FRAMING FEARFUL SYMMETRIES

DAVID BLAKE

Matador
5 Weir Road
Kibworth Beauchamp
Leicester LE8 0lQ, UK
Tel: (+44) 116 279 2299
Email: books@troubador.co.uk
Web: www.troubador.co.uk/matador

ISBN 978-1848765-764

A Cataloguing-in-Publication (CIP) catalogue record for this book
is available from the British Library.

All reasonable efforts have been made to trace the copyright holders of quoted text
or illustrations within this book. Where these have proved unsuccessful, copyright
holders are requested to contact the publisher.

Typeset in 10.5pt Book Antiqua by Troubador Publishing Ltd, Leicester, UK
Printed on acid free paper sourced from sustainable forests.

Matador is an imprint of Troubador Publishing Ltd

FRAMING
FEARFUL
SYMMETRIES

CONTENTS

Quotes from books are identified by a 'B' followed by a number, and quotes from papers in journals are identified by a 'J' followed by a number, all of which are listed in the Bibliography.

INTRODUCTION

Whilst this book includes scientific information about tigers and suggests innovative techniques for their conservation, its tigers roam far beyond physical jungles, and the reader is invited to track these tigers through personal, psychological and philosophical terrain. This book does not cover the standard 'tiger topics' of geographical distribution, life-history, size and weight, fossils, art and advertising etc. – assuming the reader interested in tigers has access to this information many times over.

Perhaps 'interested in tigers' sounds too tepid – tigers are usually associated with higher temperatures and burn brightly beyond Blake's forests of the night. Finding the exact words to describe your reaction to, or the impression made by a tiger, might be difficult and, even if found, they probably can't quite capture the tiger, or your feelings. For now 'passion for' might be preferable to 'interest in'.

Yet, passion cannot be seen from a scientific perspective and you might see a tiger in terms of biology, ecology and genetics, and what some scientists see as a refined product of aeons of evolutionary blindness and natural selection.

You possibly stand somewhere between the romantic and the scientist, somewhere between mysticism and reason, recognising functionality at the same time as aesthetic beauty and sensing something of mystery and unanswered questions. Even from a purely romantic viewpoint, you may still see ecological connections and the tiger's role in a greater scheme while, at the other extreme, a scientific view might see something silently challenging any claim that a tiger can only be form and function.

All these views can be seen from trails leading through the following chapters. Some of our questions and the difficulties we have defining our reactions to a tiger, might be answered or resolved along the way. However, complementing these, you might find that we can learn as much from questions that remain unanswered, such as those of William Blake's. Poems in addition to Blake's have relevance for our journey and, rather than relegate apt verses of poetry to decorate chapter headings, they feature in the text where they convey meanings more effectively than prose.

From wherever you view the tiger, there should be something in this book to interest you and, perhaps, something tempting you to try another viewpoint. For readers wanting to read about tiger biology, chapter II offers content which, to this author's knowledge, has not been published before, and should therefore be of fresh interest. Readers not particularly interested in tiger biology could omit most of chapter II, picking up at subsection 'Notes on Innate v. Reasoned Behaviour'. Jim Corbett is the main topic of chapter III, and we rest at his place for a while, taking a break from the exclusive rule of reason. This marks the mid-point of our journey and from there onward we consider points of view not completely constrained by logic and reason - without dismissing those that are. In chapter IV we look into some of nature's mysterious mirrors and in Chapter V learn of conservation programmes and their importance for us all.

However, trying to halt and reverse the decline of tigers, or any other species, without addressing our other environmental problems is of limited value or a waste of time, comparable to trying to save a leaf on a tree while the trunk is being sawn through. Although there seems to be an endless array of problems to address (environmentally and otherwise) many of them, when examined, do reveal common connections. In terms of the analogy just used; tracing sufficient 'leaves' backward leads us to branches, boughs and then a trunk. These interconnections cover a wide breadth of topics, not allowing an in-depth analysis of any particular one. Hence, experts on 'leaves and branches' may note much that is missing or mistaken but, hopefully, the main connections are illustrated clearly enough for readers to make their own investigations and subsequently fill in and correct as necessary.

Examination reveals many of our problems to be as old as humanity. However, unlike previous generations, the scale of these problems is now global and critical and, as we have nowhere else to go, we need to finally address them and do so without further delay. Although the most important of the solutions are of equal vintage, the suggestions presented here offer some fresh perspectives and, if these new labels on old bottles prove appealing and prompt an active response, their contents will bring benefits to the tiger, the environment, and the reader.

CHAPTER I

FORESTS OF THE NIGHT

There was no sound; he gave no cry,
The careless stars looked on serene.
The jungle's sudden tragedy
Remained unheard, unknown, unseen.

(Laurence Hope. 1865–1904)

Royal Chitwan National Park is a lush, unspoiled and truly beautiful mix of rivers, grasslands and jungle living about 75 miles south of Kathmandu, Nepal, where it rests on the border with India. In 1978, Chitwan was my destination but, at that time, there were no scheduled flights directly from London to Nepal. The journey would be via India and so, one September evening, I flew out from Heathrow and, after one stop in Germany and two in the Middle East, arrived almost 16 sleepless hours later in Delhi.

Kathmandu is only one hour's flying time from Delhi but I had arrived too late to catch the daily flight and for various reasons and mistakes, all due to my youth and inexperience, I spent another 24 sleepless hours actually getting to Kathmandu. Once there, I took a room in a basic but clean little hotel before going out to find locations necessary for the next stage of my journey. Having found them, I returned to the hotel room, where my mini backpack could finally be laid down, pockets emptied, and the tiny bathroom used to wash my clothes and myself, before laying down to sleep. After many miles, and years of great but entirely imaginary expectations, I was finally close to jungle, but still not actually there yet. Meetings that would determine those final steps would, hopefully, be held soon but, as I lay down, there was apprehension at their outcome: what if they did not go well, what if I had to move on to more places and people unknown, what if…but for now all duties and the day were done so, letting go of these cares and concerns, I slid down into a deep sea of sleep.

Unfortunately my slumbers had to be interrupted just a couple of hours later but, more importantly, I was able to arrange a forthcoming meeting with Charles 'Chuck' McDougal, Director of Operations and Chief Naturalist of 'Tiger Tops Jungle Lodge'. At the meeting and to my great relief, he kindly invited me to stay at the lodge, located in the midst of Chitwan National Park.

For the journey from Kathmandu to the lodge a few days later, I joined a small group of 'Tiger Tops' guests on a small, propeller-driven aeroplane which flew at low altitude the c. 75

miles to the lodge. Once airborne, its windows revealed innumerable terraced fields making long, curving green 'stairs' down the sides of mountains – although these are mere 'foothills' compared to the high, snow capped, remote and mighty Himalayas forming the northern border to this ancient kingdom. As we flew south, these stairs led down to a deep green 'sea' of forested plains. I was, for the time being, trapped in the metal tube of the aircraft fuselage, surrounded by structural metalwork and basic functional equipment – something like an air-worthy version of Nemo's Nautilus, on a similar voyage of exploration but, in this case, from skies above to green deeps below. I had waited fifteen years for this 'voyage' but now, from my simple seat, looking out of the little oval window, while the engines droned on, I could see that the wait and journey were almost over. The effects of thousands of uncomfortable miles still lingered about me but the keenness of thrill I felt looking down at my destination forced my faculties to function and silently anticipate my explorations of that jungle. I was exultant looking down on that vast, still, silent panorama of deep forest – there were wild tigers somewhere in that greenery! You are now invited to join these explorations, find our first tiger pugmarks, and discover where they lead…

At low altitude, air-turbulence is frequent and a short, bumpy flight was concluded by a short, bumpy landing on a grassy clearing – making many cattle move out of our way. A bright, hot sun looked down from a cloudless blue sky while we looked around us: not a single building, ground crew, facility or stick of furniture appeared in the immediate vicinity but there, in the middle distance was the edge of dense forest and, if that was not sufficient to convince us we were next to jungle, waiting there to transport us to the lodge, were the only 'ground crew' – elephants with howdahs (a box with seats) on their backs.

Those readers fortunate enough to have ridden elephants in their natural habitat will know they are the best means of transport in the forest. Few passengers complete their journey without marvelling at some aspect of the elephant's abilities. The first few times the elephant negotiates a steep bank or ravine, one feels something akin to being on a fairground ride; holding on to a rope or rail as one's seat sways out over a dizzy height before being tipped at a steep angle, ropes and wooden seat creaking under the strain, while the elephant slowly and carefully finds a secure footing down a ravine or riverbank. So begins its ponderous descent, before all strains are reversed for the ascent the other side. Able to move through rivers, ravines and the densest undergrowth, elephants are also the best way to view wildlife, which will, under most circumstances, ignore the humans sitting on the elephant's back. Not least of the impressions made is that of the elephant's strength which sometimes contrasts starkly with use of the trunk or foot that can seem more suitable for a slim-legged and graceful gazelle. I remember seeing that amazingly versatile trunk curl around a stout, living bough of approximately 6 inches (c. 15 cm) diameter and snap it off the tree after a few seconds of concentrated effort – and I knew I had not seen anything like the trunk's full power. As for delicacy; a mahout will sometimes need to halt the elephant, tell him, or more usually her, to reverse a few paces and pick up something dropped by a passenger. I have been amazed on more than one occasion to witness the elephant locate with its trunk – amongst leaf litter and within seconds – a slim black camera lens cap and pass it up to the mahout! I also marvelled at the communication between man and beast, but would learn to marvel more, as related in chapter IV.

The journey by elephant to the lodge introduced this, for me, new and exotic world and revealed some of the beauty of Chitwan National Park. The mature forests are dominated either by silk cotton trees (usually large with many branches, much foliage and some with buttressed roots) or sal trees (which have big, vertically straight, tall trunks devoid of side branches until near the top of the tree). All types of habitat are well watered by major rivers or small streams, producing lush vegetation and dense, shady groves. Another characteristic feature of the Park is its extensive grasslands. However, these should not bring to mind a neat green landscape waiting to be discovered by golfers. The grass is 'elephant-grass' and it's certainly a good idea to use an elephant to move through it. Sometimes over 20 feet in height, the tips of the grass wave over one's head – even when on elephant back!

Blades of grass they truly are since the edges of the broad leaves are sharp and will easily cut hands if unaided attempts are made to explore what, for most practical purposes, is an impenetrable wall of vegetation. The only pathways through the grass are those made by animals, notably the great one-horned rhinoceros – which is another good reason not to explore the grass on foot since rhinos can be very short-tempered and charge immediately, without asking questions.

Crossing the Reu river on elephant back, we lurched and swayed up the opposite bank to see before us the blocks of rooms, all made from local, natural materials, atop their tall wooden posts and the ground-level circular stone lodge with thatched roof where guests dined and socialised. At that time there were only two places in Chitwan which could accommodate guests; 'Tiger Tops' toward the west and, at the eastern end of the Park near a place called Sauraha, 'Elephant Camp'.

This basic but comfortable lodge was where drinks and the day's sightings were shared while, during winter evenings, a log fire crackled in the centre circular stone hearth. About one hundred and fifty paces from the lodge buildings was Chuck's, and his wife Margie's, wooden bungalow. The land between was about 25 paces wide, covered in short grass, bordered on one side by the river bank and by jungle on the other, along the side of which ran a narrow path linking Chuck's bungalow to the lodge. I found my tent on this land about halfway between their bungalow and the lodge and just a few paces away from the jungle.

The jungle! I had arrived but was not yet introduced. Since a young boy I had read books about life and adventures in the jungle but had remained, in more senses than one, at a great distance. Now, having travelled to distant deeps and skies, I was 'suddenly', and literally, next to it – after thousands of miles, it was standing a few yards away – the edge of the primeval forest.

It was the size and density of the jungle that made the first

One block of rooms to the left, the lodge at centre background and, out of sight to the right, a second block of rooms.

impression on me; a matted profusion of green life stretching away to the limits of my vision either side while it towered above me in height. It soared like a green cathedral and I was the awed pilgrim, feet on hallowed ground, lost in wonder, conscious that I would not enter and view its treasures today. From my tiny and restricted perspective the forest appeared still and silent but my formal education told me that, in addition to sheltering and supporting a multitude of life forms, that vast green, molecular machinery was turning sunlight into sugar, while lifting tons of water from the earth and giving it to the sky. The sky would later return that water to the earth. This and other biological cycles, within the forest, and those of which forests form parts, embraced millions of lives, including my own. Only my eyes roamed around it for now, probing into its depths as far as they could, not knowing then that its stillness and silence would teach me something of stillness and silence and, with further turns of the Earth, plant feelings in my head and grow unanswered questions in my heart, to teach me as much as my formal education had ever done. It would take time, but stillness and silence also speak of patience.

That vast, tall tangle of greenery hid dramatic, strange and unknown life…and was itself alive – I felt both the life *in* the forest and the life *of* the forest. Although not able to identify anything in particular, the awareness of so much hidden but rhythmically pulsing life, dwarfing me in my ignorance and insignificance, stirred a deeply buried, long-forgotten awareness. "He was sounding the deeps of his nature, and of the parts of his nature that were deeper than he, going back into the womb of Time." (B47a) I sensed somehow that something within it, was also within me – but what, I couldn't even identify, let alone understand. I was looking into a mirror – and one as strange and alive and fantastic as anything Alice ever looked into. I was young and still trying to adapt to the entirely new life, but ancient world, that I found myself in. After absorbing what little I could, in preparation for newly entering that brave old world, I turned and went to my tent. One thought kept me focussed – and thrilled – I am living with wild tigers. I might not be able to see them – but they are there!

> For many a thrill
> Of kinship, I confess to, with the powers
> Called Nature: animate, inanimate,
> In parts or in the whole, there's something there
> Man-like that somehow meets the man in me.

> *(Browning. 1812–1889)*

> "Shall I not have intelligence with the earth?
> Am I not partly leaves and vegetable mould myself?"

> *(Thoreau. 1817–1862)*

As a neighbour and daily visitor to this jungle I gradually gained an impression of what a well-populated and healthy forest looks, sounds and 'feels' like, and this has been of value in my subsequent tiger conservation work. These benefits came courtesy of Chuck McDougal, his wife Margie and Jim Edwards, Director of Tiger Tops, to all of whom I am most sincerely grateful.

I was able to stay from late September to early December 1978 so the hottest part of the year had passed and, apart from a few days of unseasonal and torrential rain, the weather was mostly pleasantly hot, with sunny, blue skies transforming into night's deep blue, star-studded skies, stunning in their clarity and presence, overarching dense black jungle.

> When sunset lights are burning low,
> While tents are pitched and camp fires glow,
> Steals o'er us, ere the stars appear,
> The furtive sense of Jungle Fear.
>
> For when the dusk is falling fast
> Still, as throughout the ages past,
> The stealthy beasts of prey arise
> And prowl around with hungry eyes.

(Laurence Hope. 1865–1904)

Rising to explore each day was another adventure – checking for animal tracks; exploring in general; wading through rivers; climbing trees, rocks and hills; finding a suitable place to sit still, to watch, listen and receive. Good, simple food, fresh air and sunshine supplied as much energy as I could spend each day. Lying down in my tent at night I often thought of a phrase in an old hunting book, the author saying that he went to bed 'deliciously tired'. This describes the feeling as well as words can but, as the reader with similar experiences knows, one's body explains it best of all.

The surroundings were both beautiful and dramatic and later, when staying away from Tiger Tops, I would have to cross the Rapti river in a dug-out canoe soon after dawn each morning. At that early hour thick mists hung over the rivers and grasslands and it seemed that both the world and I were awaking afresh to a new day, both still wrapped in a blanket of mist – the shared intimacy making me feel at one with the scene; my hazy dreaminess reflected in the world around me. All seemed still: silently steeped in mists not only of place but also of time – the world was as yet unborn, undifferentiated, sky blending as one with the water, still within the 'womb of Time'. However, the sun's bright but hazy disc gradually surfaced above the ocean of misty unity, becoming sharper and brighter while pulling, as if from some primeval protoplasm, a brilliant blue sky from its grey/white union with the water, dissolving my 'mist-ical' illusion into airy nothingness.

If the Earth's 'new born' status was illusory, mine was not. In his book 'Shikar and Safari' Edison Marshall identifies himself as a 'tenderfoot', makes humorous observations about them and gives some defining criteria. Whatever the full set of criteria might be, judging by a few of them, I too am a prime tenderfoot. Certainly, the first few times one wanders through a jungle without shoes or socks convince one of how appropriate the term is – somehow summarising the soft, vulnerable and inexperienced status of both the foot and its owner!

There is a power
Unseen, that rules th' illimitable world –
That guides its motions, from the brightest
Star to least dust of this sin-tainted mould;
While man, who madly deems himself the lord
Of all, is naught but weakness and dependence.
This sacred truth, by sure experience taught,
Thou must have learnt, when wandering all alone:
Each bird, each insect flitting through the sky,
Was more sufficient for itself than thou!

(Thomson. 1700–1748)

As experience grows and lessons are learned, one wonders how much one might be able to adapt to the natural world, how far one could walk with raw nature. I am surely not the only one to have occasionally entertained fantasies of finding a life free from the cares and worries of 'civilisation'. Whilst going 'back to nature' would bring some physical hardships, it would also bring an independence, a freedom, a sort of innocence and joy that more than compensates.

I am as free as Nature first made man,
Ere the base laws of servitude began,
When wild in woods the noble savage ran.

(Dryden. 1631–1700)

Tender feet and Thomson's lines terminated any possibilities of finding in me the man nature had first made! However, I adapted as quickly as the best efforts of a tenderfoot allowed. One technique experience teaches very quickly is that of removing leeches. Most abundant immediately after the monsoon, it is only necessary to brush past some undergrowth to find six or seven leeches attached to one's skin. If the path compels one to pass through more undergrowth before reaching a clearing, many more leeches are acquired and they move very quickly under one's clothes by 'looping' – stretching one end away from its current location, attaching it to one's skin, releasing the other end and bringing it close to the first, releasing and stretching that end…The reader is probably aware that big leeches must be made to release their jaws as they are removed from one's skin, and that salt, tobacco and lighted cigarettes can be used for this. Luckily, the leeches I am referring to were small (about four to five centimetres long) and one quickly learned to pinch their jaws out of one's skin, turn and flick them into the undergrowth in one smooth movement. A slight delay between pinching and flicking resulted in a leech attached to one's finger. Trying to pull them off demonstrated their incredible strength as they would, without letting go, stretch to a long thin string at the limit of one's ability to hold and pull them. Cutting them in two produced two living leeches. Only fire would destroy them and this was obviously undesirable from a number of perspectives, so one quickly learned to rapidly 'de-leech' after every few steps through dense undergrowth. However, because they injected an anti-coagulant in order to prolong their feed, the wound continued to bleed for some time so, after a few hours in the forest, one would emerge with one's shorts and shirt covered in large bloodstains.

The same need to remove head and jaws occurs when removing ticks since, if one is not careful, it is easy to pull the body away from the head, leaving the head in the skin as a potential irritant and point of infection. Neither leeches nor ticks could be said to be painful but ant bites were. When a tree was needed to sit in it was not always possible to find one that was ant-free, and therefore their attentions would have to be tolerated. Even though the ants were bigger than most Western ants the pain was amazingly and uncomfortably out of all proportion to their size and felt like red-hot little needles being inserted into one's skin (apparently this is due to their injecting formic acid. It seems this acid was so named due to ant nests smelling of it; the Latin word for ant being 'formica'. Its current, systematic name is methanoic acid).

Learning little techniques to avoid such irritations allows one to be at peace in the forest and begin to learn some of its deeper lessons and laws which, like the tigers within them, do not reveal themselves at first glance.

> The earth is rude, silent, incomprehensible at first,
> Nature is rude and incomprehensible at first,
> Be not discouraged, keep on, there are divine things well envelop'd,
> I swear to you there are divine things more beautiful than words can tell.
>
> *(Walt Whitman. 1819–1892)*

For persistence, patience is necessary, but nature takes care of that too, teaching the attentive that 'There is a patience of the wild – dogged, tireless, persistent as life itself – that holds motionless for endless hours the spider in its web, the snake in its coils, the panther in its ambuscade; this patience belongs peculiarly to life when it hunts its living food…' (B47a) and therefore, of course, to the tiger…

J.W. Best, hunting in the early 20th century, tells us of a man-eating tiger returning to a buffalo kill one night. As the reader may know, a full moon rises as the sun sets and sets as the sun rises. Depending on the particular night, there might be a few minutes of darkness between sun and moon…

'Against the moon I could clearly see sharply outlined the dark branches of the ebony tree in which I sat, but below me even in the moonlight it was very difficult to make out anything but the black splodge which I knew indicated where the kill was…At nine o'clock (p.m.) I heard approaching the heavy scrunch, scrunch on brittle leaves and got ready for the shot. The sound came to within fifty yards, but I could see nothing in the shadows thrown by the moonlight. After that there was dead silence. It really was a silence that could be felt. It was such a silence that you can find nowhere but in an Indian jungle or possibly in the Sahara at midnight. And the stillness was hot and smelly.

The stink kept me awake. The unfortunate buffalo below me had by sunset swollen like a balloon, and now the gas had found a way of escape.

Yet from nine o'clock until close before sunrise, I heard nothing, save when a jungle breeze rustled through the forest to which the bamboos bowed a creaking welcome. A time comes even with the best of full moons, when she must set before the greater radiance of the sun, and this one set a few minutes before the sun could lighten the earth again. In these few minutes before the sun rose, the night was at her blackest and that cunning old tiger knew the phases of the moon better than I did. As the moon set and in the few minutes before the sun rose with his tropical swiftness, a grey form crept from the shadows beneath me towards the kill; it was so dark that I could barely see it…'(B5)

Ill met by moonlight

The tiger's patience was more powerful than its hunger.

Nature as a whole has exhibited the most extraordinary patience with humans since, for literally thousands of years and tigers, the major, and sometimes only, characteristic of our relationship with the tiger has been for us to kill it whenever possible. It is understood that people will kill man-eaters and man-killers but these make a tiny fraction of the tigers killed by man, the vast majority of which never harmed a human being, despite many opportunities, and even provocations, to do so.

'Yesterday', in 1965, G.B. Schaller of the then New York Zoological Society conducted the first scientific study of the tiger in Kanha National Park, India. Just over a decade later, the Smithsonian Institute of America organised the second scientific study and first radio-telemetry tiger ecology project in Chitwan National Park, which ran for years, yielding valuable insights. By great good fortune I found myself in Chitwan during the project's early years and was able to briefly assist with it due to the kindness of Dave Smith who was then conducting the study, to whom my most sincere thanks and appreciation also go.

Chitwan gave me some impression of the abundance of animal life in a healthy forest, how the activities and movements of tigers can be tracked and followed either directly or indirectly and how one can absorb something with every day passed in nature's company. This gift of Providence, this privilege for me, was both an education and stimulation for my subsequent tiger conservation work, since nature wraps a lesson in experience like a seed in fruit.

The abundance I had been fortunate enough to see and sense was in stark contrast to so much of the countryside surrounding the Park. This impression was later reinforced in India and confirmed what study in England had indicated – that the natural world was being seriously and extensively abused by man's activities and that lessons presented by nature in microcosm, such as loss of topsoil or plummeting water-tables due to deforestation, were not only not being learned but being repeated at larger scales. Just as, collectively speaking, we were so slow to study the tiger (and many other aspects of nature); we have been even slower to address essential conservation and environmental issues but need to do so before nature finally loses patience with us. Even at time of writing, effective, long-term and comprehensive environmental protection programmes have yet to be organised globally, or even nationally. At a minimum of three decades late, the authorities have woken up to the dangers of global warming but still largely ignore pollution, loss of topsoil, deforestation and species extinctions, even compounding some of these problems by inappropriate measures to address global warming (more details in chapter IV).

In the 1970's actively contributing toward conservation was, and remains now, far from straightforward, especially for Westerners wanting to work in Africa or Asia. I had been advised that academia provided the only possible path (and a very narrow one at that) and had been fortunate enough to gain a degree before beginning my travels. I had also been advised that a further Ph.D. degree would be preferable but my passionate interests in tigers and nature could wait no longer to find their foundations and so I sought them first in Nepal.

Now in Nepal, in a properly managed and secure National Park, I could see that science could contribute to tigers' and other species' welfare, and teach us much else besides (later I would learn in other tiger range countries that this is dependent on communication and collaboration between administrative authorities and academia which, in reality, rarely occurs). The passion, the sense of wonderment and enthusiasm for nature's creations, resided in my feelings, in my heart. Perhaps,

I thought at the time, by channelling the energy of my feelings through my head, transforming their energy, via a scientific discipline, into support of conservation initiatives and environmental welfare programmes, I might be able to find a way forward, a path to follow by which I might make some meaningful contribution.

Two Types of Knowledge

In addition to the use of academic, scientific knowledge, my time in Chitwan also showed me another sort of knowledge, but it took years for me to really distinguish them and a note here might help the reader recognise them as they re-appear throughout this book, and especially as they gradually reveal a key to the survival of the tiger…and ourselves.

Science is a rigorous method of enquiry into nature measuring, by definition and agreement, physical, mechanical aspects of our experience. It has brought us much new and interesting knowledge. As an intellectual pursuit it can be as fascinating as the part of nature it studies. However, material and mechanics excludes many other experiences of our lives, which are equally valid and important, if not more important, than material and mechanics. When various experiences, not available to scientific analysis, are treated with equal respect and interest, they contribute to making our knowledge, and life, a better-balanced whole.

The example above of J.W. Best waiting for a tiger to return to its kill offers a few points to ponder in this context. From a solely rational analysis of Best's account, the tiger's knowledge of the moon's phases could be disputed and it be suggested that the tiger simply waited for the first period of complete darkness and the greater safety it brought. That the tiger waited for darkness before approaching his kill, rather than move off to hunt implies some understanding / expectation that this opportunity would eventually present itself. That the tiger moved immediately darkness arrived might indicate, in addition to hunger, an expectation that sunrise would follow in a few minutes. (Hunters' experiences sitting over kills show that predators learn to associate danger with humans near their kill. They will either abandon the kill, wait for the human to leave or for circumstances to change and provide safe access to the kill. However, if we wanted to be extremely pedantic, a purely rational analysis could dispute even these points and cast doubt on what the predator might be thinking or learning). After a rationalisation of events, we cannot be sure of any particular point: so much for reason alone.

Those who have some knowledge and personal experience of wild animals would not question their awareness or understanding of nature's patterns. All wild animals' total integration with and obedience to natural laws becomes evident to all who spend time observing their behaviour – which is why they are such a valuable guide to us; they and their lives are literally living, breathing expressions of nature's laws. They can therefore teach us aspects of those laws which our own lives, 'insulated' or 'distant' from nature, might not necessarily reveal to us. Animals demonstrate amazing and indisputable abilities such as, to mention but a few, navigation, anticipation of geophysical events and / or the weather, locating sources of water and minerals, and the avoidance of dangers due to drastic and dramatic changes to landscapes and rivers during monsoons, all while maintaining their livelihood. They probably know things we don't know we don't know. The example of the tiger's patience given above and the possible objections of pure reason, show how reason can pedantically pick over 'evidence' and lead us away from deeper truths. Reason reveals much of interest and value, and the next chapter includes some such findings but, by allowing for other ways of knowing and understanding, we can guard against some dangers of solely scientific study which will teach us about nature, as if we were separate and distant from it, while ignoring lessons from nature, which emphasise our part in it and invite our participation. Examples to clarify this distinction will crop up in the following chapters. In some senses, wild animals, and those humans still living closely to nature, know more about nature than does science or 'civilisation', but without so many abstract theories to account for what they know.

In his books, the hunter-naturalist Jim Corbett (1875 – 1955) refers to his opening a 'credit account' with the 'bank of Nature', his absorbing jungle lore and the pleasure it brought him. He used the word 'absorbed' rather than 'learnt' since he says jungle lore is not a science and cannot be learned from textbooks, but it can be absorbed, by small amounts, and increased continuously since, he tells us, the book of nature has no beginning and no end and we may open it at any time in our lives.

Biologists learn *about* animals but we can all, with or without academic qualifications, learn *from* animals, and from native human societies made up of what Dryden would have called 'noble savages'. We can scientifically study nature 'out there' and gain interesting and valuable information. However, we can also learn to 'be' with it and thereby 'absorb' knowledge, by an attentive proximity to nature. More often than not, this absorption of knowledge results not from action, but from stillness and silence, patiently watching and 'receiving'. One develops a 'feeling' for situations, perhaps the attitude or intention of an animal, some foreknowledge of weather or events, when to move out of the moonlight (even waking from sleep to do so)…This knowledge cannot be 'proved' in the conventional sense, or guaranteed with pin-point accuracy on every occasion, but it has its own validity and value. Perhaps more importantly, this 'feeling' gradually brings with it 'feeling' in the conventional sense of the word, in that as this knowledge is gained, one also gains a respect, a concern, sometimes compassion, for what is observed and for nature as a whole.

In these ways it contrasts with scientific knowledge – which by definition seeks to exclude all but reasoning and externally measured data – but is complementary, rather than opposed, to it. Moreover, science can be taught, but 'absorbing' knowledge requires stillness, silence and patience – which we can learn, but not teach.

There is a modern and increasing trend, in Western society at least, toward treating scientific knowledge as the only reliable knowledge, the closest to absolute truth. However, a true scientist would be the first to deny this and point to the limitations of science's operation, tools, concepts and practitioners. Even within its legitimate limitations the knowledge gained is, at best, only probable and usually subject to continuing and significant revisions. Modern media frequently use science as the ultimate authority and refer to whether or not 'scientists' have 'proved' something true or false, genuine or fake, valid or invalid, giving the impression that there is no other alternative.

Directly experiencing nature instils a confident knowledge, and later wisdom, that cannot necessarily be 'proved', or substantiated with 'facts', or even fully articulated, but we know for sure what we have experienced and learn in a deeper way. In these ways it shares something with poetry, which is neither necessarily logical nor immediately and completely understood – but its truth can still be sensed.

Both types of knowledge, and the feelings fostered by 'absorbed knowledge' such as care and compassion, will be seen, by the final chapter, to be essential to our survival. From here onward scientific, academic, formal knowledge will be referred to as rational knowledge and 'absorbed', personal, informal knowledge will be referred to as intuitive knowledge. Both require input from the external world. The former is received by the mind; the latter by the heart. Subsequent chapters will, hopefully, illustrate that experience teaches us how to combine both, to find truth.

Travelling far had brought me closer to nature without and within, and had begun to teach both my head and my heart. I could not then even identify, let alone see, the significance of these two types of knowledge, or their value as a key to our survival.

As our journeys continue we all learn that nature's path can only be travelled one step at a time and has to be walked with one's own feet. Indeed, in only a semi-metaphorical sense, I am sure the 'absorption' process takes place as much through the feet as the heart and head. Swami Vivekananda (Hindu mystic and philosopher 1863–1902) who represented Hinduism at the World Parliament of Religion held at Chicago USA in 1893, used to quote a saying already ancient, that to know a place one had to know it with one's own feet.

This will be a familiar truth to pilgrims walking to sacred sights and also to those who have walked in forests, who will agree that no number of miles in 4WD vehicles can replace the distance covered by one's own feet – revealing another shade of meaning to the tag of 'tenderfoot'.

Swami Vivekananda

Much of interest and value can be learned from others. We may benefit much from doing so and believe in what we have learned, but we never know it until we have experienced it. Ultimately, personal experience is the surest form of knowledge; as absorbed by one's own heart, mind and feet.

Whether rational or intuitive or both, today all perspectives agree on the critical need to protect the environment in general and the remaining forests in particular. Looking into these forests longer and more deeply, one begins to see dense thickets of entangled responsibilities. We have to try to clear a way forward by each of us disentangling our own share. From my own tiny perspective, flying over Chitwan at low altitude, I saw a 'sea' of green. However, from a global perspective, forests are now actually tiny 'islands' amidst 'seas' of cultivated, residential or industrialised land, with abrupt borders between. Isolating them in this way, while illegal and abusive activities continue within them, is gross mismanagement and dangerous for them, their inhabitants and, ultimately, life on Earth, including human populations. It is essential that the vital importance of the natural environment is more widely appreciated by people, whoever and wherever they are. Perhaps, I thought, in addition to supporting conservation initiatives and environmental welfare programmes, helping to provide education was another way that I could help.

As referred to above, science had, and still has, been gaining much prominence, and so, for this and other reasons given above, academia seemed the way forward and the route by which I might make some contribution to the tiger's welfare, and to nature and life in general. The paths of both jungle and academia can be dry and dusty, but following tiger pugmarks along them brings dry dust to life. I would now follow their trail into academia.

CHAPTER II

MORTAL HAND AND EYE

Science, scents and experiments

With regard to India in the late seventies, Indira Gandhi's Project Tiger had achieved great success and a politically stable Nepal was doing a respectable job looking after the tigers living there. Under these conditions – healthy and relatively safe populations living in properly protected and managed National Parks or Tiger Reserves – research could make a welcome addition to a conservation and / or management programme. If communications between academia and the Park/Reserve authorities are good and the acquired knowledge is utilised, it can help Park authorities make better-informed decisions. Researching a variety of ecological settings would provide comparative studies and improve our ability to efficiently manage and protect as much remaining natural habitat as possible. So, on returning to England from Nepal and India in late December 1978, I sought funding for research projects covering different ecological settings to those of the Smithsonian project.

In the meanwhile I thought I should increase my knowledge of tigers as much as practically possible. Although the behaviour of any animal in captivity must, in some respects, be a distortion of its behaviour in the wild, much directly comparable behaviour of interest and value remains. Indeed, some observations of captive animals can illuminate aspects of their wild counterparts' behaviour that decades of study in the wild might not reveal.

Before travelling to India and Nepal, and as part of my studies for a degree, I had conducted a minor behavioural research project on captive tigers. Coinciding with my return to England, the same 'safari park', after a period of closure, was re-opening to the public and needed keepers for their big-cats. So, armed with broom, pen and paper, I began my duties and observations, comparing them, where appropriate, with observations made in the wild.

The notes below are on topics which have not, to my knowledge, been previously published and they might therefore be of fresh interest. The bulk of this chapter is for those with a particular and detailed interest in tigers. In terms identified in the preceding chapter, it is largely an account of 'rational knowledge'. Readers with a more general interest in nature can skip most of it and pick up from the sub section 'Notes on Innate v. Reasoned Behaviour', where 'intuitive knowledge' reappears.

Notes on Tiger Cubs

In 1978 the safari park's group of eight tiger cubs was made up of one litter of four cubs from each of two mothers. Photographs of the tigers follow, along with the name given to them and their sex. In the following text each tiger is referred to by name, which serves the same purpose as a number and is more natural, since that's how we keepers identified each animal in order to do our work. Face and body shapes distinguished individuals from one another and the markings on each tiger are also unique, the black markings on the white patch above each eye serves as a very distinctive and easily recognisable area for quick identification. The stripes, especially on these patches, also show how the markings among one family more closely resemble each other than those of another family. Lancer, Rajah, Sceptre and Suli are of one litter, Trooper, Kamal, Topaz and Jay, the other.

When the study began the cubs were 5 and a half months old and the approximate size of the average male was 5 feet (152cm) long plus 2.5 feet (76cm) of tail, standing 2.5 feet at the shoulder. Individuals differed from this average only very slightly. All had distinctive temperaments and characteristics justifying the following brief description:

Males

Lancer: Large and adventurous but wary in new circumstances.
Rajah: Large, adventurous and bold.
Trooper: Average size, quiet.
Kamal: Small, quiet.

Females

Sceptre: Large, adventurous.
Topaz: Average, quiet.
Suli: Small, timid.
Jay: Small, timid.

The cubs would show great curiosity in anything strange or new (events or objects) and this was pronounced in Lancer and Rajah. Although there were occasional periods when the cubs would sit or lie around (usually in physical contact with each other) displaying little or no activity, for the greater part of the daylight hours the cubs played. The cubs were amazingly hardy and, although the play was very rough, no individual suffered injury or, apparently, pain. Cubs would roll over each other and their heads (describing a wide arc) would crack loudly on the concrete floor with no visible effect. Fur and skin would be pulled by another's teeth until it seemed impossible that the 'victim' could remain unperturbed which, however, it did. All the cubs played as roughly as this, with no apparent ill effects. During most of their play the cubs proved to be very clumsy, frequently tripping over, skidding along on their chins, paws slipping or not being brought into position quickly enough, tumbling over themselves or each other.

Their play took the form of several distinctive types. One type would be recognised when two cubs would stand on their hind legs and, supporting each other's forequarters, cuff and bite each other. This position would soon degenerate into both animals rolling over each other, often with others joining in, until perhaps another two would rear up in clinched positions. No vocalisations accompanied their playful activities except, perhaps, for an occasional short snarl.

Another distinctive routine was that of running and catching other cubs. The cub selected would normally be unaware that another was 'hunting' it, although a cub would still be run at and pounced on if it happened to look at the 'hunter'. On deciding on its quarry, the 'hunter's' eyes and head were 'fixed' on target and a crouch or semi-crouch would be adopted. In a semi-crouch, the head is lowered and the legs flexed while in a crouch the head is held even lower and the belly rests just above the ground. The whole foot (i.e. all the tarsal bones) of both hind legs are in contact with the ground and held very close together. One of the front paws may be held limply in the air, just off the ground. Intermittently the tiger may make a slight forward-backward rocking movement while slightly shifting its hind paws. Sometimes the cub would move forward while crouched and reduce the distance between itself and the target. This initial sequence would be followed by a loping or fast run, depending on how much effort the cub put into it, culminating in the cub springing at and bringing down its quarry. This would most often be done by the tiger flopping it's forequarters over the 'victim' while its hind legs remained on the ground. The 'hunter' would also bite the 'victim' in the middle of its back. This ended in both cubs rolling over each other on the ground. This game seemed to be 'all against all' and often a stalking cub would be brought down by another before completing its own 'hunt'.

As noted by many observers, play incorporates basic

Rajah

Lancer

Kamal

Trooper

Sceptre

Topaz

behaviour patterns needed in adult life and the sequence just described obviously includes features of adult hunting behaviour. A section below stresses that stalking, catching and killing prey represent three distinct behavioural sequences and that in the wild each have to be practised separately before they can be put together for a successful hunt. The rudiments of the first two sequences are evident in the cubs' play, including the good grip and position of the propulsive hind feet. If a cub sees that it is being stalked and moves away, the game may turn into a chase. If so, the chaser would frequently try to insert a fore-paw between the hind legs of the chased or hook them with its fore-paw as if trying to trip it. The possible significance of this and other behaviour are included in the relevant following sections along with notes on adult behaviour in the wild.

For now, the reader's attention is drawn to two points:

- an adult tiger will often abandon a hunt if the quarry detects it, whereas the cubs continued regardless of detection

- The 'hunter' biting the neck of the 'victim' was not observed in the play sequences – only the bite to the small of the back. The cubs did not bite at random or anywhere other than the same place on the spine, within an inch or two, every time. Nape and throat bites kill prey but, on the rare occasions that intra-specific conflicts escalate to a fight to the death, biting the lumbar region of the middle back is a technique used, if opportunity offers, by adult big cats fighting each other. On occasion, prey may be grasped by the back, or shoulders, buttocks and sides to bring it down, as opportunity offers but the cubs did not use the bite to the back to bring the other down, it was a brief, rapid and distinct action almost finished before it was observed. This bite, delivered in the same way but in earnest by adults, breaks the opponent's spinal cord, rendering the victim's hind legs useless. Inflicting fatal damage as far as possible from the opponent's formidable teeth makes sense and once paralysed, the animal would not be able to survive, so the opponent could leave it to die without risking further injury to itself. However, it appears that the victor does kill the disabled opponent, but not by the throat or nape bite used to kill prey. The victor's canines puncture the opponent's cranium – the author knows of a tiger found in the wild with its skull crushed (the injuries were such that only another tiger could have inflicted the wounds) and has seen film and photographs of lions using their canine teeth to puncture the cranium of an opponent after delivering the bite to the lower spine.

Social Status

The cubs established a rank order amongst themselves by some ritualised behaviour which I termed a 'pair confrontation'. The confrontations exhibited facial expressions very similar to those noted by Leyhausen, who distinguished between aggressive threat and defensive threat in the facial expression of various species of cats. In an aggressive threat the mouth is closed, or partially so, the ears erect and twisted in such a way that the backs almost face forward, displaying the conspicuous spot which many cats have there, and the pupils are small. In an attitude of defensive threat the canines may be exposed, the corners of the open mouth pulled back, the ears flattened, and the pupils large.

The confrontations observed at the 'safari park' are markedly distinct from the usual everyday chasing, confrontations, fighting and wrestling of the cubs at play. Two individuals would suddenly be noticed to be facing each other in a direct and characteristic way as shown in the following photograph.

'Pair confrontation'

Trooper   *Kamal*

Unfortunately, the photograph is poor quality but the only one available. However careful observation will detect these same postures in footage of tigers in modern wildlife programmes.

One cub, which hereafter will be referred to as the dominant, would be directly facing the other at close range (maximum distance between noses was 11-12 inches (30 cm)). It would be standing upright on all fours with its ears turned slightly inwards and slightly forward, although the ear position of the dominant was not as constant and invariable as that of the other cub (hereafter referred to as the subordinate). The dominant cub's tail would swing from side to side with increasing rapidity as the confrontation developed into cuffing by fore-paws. The dominant cub's mouth would remain closed or just slightly open. The lips were not drawn back nor would there be growling or snarling.

The other cub, the subordinate, would adopt a position with its hindquarters held very low, occasionally touching the ground. The ears would be flattened back and down and one front paw would be held off the ground. It continually snarled and hissed with lips drawn back. The pair would face each other for about a minute or less and then the dominant would hit first, cuffing the other with a fore-paw. The subordinate would return this blow but the return hit seemed tentative and would be accompanied by further crouching and snarling, while the dominant not only appeared to decide when the exchange would take place but hit in a much more positive manner. These exchanges would quickly build up into a rapid exchange of blows until the bout would end by the subordinate rolling onto its back and being nibbled by the dominant, which may roll onto and over it as in play. The bout may then suddenly resume. The greater the number of times the bouts were consecutively enacted, the quicker the dominant individual would bring it to a close by not hesitating so long before hitting the other. Either individual would then break off and move away, signalling the end of that particular confrontation.

One interesting and puzzling point about these confrontations is that the social status seemed to have been determined beforehand as shown by the positions each adopted. I never saw the dominant / subordinate change positions. The only indecision appeared to be the tentative nature of the first exchange of blows, which rapidly swung to confident hitting by the one that had assumed the dominant stance. Perhaps the experiences of the cubs in the two play sequences already described revealed the relative confidence and strength of individuals and determined the position each adopted in these ritualised 'pair confrontations'.

Snakes

I had long wondered if tigers have a wariness of snakes and if so, whether it is instinctive or taught by the mother. As the cubs had been reared without their mothers their behaviour was predominantly governed by instinct and provided an opportunity to seek an answer to my question.

A tiger's habitat usually contains extremely venomous snakes. Despite a tiger's enormous vitality and strength, a bite or bites from some of these snakes might prove fatal (not always directly but by incapacitating the tiger whilst it recovers from the venom – there being other animals dangerous to a defenceless tiger). "I found in a pool of water a large python (*a constrictor; non-venomous – author*) bitten in half by a tiger, and part of the middle eaten; and over two feet of snake in one piece has been extracted from the stomach of another. This is interesting, as cats generally have a great aversion to snakes. A captive tiger was killed in its cage by the bite of a cobra." (B12 reprinted by kind permission of the Random House Group Ltd.)

The following 'experiment' is hardly at the cutting edge of research but might be of interest to the reader. For some obscure reason, which I never discovered, on a Christmas or birthday many years ago a friend gave me a six foot rubber 'snake' coloured dark green with a white underbelly (still don't know the species!), and this became my test apparatus.

At the time I am writing about, a floor-standing 'tunnel', made of inverted U-shaped iron bars, connected the tigers' night cages to the daytime reserve. Height- and width-wise the tunnel comfortably held one tiger at a time and length-wise, all eight in a line, with plenty of space between noses and tails. Each end of the tunnel had a vertically sliding 'guillotine' door by which we keepers could control the 'flow' of tigers. The reserve-end of the tunnel fitted flush with a tall chain-link fence, which made one boundary of the reserve. Further along this fence was another and very large gate, facing into the reserve. I could stand behind this large gate and, due to intervening cages, remain invisible to the tigers in the tunnel. I had previously placed the 'snake' in the reserve approx. thirty feet from the large gate. By a fine thread, tied around the neck of the snake, I gently pulled it toward the gate. As the snake moved it looked remarkably authentic since the curves moulded into the rubber quivered realistically as they were pulled over the irregularities of the ground.

All the tigers showed distinct individual characteristics or 'personalities'. Hence, in order to see as many reactions as possible before the 'great experiment' met some unexpected end, I had, on the morning of the experiment, put the tigers into a sequence of 'gentle' or 'cautious' tigers first, followed by increasingly bold individuals up to the boldest and most aggressive individual. Fourth in line was the most dominant individual (named Lancer) who, although capable of tremendous ferocity and displays of dominance was very cautious in new situations – holding back and watching while others investigated. If any new situation proved benign and to some advantage, he would then move in and take control, dispossessing the subordinate of the object or place of value. His position in fourth place was due to his initially cautious approaches.

Jay, a small, cautious tigress was the first in line and had seen the snake from her position at the front of the tunnel as soon as I had begun to move it. Now it was stationary and I gave the signal for Jay to be released. She ran over to it and, with fore paws spread, lowered her head and inspected it visually. She then fairly cautiously put her nose next to the tail end to smell it, and then tentatively began to pick it up in her mouth, recoiling suddenly but only slightly when it began to move. She followed with interest whilst the snake moved and the second tigress (Suli) was released. Suli followed a similar pattern to Jay and both pranced about the alternately stationary and moving snake watching and following it back toward the large gate, occasionally trying to put their nose against it but drawing back when it moved. Both females showed a fully alert curiosity with ears erect and forward, muscles tensed and both were 'ready for action'.

Sceptre was next in line but things were about to change rapidly – Lancer had been watching the first two females and the snake from the tunnel. As the door was drawn up to release Sceptre, he squeezed out half beside and behind her but overtook her, going straight to the snake and, without a second's hesitation, bit it behind the head, severing the head from the body. Just a few seconds had passed since his unplanned release from the tunnel. He looked in surprise as the head continued to be drawn toward the gate (it is said that life hangs by a thread!), and began to follow it. Sceptre snatched up the remaining body section and ran off into the reserve (see photo) shaking it vigorously. Although the snake head was still outside i.e. not yet drawn fully under the gate,

Lancer turned and bounded after Sceptre who growled as if she held meat. The gate-keeper could see that the experiment was coming to a rapid close and released the remaining tigers. There was a scuffle and growling as Trooper, Kamal and Topaz investigated and Sceptre warned them off. Lancer appeared to lose interest and wandered off. Three minutes after the tigers had met their first rubber snake, Sceptre was biting it into pieces while lying on the roofed hut in the reserve.

Sceptre running off with the headless body of the 'snake' in her mouth

I still wonder about the conclusions to be drawn from this experiment! Did the females' cautious investigation, recoiling when the snake moved, indicate some innate awareness of snakes, or possibly of a moving 'animal', or just wariness of the new and unknown? Did Lancer's knowledge of where to bite (a little inaccurate at about 12-15 centimetres behind the head) was definitely innate and certainly nowhere near the tail end, which had taken the attention of the tigresses (did they assess this as the least dangerous end?) Lancer displayed no caution whatsoever and his bite was so swift it would have been a *fait accompli* whether the snake was venomous or not. He possibly prompted Sceptre to overcome any caution that she might have shown.

Years later, I talked with a keeper of seven captive tigers in Australia. The tigers spent much of their time on a grassed, open-air 'island' bordered by a moat and the rear sides of their night-quarters, but which allowed free access to insects, birds, small mammals and...snakes. He told me that all the tigers showed a distinct awareness of and aversion to snakes, watching them attentively and taking care not to let them get too close. These observations suggest that tigers do have an innate awareness of snakes, since no snake had ever bitten these tigers and all had been hand-reared without opportunity of maternal tuition.

In conclusion, it would seem that tigers, and perhaps other big cats, distinguish between venomous and non-venomous snakes, having an innate awareness of those with relatively small girths (venomous), whilst considering constrictors fair game, as and when opportunity offers – as noted by Burton with regard to the python. Jaguars have also been known to kill and eat anacondas in South America. Constrictors are necessarily large in length and girth and have no venom. However, as an exception that might prove this rule, large king cobras (hamadryads) are comparable to pythons in length, if not fully in girth but, being highly venomous, are best avoided by tigers.

Hamstringing

Hamstringing (severing the Achilles tendon of a hind leg) is a technique used on prey large enough to be a formidable challenge and tilts the odds significantly in favour of the predator. Obviously, tackling large, strong prey, often equipped with horns or sharp hooves at the ends of very powerful legs, is a dangerous business and the predator must come within striking distance of horns and hooves to inflict any sort of fatal bite. A predator's teeth within inches of powerful hind legs with hard hooves might represent too great a risk (see section on tiger teeth below) when a paw can inflict the same damage while keeping the rest of the body at more of a distance. Damage to a paw, although less likely due to its comparatively greater flexibility, is undesirable but is less risky overall than damage to teeth. If a tiger ever used its teeth to hamstring an animal (I know of no reliable record of such), the tiger presumably judges, due to the particular circumstances, that the limb is not about to move.

Corbett reports that he has seen many cases of hamstringing by tigers but that in all those cases the hamstringing was done by claws and not by teeth. He says that two of the biggest buffaloes he ever saw killed by tigers had been hamstrung by the tiger's claws before they were pulled down and killed by the tiger's teeth.

Once again the cubs in captivity provided some possible insight to this behaviour. Despite their clumsiness on many occasions, their bodily co-ordination was without fault when 'locked on' target and chasing each other at a reasonably fast run. While running, as mentioned above, the chaser would frequently try to either insert its leading front paw between the hind legs of the chased, or simply use it to hook one hind leg to trip the 'prey'. This brings to mind the cheetah which, while chasing its prey, will often try to trip it with a front paw or knock it over with a blow to the rump. However, despite the similar action, the cheetah's claws are only semi-retractile and hence nowhere near as sharp as the tiger's fully retractile claws. Apart from having semi-blunt claws, hamstringing does not harmonise with the cheetah's distinct hunting technique nor with their prey, which is rarely, if ever, of such a size or strength as to require hamstringing. On occasion, the tiger cubs would also try to bite the hind legs of the chased cub but my impression was that this might have been due to the relatively small and 'cuddly' nature of the cubs and that it was disappearing with age and increasing size, while the frequency and dexterity of the paw action might be a precursor to an adult hamstringing action.

The Right Angle

It might seem evident from the frontal view of a tiger's face that everything 'above' the eyes would be visible when a tiger was looking over some barrier or cover. However, the shape of

Diagram 1

the head is adapted to the animal's need to observe whilst remaining unobserved and, as described below, ensures that virtually nothing of the tiger is exposed above the cover it hides behind.

I was lucky enough to be taught this by the young adult tigers on a number of working mornings when arriving at their overnight cages. The upper half or two-thirds of the front of these cages were made up of vertical bars, which were set into a metal-reinforced wooden panel, forming the lower front portion of the cage. This panel was big enough to obscure the tiger from view if it crouched or lay behind it. All the tigers would be attentive to the keepers' arrival, it signalling their imminent release into the reserve after their overnight confinement. We keepers approached on a narrow tarmac road at right angles to the cages at the end of one block. Their occupants would sometimes stand looking at us as we approached without any attempt at concealment. However, on occasion no tiger would be visible at first glance. Yet, as I approached the cages I might catch sight of a slight movement or something small just, and only just, above the edge of the front panel. Once I had detected it, I fixed my gaze upon it and walked directly toward it until I reached the cage to look in. The tiger would be crouched on all fours with head lifted, the plane of the bridge of nose almost parallel to the cage floor, the forehead therefore tilted back and down (see diagram). From a frontal view only the eyes and the bridge between the eyes were visible, just above the top edge of the panel, and these had caught my eye. At that angle, no part of the face either side of the eyes is visible.

When the tiger detects an object of interest it lifts its head and points its nose toward the object. A profile view of the head clearly shows the distinct angle between the muzzle/bridge of nose and the forehead (see diagram). This angle allows the eyes to be held just above cover without revealing any other part of the head or body, except the relatively small bridge of the nose, which, with its disruptive colouration, blends easily against most natural backgrounds. Over the distance between prey and tiger, this part is reduced even further by perspective. Few animals can visually resolve objects that remain still – even fewer when the object remains still against an obscuring and visually disruptive background, such as foliage. Hence the tiger, in suitable cover, can view its prey whilst remaining virtually invisible.

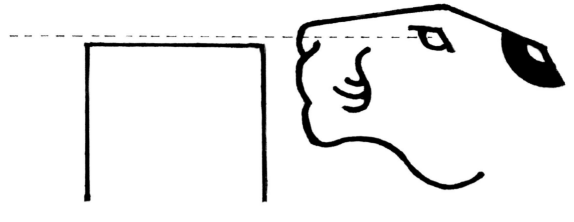

Diagram 2
SIDE VIEW

Diagram 3
FRONT VIEW

The artificiality of the dull, uniformly coloured cages combined with the certainty of a tiger being within a 'window' of approx. 7 feet square only 20 feet away allowed me to detect this feature. In a jungle, quite apart from an observer's presence almost certainly interfering with or preventing a tiger stalking its prey, the chance of having a vantage point placed just so, without any obstruction, from which to see such detail is extremely unlikely. Without the combination of circumstances in captivity providing me with such a fortunate opportunity, it would be easy to make the assumption mentioned above, that the top of the head, 'above' a tiger's eyes, would be visible when it looks over the top edge of an object.

Few people have observed wild tigers as closely, frequently or as accurately as Jim Corbett, and in his account of 'The Temple Tiger' he refers to sitting in a tree and, although he cannot see it, sensing the arrival of the tiger. He wonders if the tiger is watching him and whether the tiger's eyes *and top of its head* would be raised over the brow of the hill facing him. I am not criticising Corbett and do not even approach his degree of jungle lore. This example is given to demonstrate how difficult it is to notice this feature in operation in the wild – due to its very function.

Head in profile to illustrate the 'right angle'

Ear Spots

Perhaps the most important tuition provided by a mother for her cubs is that concerned with acquiring food. Stalking, catching and killing represent three distinct behavioural repertoires for a tiger to learn. A mother might disable prey but leave it alive, giving her cubs the opportunity to kill it and learn, in relative safety, what to do once they have caught their own prey, there being a significant behavioural difference between catching and killing. Similarly, there is a behavioural difference between stalking and catching and, with regard to stalking, there are few reliable observations of a successful stalk and still fewer of a stalk by a mother while being watched by her cubs, since in such circumstances the observer would almost certainly represent an interference with the stalk. Notes above referred to the cubs' instinctive behaviour revealed in their endless games of stalking and catching each other. However, these innate impulses have to be refined and applied selectively for future survival. The mother bridges the gap between the cub's awkward fumbling and real practice making perfect – the gap between play and prey.

If deprived of their mother, individuals can sometimes learn by trial and error, but trials take time, which could be critical (i.e. that period before starvation terminates trials) as could errors (e.g. tackling armed prey without knowledge). If we could compare graphs of 'learning curves' for motherless cubs and those raised by mothers, it is likely that the mother's presence increases the gradient of a cub's learning curve such that it reaches self-sufficiency on one axis well before it reaches maximum time without food on the other. The learning curves of individual cubs would, of course, vary according to individual characteristics and some would achieve self-sufficiency on their own. However, these are probably too few for a viable tiger population and Mother Nature designs mother tigers to bring up their litters to self-sufficiency faster than most could reach it alone.

While a few cubs mature quickly and the majority make up the 'average' rate, a few others will be unable to achieve self-sufficiency, even with their mother's help. Since the struggle to survive is a difficult one, the need to prevent energy and resources being wasted on individuals that will not survive independently, means that mothers must abandon them. This behaviour has been seen both in the wild and captivity. The latter may seem surprising since captive animals are not subject to the rigours of the wild, but this behaviour is probably innate. If not innate, what they know of their 'security' is questionable (for example; whether they 'know' that food will appear at next feeding time). Lionesses at the 'safari park' would ignore runts or cubs with some deformation, or kill, and sometimes, eat them – harsh by human standards but reducing wasted energy to a minimum.

For those brought up by their mothers, one factor accelerating the learning processes appears to be imitation of the mother. For example, big cats often use their fore-paws to hold a piece of meat while the carnassial teeth at the side of their jaws detach lumps for swallowing (see section on tiger teeth for more details). At the 'safari park' and unlike the tiger cubs, lion cubs were raised by their mothers. Lion cubs used their paws to hold meat months before tiger cubs of the same age acquired the habit and the only significant difference appears to be that the lion cubs could see lionesses using their fore-paws to hold meat (the tiger cubs could not see the lions at feeding time).

It appears reasonable to conclude, on the basis of far more evidence than can be presented here, that the mother accelerates learning and that the cubs' imitation of their mother is part of this process.

There has been much speculation as to the purpose of the striking white spots on the back of tigers' otherwise black-backed ears. Leyhausen's suggestion concerning 'aggressive' and 'defensive' threat has been noted above. The ear spots are really striking and I, amongst others, have become aware of a tiger in cover, otherwise perfectly hidden in its surroundings, by seeing these ear spots. Their stark visibility in the forest must be seen to be appreciated. There have been suggestions that they enable cubs to follow their mother but I do not think this is correct – other than in one particular set of circumstances.

When conducting the minor research project in 1978, it occurred to me that the ear spots provide a means by which cubs could observe their mother whilst she stalked prey. For a cub needing to follow its mother in circumstances other than hunting, and being in a position low down and to the rear of a relatively large four-legged animal, it is not the back of the ears, but the mother's hind legs or tail, which are most easily seen. However, when stalking, the tigress is likely to be in a crouched position, when the ear-spots are more easily seen by cubs. When standing directly behind it, I observed a tiger in such a crouched position, stalking a lion in an adjacent compound: The ear spots were extremely conspicuous and could be seen whether the head was raised or lowered and whether one's field of vision was a direct or three-quarterly view from behind. The only position in which neither ear could be seen was when I was directly behind the tiger and its head was fully down to the ground; in this position the rump obscured my view. I made my observations bent or lying down i.e. from the height that I assessed a cub would be viewing from, and therefore did not have the viewing advantage of an upright stance. Although in the natural environment the spots would occasionally be obscured by vegetation there would also be other times when, as witnessed by many observers, they would be clearly visible.

The knowledge of their mother's presence would also provide reassurance to cubs brought away from the lair (perhaps another of nature's efficiencies – the cubs' 'insecurity' ensuring they watch their mother attentively). The cubs observe the patience, movements and techniques of stalking (e.g. stalking upwind or downwind according to prevailing wind direction and position of prey) and that, to ambush or stalk a wild animal, a very close approach is necessary before launching an attack. Obviously, when stalking, the mother needs to be at a distance from her cubs (lest they disturb the prey) and, equally obviously, vocal communication is inappropriate. The spots on the back of the ear stand out as a silent marker of the mother's position. If adult tigers hunted co-operatively (I know of no evidence for this but am considering why else a silent marker might be needed), they would not be positioned directly behind each other.

Diagram 2 above, illustrates the position of the head and ears when stalking from behind cover that cannot be seen through. Obviously, the ears in their normal 'upright' position would be exposed above the level of cover. So, the ear position is not only a functional part of the stalk but also, by displaying the ear spots to the rear, indicates to a useful degree of accuracy, the position of the tiger's eyes (not visible from the rear) and hence the direction of the object of interest and how it is to be observed. The angle at which the forehead is naturally tilted while stalking further contributes to the ear spots being fully displayed. On those occasions when a tiger approaches prey without crouching and with ears upright, the spots remain rearward facing and clearly visible. A successful stalk is one situation wherein the predator will always be facing the prey and the ear spots, whether the ears are erect or laid back, will be starkly visible through gaps in vegetation to eyes watching from the rear.

Many cats have some sort of spot or mark on the back of the ears e.g. all cats of genus Panthera – lions have a fawn coloured ear with a black mark. As well as white ear patches, the leopard also has a very distinct white underside to the tip of the tail (the tips of tigers' tails are black). Considering just how well a leopard can 'disappear' in undergrowth and its relatively small size, it makes sense for nature to enhance its 'rearward signalling' capacity. The still smaller and jungle dwelling Temminck cat lacks prominent ear spots but the underside of the distal third of the tail is strikingly white. The tails of bobcats and lynxes are very short but, in a sort of compensatory way, their ears are large or long; sometimes with tufts at the tips (backs of the ears may also have a white spot as in the case of the bobcat). This apparent relationship between various species of cats' ear and tail features does not appear to have a shared significance for establishing social status, but all cat species do share the same need to teach cubs to catch prey by stealth and stalking. As tiger cubs can accompany their mother on hunts from ages of six months up to eighteen months or two years, what purpose could be served by these forays other than some form of tuition or demonstration of stalking, catching and killing techniques? After six months of age, risks to cubs left at the lair are minimal. Cubs which accompany their mother do not assist with the hunt, so their presence is potentially detrimental (more tigers mean more chances of noise, detection by prey or animal 'watchmen' etc.) and it seems that nature would not reduce the mother's chances of hunting success unless there is an overall advantage to them observing her in action.

Although this cub is not stalking, the prominence of the ear spots is clear

Notes on Tracks, Pugmarks and Stalking

Many hunter/naturalist authors refer to the tiger's ability to move silently, especially when stalking. It is understood that the tiger is able to see where to place its front paws (to avoid treading on something that would make a noise) but unable to do the same for its hind paws. Some of the available literature discusses the possibility of the hind paws being placed in the spaces vacated by the front paws.

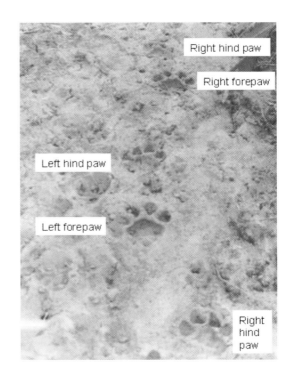

At this point it might be useful to review the tiger's normal gait and the track it leaves on a suitable viewing surface such as a sandy or muddy trail. At a normal walking pace, the hind paw is placed immediately in front of the place just vacated by the fore-paw. This leaves a 'double' track. The picture shows the pugmark trail of a male tiger (squarer pugs) walking at a brisk pace.

If the tiger increases its speed, the gap between the imprint of the fore and hind paws increases, the hind paw falling further in front of the fore paw the faster the tiger runs. Conversely, if the tiger's pace is very slow, it is possible for the hind paw to superimpose itself entirely over the print of the fore-paw. In this case a 'single', as opposed to 'double', track is left. This is the reason why hind paws are traced for census purposes in the wild, since one cannot always be sure of finding un-obscured fore-paw prints. Tracing left or right is an arbitrary decision.

However, the point of interest raised above is whether the tiger, when stalking or requiring complete silence while moving, places its hind paws in the spaces vacated by the fore paws.

Standing immediately next to a chain link fence I was lucky enough to watch a tiger within a few feet of me stalking other animals in an adjacent compound. With head 'fixed' and intent gaze, the tiger moved slowly forward in the typical stalking posture with body slung low and underbelly almost, but not quite, touching the ground. Most carefully and gently one hind leg was lifted and brought forward which seemed to initiate the fore-paw on the same side starting to lift slowly from the ground. The fore-paw vacated its position very slowly and gradually, with the rearmost part of the fore-paw lifting first and the rest following as it 'rolled forward'. The front tips of the toes of the hind paw lightly touched the back of the front paw and slid down the under-surface of the front paw until it completely occupied the space just vacated. Meanwhile the fore-paw extended for the next step.

I was struck by the smooth flow and delicacy of the operation, how carefully it was conducted and the slight touch between paws ensuring precision, which would support the idea that hind paws taking the places of fore-paws during a stalk is neither accidental nor coincidental. The underbelly is kept clear of the ground as another precaution against noise – a dry twig can make a surprisingly distinct sound on being disturbed. The underbelly is allowed to touch the ground when contact will be silent e.g. sand or mud.

Having referred to the intensity of the animal's concentration whilst stalking, it might be of interest to note some aspects of what biologists call selective attention. It is well known that we, for example, can listen to a person speaking to us in a crowded and noisy room by focusing on the speaker and ignoring the surrounding noise, while remaining aware of it. Similarly, when sleeping, we will ignore passing traffic but wake to, say, a baby's cry. When the stimulus is of sufficient importance this selectivity operates even during a sleep of utter exhaustion: the pilots fighting the Battle of Britain during the summer of 1940 would wait outside their huts in the sunshine for the next order to 'scramble' and engage the enemy. Wing Commander Ronald Adams recalled seeing them fast asleep on beds or in wicker chairs, Mae Wests around their necks and flying-boots on their feet. 'Every time the telephone rang in the dispersal hut, or every time a voice was heard booming on the loudspeaker, all the sleeping figures would wake up and listen, and if not an urgent call for them, they would fall back and be asleep in an instant. Generally, the radio was on at full blast. That did not disturb them. The roar of aircraft taking off and the clatter of vehicles passing by – those did not disturb them either. But a telephone bell had them alert and grabbing for their flying-helmets before it had stopped ringing.' (B31 reprinted by kind permission of Souvenir Press). We and other animals are somehow able to select the stimuli to which we pay attention. The example of the pilots is an extreme one and shows that these stimuli can have the very opposite of personal survival value.

Therefore the selectivity involves some input, at some level, of conscious awareness and choice.

Some well known research conducted in 1956 (J12) involved electrically measuring the auditory response of domestic cats to regular uniform sounds from a nearby loudspeaker. The oscilloscope trace of the cat's auditory response displayed regular and distinct peaks or pulses corresponding to the regular beats from the loudspeaker, indicating that the cat was registering the sound. When a mouse (in a closed bottle) was introduced to the test chamber the cat focussed its attention on the mouse while the sounds continued to beat but, remarkably, the pulse on the oscilloscope trace either disappeared or significantly diminished, indicating that the cat's auditory response to the sounds had disappeared or significantly diminished. (It is fascinating to consider that the physiological apparatus for the auditory nerve to receive the impulse remained functional, yet its transmission was reduced or nullified by some response of the cat's conscious awareness of the mouse. The brain was not just receiving information from the outside world but was able to transmit its own signal to the sensory organ to reduce or shut-off that information (the electrode was only attached to the auditory nerve)). The same result was found when an olfactory stimulus distracted the animal's attention – a similar null auditory trace was produced even though the sounds continued. Whilst the oscilloscope traces leave no room for doubt (the 'sound pulse' or peak on the traces produced when attention was distracted being distinctly reduced or absent) this work and the conclusions drawn from it have since been criticised (B52). However, the criticism concerns the exact interpretation of the data and / or the physiology of how the selection or blocking takes place, not the principle that such selection can and does occur.

I have seen stalking tigers and lions seemingly 'locked on target', interrupted by, say, an approaching vehicle suddenly break concentration, register their surroundings with a slightly dazed look, stop stalking and move off with, perhaps, a brief glance back at the 'prey' or object that was previously being stalked.

Notes on Tiger Teeth

I saw a young tigress in the wild whose body size suggested an age of about 7 months. She yawned whilst I, and a friend who was familiar with this Tiger Reserve, watched her from elephant back at a distance of 10-12 feet. As she did so I saw that she had a perfect set of adult canine teeth. The friend asked me how old I thought she was. Tigers usually gain their adult canines at about one year of age, the new teeth growing immediately next to the milk teeth and gradually pushing them out, ensuring the tiger always has the ability to provide itself with food. This evidence conflicted sharply with the body size but was at least definite – those were adult canine teeth and not milk or 'deciduous' teeth (milk canines have a 'dented' rear curve in profile and are smaller in both profile and diameter than adult teeth). So I plumped for the least possible age that I thought those teeth could indicate and said "About one year?" The correct answer was, as the body suggested, somewhere between 6 and 8 months. The friend and the local Forest Guards had monitored the cub's progress after losing her mother and reported that she was doing well and killing her own prey regularly.

This cub had adult canine teeth

So, nature, ever able to amaze us and enhance our theories, had accelerated this cub's development in at least one area of critical importance and prematurely (physiologically speaking) provided her with adult canine teeth, the most important tools for a tiger's survival. There are other examples of cubs defying probability and surviving to adulthood despite losing their mother before two years of age and there may be other accelerated physiological developments improving the cub's chances of survival. This example seems particularly fascinating, since the 'nature' part of 'nature and nurture' often defines features which are genetically determined or 'hard-wired'. Of course, some 'fixed' features can be adjusted or refined by experience, just as the stalking, catching and killing behaviour considered above, but physiological features such as tooth eruption would usually be considered genetically fixed within relatively narrow margins. Yet, as in this instance, physiological features (by which age could normally be determined) can be adjusted according to prevailing conditions, illustrating a rarely recognised flexibility of genetic mechanisms.

This example also illustrates the immense value of an unusual observation and the dangers of generalisation. The canine teeth of many, many captive cubs raised without their mother have erupted at the usual age of about one year old since, obviously, food is provided in captivity. In the wild, hunger makes the motherless cub try to catch, kill and eat animals and the prematurely frequent use of its milk canines presumably stimulates growth of adult canines (a concept so easily stated but so difficult to explain physiologically and genetically). Moreover, while the cub's behaviour is presumably stimulated by hunger, it is interesting to speculate (as it was in the case of the auditory experiments) on the element of conscious awareness / expectation involved on the part of the cub and the degree to which this might also influence the accelerated tooth eruption, as well as, say, adaptations to, or an acceleration of, territorial behaviour.

Now we turn our attention to how those teeth are used.

Prey may be killed by a throat bite, the tiger's jaws holding the victim's windpipe (trachea) closed, or by a nape bite breaking the spinal cord. Some have suggested that large prey are killed by the throat bite and medium-sized or small prey killed by the nape bite. Yet both Leyhausen and Schaller have cited cases of tigers (and lions) using either bite regardless of prey size. The only common distinction between the bites is, according to Leyhausen, that the cats (including the big cats), have an innate predisposition to learn the nape bite whereas the throat bite is only learned as a supplementary technique by experience. Indirect evidence for this are observations of the nape bite being given by cats *in addition* to the throat bite, after the prey is dead and sometimes during a pause after eating has commenced. Leyhausen never observed a throat bite being subsequently given to prey killed by a nape bite. With regard to a subsequent nape bite, given after killing the prey by another method '…the observer gets the impression that there is an air of compulsion about it, as if it had suddenly occurred to the animal that it had forgotten something essential.' (B44) Some tiger kills examined by this author have shown that both throat and nape bites have been used.

The throat and nape bites raise some interesting points. However, before considering these points, an examination of the skull, jaw and muscles will help us assess them.

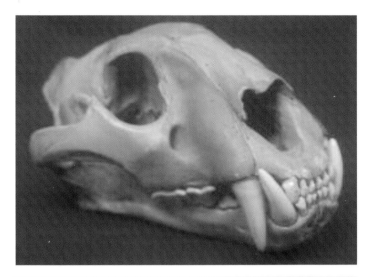

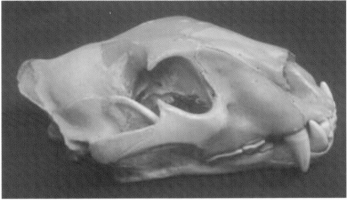

Tiger skull painted to identify the bones of which it is made: the parietal bone (yellow); the frontal bone (purple); the nasal bone (dark pink); the premaxilla bone (turquoise); two maxilla bones, one on either side of the skull (orange); two zygomatic arches, one on either side of the skull, made up of the jugal bone (light blue) and a process from the squamosal bone (light pink). The jaw is made up of a single bone: the dentary or mandible (unpainted).

© University of Edinburgh.
Published by kind permission of the University of Edinburgh Natural History Collections and with thanks to the curators.

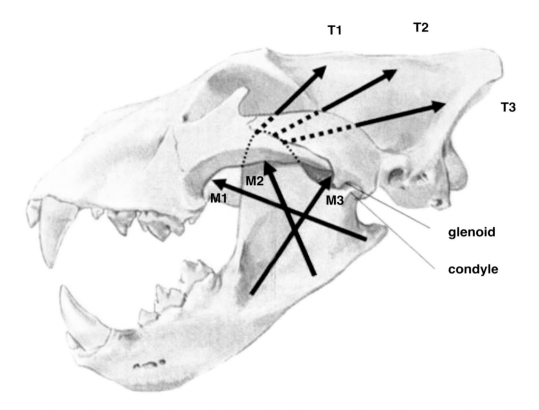

T1, T2, T3 the anterior, middle and posterior fibres of the left temporalis muscle attaching the top of the coronoid process of the mandible, located within (and invisible behind) the zygomatic arch, to the braincase and the sagittal crest – which extends along the length of the top of the braincase from neck to brow.

M1, M2, M3 the anterior, middle and posterior fibres of the left masseter muscle attached to the inner surface of the zygomatic arch and the recess of the mandible, which it fills completely.

Arrows indicate the lines of action of the muscles which close the jaws.

(After B26)

Holding vigorously struggling prey, sometimes of the size and strength of a gaur (an enormous wild ox), requires specialised teeth and great strength, both generally and of the jaws in particular. 'The jaws are short and powerful and the strong, bowed-out zygoma provides a firm attachment for the masseter muscle as well as ample space within for the passage of the temporalis fibres…the attachment area for the latter is enlarged by the development of a strong sagittal crest in the larger species and the wide, high braincase also provides a generous attachment area for neck muscles. The latter are extremely important, since the shock produced when the canines encounter sudden resistance must be transmitted back through the skull to the body. Skull architecture is in fact so arranged that stresses applied to canines or carnassials are transmitted back along smoothly curving strengthened bony arches. These strengthened arches are also so placed as to resist the forces applied to the skull and mandible when tension is developed in the jaw muscles.' (B26 reprinted by kind permission of Weidenfield and Nicolson, a division of Orion Publishing Group)

As a comparison, look in a mirror and clench your jaw tightly, you will see a slight bulging movement just above your temples, indicating the extent to which your temporalis muscles are attached to the side of your skull. In cats, the temporalis muscle continues around the side and up, over the braincase to the sagittal crest. Other muscles are associated with closing the jaws (pterygoidus, zygomatico-mandibularis) but the temporalis and masseter muscles are the two largest sets and provide the most powerful forces.

Carnivores also have a characteristic set of teeth called 'carnassials' comprising the last premolar in the upper jaw and the first molar in the lower. It is well-known that carnassials have a shearing or scissor action i.e. the teeth slide past each other, as do the blades of scissors. We know that the closing blades of scissors can push the object, if not restrained, forward and out of the blades. To prevent this, carnassials (seen in profile) have V shaped notches, in which the flesh is held. However, large lumps of flesh, bone, tendon and tissue move while the animal is eating, so the fore-paws help hold it in position. The toughness of some tendon and flesh often requires repeated slicing actions to detach a chunk and the repeated up and down motions of the jaws can make it appear as if the tiger is chewing. However, careful observation will reveal that, as soon as a chunk is finally and fully detached from the carcass, it is immediately swallowed, without being chewed. Big cats only use the carnassials on one side of their mouth at a time. The reason for this reveals a plane of jaw movement not usually recognised as possible for the big cats.

It is well known that the wide range of movement of herbivores' jaws enables vegetable matter to be ground and crushed. It is also commonly thought that, in contrast, carnivores' jaws can only move up and down, enabling them to grip struggling prey without risk of dislocating their jaws. This is not quite accurate since, although jaw movement is restricted in some ways as described below, a slight side-to-side movement is both possible and necessary, since the surfaces of the carnassial teeth do not shear past each other with each opening and closing of the jaws. There is a small gap between the outer surfaces of the lower carnassial teeth and the inner surfaces of the upper carnassials. Hence, 'To get a good scissor-like action with the cutting edges passing close together, the jaw must be moved laterally. This means of course that the carnassial teeth can only be in position for cutting on one side of the mouth at a time.' (B2)

The carnassials are used independently of the canines, dismembering prey after the canine teeth have killed it.

Jaw movements are, however, restricted in some ways: The contractions of the muscles which close the jaws contain components which can pull backwards on the inner surface, and forwards on the outer surface, of the lower jaw. This forms a twist which could dislocate the jaw (B26). In addition, as can be seen from the arrows on the skull diagrams, the temporalis and masseter muscles are so large that their anterior, middle and posterior fibres exert forces in different directions (when the jaws are completely closed T1 forms a near right angle with T3). This allows a powerful bite whether the jaws are wide open (more contribution from the temporalis) or closing shut (more contribution from the masseter). A twisting motion could also be caused by prey struggling in the grip of the jaws.

To prevent any twist and risk of dislocation, each area of articulation, the 'hinge' of the jaw, the almost cylindrical condyle at the rear of the lower jaw, fits closely and snugly into a deep transverse groove called the glenoid, in the squamosal bone. Furthermore, this groove has bony enlargements (called preglenoid and postglenoid processes), one each side, front and rear, effectively preventing any significant movement of the mandible fore and aft, and hence, in conjunction with movements in other directions, twisting. Being almost cylindrical, the hinges of

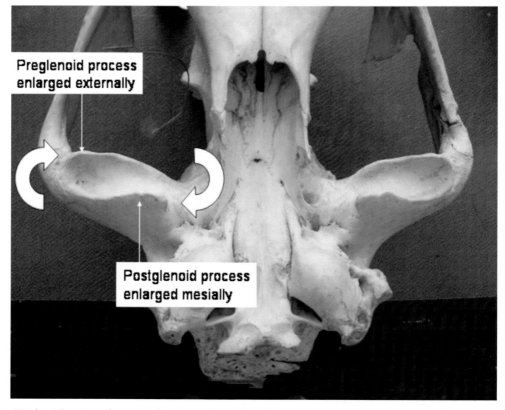

Preglenoid process enlarged externally

Postglenoid process enlarged mesially

Underside view of tiger skull without mandible. The bony protrusions or enlarged processes of the glenoid prevent movements indicated by block arrows but will allow slight lateral movement.

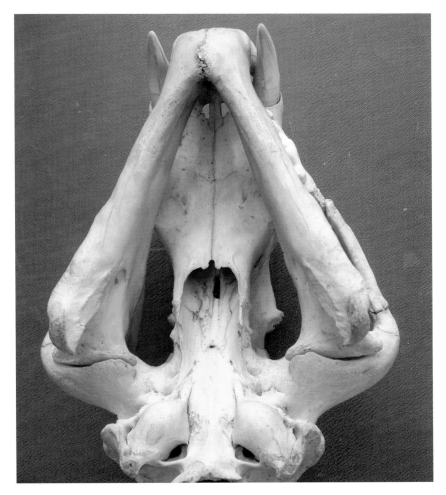

Underside view of skull with mandible in situ. The postglenoid processes can been seen curling over the inner ends of the condyle.

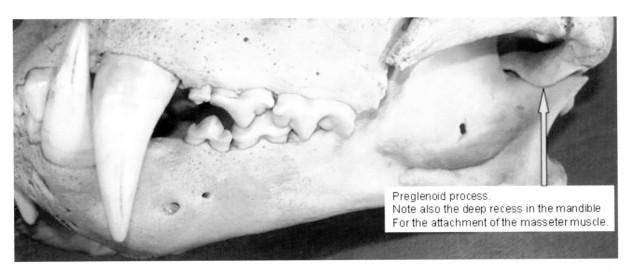

Preglenoid process.
Note also the deep recess in the mandible
For the attachment of the masseter muscle.

(With thanks to the British Museum of Natural History for the use of tiger skull 32-5-7-3)

the jaw can rotate and, within narrow margins, move laterally but the 'hinges' can neither move up or down, nor fore or aft

The skulls of tiger cubs examined (ranging from a few months old to over one year old) featured postglenoid processes but none showed any preglenoid processes – these were only present in the adult skulls examined. Although the sample size was small, this might indicate the ontogenetic development of the preglenoid process during maturation, perhaps stimulated by increasingly 'serious' use of the jaws.

These points provide a context in which we may consider the teeth and aspects of the nape and throat bites.

The size and shape of the canine teeth seem to be related to severing the spinal column. 'Although there are minor differences in skull proportion and in the size and degree of flattening of the canine teeth, the skulls of the Felidae are remarkably uniform…The (cheetah's) canines are small by felid standards and not very much flattened. This is probably correlated with a killing technique of biting at the throat (Kruuk and Turner, 1967; Eaton, 1970b, 1970d), which does not demand quite such specialised weapons as the method of breaking the spinal cord. Leyhausen has drawn my attention to the way the nasal aperture is bounded on either side by the roots of the upper canines and points out that a reduction in the size of the teeth permits the aperture to be enlarged. For an animal capable of such a burst of speed as the cheetah, increased air intake may be more valuable than enlarged canines. Strange though it may sound, it may therefore be true to say that the cheetah has small canines because it runs so fast.' (B26 reprinted by kind permission of Weidenfield and Nicolson, a division of Orion Publishing Group)

Masai Mara National Reserve, Kenya: Cheetah yawning and showing the relatively small canine teeth. Only two of her three silver-back cubs are visible.

During a killing bite the jaw muscles' enormous power is concentrated on:

- the jaw 'hinges' and
- the canine teeth

We have seen some of the adaptations of the hinges to withstand these forces and Ewer pointed out that shocks are transmitted away from the teeth along smoothly curving bony arches (another of these bony curves is formed by the canine teeth themselves since up to two-thirds of each tooth curves deeply into firm fixtures above the gum line). However, even allowing for this 'power transmitting' skull architecture, the enormous strength of the jaw muscles focused on the relatively fine points of the canine teeth might, when their shape is considered, suggest some risk to those teeth, especially when they meet solid bone. The cervical vertebrae of even medium-sized prey might be hard enough to pose a threat to the teeth. The canine teeth and their condition mean the difference between life and death for their owner (we have already considered tigers avoiding use of their teeth to hamstring and the premature appearance of those teeth when circumstances required them). Do the canine teeth, the operative tools of both the nape and throat bites, show any adaptations to prevent damage, in addition to those already mentioned?

'According to Leyhausen (J17b), the typical felid kill results from one of the canine teeth entering between two neck vertebrae, forcing them apart and breaking the spinal cord. He points out that the laterally compressed canines are admirably adapted to act in this way and much less so to bite directly on bone; (*this lateral compression makes their cross-section elliptical and is clearly, and strikingly, seen by viewing a tiger's canine teeth from the front; where they appear slim, if not slender, and from the side; where they appear broad and stout – author's comments*) indeed, he is of the opinion that the canines in different species are specifically adapted in size and shape to deal in this way with the neck vertebrae of their principal prey species. Such a technique at first sight seems incredible, since the chances against the canines striking the right place would appear to be very high. It seems too much to ask that, as it bites, the animal should search for the right spot and adjust its grip before biting home. Nevertheless, this may well be exactly what does happen. In the domestic cat, at least, mechano-receptors related to the teeth are abundant, especially around the canines (Jerge, 1963) and the jaw muscles have an exceedingly short contraction time (Taylor and Davey, 1968). Eccles and her co-workers (1968) also mention that the cat's muscle afferent nerves conduct extremely fast. The animal therefore possesses the physiological basis both for 'feeling' with its canines and for biting home with great speed once the teeth have found the correct position.' (B26 reprinted by kind permission of Weidenfield and Nicolson, a division of Orion Publishing Group)

This idea is discounted by such a seasoned tiger expert as Charles McDougal (pers. comm.) who stresses that the many tiger kills he has examined show completely broken and splintered cervical vertebrae and never any 'surgical' separation of vertebrae. Having been fortunate enough to have examined some kills with him, I have to agree that those kills did not support the theory. With a finger inserted into the holes made by the tiger's canines one can feel multiple jagged pieces of broken vertebrae, which we sometimes confirmed by cutting away the flesh and exposing the bones.

It is known that mammalian populations can develop 'cultural characteristics' including distinctive physiological and behavioural features only found in that population. So perhaps the idea has some validity in this way. Whether or not it does, it cannot be discounted entirely on the evidence currently available. We have simply not studied sufficient tiger populations in sufficient detail: the few long-term studies of wild tiger populations all put together cannot pronounce for all populations even within any one country, let alone for all tiger range countries past and present.

Notes on Hyoid Bones and Roars

The pharynx is the region of the throat just prior to its division into the oesophagus (carrying food to the stomach) and the trachea (carrying air to the lungs and held open by rings of cartilage. The upper portion of the trachea forms the larynx). There is a flap (the epiglottis) which prevents food or liquid falling into the trachea during ingestion. When the epiglottis, and hence trachea, is open, the mouth, pharynx, larynx and lungs make one continuous structure. I refer to the pharynx and larynx together as the vocal tract.

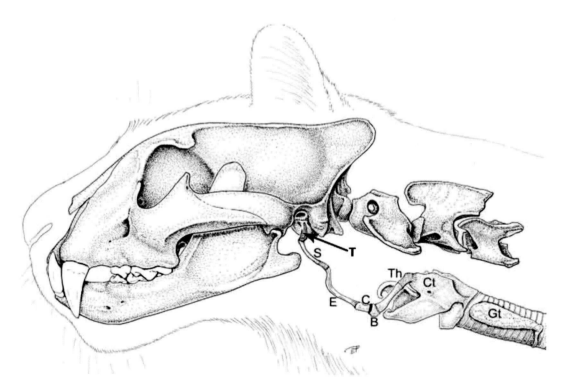

Tiger: larynx, cranial part of the trachea and the left side only of the hyoid apparatus.
T, Tympanohyoideum; S, Stylohyoideum; E, Epihyoideum; C, Ceratohyoideum;
B, Basiyoideum; Th, Thyrohyoideum; Ct, Cartilago thyroidea; Gt, Glandula thyroidea.

(Printed by kind permission of Wiley-Blackwell J31)

The vocal tract is supported by the hyoid bones (T,S,E,C, and Th in the diagram above) – one set on the left and an identical set on the right, bridged at the base by a single, shared Basiyoideum, forming a suspension structure similar, from a frontal perspective, to a 'U'. The basiyoideum also joins the root of the tongue (not shown) and the upper vocal tract. The hyoid bones of the Pantherinae or roaring cats are not fixed rigidly together but flexible, including an 'elastic' (i.e. ligamentous) epihyoid (J31).

This flexible arrangement allows the vocal tract to be lengthend and moved down into the throat. A lengthened vocal tract produces longer wavelengths (i.e. lower frequencies – deeper, bass sounds). The researchers (J31) refer to lower 'formant frequencies' which are an essential component of a roar. The reader may be more familiar with the term 'resonance'. Formants correspond to resonances, which is the tendency of a system to vibrate at peak amplitude (high energy) for any particular frequency. A vocalisation is made up of a number of different frequencies, each measured in cycles per second or Hertz (Hz) and a formant (a concentration of energy) is associated with particular frequencies, usually one in each 1000 Hz bandwidth. As a vocalisation comprises a number of 1000 Hz bandwidths, there are several formants for any particular vocalisation.

Red deer and Fallow deer also have a flexible hyoid apparatus, can also lower and lenghten their vocal tract, and also roar during the rut. Other cats (and deer) cannot lower the vocal tract, due to a non-flexible hyoid bone apparatus, and cannot roar.

In addition to this lowering of the vocal tract, the rearward aspect of the pharyngeal wall in the Pantherinae is elongated and has numerous longitudinal folds on its inner surface (when air from the lungs passes over these folds they vibrate and produce sound). In addition, 'the Pantherinae examined had an extensive and voluminous venous network…(and)…muscles (and) numerous collagenous and elastic fibres within the lateral pharyngeal walls and the soft palate' (J31).

It seems that these features together provide the ability to roar and Weissengruber et al (J31) 'offer a tentative definition of "roaring", which has till now been a confusing and elusive notion, in acoustic terms.' They suggest that roaring… 'has two distinct physiological and acoustic components:

- a low fundamental frequency, made possible by long or heavy vocal folds, which lead to the low pitch of the roar;
- lowered formant frequencies, made possible by an elongated vocal tract, which provide the impressive baritone timbre of roars.

Thus it is possible to have low-pitched calls that are not roars (e.g. a bullfrog vocalisation has a low fundamental but is not a 'roar'), or calls with low formants that are not roars (e.g. the trumpet call of cranes).' (J31) In jaguars, leopards, lions and tigers (and some species of deer), both physiological features combine and provide the ability to roar.

There has been some debate over whether big cats can purr. It appears that this vocalisation is also linked with the hyoid apparatus in that the flexible arrangement, whilst essential for roaring, prevents purring. A completely ossified hyoid apparatus allows for purring but not roaring. This author has never heard a vocalisation from a tiger that could be called purring.

The tiger has a comparatively wide range of vocalisations but it vocalises infrequently. Up to a dozen distinct calls have been described in literature but these notes attempt to supplement other published texts. Hence this last note on vocalisations concerns prusten, on which this author has read and heard unreliable reports, some even confusing it with purring.

Prusten, a term coined by the cat expert and German Professor, the late Paul Leyhausen, is a gentle puffing sound made by tigers rapidly expelling air through their mouth and nostrils, accompanied by a gentle vocal sound. Sometimes the head is lifted as the sound is made, clearly showing the lips vibrating as air is expelled. It is usually noted by observers as a greeting but cannot be restricted to greeting since it may be used by a tiger already in a group of tigers to appease aggression from another. As far as words can translate it, 'no threat' would seem to be the interpretation that covers its use on all occasions. It is important for tigers approaching each other to assess the mood and intentions of the other and prusten is used most frequently on these occasions, giving the impression that it is only a form of greeting, while the more important message communicated is reassurance to the other that no threat is intended. It is possible for humans to imitate it sufficiently well to gain the same response from a captive tiger particularly, as would be expected from the foregoing, on newly approaching the animal. Prusten is most definitely not purring (usually associated with pleasure or comfort) which, even if physiologically possible, would not (in terms of communication) be an appropriate substitute for prusten. In the author's experience prusten is the most frequently used of the vocalisations and is an important part of the tiger's social life, which we look at in the following sections.

It seems unlikely for captivity to have imposed any significant distortions on any of the behaviour described above, especially as related to young cubs. At about one year of age, a change comes over the cubs; they lose their playful cuteness and become small tigers, moving and behaving as adults. By two years of age they are fully grown in length and height, just 'filling out' in terms of bulk over the next few years. Two years also marks the onset of sexual maturity. In their first year the cubs might occasionally exhibit sexual behaviour (e.g. one cub clumsily trying to mount another) but cubs on a high-value, regulated diet, in the absence of stressful circumstances and with little else to do, are likely to explore the full range of their innate behavioural sequences and this early sexual behaviour does not indicate sexual maturity.

It is after sexual maturity that behaviour modified by captivity is most clearly seen, and includes aspects of territoriality and reproduction. The latter produces the most extreme and artificial effects imposed by captivity: cross-breeding.

Notes on Reproduction

Scientific studies in the wild and captive breeding programmes have provided much information on this topic but, as these notes attempt to offer some slightly more unusual information, only two aspects will be considered here: the first is due to some of the cubs maturing sexually during the chemical communication experiments recorded in Appendix 1. The second aspect concerns cross breeding between species of Panthera. Although never recorded in the wild, the highly artificial conditions of some captive arrangements have proved that such cross breeding is physiologically possible. Since some species share habitat, how does nature maintain reproductive isolation? It appears that both anatomical and ecological barriers are responsible. We look at anatomy first.

Unlike human females, female big cats do not ovulate at regular intervals but in response to intromission during coitus. During the days of the female's oestrus, mating takes place repeatedly, sometimes every few minutes, since the stimulation of intromission has to be repeated regularly to ensure ovulation. Thus it is likely that only vigorous, well-fed and energetic males pass on their genes.

Nature's processes are often subtle and there are surely many that we have not even begun to suspect exist, let alone study. The mating act probably has its own refinements and the multi-functionality of intromission (we have already considered three: ovulation, fertilisation and a possible selection pressure) is surely associated with the fact that all male carnivores (except those of the family Hyaenidae) have a bone in the penis (the os penis or baculum) which is species specific. Originally, examination of the baculum was thought to be a possible aid to taxonomy but it was found that closely related species had very different bacula and hence were no aid to classification. The reason for this and the link with mating behaviour is nicely summarised by Ewer 'In the mouse, pseudopregnancy can be induced by mechanical stimulation of the cervix. Diamond (1970) has recently shown that this is most successful if the temporal sequence of stimulation closely mimics the normal sequence of intromissions by the male. He is of the opinion that there is a specific coding of stimulus patterning to which the vagina is most responsive, which may serve as a reproductive isolating mechanism. It is thus quite possible that in the Carnivora, in addition to the timing of the sequence of intromissions, the characters of the baculum, by affecting the quality of the stimulation, may act in the same way. In these terms the bacular differences between closely related species are easily explicable as mechanisms contributing to reproductive isolation.'

Whilst tigers and lions are physically very similar (further details in sub section 'Predators, Prey and Territory') their bacula are very distinct (J6).

Panthera Leo (7cm)

Panthera tigris (12cm)

On rare occasions, in the artificiality of captivity, lions and tigers have been mated, producing 'tigons' (male parent a tiger) and 'ligers' (male parent a lion). Like all hybrids they are sterile. However, whilst the abnormalities of captivity can, on occasion, overcome the refinements of species-specific bacula and / or temporal sequences of intromission, the chances of such hybrids being produced in the wild is remote in the extreme due to additional 'ecological barriers'.

It is well known that the Gir forest in India is the only remaining location of Asiatic lions and holds no tigers. In India's past, although far greater populations of both lions and tigers co-existed, they would have been 'ecologically separated' by habitat requirements (tigers inhabiting heavy cover while lions lived in more open terrain – see 'Predators, Prey and Territories' below). Hence species-specific bacula, operating in conjunction with ecological barriers, helped ensure their reproductive isolation.

Although leopard habitats are co-extensive with both lion and tiger habitats, mating between tiger and leopard or lion and leopard is an even more remote possibility since lions and tigers will, given the chance, kill and eat leopards. However, once again, the abnormalities of captivity can overcome these barriers and a male leopard has been mated with a lioness to produce a sterile 'leopon', with a leonine mane and tail tuft, and a coat covered with leopard rosettes.

Notes on Predators, Prey and Territories

Volumes have been written on these topics, but we need only establish a few relevant concepts to consider the contents of this sub section.

It had long been known by local natives, hunters and naturalists that tigers tend to follow the same 'closed' or topologically circular path through their habitat and do so according to a fairly regular timetable i.e. they followed a 'beat', which they mark with various signs and scents. A basic definition of 'territory' is 'any defended area'. As tigers are known to occasionally fight with other tigers intruding on their 'beat', tigers exhibit territorial behaviour.

However, recent research, spanning different ecological settings over some decades, has revealed that tigers make more flexible use of land than simply 'staking out' portions of it in a strictly exclusive way. Hence the term 'territory' is now usually applied with a few qualifications. Some researchers refer to 'home ranges', which are areas shared by tigers and 'territories' which are areas from which other tigers are excluded by their 'owners'. However, on occasion, a home range can become a territory and vice versa.

It may be that tigers divide land use by space (area), time, and function (e.g. cover, water, prey and mating partners). Additional factors of age, sex, family relations, status of individual tigers and possibly other criteria as yet undiscovered by humans, may also affect the situation. Considering the range of tigers globally and their history in terms of millennia, recent research projects, all put together, still only constitute fragments of data. Even when we do make observations, we do not always know what we are observing in terms of the criteria just listed. Leyhausen and Wolff suggested the 'timetable' use of territory decades ago and suggested chemical communication as the mechanism for this. The idea is explored further in the sub-section on chemical communication below.

One feature thought to apply to all tiger populations was that male territories include (or at least overlap), the territories of females, with which they mate. However, even on this point different studies have provided different data. According to the Smithsonian studies in Chitwan, males mate exclusively with the females within their territory. Other studies (in Russia by D. Miquelle and his Russian colleagues and in southern India by K. Ullas Karanth) have suggested otherwise and the latter has observed a female mating with two different males within the same narrow time frame. How the following factors…

- 'territorial' aspects (areas marked by an 'owner', sometimes (or for some things) used exclusively and therefore defended physically against intruders), and
- 'home range' aspects (areas marked by sub-adults and 'visitors'/transients, shared resources (sometimes prey, cover and water, perhaps mates) with no intra-specific fighting)

interrelate will be fascinating to learn if wild tiger populations remain long enough for us to study. Traditionally the tiger was considered to be solitary, so relatively recent observations of tigers socialising stimulated great interest due to their being new and seemingly exceptional. It is now well known that the tiger, although essentially solitary, does have an active social life with obvious implications for any study of home ranges and territories. For now, tigers can still be said to be solitary and territorial but not in such a simple and exclusive way as previously thought.

Having established some guide lines regarding territories, how do they help us understand relations between predator and prey? It is well known that territorial behaviour regulates population since, in general and basic terms; animals not possessing a territory do not produce young. Hence population density is intimately related to territory sizes, and one factor influencing territory sizes is the availability of food.

However, while nature's principles are often simple to state, their practice and / or application can involve a range of diverse subtleties. For example in this context, various and reliable scientific works have shown that predator densities do not (as one might expect) increase with short-term increases in prey numbers. Nonetheless, in general and in the long-term, higher concentrations of prey tend to support higher concentrations of predators. A number of researchers have reported this for particular species of predator but, as Schaller has studied both lions and tigers, his work is mainly quoted in the following comparisons. With regard to the tiger, this section's comparisons are confined to the tigers of the Indian sub-continent and, with regard to lion prides (unless otherwise specified) all refer to East African lions living on savannah – the location of Schaller's research and, where they are quoted, of Bertram's and Packer's.

Schaller found that the area used by a pride is larger than usually needed since it, and consequently lion population density, is related to the amount of prey available in lean times (be they seasons or years) '…when fewer than the normal number of (*prey*) animals is present and the number of pride members is about the optimum. While the correlation between prey biomass and lion density is reasonably good, some factor or factors other than food must determine and maintain pride size at its optimum level when prey is abundant, a level below the one which is based on carrying capacity of the prey…The data suggest that lion density is regulated both by the food supply and by a behavioural mechanism.' (B58b).

With regard to the tiger, Schaller's conclusions are similar: 'It seems likely that there is a density level based on intra-specific intolerance which maintains the tiger population at or near an optimum both in relation to the food sources and independent of them.' (B58a).

Suggestions in the section below on chemical communication may be of interest both in relation to the 'behavioural mechanism' Schaller refers to with regard to lions, and the 'intra-specific intolerance' with regard to tigers.

For comparison with points made in later chapters please note that nature favours an optimum, rather than a maximum.

Although we know subtleties are operating, we can be confident that, from long-term perspectives and in general terms, the number of individual predators per unit land area is higher when prey density is higher, with predators occupying relatively smaller territories within that land area.

A lion's pride usually comprises a pair of related lions (often brothers) (observations of adult male numbers range from one to four (Schaller B58c), one to six (Bertram J4) or one to nine (Packer *et al.* J21) although it is unclear whether these are all adults) and five to nine related lionesses with which the males will mate (observations range from two to twelve (Bertram J4) or one to eighteen (Packer *et al.* J21). Schaller refers to 'up to about fifteen' lionesses but also cites prides (in total) of thirty seven and one of four). The pride maintains a territory of approx. 20 to 100 km² according to size of pride (Bertram J4).

Packer *et al* (J21) also refer to there being an optimal size of pride in Serengeti lion populations which can remain relatively constant for some years and seem independent of prey density. Interestingly, Packer et al found that over decades, the lion population does not (in terms of numbers of individuals comprising the pride) change gradually but in abrupt 'jumps' (J21). However, in whichever way the population fluctuates, it remains true that, in the long-term, lion numbers are positively correlated with prey numbers (provided, obviously, that other resources such as water and / or dens for lion cubs, are available). The correlation may occasionally be exhibited in the short-term if the increases or decreases in prey population are sufficiently large and sudden; for example, lion numbers have been known to show a rapid and large decline following the same in wildebeest and buffalo numbers due to a severe drought.

The Smithsonian work showed that average size of a territory for a male tiger is about 40 km² containing the smaller territories (e.g. 10 km² each) of three or four females, with which he will exclusively mate. The range of values from which these averages were calculated could vary as widely as the lion data with, for example, a very small male tiger territory measuring 19 km² and an extremely large one, 155 km². It also showed that neighbouring tigresses could be as closely related as lionesses in a pride. It was noted above that exceptions to exclusive mating by one particular male tiger have been observed. In this context, it would be interesting to know if the two male tigers observed by U. Karanth mating with one female were related.

So, comparing the data just given for lions and tigers, the lion's social structure, the pride, could, in one sense, be considered a 'compressed' version of the tiger's social structure, although both occupy (and on occasion defend) similar size areas of land. What factors allow for this 'compression'? Why do lions form prides but tigers do not?

Apart from their coats and social structure, tigers and lions share many similarities: they are generally equivalent in size and they prey on much the same sized animals while, despite occasional fatalities inflicted by other species, neither tigers nor lions could be said to be preyed upon. Research suggests that male tigers and lions show an emphasis on competing for females, whilst females show an emphasis on competing for resources to feed cubs. In terms of skeleton and musculature the lion is almost identical to the tiger. The few and relatively tiny differences (with different authorities referring to different distinguishing characteristics) include very small, and easily overlooked areas of the skull and small differences in the metacarpal and metatarsal bones (of the fore and hind feet respectively), requiring experience and expertise to identify. To the casual, or even meticulous, observer the skeletons and musculature not only appear but also are, for the most part, identical. Even amongst the four big cats representing the genus Panthera (lion, tiger, leopard and jaguar) the lion and tiger are the most similar. As mentioned above, one of the distinguishing characteristics of the genus Panthera is the ability to roar. Although one can distinguish between the roars of lions and tigers, they are more similar to each other than to those of the other big cats (however, despite this audible similarity, the arrangement of the hyoid bones does provide a distinguishing feature between lions and tigers. 'In the lion…the Thyrohyoideum and the thyroid cartilage are connected by an elastic ligament, whereas in the tiger there is a synovial articulation.' (J31)). Species specific bacula have already been noted.

That nature has produced (apart from their coats) such similar animals as lions and tigers, but with seemingly very different social structures, must surely be instructive. Coat patterns and colours correspond to habitats. That animals have to adapt to their habitats is too well known to require elaboration but what is interesting in this case is the particular features of those habitats which, it is suggested here, have determined the different social structures.

Both Asian and African habitats (prior to the 20th century) provided an abundance of various prey species supporting a high population density of tigers, lions and smaller carnivores such as smaller cats, wild dogs and hyenas, each with their specific social structures. A particular social grouping may even be flexible enough to adapt to particular circumstances e.g. the size of group in which lions hunt gazelle is smaller than that used to hunt wildebeest (B58c). However, size of prey and prey density cannot be the only relevant factors influencing pride formation since the remaining population of Asiatic lions in the Gir Forest of India formed prides amidst relatively low prey densities (more recent data explored further below) and this is not just a result of modern human-driven degradation – neither Indian nor Nepalese habitats have (at least in recent geological history) supported the size of herds seen on African savannah.

It is suggested that another critical factor contributes *firstly* and most importantly, to co-operative hunting which is then *followed by* pride formation: this critical factor is visibility. It is suggested that prides form only where, given a sufficient prey-density, predator and prey are *relatively easy to detect visually.*

Whilst lions can astound a human observer with their ability to hide in savannah habitat, merely one visit to each of savannah and jungle habitats leaves no doubt as to which represents heavier cover.

The lion behind the lioness illustrates the first point. Lifting one's eyes to view the surroundings illustrates the second

Enormous herds of large prey animals on open savannah benefit the lion by making its prey easily detectable, since a standing lion can survey large areas of ground. The disadvantage of their own greater visibility can be offset by both the predators' ability to significantly reduce their visibility (by stalking belly to ground) and by co-operative, or at least, group hunting – also made possible by the prey's constant visibility. Schaller noted that at least two lions hunting were twice as successful as one lioness hunting alone. On occasions, greater visibility actually contributes to hunting strategy insofar as a lioness may reveal her presence to prey, causing them to run away from her toward cover sufficient to conceal other lionesses lying in wait. This strategy is obviously more likely to succeed if a number of individuals are influenced to run in the 'right' direction, especially as predators will be opportunistic and allow developing circumstances to determine which individual or individuals they take (sometimes as many as five animals may be killed (B58c)). So, in summary, savannah provides high density and densely grouped, easily visible large prey, and *some* cover to hide a large, stalking predator.

In contrast to savannah, tiger habitat is densely forested, restricting visibility. The benefit of cover for the prey is offset by the same benefit to an individual tiger. If tigers in a hypothetical hunting group did stalk prey in a similar way to lions, severely restricted visibility compromises co-operative hunting not only because predators cannot see each other but also because a herd of prey running in heavy cover makes it more difficult, if not impossible, for pursuing predators to assess which individual is slower than others or; if prey takes an opportune (or simply visible) route, which prey animal is nearer to another (if any) co-operating predator(s). In dense cover, solitary hunting by ambush is a better strategy.

The importance of visibility is consistent with the importance of sight for lions and tigers, since it is the primary sense they use when hunting, the nose being of little or no significance (see section on chemical communication for more details). Schaller noted that the Serengeti lions ignored the wind direction even though they were more successful catching prey hunted upwind than downwind. It seems that the benefits of co-operative hunting more than compensate for those lost by ignoring wind direction. The solitary tiger does not use its nose to hunt but does take into account wind direction when stalking its prey.

A single large predator in wide open spaces cannot help but advertise its presence and so reduce its chances of approaching prey closely enough to make a kill. Co-operative hunting helps offset this disadvantage – even male lions looking to take over a pride are often in pairs. However, it is not suggested that lions never make a kill on their own; we are considering general trends and overall influences. It would be interesting to know whether the single hunter, the occasional lion / lioness without a pride, adapts to its situation by adopting any or all of the following behavioural techniques:

•   hunting from heavier cover
•   taking wind direction into account when stalking
•   appropriating the kills of other predators more regularly than pride-based lions.

In summary, the tiger's hunting strategy shows an emphasis on solitary ambush while lions' hunting strategy shows an emphasis on co-operation.

For carnivores, obtaining food is the most difficult and important requirement to be met – and met most regularly, amidst competition. Hence, if co-operative hunting can be established, other areas of co-operation (e.g. shared suckling of cubs by lactating lionesses, territory protection by the group) can easily follow (whereas it is not so easy to imagine the powerful and dangerous instincts associated with hunting following smoothly and co-operatively from other features of pride living). Co-operative hunting has been suggested (and discounted) by scientists as a reason for pride formation, but this author has not heard of a high visibility of predators and prey also being taken into consideration as a stimulus to co-operative hunting. However, this 'visibility factor', because it relates directly and immediately to the most powerful stimulus most regularly experienced could, perhaps, be the extra feature that elevates co-operative hunting to the principal stimulus for pride formation (provided, of course, those conditions making visibility important, such as prey density, and size of prey and predator, are satisfied).

The absence of co-operative hunting in tigers corresponds to the absence of a 'pride', but not to an absence of a highly developed social system. U. Karanth's observation of two males mating with a single tigress provoked speculation above that the males might be related. If they were, it could imply a type of 'loose' or 'extended' pride pattern emerging, but not fully forming, due to the absence of any need for co-operative hunting. Jim Corbett noted that mating tigresses might be accompanied by more than one male. Male tigers are notoriously aggressive when escorting a female in oestrus and both can be dangerously 'playful'. In a letter to a friend, Corbett referred to the two occasions on which he was forced to climb a tree and on both it was due to accidentally walking on to tigers' mating grounds. 'On one of these occasions the tigress was accompanied by two tigers, and on the other there appeared to be several, but time did not permit of my counting them.' (Printed by kind permission of O.U.P.)

It may be relatively high prey densities distributed over a variety of Asiatic habitat types (savannah-type; scrub and grassland as well as dense forest) that helps explain how tigers used to co-exist with Asiatic lions (and previously cheetahs) in India. The different types of habitat separated tigers and lions ecologically, the former in dense forest and the latter in open forest, scrub and 'savannah-type' habitat. (The now extinct Indian cheetah also required more open habitat to effectively run down prey but, as it is sometimes deprived of kills by lions (if not occasionally killed by them) and exhibits a number of other unique physiological and behavioural features, it is not directly comparable with either lion or tiger). No doubt, predators occasionally took opportunities to kill out of their usual environs but overall a separation was maintained by habitat types.

The correlation between prey density and predator territory sizes would predict that, in the long-term, as prey density decreases, territories of tigers and lions have to increase, with a corresponding reduction in tiger / lion density. However, if the pride structure can only be maintained above a certain lower threshold of prey density inhabiting visually relatively 'open' habitat, the pride would disappear below that threshold. As this model would predict, during the twentieth century, with its general decline in all large mammalian herbivores and their habitat, it is the lion in India, not the tiger, which has disappeared first, leaving the remaining and now famous population in India's Gir Forest, in which there are no tigers. The Gir Forest it is not lush, dense forest but 'very dry teak forest…with degradation stages…(of) dry deciduous scrub forest and dry savannah forests.' (Champion and Sheth 1964). The densest type of forest is only found bordering the rivers and streams, elsewhere there is scrub and grasslands (known as 'vidis'). Hence, compared to a lush jungle, the Gir Forest is dry and mixed with scrub and savannah type areas i.e. relatively open, allowing both predator and prey to be relatively easily detected by sight and therefore both conducive to, and more frequently necessitating, co-operative hunting.

Research in the 1960s and early 1970s (B44) has referred to lions in desert-like areas in South-west Africa living in pairs with their young. This would tally with our speculation since the desert-like areas would not support large prey in large herds (nor, therefore, large prides) but the high visibility of such habitat means that co-operative hunting by the pair would probably bring success rates neither could achieve alone (as noted by Schaller, albeit in a different ecological setting). The same research has also reported that smaller prides correspond to prey scarcity and has cited the Gir Forest lions as an example. However, recent observers of lions at Gir might contend that, whilst the Gir Forest has relatively low prey densities, the lion prides are large and, at time of writing, comparable to East African prides. It is suggested here that the following factors contribute to the current relatively large Gir Forest lion prides: In addition to wild prey animals, the lions take domestic stock (large herds of cattle graze in Gir Forest) and also eat carrion which significantly supplements their food supply. Due to their being a tourist attraction, the Forest Department have also been known to provide baits as well.

If, in the Gir Forest, prey density dropped still further and / or domestic animals were unavailable and / or the habitat became more densely covered in vegetation, would lions adopt the territorial structure of tigers or at least modify/reduce their pride structure? Each species is adapted to its ecological niche and cannot 'think things through and decide to change'. Lions that survived by developing behaviour such as that suggested above for solitary lions and / or other techniques such as those of the lions of South-west Africa just referred to, might well give rise to a race of lion that is essentially a solitary hunter. However, since large predators are not usually able to cope with the rapidity of ecological change driven by humans, extinction is likely to occur before adaptation. With regard to the human-driven degradation of African savannah, we can see that whilst its 'physical structure' is damaged, disturbed or reduced overall, a lion's eyes (for now at least) sees much the same 'ecological structure' i.e. as far as individual prides are concerned, relatively large herds of easily detectable prey species, in the same sort of habitat, remain.

To avoid keeping 'all eggs in one basket' the Indian Forest Department might one day relocate some of the Gir Forest lions to another Reserve – and one that might contain tigers. The above speculation suggests that factors including habitat type; prey density and how easily it is visually detected; lion density and the density of competing predators in ecological niches currently occupied, would best be considered by the Indian authorities if and when they attempt a re-location of some of those last remaining Asiatic lions. It would be interesting to see how the lions adapt to new habitat, the availability of prey and to tigers, since neither present-day tigers nor lions, unlike their forebears, have any experience of each other.

For all the variations and exceptions to rules we might point out, fundamentally the tiger is an animal of the jungle and the lion is not, and for all the similarities between these animals, the contrast in their habitats surely underlies the contrast in their social structures. Playing for a moment at being nature's designer; if we took lions out of savannah, scrub or open forest and put them into dense jungle, the vegetation would reduce the male's mane to a ruff; the jungle's smaller herds and lack of long-range visibility would compromise co-operative hunting and fragment prides. The uniform shade of coat would be broken up to match the dappled light and colours of a jungle. We would then recognise this beast as a tiger. Similarly, a tiger taken out of the jungle and put in savannah, scrub or open forest to prey on enormous herds over vast open plains, would be more successful by practising co-operative hunting. The striped coat, vivid in open spaces, would have to be changed to an overall shade blending with available cover. A male tiger's ruff might develop into a mane – and we would then call this beast a lion. If you still doubt the point, compare the number of television screenings of lions hunting, to those of tigers hunting – it is easier for cameras, and lions, to follow hunts on savannah than in jungle.

A brief review of the genus Panthera might help put all this speculation into a clearer perspective. The jaguar is not subject to predation but nor does it have anywhere near the same prey density available to it as do East and West African lions and its habitat is jungle hence, according to the reasoning put forward here, we would expect the pride form of social structure to be absent. Leopards cannot kill prey as large as that killed by lions or tigers. However, of the smaller prey species available to it, some of these collect in herds or groups on savannah, so could 'prides' of leopards form? The leopard's smaller stature and lower shoulder height mean that, even on savannah, visibility is restricted (while a panoramic view may be available from a tree, the leopard has to descend to make use of it). Presumably, the size and frequency of short grass or undergrowth (up to but not exceeding a leopard's shoulder height) combined with sizeable herds of smaller prey animals are insufficient to have stimulated co-operative hunting, and hence the formation of 'leopard prides'. The features and factors actually prevailing for leopards favour solitary hunting. Moreover, unlike lions and tigers, leopards are subject to occasional predation (by lions, tigers, hyenas and wild dogs) but nature has provided a third dimension to their territories via its tree-climbing abilities (giving a sense of balance to the leopard and the ecosystem).

A puma, while not a member of the genus Panthera, is a large cat and will attack deer. An adult North American Bison would probably be too large for it to tackle but young bison would be vulnerable. Nonetheless, in the context of this speculation, it may be that 'prides' of pumas never developed and / or that pumas are not a species of Panthera because the ecological niche for preying upon (what were) vast herds of easily visible bison was filled by wolf packs, which do hunt co-operatively, albeit with a different strategy to lions.

This speculation would suggest that the same principle explains why neither Indian wolves nor Indian wild dogs form packs anywhere near the size of, for example, Canadian timber wolves (tundra) or African wild dogs (savannah). Neither wolves nor African wild dogs stalk, but their strategy of co-operative hunting (running down the prey by successively replacing the lead dog(s)) is still primarily dependent on visibility. Indian wolves (south of the Himalayas) and Indian wild dogs, living in habitat preventing long range visibility, form very small groups or are solitary (interestingly, wolves at higher altitudes in the Himalayas – with sparse vegetation and cover – do congregate in packs of half a dozen or more).

The dog family's scenting abilities are acute and may suggest visibility is not so important for them to hunt effectively. However, sprinting and leaping prey animals disappear before there is time to scent the trail, so dogs still depend on visibility to hunt. Presumably the degree to which it is possible for groups of dogs to effectively hunt in cover is the degree to which wolf and wild dog have prospered in, say, India. The dhole or Indian wild dog lives in small family units, or several family units combined, to form a pack, but each individual animal is small – so the 'size' (biomass) of the group is small.

However, the possibility of a sufficiently large pack of dholes being in direct competition with a tiger is not only suggested by the fact that large packs will take the same prey as the tiger but also, as tradition has it, occasionally the tiger itself. To the author's knowledge there has been no reliably

From the proximity and apparent indifference of the gaur, these dholes are not about to hunt

recorded observation of such, but tales of hunters, naturalists and natives are sufficient to keep the question open, and it would fit with our current speculation. By the same token of direct competition, tigers will also occasionally kill wild dogs and / or take their prey if opportunity offers.

Do large packs of dholes confound the ideas just explored? If and when 'large' packs of dholes do occur, how can they hunt co-operatively in tiger habitat i.e. areas of restricted visibility? This author has heard reliable reports in India of observers seeing, from a suitable vantage point, that a group of dholes were somehow favourably adjusting their positions, both in relation to prey and to each other, without the dholes being able to see one another. This raises the fascinating possibilities of other means of communication, necessarily utilising very rapid transmission and response. The relatively newly researched areas of communication by sound at frequencies too high or too low for human detection suggest one possibility, especially considering the hearing abilities of dogs in general.

(With regard to the tiger, some research has investigated the 'infra-sound' components in tiger vocalisations, including that known as the 'coughing roar'. As co-operative hunting by tigers has yet to be observed, it would suggest that such communication, even if possible, has not developed for this purpose).

In summary, habitats supporting large, high density prey living in high density herds with *high visibility* provide opportunities for large, high density predators to employ *co-operative hunting, which leads to pride formation*. Large, high density prey living in heavy cover provides for a high density of large predators but the restricted visibility prevents effective co-operative hunting, and therefore, pride formation does not occur. However, the absence of prides does not mean an absence of a social system. If anything, a high density of predators requires a fully developed social system to allow predators to co-exist without wasting energy, or risking injury, in inevitably frequent encounters, and potential confrontations, with each other.

Predator Densities

We are now in a position to consider what these reviews of territories and predator/prey densities could mean for conservation.

Increasing human populations, technology, commercial activities and hunting have reduced prey and predators across all habitats. The remaining tigers were compelled to disperse through (where still possible) expanded territorial or home ranges, hunting fewer animals in heavy cover (even heavier due to being browsed and grazed by fewer herbivores). Lions maintained their pride structure in some areas of east, west, central and southern Africa but lived in larger territories where, despite fewer prey animals overall, the remaining prey still collected in large and easily visible herds. This was the situation when scientific study of lions and tigers began during the 20th century.

In this book we are primarily concerned with tigers and the following speculation will be confined mainly to them. Do we have any evidence for tiger densities before modern scientific studies? Yes, the memoirs of European hunters and the hunting records of Maharajahs and shikaris. Whilst less than scientifically rigorous, they are both abundant and consistent in that they report staggeringly high numbers of tigers killed in relatively tiny areas of India and Nepal in a matter of days or weeks during the last few hundred years – since, happily, not all tigers fell to guns, the population was even higher than the total killed. A small selection is included below to indicate the sort of density common to at least the Indian sub-continent and just, geologically speaking, yesterday.

(Today, the Sundarbans Reserve probably holds more tigers than any other Reserve in the Indian sub-continent (or even the world) but it will not be used for comparison in this context since its unique habitat and unusually high proportion of man-eating tigers introduces a bias, making both data collection and its tiger population unrepresentative. See 'Notes on Man-Eating' below).

The highest population (by far) is currently credited to Corbett Tiger Reserve (approx. 1300 km² or 500 sq. miles) which, according to the last census figures available at time of writing (the 2008 census), optimistically claims 164 tigers. A modern Tiger Reserve of around 1500–2000 km² (579-772 sq. miles) is well stocked by today's standards if it can claim c. 50 tigers.

In stark contrast, Perry (B53) refers to a George Palmer who, between 1832 and 1862, was reported to have killed one thousand tigers. The literature also records a number of Maharajah's each personally having killed more than one thousand tigers. An even more striking impression is gained by considering totals shot in shorter time periods and relatively tiny areas: in 1862, Gordon-Cummings and his companions killed nine tigers in five days hunting within an area 'half-a-mile in diameter' on a tributary of the Narbada River (central India) (B30). Even up to the early 20th century, in areas where there was little or no human disturbance and prey was abundant, high densities of tiger still occurred: In 1921 General Wardrop killed seven adult tigers during one week's hunting in one Indian State. Whilst a State is a very large area, Wardrop killed them all from the *same* tree in beats along the *same* ravine within that *one week*! (B71). Up to the mid-twentieth century, Nepal's lush southern forest and grassland held abundant prey but suffered little or no human disturbance. Smythies (B63) describes a ten week hunt in the winter of 1938-39, through the Chitwan valley (an area mostly made up by what is now Chitwan National Park – approx. 932 km² (360 sq. miles)) and neighbouring grassland and forest to the south and east, killing 120 tigers. This was just one of the hunts between 1933 and 1940 during which Prime Minister Rana of Nepal and his guests shot 433 tigers, with no noticeable effect on the tiger population (B50).

The sex ratio and ages of the animals killed would shed some light on these high-density populations and hence their social structure, but I do not know of sufficient data recorded at that time, let alone how accurate it might be. Reliable, systematic (non-anecdotal) observations relating to the natural history of tigers during the 18th, 19th and early 20th centuries are rare to the point of non-existence. The 'hunter-naturalists' such as Brander, Burton and Corbett, were relative late-comers and even then they represented a very small proportion of the hunters of their generation – most of whom were only interested in killing the animals. As Leyhausen wrote: 'If we want to examine more closely what relationships might possibly exist between individuals of an allegedly solitary mammalian species, we are in a very bad position indeed. For the main reason why so many mammals are said to be solitary seems to be that they can only be shot one at a time. Very little field work has been done on such species…' (J17a)

Science, quite correctly, only works with data collected scientifically. It cannot base reliable conclusions on anecdote or hearsay. Hence old hunting records and memoirs are inadmissible from a scientific perspective and we have no means by which we could refute or refine these records of extremely high density tiger populations. However, this is not a scientific paper and common sense allows us to see that the hunting records, for whatever they lack in detail and rigour, all taken together are a considerable corpus of consistent data and do undoubtedly indicate significantly higher tiger densities than any known during the late 20th century. To emphasise; the point being made here is not that in years gone by there were more forests, more prey and hence more tigers but many, many more tigers in any one forest (or unit of land area) than has been known for more than half a century (and, obviously, these amazingly high densities must be correlated with high density of prey species, which are also referred to in the memoirs).

Hunters' records and memoirs also provide insights to the natural world of the past and, as such, may not be such a 'poor relation' to modern scientific studies for the following reasons. They remind us of the tiny window in time and space that our modern research reveals to us. The territorial structure, ecology in general and population dynamics of the tiger as studied in a few localities in the late 20th century might only be temporary adjustments to prevailing conditions. Hence, data from the late 20th century should not be assumed to give a definitive picture of nature's original population dynamics for tigers. Quite apart from the animals dispersing or attempting to disperse as described above, modern ecology must surely be influenced by the massive increase of hunting produced by the invention of firearms in the immediately preceding centuries, an increasing human population with associated habitat degradation, reduction of prey numbers and species, general environmental disturbance and pollution. Hence we might be studying symptoms of 'ecological disease' rather than healthy nature. Compiled as this period of unparalleled destruction unfolded, the old hunting records are the only evidence available for this period.

Perhaps, as in previous centuries when far higher prey densities prevailed, the tiger's social structure is able to cope with far higher densities of tigers? Interesting hints of this are provided by the relatively recent and fragmented evidence of active socialising and grouping by the relatively few tigers remaining today, which has been recorded, for examples, in Corbett's films (see next chapter) and by C. McDougal and F.S. Rathore. Obviously, there must be upper limits to predator densities and it is also recognised that these limits are set by factors additional to prey density (as noted in the Schaller quotes above and the sub section below on chemical communication) but, whatever they are, they were, and those limits may still be, much higher than any currently known. Modern scientific studies do accept that some compression of current predator densities is possible; however, the scientific models have been developed during what is, from nature's perspective, devastation i.e. since the disappearance of vast tracts of wilderness and high density prey and predators. As a consequence, the scientific models are very modest in their suggestions. For present purposes the evidence of the old hunting records is taken as valid and, combined with the above speculation regarding 'territorial compression', used to suggest a conservation strategy.

It is well known that environmental abuse by humans includes the

- poaching of prey species
- displacement of prey species due to domestic stock
  (When domestic buffalo, cattle or goats move into forest, natural herbivores move out. However, the tiger and leopard are territorial and their behaviour patterns cannot be adjusted as rapidly as humans affect their food supply. Domestic animals also bring the risk of fatal diseases (such as anthrax) to wild populations)
- removal and / or spoiling of food sources for prey species

As noted above, one possible adjustment by predators to reducing prey density is to increase their territory size. However, since human activity also directly degrades or destroys habitat – the very compensatory factor needed to offset the other harmful human activities just listed – the threat to the tiger's (and leopard's) existence is greatly and dangerously compounded.

Do these problems also suggest their solution? Can our speculation on the high-density tiger populations of previous centuries help us conserve what remains?

Our speculation would predict that a long–term increase in prey density, in a particular area of suitable habitat, will result in a decrease in size of tiger territories and an increasing tiger population. We have already seen that artificially boosted prey density is one possible factor boosting the pride sizes of the Gir Forest lions.

(The speculation above suggests that, even if prey density is boosted, 'prides' of tigers would probably not form – at least not in terms of co-operative hunting. We have already seen that some sort of social structure would be necessary to allow for seven tigers to be found in one ravine and for those social gatherings, including the sharing of kills, which recent observers have reported. Apparently, on those occasions when tigers share a kill it is usually structured insofar as only one eats at a time, in contrast to lions where, after the dominant male(s) have fed, it is a free for all. This distinction may relate to another distinction between lions and tigers as observed by those who have worked with both species. To avoid inappropriate 'my team' mentality interfering with our assessment, let it be said that a lion is a magnificent beast and that there is nothing on Earth braver than a mating lion. However, due to the pride structure, any lion, whatever attributes it possesses or lacks, can survive provided it can get into a position at the kill to gulp down enough meat. Therefore individuals which are not necessarily the sharpest in skills or intelligence can survive to pass on their genes. In contrast, solitary hunting means total self-reliance (the social gatherings just referred to are rare). Therefore tigers (and leopards for the same reason) are far more sharp and canny than lions. When working with them in captivity one quickly learns that lions are happy to be left alone and, with rare exception, will mind their own business. Even a mating lion, which will literally attack anything that approaches his lioness too closely, will not seek conflict. Tigers have a different aura about them and usually closely observe all that goes on around them.)

Captivity provides an artificial but nonetheless valid example of extremely high population densities. In 'safari park' situations, as tiger cubs become adults, it is usually necessary for the keepers to manipulate the combination of individuals in the reserve to prevent fighting and fatalities – keeping different individuals in their overnight cages on different days. Nonetheless, even those remaining together in 'safari park' situations still represent a very high population. Moreover, social groupings observed in the wild last for a few days before individuals disperse, whereas the high density of 'safari park' tiger groups is continuous. Bearing in mind that a small territory for a wild tigress is in the region of 10 km², occasionally shared with one or two sub-adult or even adult female offspring, 'safari park' situations might hold 5 – 8 adult tigers in an area approximately one tenth of this size or less! Whilst factors including age, sex, sexual maturity and individual characteristics no doubt influence the situation, surely one factor in particular – as artificial as the relatively tiny enclosure – allows for these very high captive population densities: the regular, continuous supply of adequate food. Adequate food was also supplied by Corbett in order to make his film of tigers referred to in the next chapter. These considerations support the idea that prey influences predator social structures in more ways than one.

Could this knowledge be used for conservation purposes? If, in the long-term, increasing prey density increases predator density, the above considerations suggest that a re-introduction of prey species would boost tiger populations. Re-introducing herbivores is far less fraught with problems than re-introducing carnivores since food for herbivores is easily and continually available with no critical period during which, like predators, they need to learn how to acquire it. After a thorough investigation of the 'test' habitat, including such features as the availability of vegetation for grazers or browsers and year-round water holes, herbivore re-introduction could proceed gradually, in stages, whilst its effects on the habitat and other species were monitored. Particular prey species should be selected according to their suitability as tiger prey and there is a wealth of information from modern research available on this topic. Where abundant vegetation is growing without being cropped by naturally present herbivores a suitable number of a particular species could be re-introduced e.g. a small herd of cheetal (spotted deer) could be introduced to graze unused grassland; a small group of sambhar (large deer) could be introduced to browse leafy woodland etc. This might bring other benefits by reducing a 'dominant' species of plant (one that 'crowds out' others), allowing other species to grow, thereby increasing variety and hence stability (for other examples please see the 'Presentation to Forest Guards' in Chapter V). However, as a note on the adaptability of species to environmental circumstances, in the Sundarbans Reserve, cheetal have become browsers since, in the mangrove swamps, there is nothing to graze.

Applying this same principle to the next level down in the ecological hierarchy, would suggest that a carefully monitored re-introduction of indigenous plant species in degraded habitat (sadly, the status of much land area near, or even within, Reserves) would start to rebalance imbalanced ecosystems and may even result in increased herbivore populations without their artificial re-introduction.

A successful re-introduction of sufficient herbivores, by whatever method, must in due course, result in increased tiger (and leopard) or lion (and leopard) numbers and hence contribute to tiger / lion and leopard conservation. It might be too obvious to mention but for the sake of thoroughness, this suggestion could only ever have validity where poaching and habitat degradation has been eliminated or reduced to negligible levels. No amount of prey can compensate for too many snares, poison or bullets, or an absence of water and suitable vegetation. Under a good Director, some Parks and Reserves have significantly reduced human interference and have ideal resources but none, to this author's knowledge, have ever launched reintroductions of, or population boosts to, prey species, or a significant, structured re-planting of indigenous plant species.

While we gain some encouragement from modern research which allows for the possibility of some modest 'compression' of territory sizes, consideration of the old hunting records suggests that the compression need not necessarily be modest. The exact degree of compression possible and the value, if any, of the historical records and / or any of the above speculations, is not important compared to the conservation possibilities they suggest, which have a validity of their own. The tiger situation being critical, they should, in this author's opinion, be seriously considered by the relevant authorities as soon as practically possible. Although modern scientific research has pointed to the importance of prey species for the welfare of the tiger and the dangers of it being reduced by human interference, no suggestion, to this author's knowledge, has ever been made to reintroduce prey species, yet the gravity of the conservation situation 'on the ground' is no longer academic and effective action is urgently required.

Conservationists often lament that the relative ease with which herbivores can be reintroduced does not apply to carnivores. Yet, in this sense it does – if we reintroduce herbivores, nature will 're-introduce' the carnivores (where there are still some remnant populations). The author has first-hand experience of Tiger Reserves and surrounding degraded habitat where experimental reintroduction of plants and / or herbivores would be relatively easy and inexpensive to organise.

With the tiger at the apex of healthy Asian ecosystems it is well known that conservation of viable tiger populations results in the conservation of the whole ecosystem. The tribal people, who know little or nothing of science, or reading, or writing, refer to the tiger as the 'guardian of the forest' which says the same thing in a more poetic way. The cycle incorporating the two is described in an Indonesian proverb used in the Guards' presentation reproduced in chapter V: "Tigers are killed without forest and the tiger-less forest is cut down – so the tiger should guard the forest and the forest should guard the tiger." In this sense, tiger conservation would be greatly invigorated if indigenous trees were planted in accordance with the decades of forestry knowledge accumulated and now stored in the Indian Forest Department. It has often been said that the Forest Department has had much to learn about animals since it became responsible for the wildlife within the forests in the late 20th century. Yet, much of its knowledge of maintaining healthy trees could help tigers and all other forest life – all things are connected and trees form a foundation for terrestrial ecosystems.

These types of re-introduction are strongly recommended as conservation strategies regardless of any validity the comparisons between lion and tiger social structures may have. Similarly, although the evidence of very high tiger population densities in previous decades or centuries is considered valid by this author, it too is unnecessary to establish the validity of these re-introduction programmes. All that is necessary is a serious and sincere attempt 'on the ground'. It is hoped that some herbivore and / or vegetation re-introduction programmes be put into practice in the wild and their validity or otherwise established for tiger, and hence all other Asian species' conservation (more on conservation issues in Chapter V). Just after completion of this section the author became aware of a programme of replacing lantana (a non-indigenous weed) with indigenous plants in Corbett Tiger Reserve. There have been numerous lantana eradication schemes in many Reserves but they are not usually accompanied by re-planting schemes. No details were available with regard to species selected, densities of planting and associated insect/animal activities – but all credit to them and best wishes for the continuation and full development of their scheme.

Developing co-ordinated re-planting and breeding programmes for herbivores (and some omnivores) for reintroduction to particular natural habitats is where zoos and botanical gardens could really make simultaneous and constructive contributions to conservation, education and the environmental crisis. This requires active communication between the relevant authorities, which often exist in remote isolation from each other while species die out to the dismay of all. Before looking at another aspect of how useful zoos can be for research, a note on zoos' 'environmental enrichment' techniques might benefit some current and future occupants of zoo compounds.

Notes on Environmental Enrichment for Animals in Captivity

With the welcome intent of making the daily routine more stimulating for captive animals (and often for the keeper and public too), zoos and parks have in recent years introduced various activities under the general umbrella of 'Environmental Enrichment'. Often the new stimuli would focus on the most powerful incentive likely to tempt an animal to explore both its behavioural repertoire and its enclosure – food. For example, carnivores might have to search for and / or retrieve their meat from unusual locations. This exercises both bodies and minds and for these reasons is usually beneficial to the animals.

However, one practice introduced for tigers (and possibly lions) is, in the author's view, potentially very dangerous to the animal. The tiger's meat ration is either placed at the top of a tall, vertical pole, or suspended from it or from the branch of a tall tree, compelling the tiger to either climb or jump vertically to a considerable height (sometimes seven metres or more) – the height usually adjusted to a near maximum in order to provide the most impressive spectacle for the public. Do tigers in the wild leap vertically or climb trees or poles seven metres or more to get their prey? The answer is an emphatic and unequivocal 'No'.

Quoting from the research project referred to above '(the cubs) appeared loath to jump very high, or more precisely, to take their hind legs far off the ground. To immediately place this assertion in perspective I did see a cub jump much higher than necessary over another with its hind legs tucked up under its belly. On a couple of other occasions a cub jumped straight onto the 1.5 metre platform in the middle of the enclosure. It was this platform however, that first drew my attention to their apparent reluctance to jump high – many were the times that, in an attempt to leap onto the platform from the ground, a cub would not achieve it and would hang on by the claws of the fore-paws while its rear end and hind legs swung in the air. By extending the hind legs to the ground, it seemed that they would only need a slight spring to carry them up onto the platform, but this did not happen and, if the hind legs could not clamber up, the tiger would give up and drop back to the ground. If, on other occasions when cubs were walking up the ramp on one side of the platform, their hind legs slipped off, rather than showing a quick neat spring back into position, one hind leg would seek for a hold whilst the other leg would follow up as the cub righted itself.

On rare occasions the tigers would start to climb the chain-link fence using mainly the strength of their forequarters but, after the hind legs had tentatively taken hold for literally a few seconds, they would drop back to the ground. The physical structure of lions and tigers indicates that the hind-quarters are mainly concerned with propulsion and look almost spindly in comparison to the large muscle development of the fore-quarters. It is the fore-paws which grasp, hold and pull down large, struggling prey before the jaws deliver the lethal bite.

Although slightly blurred, this photograph of a male in Corbett Tiger Reserve illustrates the relative proportions of fore and hind quarters

In terms of motion, the forelimbs are mainly used for 'braking'. This arrangement of propulsive hind limbs and 'braking' forelimbs is common to the vast majority of mammals. However, an exception reminds us of the observations on the elephant made in the previous chapter, since work in 2010 by the Royal Veterinary College in Hatfield, U.K. has shown that elephants can use all four legs to accelerate or brake, literally being a 4x4 all-terrain vehicle! (J24)

Sometimes while running or bounding, the tiger cubs' potential for long jumping seemed great, and long distances would be covered in single bounds. Those authors that give examples of tigers leaping almost invariably describe a long jump (e.g. B8 B4) rather than a high jump. Bazé says the tiger is better at the long jump than the high jump and that he often used to think, when watching a cat jump easily up onto a side-board, that a tiger should be capable of a similar feat, but experience convinced him he was wrong. Bazé also measured an enormous 'long jump' by a tiger at 22 feet (*almost 7 metres*) from the bush he started from to where he landed'.

The bodies of tigers and lions, whilst capable of high jumps if pressed by circumstance, are not designed to regularly perform them. Even tree climbing does not feature as part of their natural behaviour and occasional observations of a lion or tiger in a tree (on the lowest branches) only emphasise how rarely it is seen, how cautious the animal is and that it is the exception rather than the rule. Examples of lions with all four paws on the back of a buffalo or even jumping at the rump of a giraffe or onto running prey do not represent heights of seven metres or more and are stimulated by the particular set of circumstances – they are not repeated daily. A comparison with leopards and jaguars leaves no doubt about relative abilities and agilities in climbing trees – leopards in particular being the essence of graceful agility. Corbett referred to many cases of leopards 'riding' animals, including sambhar, cheetal, and a horse, preparatory to killing them but refers to only one case of a tiger doing the same. Tigers and lions are the 'heavyweights' of the cat world and their normal behavioural repertoire, whilst allowing for some spectacular physical abilities, does not allow for that heavy body being too far off the ground too often, except for emergencies, that are, sadly, being produced for them everyday by well-meaning but misguided keepers and / or zoo authorities. Neither tigers, nor lions, should be given incentives to climb vertical poles or jump vertically to great heights.

'Excess enrichment' might also be a label we could apply to some food supplements or substitutes! Humans often tend to think that if 'some is good; more must be better', preferring 'maximum' to 'optimum'. Yet nature favours an optimum – a balance between extremes. For example: a zoo-bred female tiger cub, about one month old, was showing a disturbing assortment of symptoms including shaky, unsteady legs, virtual blindness from cataracts to the point of walking head-on into objects and, according to the vet, problems with various viscera. In the case of this little tigress, the keeper and I examined the powdered mix used for feeding and found its protein content, at the dilution recommended by the manufacturer, was c. 30%. Data available at that time for comparison indicated that the proportion of protein in human mothers' milk is approx. 1%; in cows 4%; and in lions and tigers 10% – which helps explain how cubs grow so rapidly (e.g. from vague white circles under its gums in the morning, a tiger cub can display the tips of canine teeth by evening). Following the principle that one cannot improve on nature, yet always wary when experimenting with a life, we decided to double the dilution and observe the results. If the results were encouraging, we would triple the dilution such that the artificial food was as similar to nature as possible in terms of protein content. After signs of improvement, we duly did triple the dilution while ensuring plenty of sunlight for and physical contact with the cub. The transformation was remarkable, within a couple of weeks she was walking strongly and steadily, was free of any internal problems and seeing perfectly since all traces of cataracts had disappeared. The surprised vet asked what we had done, and lost interest when told.

This puny example contains powerful principles: nature offers the best model; nature favours an optimum; and solutions can be simple and inexpensive. This is neither the last time, nor only with regard to tigers, that we will contemplate the benefits of properly balanced nutrition, fresh air, sunshine and a touch of care.

If keepers, management and academia co-operate, zoos can provide unique learning and rich research opportunities. If all the same co-operate with Forest Departments and other wildlife authorities, the potential for conservation is great and may yet prove decisive with regard to preventing extinctions.

Notes on Chemical Communication

Chemical communication between animals is a good example of how valuable zoos can be for research since the chances of obtaining uncontaminated scent samples from the wild are very small, yet such samples can be collected in captivity with a little effort and luck.

Chemical communication in terms of scent is one among a number of distinctive signs and marks tigers make around their habitat. Marks include deep claw marks, made while the tiger stands on its hind legs and draws its front paws down tree trunks (and along, and very occasionally across, fallen tree trunks. That this serves to mark territories and / or home ranges has superseded the old idea that tigers were sharpening their claws); 'scrapes', made by alternately drawing the hind paws backward on a patch of ground, and grass flattened by the tiger rolling and writhing on its back over a particular patch. Since tigers have sweat glands on their cheeks, between their toes and around the anus, it maybe that the claw marks, scrapes and flattened grass also carry scent of some kind and hence chemical messages.

Signs include exposed scats – sometimes left on a scrape. When working with tigers in captivity, we keepers would provide some local farmers with lion and tiger scats which they would place at the edges of their fields to keep deer away from their crops. As these 'English' deer would have never in their lives been aware of the existence of lions or tigers, this practice gives us a fascinating insight into some sort of 'genetic memory'. Nor is this an isolated incident but well established enough to attract scientific research (J1). (Marking its territory with deer-repellent scats would seem disadvantageous to a tiger. However, nature's efficiency ensures that scats are produced not long after feeding (protein is easy to digest and cats have a relatively short gut) so, if there is a detrimental effect on a tiger's hunting prospects due to its exposed scats (or other marks and signs) the tiger is not disadvantaged since, having recently eaten and freshly marked this part of its territory, the tiger moves on). Tiger signs also include urine-carried scent marks deposited on tree trunks, prominent rocks, bushes or scrapes. These scent marks may utilise chemical compounds that could be detrimental to the tiger if not expelled (more detail below). Hence, habitat marking with scats and potentially harmful chemicals, timed to ensure no disadvantage to the tiger in terms of prey reaction, its energy requirements or subsequent patrolling / hunting may be evidence of nature's further efficiencies.

After a brief review of chemical communication in the animal kingdom in general, the tiger's urine-carried scent marking will be examined in more detail.

The reader might have left messages for friends or family; identifying yourself, your whereabouts, when you were passing and, less likely perhaps, your social status and whether or not you were physiologically ready to mate. Many animals, including tigers, leave these messages (and, perhaps, others we have not yet discovered or thought about) by marking objects in their environment with their scent.

In this modern age of electronic gadgets, it would seem impressive if we could pass some sort of sensor over a small surface area and get an instant 'read-out' telling us all the information suggested above. Even more impressively, consider that, just by reading the information, immediate and involuntary physical effects are produced in the reader! Such a sophisticated sensor exists – it is called a nose, working in conjunction with a specialised organ within it called the vomeronasal organ (or VNO – named after the vomer bone in the hard palate of the skull (the 'roof' of the mouth), over which it lies) or Jacobson's organ (named after the Danish physician whose research during the 1800's expanded on the original description by F. Ruysch in 1703).

Comparisons between embryos confirmed the presence of a VNO in such diverse classes as mammals and reptiles but, although it was found to be present in most terrestrial vertebrates, it was considered to be vestigial or even absent in humans. However, research published in 1991 finally established that it is both present and functional in humans. Fascinatingly, this work showed that, in general, molecules stimulating the olfactory epithelium (resulting in our becoming consciously aware of a smell) need not necessarily stimulate the VNO. Conversely, molecules stimulating the VNO need not necessarily stimulate the olfactory epithelium – meaning that we do not always consciously 'smell' what the VNO is 'reading' but the information might still influence us mentally or physically. Such little work has been done it is not yet possible to present a comprehensive account of the VNO's functionality in humans, or for that matter, any other species (no one knows!). However, the well-known 'right chemistry' between two people might be an apt term. Indeed, research on the human VNO has been funded by the perfumery industry hoping to profit from a perfume that bio-chemically increases the wearer's attractiveness to the opposite sex.

Chemical communication between insects and a few species of small mammals have been studied since the mid-twentieth century and the term 'pheromone' was first used by Karlson and Luscher in 1959 to describe chemicals emitted by an individual, evoking response in members of the same species, and sometimes other species. Pheromones have been described as chemical messengers but that doesn't quite say it all: pheromonal messages may automatically achieve their purpose – the 'reader' cannot help but react in accordance with what they have read. For example, while the stud mate's urine has no effect, on exposure to the urine of a strange male a pregnant mouse will terminate her pregnancy and resorb her embryos (J27). Please note, not abort (which would also be impressive) but resorb. A moment's reflection on such complex and dramatic physiology being triggered by a scent confirms the power of these chemical signals. Other chemical messages might offer a challenge, to which there maybe a variety of responses. Even those which seem to offer plain information might have further functionality e.g. the scent which informs a male reader that the female donor is in oestrus might also have physiological effects in the male.

Hence it was suggested by early researchers that pheromones producing long-term physiological responses, in contrast to those stimulating short-term behavioural responses, be classed as distinct pheromones (primer and releaser pheromones respectively) but, due to some pheromones' multi-functional capabilities, confusion and disagreement resulted. The general term 'semiochemical' was defined as a chemical signal, mediating behaviour between organisms in a shared environment. However, this can include signals that stimulate the olfactory system (but maybe not the VNO) and therefore include a learned component in the response, which resulted in further uncertainty. Hence, without clearly defined terminology being currently available, the term 'chemical communication' is used for the purposes of this section.

Before the first scientific study of the tiger in the wild by Schaller in Kanha during the early 1960's, the only source of published information on the behaviour of wild tigers was that of hunters, particularly those 'naturalist-hunters' who tried to make detailed observations of the animals and report their findings in their memoirs or books. A number of seasoned authorities on tigers including A.A. Dunbar Brander, R.G. Burton, F.W. Champion and J. Corbett all report, particularly with regard to hunting, the relative unimportance of the tiger's nose as compared to its eyes and ears, and they held that the tiger has a poor sense of smell. Brander recalls that his tame tiger, if his food was taken away and hung on a branch, was unable to find it. If the meat was removed and dragged along the grass, the tiger never even attempted to follow the scent trail, but looked around in circles until he discovered it. He had seen a wild tiger do the same when his kill had been moved (B8). Corbett has often been quoted for saying that the tiger has no sense of smell and there has been some debate as to whether he meant this literally. However, the answer is contained in his books. In 'Man-Eaters of Kumaon' he comments that tigers are not aware that human beings have no sense of smell. Yet in his book 'Jungle Lore' he refers to human appreciation of nature and writes of the air being filled with the smell of flowers and the wind bringing the scent of flowers. Hence Corbett's 'no sense of smell' is one of his expressions, meant relatively, not literally, indicating the relative weakness of this sense in humans – and tigers – in contrast to its acuity in other species.

With today's knowledge of the importance of scent marking, it is easy to conclude that those who dismissed the tiger's nose as unimportant were 'wrong' since the tiger does use its nose, at least for intra-specific communication, and some investigations of its surroundings, especially new objects or situations. However, those who held this view were mainly concerned with aspects of its hunting behaviour and concluded that the tiger seems not to use its nose either for hunting or to detect humans hunting it. It is instructive to recognise that, for example, Corbett's view was more than 'opinion' since, unlike many investigators, he risked his life on his knowledge and conclusions – and not once but many times. Bhils are one of the ancient indigenous tribes of India and an old Bhil shikari said to Stanley Jepson "Sahib, God gave the tiger the finest sight and the finest hearing; if he had given him a fine nose also, no animals would be safe. That would be too much!" The wisdom of the wild!' (B35)

Scent marking by tigers (described in detail below) went almost totally unnoticed, or at least unrecorded, until Schaller's study. The exceptions were noted by Perry (B53) and included the jungle people who knew that (at least) male tigers sprayed tree-trunks and bushes with their urine; and the naturalist Leslie Brown who observed a tiger walking along a path 'sniffing the boles of trees carefully and sometimes urinating, tail curled over back, like a dog at a lamp-post. It has been confirmed by Locke (*Locke, A. The Tigers of Trengganu. Museum Press. London 1954*), who states that Malayan tigers eject a pungent-smelling secretion from glands at the root of the tail, and that traces of the fluid can be detected on the surrounding vegetation and the undersides of the leaves on low hanging branches, since it is expelled upwards with surprising force. Tigresses in season also leave their signs by squirting sprays of urine and anal secretions to a distance of as much as ten feet.' (B53)

Although the tiger lifts its tail while spraying, it does not, like a dog, also lift a leg, just turns its hindquarters to point in the required direction. This author does not know on what basis Locke suggested the anal glands as the source of the scent marking substance. Schaller says in 'The Deer and the Tiger' that the marking fluid "…consisted of a clear, pale yellow liquid, apparently urine. Several clumps of a granular, whitish precipitate were in it…apparently a secretion from the anal glands, which are also found in the house cat" and cites both Locke and Perry as references. An update on this point follows shortly.

It appears to be these latter scent marks that are (to human observers at least) most obviously associated with chemical communication and the tiger's VNO. Tigers deposit these marks around their environment by swivelling their hindquarters toward, say, a tree trunk, lifting their tail vertically and spraying the target with squirts of scent. The scent appears as a milky white substance/liquid in the urine. Scent marking is distinct from urination which is accomplished by the animal lowering its hindquarters and squatting for some time (maybe half a minute or more) with hind paws held apart – a completely different posture to their scent-marking stance – and a puddle of urine on the ground does not contain the milky white substance/liquid. I have seen a tigress scent mark a tuft of grass but, although she obviously had to lower her hind quarters, the hind paws were close together and a few short squirts scent marked the grass, before she moved on, the whole process taking a few seconds at most.

The following references to scent marks are only to those carried by urine, which is thought to convey a variety of information that includes:

- The identity of the donor
- If the donor is female, whether she is in oestrus or not
- A chemical declaration of 'ownership' of a territory – these marks are most frequently sprayed at territorial boundaries, the interface areas between adjacent territories.
- A chemical representation of an individual's social status.
- Other information, currently unknown to or unimagined by humans.

As an example of the type of information that could be included in the last category and which may well have never been considered by a casual human observer, Beauchamp et al (J3) have shown that mice are able to detect a difference of only one gene in a related companion by smelling its urine, while Hepper (J11) has given evidence of a similar ability in the rat.

Collecting uncontaminated urine-carried samples from tigers in the wild would be very difficult, as would the presentation of scent samples and chemicals to individual tigers under controlled conditions. Both can be achieved with captive animals. Hence, if academia and zoos co-operate, there are good opportunities for both researchers and zoos to increase our knowledge of the natural world.

At the 'safari park' referred to above, the tigers frequently sprayed the cages and objects in the reserve, so I tried to find out a little more about this method of communication. Getting down to the cages extra early before the day's duties began, I was able to collect some samples of the scent and conduct some simple experiments. After I had completed a series of experiments, I met Dr. Michael Stoddart, a world authority on chemical communication, then at Kings College, University of London. He was interested in my work and due to his kind and considerate help, a brief summary of the experimental results were published as 'Reactions of Tigers to the Scent of Conspecifics' in Journal of Zoology (*J.Zool., Lond. (1981) 194, 263-265*). Reprinted in Appendix I is a copy of the original version (of which the published paper is a summary). The additional information it contains might be of interest to tiger enthusiasts. The tigers' names relate to the same individuals and their photos as in the 'university research project', referred to in previous sub-sections of this chapter.

My research involved observing tigers investigate scent marks and noting their responses. The responses are listed in Appendix I and one of them is a gesture known as 'flehmen', a word coined by Leyhausen, to describe the facial grimace with wrinkled lips, mouth open, tongue lolling out with, sometimes, visible salivation (many animals, including herbivores, make this grimace in similar circumstances).

The ancient Greeks seem to have been as careful observers of nature as innovators of philosophy and mathematics, if we judge by this illustration of a sculpted lion's head from a temple in Sicily (where the Greeks also founded colonies) exhibiting the flehmen gesture.

(B54)

However, the ancient Greeks may not be so impressed with us, since two and a half thousand years later we still do not understand the function of flehmen. For some currently unknown reason, only some scents stimulate flehmen, which is thought to be associated with further investigation of the scent using the VNO.

This author is not aware of any research concerning the VNO of the tiger specifically, indeed; we are without complete details for the VNO of any particular species. Since there is some variation in connections to ducts or organs and proportionate sizes between species, the tiger's VNO is here assumed to share the most common characteristics of those studied so far, in particular that of the cat (J8).

The VNO consists of a pair of mucus filled tubular structures lying within connective tissue and cartilage over the vomer bone, one each side of the nasal septum (the thin, vertical bone and cartilage dividing the nose into two halves). The VNO is 'blind' or closed at the posterior end.

Researchers have identified nerve fibres attached to the closed ends of the VNO 'tubes' which, as they are traced further rearward, become the vomeronasal nerve. Hence, information gathered by the VNO is presumably transmitted via these nerves to the brain. Each anterior, or front, end reduces to become a narrow duct leading forward and down, through a nasopalatine canal (connecting the nasal cavity with the oral cavity) and terminating in two tiny lateral vents in a little 'pad' of tissue called a papilla immediately behind the upper incisor teeth.

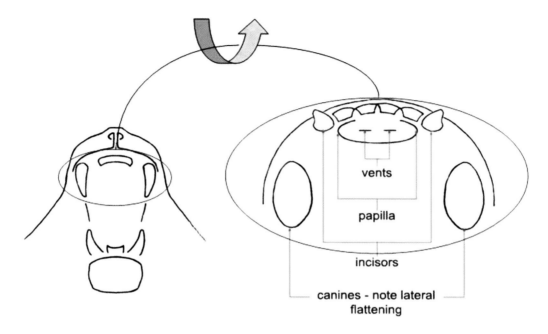

In the diagram, the vents and the little pad of tissue in which they are located have been emphasised to aid illustration. In reality, the little pad of tissue is nigh on invisible unless you know what you are looking for. Its two tiny vents are also invisible when closed but can be seen when opened slightly by a finger gently pressing on the rear edge of the little papilla.

Even when open, the narrowness of the ducts would only permit very slow induction of scent by diffusion, whether airborne or dissolved and, for the same reason, very slow clearance of the VNO (J8). This has led to speculation about possible pumping mechanisms, since a tube with one end closed (essentially the VNO is two such tubes) will, when compressed and released, produce some pumping and suction effect. However, without muscles or tendons attached, how can the VNO be compressed or dilated? Some researchers have suggested that, since each 'tube' of the VNO contains relatively large blood vessels, compression and dilation might be at least partially achieved by the dilation and constriction of those blood vessels – forming a "vomeronasal pump". The expanded and restricted blood flow would vary the volume of the VNO tubes and pump in or pump out mucous with its dissolved scents through the little ducts already mentioned (Meredith and O'Connell quoted in J16). A number of researchers note great quantities of mucous associated with the VNO and its ducts.

Few large animals have been examined with regard to either the gross or microscopic anatomy of their VNO. However, one of the few that has been dissected could hardly get any larger; the VNO of the Asian elephant (J23). In one diagram the researchers indicate an 'accessory duct' connecting the nasal cavity to the 'VNO duct' (that joining the VNO with the vents behind the incisors). This author could find no elaboration on this duct in the text of the paper and has never seen any reference to it with regard to other species. Until a tiger's VNO is examined thoroughly we can only speculate as to whether it too has such a duct. However, such speculation is prompted by a few of the author's first-hand observations during which copious amounts of liquid / mucous flowed from tigers' nostrils while smelling the scent of other tigers.

On some occasions a tiger smells a scent and leaves the investigation at that. On other occasions, further investigation is stimulated and the mouth opens, which would allow airborne access to the ducts behind the incisors. If investigations proceed to flehmen it seems that it might facilitate the transport of scent from the oral cavity to the VNO (J19). Perhaps flehmen helps to constrict and / or dilate blood vessels of the VNO and / or is part of some other pumping mechanism. Whatever mechanism is involved, it seems to be maintained until flehmen is relaxed. If more information or longer examination is required, flehmen is repeated, perhaps to 'run the pump again'. Exactly how this aspect in particular, or flehmen in general functions remains uncertain. Whatever the method of transport may be, the VNO presumably gleans further information from the scent than is gained by smelling alone.

Hopefully other researchers will have more luck than this author did in finding funding and we shall all learn more in due course, not only about the VNO and flehmen but also about the source of the scent carried in the urine which, to my knowledge, also remains unknown. We saw above that Locke, Perry and Schaller referred to the anal glands in connection with the urine-carried scent and a number of later researchers (including me!) failed to establish this for themselves. There is one gland each side of the tiger's anus, holding a thick and pungent substance. Since urine does not always contain the whitish, milky scent and there being no other apparent source of that scent, I repeated the mistake in the published paper of 1981 by mentioning the anal glands as the source of the scent. Work done later by Cheryl S. Asa (J2) in 1993 has shown that anal-sac secretions do not appear in urine marks or on faeces. However, even books on tigers published up to 2005 (the most recent I have seen) are still printing the same error. Although we now know that the anal sacs are not involved with urine-carried scent marks, what role they, or their secretions play, also remains unknown.

A number of books state that flehmen is exhibited by a tiger smelling its own scent while other books claim that flehmen is used to assess oestrus in the female scent donor. The simple experiments conducted with the captive tigers (Appendix 1) revealed that, out of all trials conducted (apart from what might be one aberrant result) no individual responded with flehmen to its own scent. In addition, the work showed that both females and males may respond with flehmen to the scent of males, indicating that the function of flehmen is unlikely to be confined to assessment of oestrus.

In addition to these insights the work indicated a number of other areas of potentially fruitful research: two tigers produced copious streams of clear liquid, running out of their nostrils while eagerly smelling, and exhibiting flehmen, in response to a strange male's scent. This would seem to refute – at least for tigers – a suggestion that the nostrils are closed during flehmen. It also, as referred to above in the case of the elephant, raises the possibility of a connecting duct between the VNO and the nasal cavity, since we know the VNO is a source of plentiful liquid / mucous.

It is well-established that the sense of smell is very closely related to the sense of taste (smell has been described as a sort of 'long-range taste' (B67)). If the tongue, which is extended during flehmen, catches liquid either running down from the nostrils and / or mouth saliva holding scent in solution, further information may be gleaned by 'tasting the smell'.

The liquid running down from the nostrils to the region of the upper lips, the incisors and the VNO vents, may also present a reinforced and / or repeated stimulus to the VNO. Whether or not this speculation is correct, the tongue does seem to play an active role in chemical communication. On occasion, tigers lick a scent mark once or twice (perhaps to put a dried scent mark into solution) before investigating it. However, on one occasion I saw a male tiger lick the scent of another male so vigorously and repeatedly the only sensible interpretation seemed to be that he was licking the scent mark off. This was supported by the fact that the males in question were close and frequent rivals in status (further details in Appendix I). The tongue may serve other functions as well and the author has seen tigers, usually in repose (never when actively investigating scents), with their jaws closed and just the tip of the tongue projecting and resting on the chin. In this position the portion of the tongue just rearward of the exposed tip would be lying over the vents behind the upper incisors. The exposed tip can also be flipped up to touch the rhinarium and nostrils. The possibility of pheromones or some other sort of 'meaningful molecules', being in solution on the tongue also opens the possibility of them being ingested. Whilst we have noted extreme physiological reactions to scent alone, an additional mechanism might be formed by ingestion, in conjunction with the VNO and the brain, allowing chemical communication to influence or regulate the internal environment and physiological functions, including perhaps, fertility (explored further below). If the amounts being ingested would seem too tiny to have much effect, remember that the human sex hormones which initiated all of your relatively dramatic and wide-ranging secondary sexual characteristics at puberty would, if placed on your finger tip, be invisible to your naked eye. Hormones and other biochemicals can be immensely powerful in tiny concentrations.

In addition to playing some role in fertility, scent marking might facilitate subtleties of territorial marking. The concentrations of scent marks tend to diminish with time and some compounds decompose while others form, meaning that time is relevant to chemical communication, not just in terms of affecting the information imparted (e.g. strong signal or weak signal) but also in terms of consequential behavioural adjustments. 'Leyhausen and Wolff have demonstrated the very interesting possibility that the distribution of animals of a certain species over the available biotope can be effected not only by a space plan but also by a time plan. They found that in domestic cats living free in open country, several individuals could make use of the same hunting-ground without ever coming into conflict by using it according to a definite timetable. An additional safeguard against undesirable encounters is the scent marks which these animals deposit at regular intervals wherever they go.' (B48) The timetable aspect of chemical communication might be linked with this author's observations that flehmen (i.e. more-detailed investigation) is most often exhibited in response to very fresh scents.

We read above of distinctions between 'home ranges' and territories. Under some circumstances tigers undoubtedly defend their territories, sometimes to the death (although these occurrences are rare). This 'use by timetable' suggests a co-operative sharing of resources in that 'visitors' or transients to an owner's territory, while not welcome, might be tolerated (while potential usurpers will be neither welcome nor tolerated). Maybe chemical communication is the mechanism in a tiger's 'land management system' that allows for 'home ranges' as opposed to 'territories' and / or defines each. If so, it is just one function amongst a range of social communication, perhaps with more varied functions than we have yet imagined. Hopefully, further study and observation will tell us more.

I have lost count of the number of applications I made for grants to continue investigating chemical communication but, just like my applications for funds to conduct ecology projects, they never met with any success. However, after attempts spread over 15 years to progress the work, I met some chemists who were investigating the chemical composition of the scent and I was able to make some contribution by providing samples of tiger scent for analysis. This led to me finally registering for a PhD researching into behavioural aspects of chemical communication in tigers, which I was happy to finance myself. Working in conjunction with a chemist, I would continue and expand my behavioural observations while our individual findings would guide or at least educate each other as we pursued our different but related studies.

Frustratingly, and within a short time of starting my research, I became aware of just how critical the situation had once again become for wild tigers. After the wonderful successes of Project Tiger in India and the growth of tiger populations and Tiger Reserves since 1972, Indira Gandhi's assassination in 1984 heralded difficult times ahead for the environment (at the time of writing, all Indian legislation protecting the environment and / or wild animals is due to Mrs. Gandhi). Her son, Rajiv Gandhi, who succeeded her as Prime Minister, was still protective of wildlife but not quite so actively as his mother had been and, just prior to his own assassination in 1991, it became known how badly the tiger in particular was suffering from poaching, then driven mainly by the Chinese tiger bone medicine trade. Tiger populations declined and were approaching the critical numbers that had triggered Project Tiger in the first place. The extinction or otherwise of the tiger or other species is dependent on socio-economic and political factors. As would be expected, academia and research can only be supportive, not actually determine the fate of species, so, for reasons given at the end of this chapter, I chose to leave my academic studies and try making some contribution to their survival in the wild.

One of the chemists was Glyn Banks, who earned his PhD by investigating chemical communication between tigers. The following passage is quoted from Dr. Banks' thesis ('marking fluid' refers to the urine-carried scent. It may also be of assistance to mention that compounds of nitrogen and hydrogen are called amino groups, such as ammonia (NH_3). If a hydrocarbon radical replaces one of the hydrogen atoms in an amino group the new compound is called an amine. When the hydrocarbon radical is made up of carbon, oxygen and hydrogen, the amine is an amino acid. The particular amino acid is determined by which, if any, other carbon and hydrogen atoms are attached).

> '…chemical analysis of the amine fraction of both "marking fluid" and anal sac secretion of the tiger revealed the presence of 26 amines of which trimethylamine and triethylamine were the most common. The anal sac secretions of the leopard, cheetah, lion and jaguar also revealed similar amines. Chemical analysis of the whole marking fluid of the tiger identified 27 other compounds (in addition to the amines).
>
> 2-acetyl-1-pyrroline was identified as the principal component of the characteristic odour of the marking fluid of the tiger following vacuum distillation, gas

chromatography and / or mass spectrometry and as sensed by the human nose. A further component of the characteristic odour identified is 4-hydroxy-3-methoxy-benzaldehyde (vanillin).

…it is concluded that the characteristic odour of the marking fluid of the tiger is primarily due to the presence of 2-acetyl-1-pyrroline. Although this compound is unstable in concentrated form…it is apparently more stable in dilute form. Other compounds present in the marking fluid may act as stabilisers to ensure longevity of 2-acetyl-1-pyrroline as it has been detected in the marking fluid of the tiger in minute quantities (close to the limits of detection for the available technology) and would seem to be relatively stable in the tigers' natural environment (Schaller, 1967; Brahmachary and Dutta, 1981; Smith et al., 1989). 2-acetyl-1-pyrroline has an extremely low odour threshold of 0.02ng/L (Schieberle, 1995) providing the characteristic smell of tiger marking fluid and has been reported as an important flavour in fragrant rice (Buttery *et al.*, 1982), wheat bread crust (Schieberle and Grosch, 1987) and popcorn (Schieberle, 1991, 1995)…vanillin also contributes to the odour of the marking fluid of the tiger as appreciated by the human nose.

2-acetyl-1-pyrroline and vanillin, detected at low concentrations by humans, offer insight into the potential for undiscovered information in odours and also an understanding of the power of the olfactory sense in other mammals. It is possible that other important odorous compounds are also present at very low concentrations as (*discerned by the*) human olfactory sense. These should be further investigated as these may offer important contributions to the olfactory picture available to the tiger. It is however, supposition to assume that the tiger perceives the same odour recognition of odour thresholds as humans. Behavioural studies should be undertaken to monitor the reaction of tigers to pre-determined responses on exposure to these compounds.

…Marking fluid has been established as the important scent-mark of the tiger (*and*) there is undoubtedly a large amount of information contained within the odour of the marking fluid enabling an individual tiger to adjust its behaviour accordingly, for example for reproduction or territorial purposes (Smith et al., 1989). It is interesting to note that the compounds identified as being of primary olfactory importance to humans, are at very low concentrations whilst other compounds of relatively high concentration, such as the long-chain carboxylic acids, have little olfactory significance to humans. These compounds may have other purposes such as ensuring the longevity of the scent-mark by acting as a fixative offering a slow-release mechanism…volatile amines will also add to the odour of the scent-mark and together with the lipid fraction coupled with bacterial activity may act as a time-measuring device interpreted by the tiger…This study has investigated the volatile fraction of samples only and so further work should also be directed at the non-volatile fraction which is likely to convey semio-chemical information in solution via the vomeronasal organ. This may be achieved with the use of high performance liquid chromatography coupled with a mass spectrometer (HPLC-MS).'

(Printed by kind permission of Dr. Banks)

Obviously the topic promises much for further research: if 2-acetyl-1-pyrroline is the 'tiger pheromone' how does it and associated compounds vary to distinguish individual tigers and furthermore, varying physiological (and psychological?) states of individuals? If it is via various combinations of this chemical with others mentioned or not yet identified, or with hormones, what parts are played by the olfactory epithelium and the VNO in detecting them? If flehmen is associated with the use of the VNO, my work would suggest that the nose (olfactory epithelium) by itself can identify an individual and detect if new, or changed, information regarding that individual is also available, which then induces flehmen and the VNO to investigate the scent further. What flehmen and the VNO are actually doing remains to be discovered – along with answers to innumerable other questions.

As one of the most solely carnivorous families of the order carnivora, cats ingest protein almost exclusively. The essential and main components of protein are amino acids. Amino acids are comprised of their amino group (NH_2), a carboxylic group (COOH) and, between these two groups, other carbon and hydrogen atoms – the hydrocarbon radical, the composition of which determines the particular amino acid (e.g. the simplest amino acid, glycine, is made up by the characteristic amino and carboxylic groups plus a further carbon atom joined to two hydrogen atoms). Disposing of carbon, oxygen and hydrogen does not normally present an animal with problems. This leaves the cat with lots of amino groups or, combined with carbon, amines. (The reader will recall their close chemical relation to ammonia (NH_3) and this was left in no doubt to keepers every morning when cleaning out urine-soaked sawdust from tigers' overnight cages. Any keeper with a cold was given this duty as the acrid fumes would be sure to clear his nose!) Using amino groups and amines for chemical communication would be a neat and efficient method of disposal. Scent marks are made up of whitish, and sometimes granular, suspensions in urine, and all amino acids are white crystalline solids soluble in water (albeit that their solubility varies considerably), so it is tempting to speculate but, obviously, we need further research to establish if this coincidence has any significance.

(Nature's efficiencies and economies can be impressive but it would seem, in this instance, that the balances are finely tuned and easily upset. Even if used for scent marking, high levels of nitrogen (and sulphur and phosphorus) still need to go into solution for excretion and there are references in the scientific literature to the excretion of ammonium salts (including ammonium sulphate) in the urine, but also to these salts tending to come out of solution in very concentrated urine. Such deposits may lead to a blocking of the ureters and urethras, a not uncommon condition referred to as uroliathiasis. Sulphur is also excreted in association with nitrogen by the formation within the kidney of a sulph-amino acid called felinine (which, it has been suggested, may be a pheromone in various species of smaller cat). Meat has a high water content and provides most of the cat's water requirements, leaving the cat little need to drink, other than in exceptionally high temperatures. However, even when sufficient water is available, the kidneys are presented with a continuous and significant workload. Of the tiger deaths which were followed by post mortems known to this author, kidney malfunction was often identified as the principal cause of death.)

Chemical communication is a new and fascinating area to explore holding, no doubt, new directions and surprises for us, such as the resorption of embryos in mice, already referred to. The research that discovered this effect, conducted by Hilda Bruce many decades ago, also showed scent-induced inhibition of the reproductive cycles of females of various mammalian species. This is now known as the Bruce Effect, and brings us back to the tiger.

The following observation has been made in Chitwan National Park, Nepal – one of the few locations where there have been long-term scientific studies of tiger populations: When the tiger population is relatively large and the available territories are occupied, litter size goes down. In contrast, when the population is relatively small, litter sizes go up (McDougal pers. comm.) – a factor which should be taken into account when reading about 'average litter sizes' as given in popular books on tigers. No mechanism has, to my knowledge, been suggested to account for this remarkable adjustment by nature and it remains an open question. Could chemical communication be part of the answer? I believe that regulation of litter size is influenced by scent marking i.e. tigresses repeatedly and widely smelling marking fluid indicating that home ranges or territories are occupied and / or that numerous other adults and sub-adults are present as 'transients', influences (hormonally or in some other biochemical way) their reproductive physiology to decrease litter size, and vice versa in the reverse scenario.

Chemical communication may also be involved with a further refinement of this process by adjusting the sex ratio of litters. In general, males tend to move away and establish new territories while females tend to share and then establish new territories with and within their mothers' territories. Hence, when territories are 'full' perhaps there is, as well as a reduction in litter size, a shift to a higher proportion of males in the litters – and vice versa in the reverse scenario. As yet, I know of no evidence to support this suggestion in the case of tigers but there is evidence from studies of African spotted hyenas (J13). These hyenas show similar territorial patterns of behaviour (males move away while females tend to stay near their mother) and exhibit this adjustment of sex ratio in their litters according to territorial circumstances. During lean times the ratio of males increases. Their departure will relieve the pressure on limited resources, unlike females which tend to stay with or near their mothers and help find food. In times of plenty, such as when a third of one pack departed to colonise newly-vacated territory, 'those remaining reacted by shifting the sex ratio of their young. In the two years before the clan divided, its members had produced 28 males and 20 females. But in the three years following the split, female offspring outnumbered males two to one.' The suggested mechanisms that might achieve this effect include "The viscosity of vaginal fluid… (*which*) affects the chances of a male-determining or female determining sperm fertilising an egg. Other experiments have shown that levels of hormones circulating in a female's bloodstream can make male or female foetuses more prone to miscarriage." (J13). While there is similarity in their offspring's dispersal patterns, we may remember from the sub section above on reproduction that, unlike tigers, male hyenas have no baculum, but how this may or may not affect fertility and / or the female's other physiological responses to mating is currently unknown.

There is already much evidence that the nose is closely linked with both the behaviour and physiology of sexual reproduction. Professor Stoddart tells us that the sense of smell and sexual reproduction developed in tandem and that the olfactory membrane and the anterior pituitary are closely related embryologically (*the anterior pituitary regulates the levels of hormones in the blood – author*) and hence it is no surprise to find the nose 'heavily committed in reproduction. That the nose plays an active part in vertebrate sexual behaviour patterns is beyond any doubt…It has even been suggested that the role of the sex hormones is as much as olfactory messengers as governors and regulators of the internal environment." (J27)

This topic alone could constitute another book; however, I believe we have sufficient clues to justify investigating correspondences between an animal's internal environment and its external environment, at least in terms of conspecific chemical odours. These could be mutually interdependent and form 'feedback loops', especially since the scents are not abstract symbols but 'airborne or waterborne small parts of the…(animals) themselves.' (B67)

Chemical communication's influence on litter size and / or its sex ratio in conjunction with territorial behaviour could also be the unknown mechanism referred to by Schaller that maintains predator populations at optimum levels, even when prey is abundant and available (this same mechanism maintaining tiger populations as Schaller suggested 'at or near an optimum both in relation to the food sources and independent of them.') Even more fascinatingly, chemical communication, fertility, litter sizes, sex-ratios and territorial behaviour might all relate to the suggestions above concerning relationships between prey density and territory sizes e.g. high prey density – plenty of food without travelling far to get it – smaller territories marked by more numerous predators – influencing reproductive physiology of females (and males?) to optimise conditions. These conditions would vary according to habitat i.e. animals within high-density prey areas (with other necessities such as water, minerals etc.) will be exhibiting reduced litter sizes with perhaps a bias toward male offspring. Near the borders of the population (where the males migrate to) litter sizes will be relatively larger with perhaps a bias toward female offspring until the population reaches sub-optimal habitat, which may mean the composition of scent marks alters again to modify reproduction.

Whether or not any of these suggestions have any validity, our knowledge of nature's efficiency makes the idea of dual or multiple purpose odours (hormonal or otherwise) possible if not probable. Nor are these subtleties confined to fertility or territorial behaviour e.g. the amino acid tryptophan is a component of red meat and also the main component of serotonin, a compound found in the brain and regulating sleep. Carnivores 'sleeping off' a heavy meal suggest a possibility of diet influencing behaviour. Conserving energy during long periods of inactivity is affordable due to the high energy value of meat which, in and of itself, helps induce the sleep, in another of nature's efficient cycles.

The investigation of chemical communication may have practical applications in conservation work and National Park and Tiger Reserve management. If we are able to understand how and what tigers are communicating, it might prove possible either to monitor movements and individuals via scent (in combination with other tiger signs and marks) or influence tigers' behaviour and thereby help manage them non-invasively. Two quite vigorous reactions to scent provide examples in this context: I presented the scent of one male tiger to another by holding the impregnated chemically-inert paper against the chain-link fence that separated us. The tiger in the compound did not know of the existence of the 'scent-donor' tiger, prior to smelling its scent. Alarmingly, the tiger started to bite the fence; pulling, twisting and distorting the wire mesh with its canine teeth so aggressively that the fence would not have remained intact for long, so I hurriedly removed the paper and walked back a few metres, after which the tiger's interest, thankfully, subsided. A fellow researcher presented the scent of a strange male to a young tiger, which immediately retreated and swam the surrounding moat in an attempt to leave the enclosure.

Some Parks and Reserves in the wild have no buffer zone, so protected forest suddenly finishes and directly abuts, say, a paddy field. The author has first-hand experience of some

Reserves where the boundary makes a distinct and sharp line between forest and cultivated fields, allowing no gradation between jungle and cultivation. These abrupt changes inevitably lead to clashes between wild animals and man and / or his livestock – with wild animals ultimately being the loser. Hence, it might be possible to influence movements of animals near these zones by careful and monitored use of natural or artificial scent. If not possible to influence the tiger's movements directly via chemical communication it may be possible to influence the prey (and therefore the tiger) by the same means (J20), to help with management of both prey and predator.

Notes on Man-Eating

Much has been written on this topic and so the following few points are restricted to aspects of it which this author has not seen in print. Before looking at them, we shall keep some perspective by recognising that man-eating is very rare. Not only tigers, but the vast majority of large carnivores (hungry or not) go about their lives doing everything possible to avoid contact with humans and will, even when forced into their close proximity, still exhibit great patience and tolerance. The author has been fortunate enough on a few occasions to be in positions (usually in a tree) from which he could see both a tiger and a party of human beings, who were unaware of the tiger's presence. The tigers did all they could to avoid the people and quietly moved away, leaving the people unaware of how close they had been to a tiger. Even when a tiger is being provoked by people, the tiger's patience is impressive and on one occasion this author recalls, when eventually pressed into responding, it confined itself to a roar to frighten the intruders away (reminding us of Corbett's assessment of the tiger as a 'gentleman'). The vast majority of tigers and leopards (and lions and jaguars) never molest a human being and why this should be i.e. why man is not the natural prey of large terrestrial carnivores, is another topic.

With regard to the relatively few animals which turn to man-eating (i.e. those regularly preying on humans for food, not those which kill a human in defence of their kill or cubs), Corbett's experience showed that the majority were unable to hunt their natural prey due to wounds and / or old-age. Yet, in recent decades physically healthy man-eaters have occurred and some have taken this as evidence that Corbett's conclusions were incorrect. However, both Corbett's conclusions and physically healthy man-eaters can be accommodated by considering sub-optimal habitats, which offer very few prey in terms of type or number. In Corbett's time, the foothills of the Himalayas, where he hunted his man-eaters, represented sub-optimal habitat. Among the tigers resident there, it would be the physically and mentally fittest which would succeed most often in hunting what few prey were available. Therefore, in sub-optimal habitat, old age or infirmity might be one negative factor too many for a predator, leaving it virtually no chance of survival unless it turned to man-eating. If the balance is tipped still further out of equilibrium by, for example, the mechanised, if not industrialised, degradation of what is already sub-optimal habitat, even the fittest predators will be hard pressed to find sufficient food and the probability of finding physically healthy man-eaters increases. Hence, in the late 20th century, with its extensive destruction and degradation of natural habitats, we would expect physically healthy man-eaters to occur more frequently than in Corbett's time. The obvious common factor is pressure from a persistent and serious lack of food; whether this is a consequence of wounds, old-age and/or a diminished prey base.

Scarcity of prey in the Himalayan foothills might be due to altitude restricting vegetation and hence herbivores, or it might be due to human activities, which are too often thoughtless and careless commercial enterprises. A relevant example (although in this case it refers to leopards), is that in recent years, naturally indigenous trees and plant species of the western Himalayas have been cut down and replaced with fast-growing conifers for commercial purposes. The unnatural excess of pine needles from these trees acidify the soil to the extent that naturally occurring plant species die off, disturbing the ecosystem. One result is that herbivores move away to find food but the resident leopards (prey and cover are too small or scarce for tigers) are territorial and cannot move so easily (they may already be in sub-optimal habitat due to not being able to secure territories in optimal habitat at lower altitudes). In consequence, these areas have recently suffered dramatic increases in the numbers of man-eating leopards and, obviously, human lives lost to them.

Turning to man-eating is not meant to imply a rational process on the part of the predator 'choosing new menu items'. Corbett gives the example of the Muktesar tigress, blinded in one eye and with some fifty quills in her fore-leg after an encounter with a porcupine, lying up and unable to move easily. When a woman cutting grass (unknowingly) approaches too closely, the tigress kills her in self defence but leaves her body untouched. In similar circumstances she later kills a man who had been working without his shirt on, and blood flows from his wounds (Corbett speculates as to whether this gave the tigress the idea that humans could satisfy her hunger). Before leaving the dead body the tigress eats a small portion from the man's back. Her third kill is not made in her own defence but deliberately to provide herself with food, and thereafter she regularly preys on humans. Hence, chance can be included among that combination of circumstances which produce a man-eater. However, since all wounded and / or old tigers, all those without adequate prey, and all of those favoured by chance, do not become man-eaters, other circumstances or factors must also be operating.

The Sundarbans region, situated in the Ganges delta of Bangladesh and north-eastern India, has long been infamous for its numerous man-eating tigers, the records for which date back centuries. Like all remaining natural habitat, the Sundarbans has suffered from poaching and human-driven degradation, but its prey base has not been reduced on anything like the scales suffered by other areas of India, and is largely, by comparison, unspoiled. The main problem with the prey base in the Sundarbans is its distribution, which is not even, but irregular – no doubt affecting, as the notes above would indicate, the territorial distribution of the resident tigers. However, even when possible territorial complications, prey distribution and the rigours of old age and wounds are allowed for, the number of man-eaters in the Sundarbans still exceed all expectations.

One serious attempt to solve this mystery was made in the early 1970's by Dr. Hubert Hendricks who began to draw a correlation between man-eating and the ingestion of brackish water (i.e. saline water; the Sundarbans being a mangrove swamp, where the fresh water of the river tributaries forming the delta mixes with the salt water of the Bay of Bengal). Unfortunately, his work was interrupted by the war which gave rise to Bangladesh and he had to make his escape as best he could, leaving his work unfinished. The 'salt connection' remains unexplained but the reader may find some of the following speculation of interest in this context.

Drinking salt water would result in severe dehydration (due to osmosis, by which the concentrated saline solution is diluted by water drawn from (previously) healthy body cells, leaving them dehydrated and shrivelled). It would also over-stress the kidneys and liver, raise blood pressure and render many cellular processes dysfunctional. Of course, low concentrations of salt (i.e. sodium chloride) acquired in food, are essential for many metabolic processes, one of which is the transmission of nerve impulses (due to differences in concentrations of sodium ions across neural membranes). Imbalances in salt intake may result in imbalances of sodium ions, which could affect neuronal transmissions (muscular cramp is an obvious example) and hence, physical and mental states. These, and any of the adverse physiological effects just referred to, might contribute to aberrant behaviour. The dehydration factor could be offset (for successful predators) by the high water content of meat, but those predators unable to kill prey, either due to disabilities and / or its scarcity, will be subject to all the anatomical and physiological problems of ingesting salt water.

Yet how can salt be a contributory factor if man-eating occurs in areas where only freshwater is available? Focussing on the potential neuronal disturbances associated with sodium; is it possible that, while in the case of the Sundarbans the problem is excess sodium, in other geographical areas the problem is lack of sodium? A prolonged lack of food results in a severe lack of salt (sodium) and, over a sufficiently long period, due to its crucial role in transmission of neuronal impulses, it may cause neuronal and, perhaps, behavioural changes.

Are there other sources of salt/sodium available to tigers? The use and value of 'salt licks' in natural habitat is far from understood and other minerals in addition to (or perhaps instead of) salt may be acquired at these sites. However, this author has never seen or heard of carnivores using such sites, only herbivores. When eating their kill from off the forest floor tigers must, probably inadvertently, ingest at least some soil, which presumably supplies some nutritional minerals (tigers do not eat the vegetation inside their prey's stomach but remove the stomach whole). However, in the case of man-eaters we are considering animals not able to acquire natural prey, so they will not be ingesting minerals via soil in this way and, just as there is no record of tigers using a salt lick, there is no record of them directly swallowing soil. So it would seem that, for the tiger, the only significant source of sodium is meat.

We would expect tigers (and most other carnivores) to have adaptations to low sodium concentrations (within limits), due to the naturally occurring intervals between kills – usually a week and often longer. The ingestion of excess sodium in salt water is a scenario we can understand nature not normally allowing for – at least for terrestrial carnivores – and would qualify as a rare and extreme exception, producing rare and extreme consequences, such as, perhaps, the very high incidences of man-eating in the Sundarbans. In the context of this speculation, the historical record would be consistent with man-eating due to a lack of sodium occurring far less frequently (proportionally speaking) than that due to an excess of sodium.

Although almost exclusively carnivorous, tigers have been known to very occasionally eat vegetation – apparently a jungle fruit called a durian, and sometimes grass. This author has seen tigers occasionally eat grass and has also seen them, sometimes, vomit it later. Apparently tigers, and other cats including the domestic variety, will eat grass when unwell and it is thought possible that vegetation provides some medicinal effect (in addition to being a possible emetic). Tigers unwell in the sense of being wounded will, apparently, eat larger amounts of vegetation than they otherwise would (this author has no first hand knowledge of this). If this is true, it may be linked with these speculations since plant food is high in potassium and potassium is another element involved with neuronal transmission. Hence, imbalances in potassium may also have physiological, and hence behavioural, effects. However, perhaps more importantly with regard to our considerations here, potassium displaces sodium. Amongst, no doubt, other effects, the displacement of sodium by potassium has some anaesthetic effect (this is the basis of toothpastes which alleviate pain from exposed nerves around teeth and gums. The toothpaste contains potassium chloride or potassium nitrate, the potassium of which displaces sodium and thereby interferes with the transmission of painful sensations). Such anaesthesia may be one reason for the increased ingestion of plant food by wounded tigers. If these wounds have prevented the tiger catching and / or killing its prey, its sodium concentrations would already be low. Ingesting potassium may depress them still further and, in sufficient quantities, impair neuronal transmissions which, in turn, might contribute to aberrant behaviour (e.g. eating humans).

Another factor, which may operate either in conjunction with this effect or independently of it, could be that low concentrations of sodium activate some biological feedback system which stimulates the animal to seek sodium in the only form it can acquire it i.e. meat, and the saltier the better. Unlike most furred or feathered animals, humans have sweat glands all over their skin and, especially in hot climates, readily perspire (and perspiration contains salt). So a relatively high concentration of salt would be on the surface of the skin, which, due to few clothes, would be mostly exposed. Perhaps animals can sense salt concentrations by some sort of 'smell' and / or VNO involvement? Maybe the Muktesar tigress sensed salt on her second victim's back and it was this, rather than, or in conjunction with the blood, that induced her to eat a portion of his back.

Sodium concentrations in the body are regulated by the kidney and we have seen above that all cats' kidneys are under a heavy workload due to their diet, so maybe overstressed and / or malfunctioning kidneys (whether due to sodium imbalances or not) are a further physiological factor contributing to man-eating. Individual variation among tigers will make some more sensitive to particular circumstances than others and so, perhaps, any one, or some combination of old age (which brings not only physical incapacities but also its own disruption of biochemical

processes), injury, prey scarcity, kidney stress, 'sodium stress', chance and opportunity, combine to produce a man-eater. Whilst we cannot be confident of what causes man-eating, we may be more confident of what does not cause it.

With evermore casual attitudes to accuracy and detail, some popular accounts have linked man-eating with aggression and seek factors that make tigers more aggressive in order to help explain why some become man-eaters. This is an invalid premise. Tigers (or any other carnivore) are not aggressive toward their prey, even when hunting and killing it. The prey is simply food. When big cats hunt and kill prey their behaviour is, obviously, violent but it is not aggressive. Contrast their behaviour and facial expressions in intra-specific confrontations (when growls, snarls, body movements and facial displays exhibit aggression) with the complete absence of such behaviour when hunting or killing. Obviously, their 'prey catching and killing equipment' serves purposes in both hunting and intra-specific confrontations but in the latter situation the reader is reminded that its use involves the bite to the lumbar region and cranial puncture. Big cats are, for obvious reasons, silent and composed when stalking, catching and killing prey. There is definitely no growling, snarling or any other sign of aggression. The Hollywood tradition of 'pressing all buttons at once' for the greater stimulation of the audience results in scenes of big cats (dubbed as) always growling or snarling while hunting, or even simply moving. In reality such a predator would never eat (even worse editing has members of the genus Panthera dubbed with vocalisations of cougars (genus Felis), and the lack of timbre makes the scene even more incongruous). Killing to eat is a functional business to satisfy nature's most persistent and ubiquitous stimulus. As Konrad Lorenz writes in his book 'On Aggression' "The buffalo which the lion fells provokes his aggression as little as the appetising turkey which I have just seen hanging in the larder provokes mine."

Having said all that, and as always in nature, the situation is far from simple and there is some possibility of a carnivore experiencing, for want of a better term, a 'psychological attitude', stimulated by its food and contributing to its killing behaviour. In what could be another example of nature's efficiency, the very diet of blood might contribute to the ability to acquire more of it, including perhaps, the psychological attitude necessary for killing, and to persist if and when that

food fights back. Obviously, humans are the only species we can question and modern dieticians do cite too much red meat in Western diets as a cause of violent behaviour in humans, and the Masai tribe of Africa would gorge themselves on blood in preparation for battle. However, violence, even in battle is not always, if ever, associated with aggression. Even when it is present, what may manifest as aggression in humans may not be the same as the 'psychological attitude' prompting killing behaviour in carnivores. Moreover, in the case of animals that become man-eaters, as we have seen, psychological states may also be influenced by a variety of biochemical conditions in addition to any that might be produced by ingesting, or having ingested, blood. (Here it might prove interesting to investigate the biochemical effects of iron concentrations (perhaps in conjunction with sodium and potassium concentrations) since iron is ingested in relatively large quantities due to an exclusively carnivorous diet (the scats of wild cats are usually black, due to a high content of iron which, in turn, is due to a high content of haemoglobin which, in turn, is due to a high content of blood)).

Aggression, as we normally understand the word, is most often associated with intimidating opponents, of the same or different species, and in either case actually contributes to the avoidance of physical violence, when one contender backs down in the face of it. Although there is undoubtedly aggression involved in some intra-specific confrontations it need not always be the case. In this author's experience, when the predator's intent is to kill, there is an expression in the animal's eyes (quite chilling to behold at close quarters) but it is unaccompanied by any sound or ritualised display – the tiger is focussed and very 'business like' (its silent and focussed efficiency is part of the chilling effect). This author has witnessed conflicts between tigers in which the attacking tiger wastes no time or energy with aggressive displays. In the context of chemical communication, Appendix I refers to the most dominant male, Lancer, having tried to kill another male, Kamal, whose scent at that time was the only one Lancer had responded to with flehmen. However, Lancer's attack also offers us something to consider in our current context of aggression since, during the ferocious attack, there was silence, except for the impact of the bodies on floor and walls. At the crux of the fight, Kamal was on his back and pushing with both his forepaws against Lancer's chest, while Lancer, with jaws open, strained to get his enormous canines closer to Kamal's throat (whether Kamal's throat was Lancer's objective, or merely the best target in the scrabble and confusion of the fight, is unknown, but no attempt to puncture the cranium or bite through the lumbar region of the spine was seen. Perhaps the confines of the cage, or other aspects of captivity influenced behaviour). Observing the attack from less than two metres away, and therefore well within its 'field of energy' or 'vibe', the power and forces present were nigh on palpable, and made a dramatic and intimidating impression. Aggression, as we normally understand that word, was absent. Only a cold, implacable force, physically embodied in Lancer as a striped 'killing machine', totally devoid of any other faculty or function, was present. Kamal's prusten broke the vocal silence but had no visible effect on Lancer, nor received any response. Lancer continued his attack with the single-minded determination of a programmed automaton. In contrast to the ferocious energy concentrated at that place and time, only the emptiness, the void and vacuum of death could be sensed, and it was distinctly dispiriting to be in its immediate vicinity. It was so powerful, it had a numbing effect on heart and mind, successively shutting down peripheral perceptions which, in one way at least, makes sense, since it was extinguishing life. After Kamal somehow escaped to another cage, constantly vocalising prusten, Lancer turned quietly and calmly and took a couple of paces to the bars of the cage, sat on his hindquarters, lifted his enormous head, slightly turned it to face me, and looked down his long nose into my eyes. His eyes were as ice – flat, cold and dead. No aspect of his demeanour, body, aura or behaviour was 'aggressive', or even evident of his having just been trying to kill Kamal, unless we make 'aggression' synonymous with violent attack.

Notes on Innate v. Reasoned Behaviour

Animals may perform instinctive actions without understanding those actions to the degree that they can choose to omit them when circumstances render them useless e.g. caged tigers on clean floors have been known to perform fore-paw movements to cover (and thereby hide) their meat, despite the lack of vegetation or soil. Many animals, especially mammals, also exhibit behaviour consistent with reasoning and decision-making regarding what, if any, action to take in response to a given set of circumstances. A fascinating area is where, when and how these two modes of behaviour combine or divide (using the previous example, not all captive tigers will try to hide meat nor will any one tiger necessarily always do so. That a pointless attempt is made at all is evidence for the behaviour's innate origin but learning and individual variation allow for adaptation).

With regard to chemical communication, some chemicals might stimulate involuntary responses – those not consciously reasoned or decided upon (e.g. resorbption of embryos) while others convey information which may or may not stimulate voluntary responses – those consciously reasoned or decided upon (e.g. perhaps Lancer's attack on Kamal as described in Appendix I). For some scientists, involuntary responses are associated with mechanistic or instinctive behaviour, while voluntary behaviour and the involvement of conscious awareness elevate an event above mechanism or instinct. However, other scientists and some relatively recent philosophers, follow a modern trend that maintains even conscious awareness is also ultimately, a product of mindless mechanisms. Animals, regardless of any reasoning abilities or emotional feelings they may possess or experience, can be seen as genetic automata, eating, surviving, reproducing to…eat, survive, reproduce…and that, some suggest, is all there is to life, including our own. All organisms from bacteria to blue whales, including humans, can be seen as collections of genes responding, albeit sometimes flexibly and intelligently, 'automatically' to environmental cues and circumstances.

This view fits well with the relatively modern and broader view of the blindness of natural selection, evolutionary purposelessness and, as an ultimate consequence, life as meaningless. Anthony Smith wrote in his very interesting book 'The Body': 'The predator seeking out the prey has no greater objective than the grass growing, the rain falling. If there seems to be a purpose in evolution, said Sir Julian Huxley, it is only an apparent purpose. "It is just as much a product of blind forces as is the falling of a stone to earth or the ebb and flow of the tides. It is we who have read purpose into evolution, as earlier men projected will and evolution into inorganic phenomena like storm or earthquake."' (B62) We, of course, are included in this analysis and it seems that scientific reasoning has emptied our lives of meaning. This author suggests that this is neither a valid, nor a scientific, conclusion.

The Limitations of Science

Some may smile condescendingly at 'savages' such as perhaps, Huxley's 'earlier men', who think the gods are angry when a thunderstorm rages, since science can now measure air pressures, temperatures and electrical charges. The concept of gods being angry might even be dismissed with contempt. However, the true scientist says 'I do not know whether or not the gods are angry. I am only able to measure air pressures, temperatures and electrical charges. Whether or not the gods are angry I, as a scientist, cannot even comment upon.' So, is it suggested here that the gods are angry? It is suggested that orthodox science cannot tell us. Yet, this open-minded attitude, and correct conclusion that we do not know anything about the gods in this context, has been replaced by the unscientific conclusion that we do. Compounding the scientific error, some 'scientists' do not restrict themselves to particular sets of circumstances but generalise to conclude not only that the gods are not angry but that they do not even exist – if a scientist cannot measure it, the conclusion is not (as it should be) that we cannot currently study it, but that it cannot exist! These conclusions are unscientific, but believed by some scientists and many lay people. Non-measurement equates to non-existence *scientifically* but that does not necessarily mean non-existence.

Orthodox science is not equipped to draw conclusions on such issues and it is a mistake to seek them through science. It is an even bigger mistake to conclude that science's inability to attribute purpose, equates to an overall human inability to attribute purpose. To conclude this chapter, we remind ourselves that one reason science can progress so rapidly and effectively is due to its agreed limitations (e.g. its dependence on measurement; matter in motion; its approximations and assumptions; and its answers which multiply questions). Yet these limitations are forgotten in the enthusiasm over its successes – achieved partly because of those limitations. Too often and for a variety of reasons, more is claimed by some scientists than science can justify.

To keep a well balanced perspective it is also helpful to remember the distinction between technology / engineering and science. A common modern assumption is that we enjoy so many technological inventions due to science. This is not the case (even though, as these disciplines grow more interconnections, science shares increasingly larger amounts of common ground with technology and helps to refine and initiate further developments). Inventions are usually the product of practical men's hands and eyes making materials into new machines while working independently of 'science' (even if science can later describe the principles and laws involved in that work which, at the time, the inventor knew little or nothing about). The point can be illustrated by selecting a few inventors / engineers and inventions known to all: the amazing Thomas Alva Edison and his light bulb (just one of his many inventions in a long and remarkable career); Marconi and his radio; Wilbur and Orville Wright and their aircraft. The latter two gentlemen were bicycle mechanics. Marconi performed poorly at school, failed to gain admission to a university and said of himself that he was not a scientist (and not much of an inventor!) Edison had no formal education, attending one school for three months and then others sporadically and briefly. Nearly all his childhood education took place at home before he started working, at 10 years of age. So strong is the misconception of all technology being due to science and scientists that one may find, from supposedly reliable sources, references to Edison as an inventor/scientist without the latter label being justified, and the falsehood is strengthened by readers accepting it at face value without checking for themselves. This author has heard a professor of physics refer to our debt to science whenever we fly on an aircraft or use a mobile telephone. The above examples remind us that neither aircraft (including the later development of the jet engine by Sir Frank Whittle) nor the practical, general use of radio transmission and reception (a mobile 'phone is a miniature radio receiver and transmitter combined) are consequences of development by science or scientists. Whilst science played no part in the work of the Wright brothers, it is true that radio waves were first predicted and then detected by scientists but scientists neither explored nor developed radio's practical potential for society (some reasons given below). That a professor of physics appears unaware of the distinction speaks of powerful social trends and the way that even 'facts' can become twisted and entangled with falsehoods. These facts are gradually incorporated with other facts into future knowledge which becomes corrupted, making it inaccurate at best or false at worst. Of course, science has made many and valuable contributions to our lives but we need to keep a balanced view of it, lest we deify it - whilst denying deities.

However, while scientists may not have physically put the inventions together, surely they knew and understood the principles that governed these inventions and could have at least predicted them – put them on paper, if not on the bench?

Despite many previous successful inventions, Edison's light bulb was derided by eminent contemporary scientists such as Sir William Siemens, Professor Henry Morton (who refused an invitation to witness the bulb working but nonetheless declared it a fraud!) and Sir William Preece who pronounced the parallel lighting system Edison was successfully working on as not practically possible. Various scientists told Marconi that his radio transmissions could not possibly cross the Atlantic. (It was known then that radio waves (on the scales of matter, space and time concerned) would travel in straight lines. Hence, transmitted from England, intended for reception in America, they would, in theory, travel off into space at a tangent, due to the curvature of the Earth between England and America. In practice, the radio waves were reflected by the atmosphere, allowing their reception in America.) After Marconi's success, the physicist Lord Kelvin declared that "Radio has no future". Lord Kelvin had also declared that "Heavier-than-air flying machines are impossible". In this he was echoed by Prof. S. Newcomb of Johns Hopkins University who declared powered flight by humans impossible. Other scientists derided the claims of the Wright brothers to have flown (without going to see for themselves) as did the magazine Scientific American – more than two years after their first flight!

These are not just a few isolated examples, others are plentiful, throughout the history of science and, of course, they must be, since science is just another human endeavour, and therefore plagued by mistakes, or ignorance, or arrogance, or ego…

The Purpose of Science

Despite and because of its limitations, science is a fascinating, educational and useful human discipline, stimulating us intellectually and, when used properly, contributing to our lives and welfare. Since science is so valuable, it is important to maintain its purity and integrity and use it appropriately – to use science scientifically. Science can and has produced much worthwhile data: amazing insights to space and time, energy and matter, the geophysical features of our planet and all life on it. Science has revealed fascinating insights to animal life, connections within and between ecosystems, locally and globally, explaining the practical importance of conservation in general and of individual animal species, such as the tiger, in particular (some details in chapter V). It has identified the dangers of human industrial / commercial activities and environmental abuse while numerous scientists have declared publicly that we (as a species) are on a collision course with nature and that scientists cannot deal with the consequences.

Science can tell us much within its limitations but beyond them we should not expect answers from science since, in these areas, it cannot even ask questions. Science studies matter in motion, (even the presence and properties of fields are detected and assessed by matter in motion) and it does so through information relayed via five senses (or six if we now include the VNO), either directly or through instruments. Science studies those material aspects of our world which can be measured or quantified. If it cannot be measured, science cannot study it. All this is fine – for as long as we're interested in material and mechanics and bear in mind that, even when confined to these concepts, all scientific knowledge put together, by science's own standards, is fragmentary and far from certain. Science has not yet incorporated all its own study material – physical phenomena – into a coherent and consistent body of knowledge.

Still less by far can science study or comment on the much richer, broader set of experiences that our lives present us with, for examples, compassion, wishes, judgements, innovations, right, wrong, love and purpose. These aspects of life are as real as any other experience but, by definition, science is not concerned with them and they remain inaccessible to conventional scientific analysis.

Recent systems theories (which are scientifically rigorous) maintain that systems give rise to properties impossible for the component parts to exhibit in isolation. Some scientists suggest that purpose, emotion, values etc. are also these, so called, 'emergent properties'. They claim that all is ultimately the mechanical results of multiple levels of matter in motion (this is unimpressive intellectually since, from an orthodox scientific perspective, matter/energy is all anything can originate from and hence, it is a default option). Some believe that it is only a matter of time before science eventually explains all natural phenomena and all aspects of our experience (chapters IV and V will challenge this view) and that life as a whole, including all that remains unknown within and beyond science, is a meaningless, purposeless chain reaction of matter in motion. Since so many studies are still in their infancy and all-encompassing conclusions impossible to draw, this is a massive, unwarranted and unscientific assumption; and currently at least, opinion, not science

'Knowledge is proud that he has learned so much;
Wisdom is humble that he knows no more.'

(William Cowper 1731 – 1800 English poet)

That all the amazing complexity, creativity, beauty and drama of nature could be completely determined by the mechanics of atoms in motion has drawn doubts ever since its proposal and these are perhaps best expressed by Durant referring to Henri Bergson's scepticism about such an all embracing determinism: 'Finally, was determinism any more intelligible than free will? If the present moment contains no living and creative choice, and is totally and mechanically the product of the matter and motion of the moment before, then so was that moment the mechanical effect of the moment that preceded it, and that again of the one before…and so on, until we arrive at the primeval nebula as the total cause of every later event, of every line of Shakespeare's plays, and every suffering of his soul; so that the sombre rhetoric of Hamlet and Othello, of Macbeth and Lear, in every clause and every phrase, was written far off there in the distant skies and the distant aeons, by the structure and content of that legendary cloud. What a draft upon credulity. What an exercise of faith such a theory must demand in this unbelieving generation! What mystery or miracle, of Old Testament or New, could be half so incredible as this monstrous fatalistic myth, this nebula composing tragedies? There was matter enough for rebellion here; and if Bergson rose so rapidly to fame it was because he had the courage to doubt where all the doubters piously believed.' (B23 reprinted with the permission of Pocket Books, a division of Simon & Schuster, Inc., from THE STORY OF PHILOSOPHY by Will Durant. Copyright © 1926, 1927, 1933, 1954, 1955, 1961 by Will Durant.. All rights reserved)

Since the advent of quantum physics, scientists themselves have found, for examples, that cause need not precede effect; that some things can be in two places at one time; that some physical entities can be both wave and particle. Foundation stones have disappeared without any substitutes being found. Yet still, mechanism and reductionism hold a great power over the minds of many scientists. Science itself is a human product, a subset of our abilities and faculties to study subsets of our experience, so when we try to make it 'explain' or give insights to areas that fall outside its methodology, up to and including the meaning of life, we are trying to make the subset explain the set of which it is a part. Trying to force life as a whole (including all that was excluded as unscientific) into science's restricted criteria is like trying to put a quart into a pint pot, which is unscientific – to say the least.

Scientists who conclude all is pointless and meaningless ignore why they want to publish their research (which must also be meaningless?) and the purpose of publishing texts about purposelessness. Science, when examined in depth, is inevitably influenced by personal, emotional and non-scientific factors – since it is the product of humans mostly studying the work of other humans. Ignoring their humanity is an agreed artifice adopted by orthodox scientists for use in their work – but some try to apply it to that which invented the artifice; humanity! Scientists are part and parcel of humanity and they proceed unscientifically if and when claiming science's subject matter as the only reality and the one from which all else derives.

For some scientists and lay people, a psychological motive has helped this view gain ground since it allows people to live in a world without personal responsibility – we're all genetic automata: don't blame me for my actions or my character; blame my genes, or the way I was nurtured – and it's all meaningless anyway. Undoubtedly nature and nurture are powerful influences on us but our system of law, and society itself, breaks down without the concept of free will and practice of personal responsibility, not only to each other but also to other species.

Whatever weakness of character may contribute to its popularity, determinism or pure mechanism also impoverishes philosophy since focussing on material and mechanics as the only and ultimate reality, while living in a bigger world that indubitably comprises more than mechanism can explain, unnecessarily and artificially restricts the scope of any sincere search for truth, which is a vastly greater field than science alone can cover.

As the concepts of information, knowledge, wisdom and truth will be referred to again, it will be helpful to describe some elements of each, as relevant to the context of this book: data such as letters and numbers may be collected into arrangements of words and sentences that provide information e.g. that contained in a telephone directory. Continuing with this example, 'knowledge' includes recognising to whom some of the directory entries refer and also their work, homes, families and who is neighbour to whom, by street or area (i.e. perceiving more relationships, more connections). Attempting to define wisdom would not be wise! However, from our perspective, it includes an understanding of the meaning of knowledge, of those connections, and hence how they will develop over time; an understanding of where they will lead. Wisdom cannot be learned from books, or in any other academic way. It is acquired through personal, direct, first-hand experience and helps us make choices to promote, or prevent, the developments foreseen, according to their anticipated consequences, and hence is a good companion for purpose. Wisdom is also a product of a well-balanced heart and head or, in terms of the previous and subsequent chapters, intuitive and rational knowledge.

Although we can only search with mortal hand and eye, we seek immortal Truth – an all embracing concept of inviolate purity subject to neither correction nor corruption. Chapters III to V will argue that science alone will never be able to explain all of our experience and therefore never provide a complete and consistent account of truth. They also argue that these other, scientifically inexplicable, experiences are a necessary and fundamental part of the truth and that we can only find something of the whole truth by balancing our heads with our hearts and taking action to face our responsibilities, which provides us with purpose. With this balanced approach, time turns purposeful knowledge into wisdom, which is useful in its own right and also helps with our search for truth. Building on this base, further comments on 'truth' as a concept are made in chapters IV and V. Part of the truth is that science itself has no value independently of human purpose. Research has been producing results now for centuries and a vast, dead body of information, and some knowledge, has been accumulating. A living body of knowledge grows when we combine it with purpose – the application of that knowledge – beyond personal promotion or profit.

Dangers arise when scientists and / or philosophers citing theories and / or practical achievements try to persuade us that neither purpose, nor morality, nor virtue, nor responsibility need accompany us on the path to truth, in fact are an obstruction on that path, which can be found more easily without these considerations. 'Science is analytical description, philosophy is synthetic interpretation. Science wishes to resolve the whole into parts, the organism into organs, the obscure into the known. It does not inquire into the values and ideal possibilities of things, nor into their total and final significance; it is content to show their present actuality and operation, it narrows its gaze resolutely to the nature and process of things as they are…But the philosopher is not content to describe the fact; he wishes to ascertain its relation to experience in general, and thereby to get at its meaning and its worth; he combines things in interpretive synthesis; he tries to put together, better than before, that great universe-watch which the inquisitive scientist has analytically taken apart…For a fact is nothing except in relation to desire; it is not complete except in relation to a purpose and a whole. Science without philosophy, facts without perspective and valuation, cannot save us from havoc and despair. Science gives us knowledge, but only philosophy can give us wisdom.'

Personal Limitations and Personal Purposes

While science may not be able to find purpose, I could find plenty, but no funding – either to continue the chemical communication research or to conduct an ecology project. I had also failed to find a position on what was then a forthcoming tiger research project in the wild.

Hopes that I might be able to make some contribution to tiger conservation through science had faded with the years, not only due to my failures to find funding or relevant work, but also because of reducing opportunities for 'pure' research, due to research in general, across all disciplines, being increasingly funded, not by government but by industry, seeking only knowledge that led to financial profit. There was also a trend to find facts for their own sake, or to publish papers to promote careers or for personal aggrandisement. Moreover, regardless of funding agendas and / or trends of counting papers published, even in 'pure' or ideal circumstances, academia neither can, nor should be able to determine the future of a species; its role is advisory and supportive. Yet even in this capacity science was having little or no significant effect at the grass-roots level where tigers and other species were living and, more worryingly, dying. Hence, my own failures and a growing awareness of academia's restricted ability to help prevent species extinctions troubled me and I began to consider other options.

At the time I am writing about (late eighties, early nineties) a renewed tiger crisis became apparent due not only to the usual threats of diminished and degraded habitat but also to an additional and enormous commercial pressure from Chinese Traditional Medicine's trade in their body parts. My decision to work, somehow, somewhere, full-time on tiger conservation in India terminated my academic work completely. Although I had failed to find funding, my self-financed PhD was actually happening and it felt good to progress the work begun years before. Hence, leaving the research work brought real regrets but, as the reader is possibly thinking, how can benefits for oneself outweigh the importance of trying to contribute to the tiger's survival and to environmental health in general?

As a boy, my fascination with the tiger and a growing awareness of our collective abuse of nature had found embodiment in Jim Corbett. His books had focussed these feelings and awareness on India. Of the remaining tiger populations in the world all are endangered; their populations numbered in three figures, except one – the Indian population which, just about, makes four figures 1000 – 1400? A number of legally protected habitats, an official Forest Department and existing protective legislation, could possibly serve as a foundation on which to base conservation efforts.

If extinction was, and is, to be averted, complex socio-economic and commercial factors along with enormous problems such as criminal activities and corruption, all operating amidst a vast arena of basic human survival problems, poverty and lack of literacy (let alone education) had, and still have, to be faced. I did not know how to tackle problems on such a vast scale and within such a rapidly diminishing time scale. Nor, even if I had some ideas about this, did I know how to turn them into action. Nor did I like spicy food! I had lost the pugmarks but, somewhere between academia and India, I hoped to pick up their trail.

We can still learn much from Jim Corbett and, if we visit his place next, we can rest from the exclusive rule of reason and explore a balance between intuitive and rational types of knowledge, while I cast around to pick up the pugmark trail again.

This map of 'Corbett country' is a section from a map of the Western Himalayas compiled by T.G. Montgomerie in 1860 for the Survey of India with additions and corrections to 1883 and additions to railways to 1893 (there is still a railhead at Kathgodam but now also one at Ramnagar, where the administrative headquarters of Corbett Tiger Reserve is located). Some spellings of place names differ from those used in this book but can be identified phonetically, for example Pithoragarh, Lohaghat, Naini Tal (– just about!) and Rudraprayag. The latter is associated with one of Corbett's man-eaters, as are Champawat and Mohan, also marked on the map.

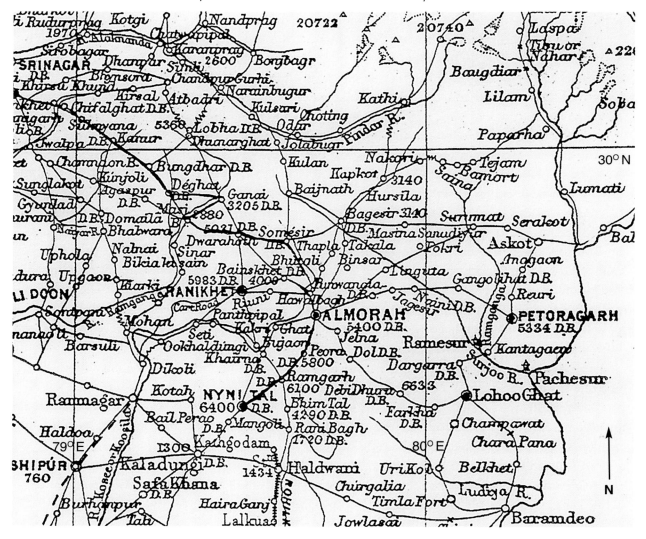

CHAPTER III

TO SEIZE THE FIRE

As we shall visit Jim Corbett's bungalows, some introduction to our host will be appropriate. Being interested in tigers, you are probably familiar with at least his name, if not his life. India's first National Park (and now Tiger Reserve) is named after him and his books became popular classics after their publication in the 1940's and 50's. If, as a tiger enthusiast, you have not yet read them, I believe you have some treasure to find – 'X marks the spot' over the library on your town map, Corbett's treasure trove includes some pearls of wisdom, green materials more valuable than gold or silver, and black, orange and white gems. Some philosophical nuggets may also be mined and, as we work more deeply into this chapter, we shall try to extract a few.

In the preface to his first book, 'Man-Eaters of Kumaon', Corbett wrote that half a century had rolled by between a tiger walking out from under the plum bush at his feet and the writing of that preface. At least another half century rolled by between his writing that, and my attempts to write this. While the world turned through that century, various perspectives, attitudes and values have become twisted and entangled, and some can no longer be seen clearly. We need to spend a few pages disentangling the warp and woof that wove Corbett's cultural era in order that we recognise our host.

Corbett was British but what that meant then (beyond a label of citizenship) is not completely the same as what it means now, and the contrasts illustrate some of those twists in perspectives. We will better understand Corbett and his contemporaries if we return to an era when self-sacrifice and self-effacement were ideals and when one's duty and devotion was not to oneself but an entity larger than oneself (e.g. families, professions, institutions, communities, and nations. In turn, nations could and should now be working together for the health of the world but sadly, conflicts at this level reflect conflicts at lower levels – due in part to the loss of values we will be considering). These ideals and dutiful attitudes are healthier for all, since, by contributing to the health of our various communities, we contribute to our own health and security. As Rudyard Kipling (British author and poet 1865 – 1936) told us 'The strength of the Pack is the Wolf, and the strength of the Wolf is the Pack.' Nature repeatedly illustrates this interdependency at many levels and now, most critically, globally and environmentally.

Ideals, Character and Ideal Characters

Neither Corbett nor many of his contemporaries would recognise many of the modern (or at least Western) world's priorities: me first – others later (if at all); money before morals; fun before duty (and when duty is done, its main focus is to benefit ourselves, if only in terms of a salary); personal before professional; superficiality before serious; casual before formal.

In contrast, a key characteristic of his cultural era was exemplified by Corbett's response to over-hearing a group of men in a social setting declining an invitation to hunt a man-eating leopard. The following day he quietly and privately approached the government official who had made the invitation and offered his services. His response not only conforms to the qualities just mentioned but also stands in contrast to other typically modern responses: to find insurance, media coverage, to advertise, seek sponsorship or sell 'rights'. He did not sell rights; he just did them, privately, at his own risk and expense. Such was the culture and such was his character and, as they do for all of us, each influences the other.

It seems that respect and admiration for character is almost extinct, or at least unfashionable, due in part to the relatively recent trend of public 'character assassinations' by the media – sometimes executed just for spite and / or without real foundation. In a modern climate of cynicism, extolling Corbett's virtues provides material for ridicule and dismissal. Of course, Corbett had his share of human weaknesses and failings. The important point is the balance point, the degree to which he governed, or was governed by, these factors – as it is for all of us, and it is often our own failings that prompt us to ridicule others with whom we cannot compare: if we can't get up to their level, let's bring them down to ours. It is suggested that both his character and the characteristics of his era were generally made of better materials than most of what we see around us today – and declining standards and values are partly the result of being without ideals and characters to admire or aspire to.

An ideal helps us see in what ways our character falls short by comparison and by how far. Hence, it is also a standard against which we may measure our progress. We always have the potential to progress or regress but modern society presents few incentives to realise our positive potential. Some 'accomplishments', skills, talents or technical abilities are offered us for admiration but few ideals in terms of characters, virtues or morality. Yet any accomplishment, born of whatever physical or mental ability, can and will be equalled, surpassed, rendered irrelevant by changing times, or simply forgotten (as the Beatles song says 'There's nothing you can do that can't be done. Nothing you can sing that can't be sung...Nothing you can make that can't be made, no one you can save that can't be saved...but you can learn how to be you in time...' We will consider the conclusion, that all we need is love, in chapter V). The only completely unique aspect each of us holds is our character. Unique in the universe for all time, it can never suffer the same fate as a technical achievement. Being unique, one cannot 'fail' as compared to others, one can only fail oneself. We may consider that we have few, if any, skills or talents, yet truly worthwhile qualities can be ours: 'Cultivate these, then, for they are wholly within your power: sincerity, for example, and dignity; industriousness, and sobriety. Avoid grumbling; be frugal, considerate, and frank; be temperate in manner and in speech; carry yourself with authority. See how many qualities there are which could be yours at this moment. You can allege no native incapacity or in-aptitude for them; and yet you choose to linger still on a less lofty plane.' (Marcus Aurelius 121 – 180). Doing one's best, in accordance with virtue and morality, makes one 'first class' whatever one's background socially, financially or technically. Moreover, it is only our character that we might, and the only thing that we could, take with us after death. Of course, no-one knows for sure – but we do know for sure that we can take nothing else.

> '...our ideal...is far away, no doubt, but at the same time, we know that we must have it. We must even have the highest ideal. Unfortunately in this life, the vast majority of persons are groping through this dark life without any ideal at all. If a man with an ideal makes a thousand mistakes, I am sure that the man without an ideal makes fifty thousand. Therefore, it is better to have an ideal...'
>
> (Swami Vivekenanda).

> 'Enthusiastic admiration. It is by our passionate admirations that we grow.'
>
> (Karin Michaelis, Danish author 1872-1950).

Modern times are short of heroes and ideals, yet it is hoped, for all our sakes, that society has not become so cynical and decadent as to dismiss or ridicule such qualities where they can still be identified. Declining standards are intimately connected to various modern crises, including the environmental one, as explored in the following chapters. As decadence deepens and cynicism becomes realism, it is evermore important to find and aspire to healthy ideals. These help heal us and reverse the current dangerous decline that threatens our tigers and, ultimately, our tenancy on the Earth.

Corbett's characteristics are not only apparent from his books but also from his biographies, which record that his qualities were outstanding and noticed in numerous situations beyond those described in his books, including his service in France during WWI and training troops for the Burma campaign during WWII. If Corbett were contemporaneous with the trend of 'character assassination' (itself an incongruity that speaks volumes) and, being subjected to it, in some way proved a fake (and nigh on half a century after his death, this author found his name and reputation still revered both where he lived and in the areas where he hunted man-eaters) the ideals and qualities identified in this chapter remain as such, since they are 'eternal' or of life itself, written in the 'book of nature', and hence it is unhealthy *not* to admire them. What we know of Corbett's qualities are taken here as a model of general principles which are important for fulfilling our lives and destinies, regardless of the degree to which Corbett does, or does not, fit his current public image.

In addition to his personal characteristics, the settings of his stories provide physical analogues to spiritual principles. For example, his cheerfully walking long distances up steep and difficult paths under a blazing Indian sun, noting nature's beauties along the way, to voluntarily relieve villagers of a man-eating tiger or leopard, is a physical manifestation of Hesiod's metaphor that 'before virtue the immortal gods have set sweat, and the road thither is long and uphill and rough at the outset, though when the summit is reached, the going is easy, for all its hardness' whereas '"the path to vice is smooth" and being short, can be travelled without sweat.'(B32) (Hesiod: Greek poet. 8th century BCE (exact dates unknown)).

Modern trends are to admire material goods or other ephemera, which are never really 'ours', but not character, which is. Hence, admiring character – as opposed to goals scored, 'movies' or monies made – now seems naïve and misguided, since science and commerce have convinced us that life is meaningless and the promotion and indulgence of self, the only passing purpose. The apparently prevailing attitude is that we're all the same really, driven by ego and self, and should be 'out there' scrabbling for the most we can get, admiring those who get larger slices of the cake, condescending to or despising those who get a smaller slice, and being friends with those who get similar slices. This is a dangerous development distancing us from duty (which is essentially service to others – an important character-building activity), while promoting its opposite, which is self.

Duties done decently and courteously, with a sense of decorum and polite reserve make a refreshing substitute for, and stark contrast to, the all too frequent 'news' of another incident involving 'celebrities', which might leave us with a vague feeling of unease as we sense the deeper implications, not only of the incident but also that such material makes national 'news'. However, because of the modern prevalence of image over substance, vulgarity over decency, and publicity over privacy, a member of the 'old school', especially one who was exemplary even by the standards of that era, can seem too good to be true, especially by comparison with today's media-manufactured, often image-only, 'heroes' and idols. The trend is evident even in nature's remote arbours where we find TV 'experts', a few scientists, or enthusiasts like me, who have spent some time in forests – usually with our 4WD's and cameras; comforts and conveniences not too far away. No harm is done – for as long as we conduct ourselves with due regard for the animals and the environment, while retaining real standards for comparison and contrast. A danger arises firstly when these perspectives are lost and secondly and worse when, as the pendulum continues past its lowest point, doubt begins, becomes belittlement and at the opposite extreme of the swing, false 'image-only experts' criticise genuine expertise.

When I read criticism of previous authorities such as Corbett, I wonder if the author of such criticism would be able, literally or metaphorically, to keep pace with them on a jungle picnic, let alone be able to locate and deal with a man-eater, or has any fraction of the knowledge and hardiness required to do so. The pendulum has swung past times when men were made of better mettle; those whose commonplace deeds would be exceptional today. For example, measured by modern standards, enduring extremes of weather for days and nights (without outrageously-priced special clothing, equipment and, of course, a mobile 'phone ('I'm on the mountain…')), walking alone, perhaps for 28 miles, over difficult and mountainous terrain, being able to eat from trees or plants and keep ourselves warm, dry and clean along the way, would be rated as achievements. It puts Corbett in some perspective to recognise that these activities were merely *preparatory* to his hunting a man-eater, and were so when he was well into his sixties. Irritations such as leeches, ticks and ants are not even mentioned and would be only by a tenderfoot.

Characters of Communities

It seems that characters in general have atrophied as compared to those formed before the infernal combustion engine (yes, that's meant to be an 'f', not a 't') and before electricity generated our current insulation from nature. In the West at least we have been softened, and wrapped in cotton wool, both by technology and imbalanced social trends, including the rise of a collective mentality amongst legislators that protects us from paper pricks – while the planet dies around us. When the law requires people to erect scaffolding to change ceiling light bulbs and children are advised to wear goggles to play conkers, whilst other people are without any ceilings and whole forests fall, there are serious and dangerous imbalances in those offices and officers we pay to administer society.

With the vast increase in specialised technical information and the absence of any authoritative body with a comprehensive overview, 'knowledge' has also become 'imbalanced', too finely focussed, the exclusive purview of specialists and experts, 'out of touch' with other groups within society, including most of us and our personal experience. 'Experts' are consulted on behalf of the whole population, laws are passed and society changes in accordance with minorities, not majorities. Continuity and communication between members of and groups within society has been lost and fragmentation, disaffection and more splinter groups result. These then influence the character development of their members in ways which segregate them still further from other, and multiplying sub-groups.

Ideally, shared experience integrates knowledge and, by following nature's guide, and adhering to moral codes and virtuous conduct, healthy characters and unified communities develop. Experience teaches us that knowledge of some entity, although always only probable, grows as we grow to be 'a part of' that entity. We have to be part of a community in order to contribute to, and receive from, that community. Similarly, to contribute to and receive from nature we have to recognise ourselves as part of nature and this can be achieved by experiencing nature at first hand, if only by regularly walking in the woods – provided we walk with interest and actually look at what we see. The unification cannot be forced or driven by us. Happy to receive what nature returns as interest for time invested in her company, understanding grows, followed by respect and love for nature's glory and beauty. Fragments of knowledge collected by forcibly taking only what 'I want' from nature (or the community) according to one's own immediate, short-sighted and restricted view, for purposes of profit, self promotion or self-indulgence, leave one forever ignorant. Sadly, in the modern Western world, cultivating a real understanding of nature and spending time with it is mainly 'for the kids' and 'real life' is made of the office, supermarket and television.

For our purposes, Corbett represents an ideal. He made many and various contributions to the welfare of natural habitats and human communities locally, nationally and internationally.. He educated himself by experiencing nature at first hand, acquiring a healthy balance between formal, technical, rational knowledge and skills, and natural, 'absorbed' intuitive knowledge and skills. He learned stillness and silence, which together breed patience and humility.

Rational Knowledge and Intuitive Knowledge

An open mind and heart, spending time with nature, absorbs a sort of 'intuitive knowledge' that is as valid as any other form of knowledge. A variety of modern cultural trends have tended to make 'rational knowledge' (which can be taught with text books), particularly scientific knowledge, seem superior to any other sort. While science surely has validity and value, we impoverish ourselves when we discard other forms of knowledge or dismiss people who hold such knowledge.

One of Corbett's notes for introducing his films of wildlife included the following passage: 'If you were in the jungles with me and four cheetal called at the four points of the compass, I could tell you that the one to the north was calling to a young one that had strayed, that the one to the east was warning the jungle of the presence of a tiger, that the one to the south was warning the jungle of the presence of a human being, and that the one to the west was calling because it could see a leopard on a tree or on the ground or while it was killing another animal. Now if you were to ask me how I could distinguish between the different calls – I could not tell you, any more than you could tell me how you could distinguish between the scent of a rose and the scent of a violet.' (Printed by kind permission of O.U.P)

Knowledge born of our direct, personal experience is the surest knowledge we can have but it cannot be taught to others. We can only guide them to, and sometimes guard them in, situations wherein they can gain their own experience. The same applies to practical abilities learned through experience. 'He could steer in anything short of half a gale from the feel of the wind on his face, humouring the (*schooner*) just when she needed it. These things he did as automatically as he skipped about the rigging, or made his dory (*a little, flat-bottomed boat*) a part of his own will and body. But he could not communicate his knowledge to Harvey.' (B42b)

And it is one's free will, directed with interest, which has to be exercised in order to learn and remember. Corbett considered the level of interest to be critical as to whether or not events are remembered and refers to why events in childhood remain fixed in one's memory while recent events can only be recalled – if at all – with an effort. He had read a suggestion that in childhood our young minds are more receptive but Corbett disagrees with this and writes: 'When we are young our horizons are limited and the few things that interest us are indelibly etched on our memories. As we grow older our horizons enlarge and an increasing number of things interest us and the impressions are not etched in for the single reason that we have neither the time nor the inclination to make as detailed and as clear etchings as we made when we were young. The mind is not at fault for distorted and faint impressions for I believe that our minds – up to a point – remain receptive throughout our lives and the fault of making bad and faint impressions instead of good clear cut ones is not due to an enlarged horizon, but is due to a lack of concentration and interest.' (Printed by kind permission of O.U.P)

He then describes an incident with a nightjar and goes on to tell us:

'Part of the events I have narrated took place yesterday and part took place today and I am confident that if you were to question me about them tomorrow, or ten years hence, I would from memory be able to retell you the story of the nightjar word for word as I have told it above. And this cannot be attributed to my mind being young and receptive, but it can be attributed to my having taken an interest in the scene which is now indelibly etched into my memory.' (Printed by kind permission of O.U.P)

The acquirement of both rational and intuitive knowledge is facilitated by the exercise of interest and both may be employed in practical applications. However, some practical applications, including wood-craft, and those who are able to apply them, can often be considered the 'poor relation' to the modern scientist and scientific knowledge, the assumption being that the scientist could do what the other does. Even though some scientists, given the opportunity, would prove very capable at learning wood-craft, experience teaches us that this would not always be so. Academic abilities often preclude practical abilities and vice versa. A related point was made at the end of chapter II that, although technology shares some territory with science, as a practical discipline it remains distinct from it. Even within any one discipline, different individuals are suited to different depths, or levels, of learning – there is much truth in the old story of the professor of mathematics arguing with the 'bus conductor over his change – and being the one in error! Practical 'know-how', feeling / absorbing knowledge and intuition are not poor relations, but partners to academic knowledge. Neither scientific knowledge nor scientists are superior to practical knowledge and ability. Nor is it true that science will eventually explain or supersede the sort of knowledge Corbett represents. This and later chapters will, hopefully, explain why.

Our survival as a species in a challenging environment is proof that academic knowledge is only of value once particular practical survival problems have been solved. Of course, once we have ensured our survival, academic knowledge can help us improve (by its practical application) our survival techniques. Further developments and comforts can follow. Yet all is based on our original need for, and ability to acquire water, food and shelter – the acquisition of which has come to be looked down upon from the socio-academic structures these foundations have allowed us to build. We tend to take for granted or despise that on which we stand.

'But 'tis a common proof
That lowliness is young ambition's ladder,
Whereto the climber upward turns his face;
But when he once attains the upmost round,
He then unto the ladder turns his back,
Looks in the clouds, scorning the base degrees
By which he did ascend.'

(Shakespeare's *Julius Caesar* Act II, Sc.I)

The same arrogance and illusory security is exhibited in the current environmental crisis wherein technological and industrial Man imagines he can without limit, damage, degrade and despise natural resources, the source of his air, water and food, for the sake of his various manufactured products (of dubious value) and short-term material profits – none of which have any value at all without the resources he is destroying to produce them. Intuitive knowledge breeds humility whereas rational knowledge, which forgets its origins, can easily breed arrogance. This is particularly the case when rational knowledge is acquired simply to pass an exam or achieve a target, such as a publication, promotion or pay rise.

Trends toward scientific dominance, looking down on life-styles, people and practices that have preceded us, can blind us to valuable insights and learning opportunities – which together are called history. And it is history, albeit inevitably selective, that presents us with what are, to the best of our knowledge, real events and achievements. Our appreciation of *real* achievements has been dulled due to saturation, not only by fiction in and of itself, but also due to the spectacular feats and special effects in modern films which our formal, technical knowledge has allowed us to make, but which are mostly *false*. This chapter will refer to Corbett risking his life to protect others by killing a man-eater. During the hunt he would have to avoid death, in a most horrific form, that was actively seeking him. These are real, worthwhile and impressive achievements in any wood but Hollywood. One reason for this trend is that so much of what now happens in Hollywood is concerned predominantly with money. The quickest and easiest way to attract maximum money, i.e. maximum audiences, is to offer their most basic impulses gratification, and so we see innumerable rehashes of the same recipe of few ingredients. The art form, the potential to elevate the makers, the actors and the audience, is lost. In some cases the art form can stimulate interest and, in others, interest seeks out the art form. Cause and effect can be interchangeable. Either way, some effort must be made by the viewer. Too much junk food, junk films and junk television can dull our faculties and turn us into dullards, not motivated to make any effort; uninterested and, consequently, uninteresting. Too much junk provided too easily results in no exercise spiritually, mentally or physically, and leads to boredom and ill health.

An idle poet, here and there,
Looks round him; but, for all the rest,
The world, unfathomably fair,
Is duller than a witling's jest.
Nature wakes men, once a lifetime each;
They lift their heavy lids and look;
And, lo, what one page can teach,
They read with joy, then shut the book.
And some give thanks, and some blaspheme
But most forget and either way,
This and their unheeded dreams
Is all the light of all their day.

(with apologies to Coventry Patmore of whose original and wonderful poem 'The Revelation' this is, almost, an exact copy. The original has 'love' instead of 'Nature'. Chapter V will consider that they can be interchangeable)

Nature woke Corbett and he continued to look and read with interest. He saw that the book, as he put it, had no beginning and no end but, even so, he never shut the book. Nor did he forget what he had read, which lent a constant light to his life, by which he and others could find their way.

We have looked at rational and intuitive knowledge with respect to science and wood-craft. Whether or not we live next to nature, these two types of knowledge inform all our activities, and all our activities inform these two types of knowledge. From basic practicalities to our highest cultural expressions, both types of knowledge are involved in our understanding. The better balanced they are, the healthier and / or better our understanding.

Having stressed some elements that made Corbett a man of his time, there were also ways in which he was ahead of his time: his advocating and promoting conservation is an obvious example. Not so obvious, is his wildlife photography.

By imitating their calls, providing food, and using his knowledge and some wisdom, Corbett drew seven tigers together in one ravine and filmed them. The last eleven words hardly seem adequate to describe the enormity of the accomplishment. Quite apart from being able to draw the animals to the particular location he wanted, the film was shot over a period of four and a half months and so, each day for many weeks, he would have to arrive, film and leave without detection. This might be difficult enough with just one or two tigers, yet to achieve this without one of six sets of sensitive ears and eyes detecting him, is an astounding accomplishment (one tigress left the day after her arrival). He says the heavy early morning dew enabled him to do this but still, readers with some experience of wild animals will know that, even with the heaviest dew, approaching any animal, let alone a group of tigers, and filming them from ten to sixty feet, every day for weeks on end, would seem nigh on impossible and the film, quite apart from its value as a record of the natural world (all the animals are unaware of being observed), has another intrinsic value as self-referential proof that such a film can be made! Readers should also remember that early cameras had no zoom lenses and the object in the viewfinder would appear minuscule. Therefore footage wherein the tiger(s) fill a large part of the screen is another striking accomplishment, largely unrecognised today due to our being familiar with footage filmed with extremely powerful zoom lenses. Corbett's feat also provided clues that the supposedly 'solitary' tiger did have a more active social structure, another aspect ahead of its time and making the observations of social grouping of tigers in the 1970's and 80's not quite so revelatory.

With these perspectives in mind we can return to our host, bearing in mind that the values of a previous era set the context of this chapter. It is suggested that their disappearance is not part of cultural progress but symptomatic of a malaise, another manifestation of decadence and the declining health of people and the planet. Such, it seems, are the times, and if they are our viewpoint, we shall not be able to see Corbett clearly.

This introduction asks the reader to adjust, if necessary, their viewpoint to focus on people and events across the distance of a century. If we keep at least some traditional values in view, we shall benefit from, and enjoy getting to know him better.

The Biography

In 1947 Jim Corbett and his sister Maggie moved to Kenya. After living in a few temporary locations, they eventually settled in the grounds of the Outspan Hotel, Nyeri, approximately 100 miles north of Nairobi, in a cottage called 'Paxtu' (a name given the cottage by its original occupant, Lord Baden-Powell). In this cottage Corbett wrote his later books; My India, Jungle Lore, The Temple Tiger and Tree Tops. The Outspan was built and owned by the Sherbrooke-Walkers, who also built the original Tree Tops hotel. Still today, at time of writing, to stay at Tree Tops one has to depart from and return to the Outspan.

Outside Paxtu a wooden display board gives some information about Baden-Powell and briefly refers to Corbett (and should, strictly speaking, refer to 'northern' rather than 'central' India) but the memorabilia inside the cottage are only of Baden-Powell.

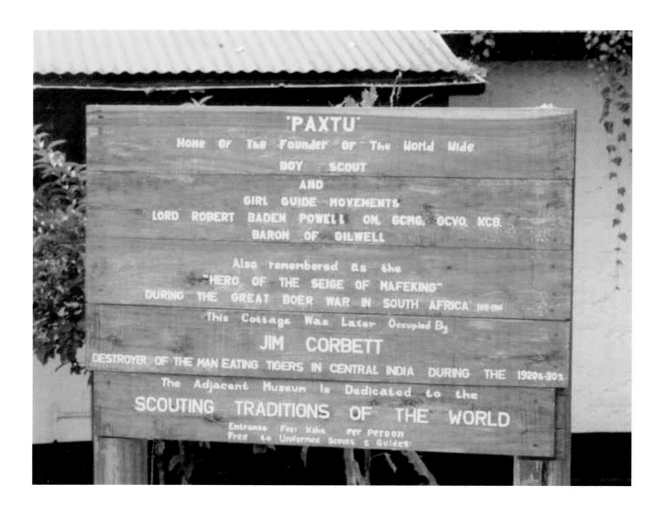

The entrance drive to the Outspan, with an end view of Paxtu in the right background. Although not visible from this angle, running the length of its right-hand side is the veranda (below) on which Jim and his sister Maggie would sit.

This author was fortunate enough to visit this cottage in 1993 and, in response to my enquiry, the manager said he would be pleased to display any Corbett biographical material I could provide. The poster partly reproduced here has been on display in Paxtu since August 1994, courtesy of J. Jaleel, an authority on Corbett, who kindly collected it from me at London airport, en route to Africa and Nyeri. The main purpose of Mr. Jaleel's visit was achieved when he successfully re-set the subsided headstone of Corbett's grave.

Jim and Maggie sitting on Paxtu's veranda.

(With thanks to Brian Stutchbury, their nephew who took, and kindly gave permission to use, this photograph).

POSTER

Long before "conservation" was a word in everyday use and well before its importance was widely recognised, Jim Corbett was actively urging the protection of the forests and their inhabitants. Born in Naini Tal, Northern India in 1875 of a domiciled British family, he grew up within walking distance of the jungles and grasslands surrounding his home. Regularly exploring these areas he gradually learned more and more of the habits of wild animals and birds, developing at the same time a true love and respect for wildlife and the environment. Hunting was as natural a part of his life from boyhood onwards as perhaps fishing or even harvesting remain natural parts of modern life. However, gradually Corbett came to oppose hunting and by middle age had set up an association to promote nature conservancy and published a magazine

(Indian Wild Life) with the same theme. In the 1930's these were unusual and in many circles unpopular actions, indicating Corbett's independent thinking and the strength of his convictions. Putting aside his gun he took up the cine camera and by employing his remarkable knowledge of jungle lore filmed many unique scenes, some of which have not been equalled to this day.

However, there was one type of hunt that he would still agree to undertake – that of a man-eater. Provided he was convinced that a tiger or leopard had taken to regularly preying on human beings (i.e. a human death was not due to the animal defending its cubs or food), he would embark on an often prolonged and hazardous hunt until he accounted for the animal.

It is difficult for many of us to imagine the terror that is a part of everyday life for people living in an area inhabited by a man-eater. Having to move about the forests in order to maintain their livelihood many, many people (death tolls often numbered hundreds) suffered tragedies either as victims or as part of a family whose members were taken and eaten. Often it was not possible to find any physical remains to cremate and hence, being Hindu, families were unable to find peace of mind even in their religious beliefs.

Corbett's accounts of his hunts reveal his deep understanding of animals and are told in an unassuming, straightforward manner which somehow heightens the excitement of the stories. Frequently he will point out that the tiger or leopard was only breaking man's law, not nature's, and will often explain why a particular animal had become a man-eater, unlike the vast majority of tigers and leopards living in peaceful harmony with the farmers and villagers of the area. To give some idea of these narratives a couple of excerpts follow:

The poster in Paxtu features at this point a brief excerpt from The Mohan Man-Eater in 'Man-Eaters of Kumaon' wherein Corbett is returning to camp at sunset and suddenly feels that danger is hidden behind a particular overhanging rock. He stands perfectly still and watches. Despite not being able to see any evidence for it, he is sure the man-eater is on the rock. After weighing his options in terms of daylight remaining and the distance to his camp, he flips off the safety-catch, puts the rifle to his shoulder and starts to pass the rock.

It is followed by a brief excerpt from 'The Muktesar Man-Eater' in 'The Temple Tiger' describing the conclusion of that hunt, in which he narrowly avoids death.

In addition to danger, the accounts contain descriptions of breathtaking scenery, animal behaviour, observations of human character and life in general, as well as rugged adventure.

An examination of the biographical material available presents a retiring and gentle yet strong and resolute, generous and courageous man, eager to see justice done and equally at home with royalty or peasants (both of whom he found himself mixing with). He was extremely hard-working and during his long career served in both world wars. So apart from his exploits in ridding a community of a man-eater, Corbett earned enormous respect and admiration from the residents of and the visitors to Kumaon (part of the U.P. – then the United Provinces, now Uttar Pradesh and Uttaranchal).

In 1944 his first book to be published and made generally available was *Man-Eaters of Kumaon* from Oxford University Press. Corbett and O.U.P. followed with:

The Man-Eating Leopard of Rudraprayag
My India
Jungle Lore
The Temple Tiger and
TreeTops

After India gained independence in 1947 Jim Corbett moved to this cottage where he lived until his death in 1955. A frequent visitor to Tree Tops, he was honoured and thrilled to be invited to join the Royal Party of the then Princess Elizabeth who visited Tree Tops in 1952. Corbett spent the night at Tree Tops with the Royal Party, during which time the King of England died making Elizabeth the uncrowned Queen. These events gave rise to Jim Corbett's last book as listed above. He is buried only a short distance from here in the little graveyard of St. Peters in Nyeri, along with his sister Maggie who also lived here and died in 1963.

Please note that at time of writing what was 'Uttaranchal' is now called 'Uttarakhand'.

The headstone before it was re-set by Mr. Jaleel

END OF POSTER REPRODUCTION

Hopefully this 'poster' has given some introduction to Jim Corbett. His birthplace, Naini Tal is at c.2000 m altitude amidst the foothills of the Himalayas. This elevation provides a comfortable summer climate and made Naini Tal a popular retreat from the heat of the plains for the British and the wealthier Indians and, as a hill station, was as popular as the likes of Simla and Darjeeling.

Naini Tal, looking south. The Corbett residence 'Gurney House' (not visible) is situated approximately half-way up the higher part of Ayarpata Hill on the right.

During a visit to Naini Tal in 1999, I met Mrs. Stephens of 'Glencoe', an elderly British resident, who had known Corbett when she was a young girl. She remarked on Corbett's extreme shyness and reserve in company, yet also on his being a prankster and recalled being frightened as a little girl on hearing growling close by only to see Corbett laughingly emerge from hiding before he caused her too much distress.

Corbett's quietness and self-effacement in company mirrored his silence and self-effacement in the forest. Moreover, time spent silently with nature does not provide gossip to trade with others or the latest 'in the rivalries of political cliques, in meetings, dinners and merrymakings with flute girls…whether any fellow citizen is well- or ill-born or has inherited some defect from his ancestors on either side…' (B32). It was also due in part to a more important and subtle reason:

his experiences with nature were first hand. Events discussed or described must be second hand. Whilst second hand accounts may contain great interest and knowledge, personal experience, especially of rich, exciting or profound events at first hand makes the passing or receiving of 'second hand knowledge' pale by comparison. Corbett's knowledge was directly imbibed from nature.

> He who knows does not speak;
> He who speaks does not know.

> *(Lao-Tzu. Principal founder of Taoism)*

Having spent the summer at Naini Tal, the Corbetts would return in November via the 'old road' to Kaladhungi, about 15 miles south and situated on the plains. This road still exists and, about half-way down, it presents the traveller with a spectacular view of the plains stretching as far as the eye can see. Continuing southward and downward eventually brings you to a T-junction, where you will see Corbett's bungalow standing opposite you (the previous Corbett residence in Kaladhungi, 'Arundel', is in ruins). Corbett lived here during the winters from 1921 until 1947 and it is now preserved as a museum. Even when in use, this property was sparingly furnished and used almost as a camp next to the jungle (Gurney House being more comfortably and fully furnished with, amongst other modest comforts, books and a piano).

Jim Corbett and his sister Maggie in front of their 'Irish cottage' at Kaladhungi.

Hence it is not so surprising that the rooms of the Kaladhungi property are now quite bare and, other than a broken walking-stick, teacup and a few odds and ends, nothing remains. The walls exhibit enlarged photographs, paintings, excerpts from his books and correspondence – some recording his generosity to local villagers both during and after his time in India. The Indian authorities now keep the house and grounds clean and in a good state of repair.

Corbett's bungalow at Kaladhungi

The well-known photograph in 'Man-eaters of Kumaon' of Corbett with the enormous tiger called the 'Bachelor of Powalgarh' was taken in this garden, which also holds the graves of two dogs including 'Robin' (a chapter in Man-Eaters of Kumaon is devoted to this dog) and, now, a bust of Corbett (just visible in the photograph). It was at Gurney house and here in Kaladhungi that he wrote some of the stories for the first three books; 'Jungle Stories' (printed privately), 'Man-Eaters of Kumaon' and 'The Man-Eating Leopard of Rudrayprayag'.

While many British people developed a genuine regard, if not love, for the people under their authority, few, if any, made such close relationships as Corbett did with the Indian people and, more particularly, the poorest people; yet he had no official duties or responsibilities to care for these people. Officials remained official, and eventually were posted or otherwise moved on, while Corbett's compassion and care for the Indian people around him were constant, continuing after he had left India and even after his death.

With regard to the ever popular 'shikar' or hunting, some British officials and / or military personnel might have supervised hunts but it was usually the locals who led the hunter to the animal or 'beat' the animal to the hunter. Even those officials who learned some jungle lore and wood-craft had not been born to it as had Corbett and couldn't really compare with his knowledge and experience (for example, I remember an accomplished 'White Hunter' in Africa telling me that, for all his experience, he couldn't sleep in a tree as Corbett could – a tree, that is, without a platform or 'machan'). While many hunters had a favourite tracker or servant, none were closer to the people amongst whom they lived than Corbett, and while some of those hunters might 'sit-up' for a man-eater or two, none devoted themselves to the relief of so many people over so many years from so many man-eaters. They would complete their tour of duty and move on and, compared to Corbett, they might aptly be termed 'tourists' albeit, on occasions, able, caring and stalwart ones.

Of the many books of memoirs and accounts by hunters, Corbett's seem (like their author) to be in a class of their own. "The heroes of the big-game camp are not men like Frederick Courtenay Selous or Rowland Ward, nor many of the authors of the big-game hunting books written today, but men like the late Jim Corbett and others who risked their lives for their fellow men, not for pride or boasting, but in order to protect human lives. These are the true hunters and the genuine lovers of wildlife." (B33).

The Books

Whether it is measured by direct comment or review, by book sales or by the number of translations and reprints, the vast majority of readers, have shown an almost universal approval of, and enthusiasm for, Corbett's books. None were more surprised than Corbett at the popularity of his books.

Whence this appeal?

Perhaps most importantly, his love for the people, the animals and nature in general is held firmly between the lines of each book. 'He writeth well, who loveth well, Both man and bird and beast.' (With apologies to Coleridge. (Samuel Taylor Coleridge 1772 – 1834 English poet)).

The memoirs of many hunters who hunted for thrills or trophies (rarely including man-eaters) each conclude when the trigger is pulled; the memoir dies with the animal. Even those who write of their sense of deflation or regret, even guilt, when they stand over the dead animal, refer to little or nothing else but the hunt in their accounts. The end of the hunt reflects the end of their interest. In contrast, Corbett's accounts are more than the hunting and death of an animal. We hear details of the post mortem skinning, learning the reasons why the animal became a man-eater (which are all too often man-made); we meet real characters who play parts in the drama, making the account more than just the record of a hunt; and we hear of stock replenished, wounds healed, peace restored and fear removed.

Corbett's concise accounts of hunting individual man-eaters also represent, in many respects, a miniature model of life – the struggle against nature's elements with limited resources and time, sometimes wasted on false leads or unreliable accomplices; the need for patience and persistence; determination and courage; the mastery of certain skills and knowledge, absorbed by patient attention and humility. Alongside those abilities and knowledge, uncertainty and unanswered questions always remain, as does the necessity to press on in spite of them. Moreover, his efforts were motivated, not by worthless objectives or self-promotion, but by benefit to others and, although he was righting wrongs and healing wounds caused by others, his self-imposed tasks required much self-sacrifice.

Close association with nature breeds a healthy body, mind and soul – and each of these sustains the others in a balanced, dynamic and harmonious equilibrium. Maintaining this balance in the face of nature's omnipotence, cultivates humility and gratitude. It also develops a sense of proportion and an awareness of the necessity of work to earn and maintain something of nature's bounty, which in turn bring further senses of satisfaction and purpose. Corbett's writings reflect these values of universal appeal and the contents are natural, healthy and wholesome, appealing to our appetites as much as natural, healthy and wholesome food.

In contrast, too close and regular association with the city – or Fennimore Cooper's 'settlement' (please see quote below) – results in imbalance, disproportion (excesses), arrogance and a casual lethargy which in turn bring senses of dissatisfaction and pointlessness. To redress this imbalance, few physicians today would prescribe a regimen of hard work helping and caring for others, with a diet of properly balanced nutrition, all taken with liberal doses of fresh air and sunshine. Whether or not this should be a prescription, it is definitely a description of Corbett's stories. Following this regimen, he redresses imbalances while promoting and preserving nature, making his voluntary work that of a sort of physician of the life principle, the life force itself. As he contributes to nature, so he receives from nature, in another natural cycle.

All this the stories deliver with simplicity of style, plot and content, set against a backdrop of nature's rich but hard grandeur, full of beauty and danger. We know that some of nature's beauty and danger is compressed and condensed into the form of a tiger and lie together like orange and black. We want to get closer to those flames and seize the fire – but without being burned. We can, courtesy of Corbett, from the safety of our armchair. From those armchairs few of us today tend a real fire for warmth on a winter's night, yet most will recognise the human fascination with a fire that appears to be universal. Some are content to stare into the ever-changing, flickering flames while others must constantly prod or touch the fire – risking their fingers and trying not to pay the price of playing with fire. The tiger's fire kindles the same fascination, and dangers.

Fire is also an essential element for most alchemical transformations and carbon is the principal element of all living organisms. Carbon forms a great variety of substances, but only occurs in pure form as graphite ('sheets' of a lattice of carbon atoms one layer thick, laid one on top of the other), 'nanotubes' (microscopic tubes formed when opposite sides of a lattice join) and diamond (a 3-D crystalline arrangement). I don't know if it is physically possible, but in principle at least, some carbon compounds and / or graphite could be compressed into diamond. Whether or not scientifically true, it provides an appropriate metaphor for Corbett's accounts since, in those stories, the tiger's fire and Corbett's alchemy have compressed the principal elements of life into little gems.

It was mentioned above that science (mechanism and determinism) and commerce (materialism) can kill our sense of purpose and meaning, often contributing to an abandonment of personal responsibilities and to a sense of apathy. However, even from these rather bleak perspectives, death is not usually considered a welcome alternative. Whether or not we are at peace with our own mortality, most of us try to avoid our appointment with death for as long as possible. Since violent death is unpleasant and disturbing, most of us hope that the meeting, when it does come, is a quiet and peaceful one. The idea of avoiding the meeting altogether; to defeat death and achieve immortality, is a universal theme common to all cultures, religions, alchemy, aspects of science and medicine, and many myths, stories, fables, films and plays. One aspect of this universal concern is buried in Corbett's stories since to kill a man-eater is to deliver death to Death; a mythical, mystical theme usually associated with the most ancient and arcane disciplines of past civilisations. Mortal men gain some comfort from the idea that other lives, especially of those who have known them personally, will succeed their own. The life and death of individuals in order that life itself continues will be considered again from another perspective in the next chapter.

Whatever our philosophical views may be, a close approach to death concentrates all energies and sobers, if not erases, any and all philosophical musings: 'When we "prove" or "disprove" a philosophy we are merely offering another one, which, like the first, is a fallible compound of experience and hope. As experience widens and hope changes, we find more "truth" in the "falsehoods" we denounced, and perhaps more falsehood in our youth's eternal truths. When we are lifted upon the wings of rebellion we like determinism and mechanism, they are so cynical and devilish; but when death looms up suddenly at the foot of the hill we try to see beyond it into another hope.'

The Balance

Applying determinism and mechanism to all of nature's phenomena is an extreme (i.e. imbalanced) use of the power of reason. As will often be repeated in this book, skilful use of our powers, of reasoning or otherwise, lies in finding the optimum, the balance point, neither rejecting, nor slavishly obeying, any particular practice, school of thought or discipline. Reasoning itself is not being rejected: what we are seeking is the ideal balance between reason and intuition. Corbett is being used as our example not only because of his personal characteristics but also because he represents that balance between 'rational' and 'intuitive' knowledge.

With regard to rational knowledge, and his hunting of man-eaters, the animal had to be dealt with by precision shooting from an efficient weapon and a knowledge of altitude, angles, drop, calibres, sights and the trade-off between accuracy, range and 'stopping power'. All applied reasoning, some concerning technology, and all of which could sit comfortably with scientific analysis. Having located a man-eater, logic leads to conclusions and then results – deductions based on animal tracks; a broken stem of grass; the shape and colour of a drop of blood; the calls or behaviour of various animals and birds. Clues and Corbett's knowledge reconnect past events in sequence and lead forward. A comparison with detective work, while obvious, remains relevant. Corbett's deductions share similarities with a generalised example of Sherlock Holmes' deductions at a crime scene, which might run something like the following:

The criminal is a large male past his prime and walks with a limp. Three days ago he approached his victim from this direction and waited behind this cover for at least one hour, no doubt awaiting the right opportunity. This was provided when, as you can see from her footprints, the victim turned her back in his direction. This was his moment! He moved very quickly across this ground to catch his victim from behind. Having seized her, he did not release his killing grip, which is why no blood trail appears, but immediately carried his victim away; clear of the ground, leaving no trace of his burden on the path he followed. Having crossed the stream onto hard ground he has left us no more clues to follow, so we must content ourselves by trying to predict his likely location, and next move, from what we have learned so far and according to the habits of his type.

Substitute 'man-eater' for 'criminal' in this example and there would be nothing to distinguish Holmes from Corbett – except that the former is fictional and the latter factual. Corbett himself refers to jungle detective stories in Jungle Lore and comments that all of us could compile a jungle detective story provided we do not start with the assumption that we know all, before we know anything.

Both science and tracking depend on one or more of the five senses (or perhaps, since the discovery of a functional VNO as mentioned in chapter II, we should say six senses). Science depends on what it can measure, directly or indirectly, with either unaided senses or those aided by technology; machines, gauges and dials. As we have other senses (e.g. of balance, thirst, temperature, pain etc.) it is sometimes asked why the 'five senses' are so-called and seem to imply a complete set. As far as this author can see, the 'five senses' tell us of the 'outside world', the world outside our bodies, while the others tell us of our inside world. Using those five senses is one way, and currently the dominant scientific way, of exploring – we look outside ourselves to see what we can know. However, in this and the next chapter, we will see something of what can be learned by looking within, while still using the clues nature provides to find connections and patterns.

For present purposes, Corbett is representing a balance. So, having seen some ways in which he used 'rational' knowledge born of logic and reasoning, we will balance our view by looking at his use of another, complementary type of knowledge – 'intuitive' knowledge; his jungle lore. Often his experience would indicate the path a tiger had taken without any supporting hard evidence being apparent. Some way down the path signs would confirm that the tiger had indeed taken it. The poster text reprinted above referred to his sense of impending danger – again without physical evidence to support it, yet it invariably proved correct. The use of his rifle required rational knowledge but bringing it to bear on the man-eater also required these sorts of intuitive knowledge. He says himself that jungle lore is not a science that can be learnt from textbooks but that it has to be absorbed a little at a time. 'Absorbing' or 'feeling' knowledge enhances intuitive knowledge. It also acquires other heart-felt feelings (e.g. a respect and love for nature, compassion for victims and their families – human and animal), which lead us to views complementary to those of the physical senses, providing other insights to tigers, nature and ourselves. When tracking a man-eater, Corbett needed his 'absorbed' knowledge and intuition as much as his mind and reasoning abilities, both to follow the trail and to survive.

These types of knowledge are aspects of another and fundamental balance, summarised in the age-old and universal Eastern principle of yin and yang whereby, along with innumerable other complementary pairings, yin is female and yang is male. 'The whole wide world is only he and she' said Sri Aurobindo (Indian poet, philosopher, and yogi. 1872 – 1950). A well-balanced combination of these types of knowledge (because, in this context, they develop feeling and then purpose) also contributes to character development. Corbett's stories reveal his self-discipline, persistence, courage and commitment to completing a job, even when it brought discomfort, danger or personal sacrifice.

Corbett represents another manifestation of this eternal duality in that, if we are all products of nature and nurture, Corbett was British born in India, so the West was in his nature, but the East nurtured him, and hence he can be seen as a blend of East and West, of yin and yang respectively. Another famous blend of East and West was Kipling. Corbett's books and Kipling's Jungle Book have obvious common ground but beyond the animal stories there are also similarities between the values, virtues and morals of each and, when viewed from this perspective, so too between Corbett's and Kipling's tigers – and both with Blake's (as on the inside front cover).

While considering qualities of character, Corbett also qualifies according to a number of Kipling's criteria for a man…he kept his head while others about him were losing theirs. He could wait and not be tired by waiting, yet he didn't look too good nor talk too wise. He heard the truth he'd spoken twisted by knaves to make a trap for fools and no doubt forced his heart and nerve and sinew to serve his turn long after they were gone, and so held on when there was nothing in him except the Will which said to them: "Hold on". He talked with crowds and kept his virtue, and walked with kings – without losing the common touch. All men counted with him. In his career hunting man-eaters he filled many unforgiving minutes with sixty seconds' worth of distance run, under a cold moon or burning sun.

Corbett also qualifies according to Shakespeare's criteria:

> His life was gentle, and the elements
> So mix'd in him that Nature might stand up
> And say to all the world 'This was a man!'

(Julius Caesar Act V scene V)

Jim Corbett was a gentleman by nature and a large-hearted one at that. Plato (c.428 – c, 348 B.C. Greek philosopher) describes the ideal character combining bravery and gentleness as warp and woof, while east of Athens the same was said in a different way since bravery is yang, and gentleness, yin.

Some aspects of his jungle craft have been compared above with deductive reasoning, accuracy, detail and logic i.e. characteristics of Western culture (yang) and, one of its products, science. Aspects of yin in his jungle lore have already been referred to and we may add his belief in the values and traditions of Eastern spiritual disciplines – he closely associated himself with the Indian people, respecting and observing their customs and making contributions to roadside symbols of their deities. His compassion and care for people and animals, and his 'absorption of knowledge' are also characteristics of yin. So, for our purposes, he balances logic and intuition, boldness and caution, silence (did not promote conversation) and outspokenness (did promote conservation). As an insightful critic wrote of Bizet's opera Carmen 'It has a perfect internal balance between passion and dignity, between gesture and restraint, humour and tragedy.' (Regretfully the author has been unable to identify this critic). Even very experienced opera professionals refer to Carmen as the perfect opera.

This balance between yin and yang is the key to health and life. When man upsets this balance, anomalies are made, such as man-eaters. Man-eaters are, most often, man-made – the result of wounding animals but not killing them and / or depriving them, directly or indirectly, of their natural prey and / or habitat. Whilst Corbett hunted man-eaters (i.e. opposed the results of imbalances) he promoted respect and care for nature and its conservation (i.e. promoted healthy balances) in the face of unpopularity and ridicule. He exhibits attitudes and actions that are needed now in a larger context – the environmental crisis – that is also born of our abuse and unbalancing of nature, turning nature as a whole into a potential man-slayer of global proportions.

The Book of Nature

We have referred to balances between reason and intuition, predators and prey, yin and yang and, of course, body and spirit. In accordance with the ancient Greek medicine of Hippocrates and the even more ancient Hindu Ayurvedic medicine, full health might yet be seen to be a balance of balances. Balance, health and symmetry are intimately related. The concept of balance is fundamental and, of course, a type of symmetry, which appears and reappears throughout nature in myriad manifestations. Even the acuity of our senses can be seen as symmetry between what is perceived and our perception of it.

Acute senses are one result of good health and they have no harder test than tracking and stalking wild animals. By comparison with Corbett's senses we can assess the condition of our own, and thereby, our health. Certainly in the modern technological world we have lost much of our ability to use our senses. Lack of use, lack of interest and various 'imbalances' in our lives such as junk food, contaminated water and air, excess material indulgences along with a decline in morality, manners and courtesies have had their effects physically, mentally and spiritually, which then exacerbate the problems. As a result, all that we produce – arts, architecture, sciences, media, politics or other disciplines – decline together and become multiple symptoms of our collective ill health.

If good health is a balance between various factors, ill health can be described as an imbalance ('dis-ease') between those same factors. Hence, in heavily industrialised nations, materially wealthy, over-indulged sections of society can often be considered 'ill' – not only as individuals but also as communities, or even nations. Initially the over-indulged become obese and, if balance is not regained, ill – physically, mentally and spiritually. The process compounds itself since, as we become more imbalanced globally, we destroy more of the natural world that could guide, teach and heal us. This disease has now advanced to a stage that is possibly, if not probably, terminal.

In addition to providing all we need for our bodies, mind and soul, nature offers us a model on which we can base our own activities and affairs. It can act as a tutor at many different levels. Firstly, and literally, at grass roots level:

In a book by Dr. C.W. Doyle (Corbett's half-brother from his mother's first marriage) called 'The Taming of the Jungle', published in 1899, is the following scene of an Indian girl, who had been adopted by a British family and lived in England, but who is now back in India, in some emotional distress:

"'Educated me, forsooth!' she exclaimed with scorn, her nostrils twitching; 'they robbed me of my five senses, and gave me instead – accomplishments. Can you tell the time of the day from the sun, sir? Can you say when the sambhur (*a large deer*) passed whose track is at your feet, and how many wolves were in the pack that followed him? Would your sense of smell lead you to a pool of fresh water in mid-jungle? Can you feel the proximity of a crouching leopard without seeing it? What sort of education is it that neglects the senses? Oh, the highest product of your civilisation

– your poet laureate, Tennyson – felt the same thing stir in his pulses when he wrote Locksley Hall, and deprecated the 'poring over miserable books' with blinded eyesight…No, I have no feeling of gratitude towards those you speak of; for the large freedom of the Terai they gave me a brick cage in London; they gave me endless crowds of miserable men and women for these, my green brothers, who are always happy,' and she put out her hand and caressed a tree that grew beside her…

'But don't you miss your books, and the keeping in touch with the progress of civilisation?' I asked.

'Must I quote "books in running brooks"* to you? What book is there like this book of God's?' and she swept her arm round her."

*(In Shakespeare's 'As You Like It', the exiled duke lives in the Forest of Arden, far from the shallow life at court and discovers
'… our life exempt from public haunt
Finds tongues in trees, books in the running brooks,
Sermons in stones and good in everything.')

Books! 'tis a dull and endless strife:
Come, hear the woodland linnet,
How sweet his music! On my life,
There's more of wisdom in it.

And hark! how blithe the throstle sings!
He, too, is no mean preacher:
Come forth into the light of things,
Let Nature be your Teacher.

(From 'The Tables Turned'
by Wordsworth. English poet 1770- 1850)

St. Bernard of Clairvaux (1090? – 1153) invited us to 'Listen to a man of experience. You will find more in woods than in books. Trees and stones will teach you that which you can never learn from masters.' In another letter he wrote 'What I know of the divine sciences and Holy Scripture, I learnt in woods and fields. I have had no other masters than the beeches and the oaks.'

Karen Blixen: 'Out in the wilds I had learned to beware of abrupt movements. The creatures with which you are dealing there are shy and watchful, they have a talent for evading you when you least expect it. No domestic animal can be as still as a wild animal. The civilised people have lost the aptitude of stillness, and must take lessons in silence from the wild before they are accepted by it. The art of moving gently, without suddenness, is the first to be studied by the hunter, and more so by the hunter with the camera. Hunters cannot have their own way, they must fall in with the wind, and the colours and smells of the landscape, and they must make the tempo of the ensemble their own. Sometimes it repeats a movement over and over again, and they must follow up with it. When you have caught the rhythm of Africa, you find that it is the same in all her music.

What I have learned from the game of the country was useful to me in my dealings with the native people.' (B7)

We cannot have our own way, 'madly deem ourselves the lord of all', we must fall in step with nature, listen to her music and move with her rhythm. Technology taught us arrogance and produced more illusions than moving images – one of the more dangerous being that we are independent of nature and can choose to dominate it and / or exploit it with impunity. Older wisdoms born of working with, and learning lessons from nature have been rejected and / or forgotten.

An obvious but, until recently, neglected lesson, is that whilst every element is re-used by nature in endless interconnected cycles, the consumer society has only just realised that we cannot continue to use resources in a manner that prevents re-use, or at rates exceeding their rates of production. Re-cycling is one of the most obvious lessons, but one only recently learned by Western human societies. Nature has innumerable other lessons but requires us to look for them.

Animals can also teach us in practical ways: construction (e.g. air-conditioning in termite mounds, the strength but lightness of honeycombs in hives), co-operation (e.g. swarming flight of birds, societies of insects, monkeys and apes), storage of resources (e.g. birds and squirrels), echo-location (e.g. whales, dolphins and bats), propulsion (e.g. squid and octopus), electricity (eels, catfish or rays), light (fireflies, some microbes and plants), aerodynamics (e.g. small birds, bats and insects), industry and organisation (e.g. ants and bees) – best put, as usual, by Shakespeare:

> Therefore doth heaven divide
> The state of man in divers functions,
> Setting endeavour in continual motion;
> To which is fixed, as an aim or butt,
> Obedience: for so work the honey-bees,
> Creatures that by a rule in nature teach
> The act of order to a peopled kingdom.

(Henry V Act I Sc. II)

Our own search for knowledge can be stimulated by witnessing animals applying their knowledge (e.g. the phases of the moon; finding water) and their wisdoms (when the weather will change, when catastrophe approaches). Apart from these, by no means unimpressive, general abilities there are also numerous verified accounts of outstanding actions and abilities (e.g. dolphins saving human swimmers from sharks and from exhaustion; various species, including elephants, parrots and chimpanzees learning to communicate with humans; and there have also been reports of pet dogs, one of which could sense the approach of its owner's epileptic fits and the other which could sense peoples' imminent death).

Their mysteries and powers are beyond our immediate perception and Shamans, witchdoctors and their like have known of and sought to capture them for millennia. Indigenous peoples accept that people and animals share spiritual realms and do not recognise a sharp division between the consciousness of members of each category. We can also gain spiritual clues from animals (e.g. patience, repetition, living in the present – in the 'now') and chapter IV will consider still more animal abilities.

If we take time to look and listen, exercise our interest as Corbett reminded us above, any aspect of nature reveals a sublime beauty and / or intricacy that, for those who have their senses still, cannot but engender a further sense of wonder. As G.K. Chesterton remarked 'The world will never starve for want of wonders, only for the want of wonder.' Those still living close to nature usually retain their sense of wonder (since it receives regular stimulation).

The intimate connections between nature and such people, and their minds and hands, are caught by Kipling referring to a people of the remote Himalayas 'Theirs was an almost obliterated Buddhism, overlaid with a nature worship fantastic as their own landscapes, elaborate as the terracing of their tiny fields…' (B42c) Kipling neatly relates land, labour and belief – which is cause and which effect?

For some, it is but a small step from the contemplation of nature to the contemplation of a Creator, and more than one religion refers to two books; one of nature and one of scripture – and their equivalence. The 'Book of Nature' is also referred to in James Fennimore Cooper's 'The Last of the Mohicans' where the woodsman and scout Hawkeye says 'I have heard it said that there are men who read in books to convince themselves there is a god. I know not but man may so deform his works in the settlements (*the beginnings of towns and cities*), as to leave that which is so clear in the wilderness a matter of doubt among traders and priests. If any such there be, and he will follow me from sun to sun, through the windings of the forest, he shall see enough to teach him that he is a fool, and that the greatest of his folly lies in striving to rise to the level of One he can never equal, be it in goodness, or be it in power.'

Cooper wrote of his creation Hawkeye as 'a being removed from the every-day inducements to err, which abound in civilized life, while he retains the best and simplest of his early impressions; who sees God in the forest; hears him in the winds; …in a word, a being who finds the impress of the Deity in all the works of nature, without any of the blots produced by the expedients, and passion, and mistakes of man.'

Anyone who has read Corbett and the biographical material on him will realise these words are directly applicable to Corbett. Hence it is not so surprising to learn that Jim Corbett was much influenced by Cooper's writing. In chapter six of Jungle Lore, Corbett refers to Cooper's thrilling books and D.C. Kala tells us in 'Jim Corbett of Kumaon' that Fennimore Cooper was a favourite author of Corbett's from boyhood: 'We find him all the time unconsciously playing the role of the Cooper heroes …upholding the principles (*they*) stood for…(*and similarly concerned with*) the westward march of White civilisation and the wanton exploitation of nature's bounty by the "Palefaces"…the wrong being done to nature…(*and knowing*) the wilderness (*is*) the creation of God in which man could learn humility and restraint.'

Henry David Thoreau (1817–1862) was an American author, naturalist, tax resister, pioneer environmentalist and philosopher. His words (in 'Cry of the Human') describing views of Red Indians distant from 'civilisation', apply equally to Corbett: 'By the wary independence and aloofness of his dim forest life he preserves his intercourse with his native gods and is admitted from time to time to a rare and peculiar society with nature. He has glances of starry recognition, to which our saloons are strangers. The steady illumination of his genius, dim only because distant, is like the faint but satisfying light of the stars compared with the dazzling but ineffectual and short-lived blaze of candles.'

Nature revealed the Creator for Cooper, Corbett and others:

So ye learn within my arbours
Where the sleeping wild things lie,
A reverence for nature
Which the city's streets deny.
Ye learn the real value
Of the man made from the loam;
And ye kneel and thank your Maker,
As ye wend your footsteps home.

(W.J.K.S.)

(The author has searched anthologies, the Internet, consulted and advertised through London's Poetry Library but not been able to identify 'W.J.K.S.')

Rousseau: "I rose every morning before the sun and passed through a neighbouring orchard into a pleasant path which led by a vineyard and along the hills toward Chambéry. While walking I prayed, not by a vain motion of the lips, but with a sincere lifting up of my heart to the Creator of this beautiful Nature whose charms lay spread out before my eyes. I never like to pray in my chamber; it is to me as if the walls and all the little works of man come between God and myself. I like to contemplate Him in His works, whilst my heart lifts itself up to Him." (Confessions of J.J. Rousseau volume VI)

Regardless of our personal views on deities and / or religion, it seems that most of us share similar ideals (whether or not we are able to achieve them) and a sense of lost innocence, a health, simplicity and happiness which, although lost, we still appreciate and seek. We can get closer to it by getting closer to nature.

Corbett refers to the time he spent in jungles being uncontaminated happiness and traced his happiness to wild life being happy in its natural habitat. He could not see sadness or regret in nature's creatures. Sitting in beautiful, natural surroundings, smelling the scent of flowers and listening to birdsong, the hardships of the human world could be forgotten and the law of the jungle appreciated which, he says, is older and incomparably better than laws made by men. Dangers keep every individual vigilant but without reducing the joy of life.

Corbett seems to personify Wordsworth's lines:

'With an eye made quiet by the power
Of harmony, and the deep power of joy,
He sees into the life of things'

(From 'Tintern Abbey')

and his knowledge of nature is captured by Wordsworth's summary of nature's riches:

She has a world of ready wealth,
Our minds and hearts to bless
Spontaneous wisdom breathed by health,
Truth breathed by cheerfulness.

(From 'The Tables Turned')

Martin Luther (1483 – 1546 German priest and theologian who initiated the Protestant Reformation) explained that 'since the Fall human beings can no longer fathom the disposition of the animals: we lack insight into that fullness of joy and bliss which Adam derived from his contemplation of all the animal creatures. All our faculties today are leprous, indeed dull and utterly dead. Who can conceive of that part, as it were, of the divine nature, that Adam and Eve had insight into all the dispositions of animals, into their character and all their powers? ...that we should know all the qualities of trees and herbs, and the disposition of all the beasts – is utterly beyond repair in this life.' Perhaps Corbett got closer to this ideal than many of us. He recalls training troops for jungle living during the Burma campaign of WWII and refers to; finding edible fruits, flowers, roots and tubers; the medicinal properties of various plants, barks and leaves; barks and creepers that can be made into stretchers or ropes; preventing trench feet and prickly heat; making fire, even in a wet forest; killing game without guns and how to cook without metal utensils; a substitute for salt; proper behaviour in jungles in order to live at peace within them and with their inhabitants. If Corbett was a little closer to Luther's ideal, what can we say for ourselves? For most of us; not much.

When in the presence of something, or someone, close to nature's elemental but profound simplicity, especially when harmonised physically, mentally and spiritually, human words and gestures fail us. Much of our communication relates to trade, toys, playtime or human vanities. When conscious of the sublime, silence may be a more eloquent response than speech. After a screening of his films of Indian wildlife to a small audience in what were then the London offices of his publishers, Oxford University Press, one of those present, A.C. Ward, wrote an account for the in-house magazine, confiding that 'Though he (Corbett) was warmly and generously thanked for his generosity in providing a unique experience, thanks seemed something of an impertinence and an irrelevance, for as a member of the audience said privately afterwards, "Jim Corbett is the nearest to a saint that any of us are likely to see."' (J29)

Surely these qualities and closer approach to Luther's ideal were partly born of his living so closely to nature. Corbett had absorbed qualities inherent in nature, through his head, heart and feet, often in stillness and silence, and this was reflected in his stillness and silence in social settings. We would be missing an important lesson to say 'Corbett was accomplished in jungle lore and, by the way, he was also a man of many virtues'. These are not distinct and independent characteristics, each reinforces the other. Despite being immensely complex, many aspects of nature manifest as a sort of simplicity (for example, the immense complexity yet recognisable regularity of seasonal weather – before we began interfering with it). Corbett also radiated a kind of 'simplicity', which we shall explore a little more as we approach the end of chapter V. The ground covered en route will provide us with some additional material by which we may gain a better understanding of this sort of 'profound simplicity'.

Wordsworth shared Rousseau's immediate appreciation of, and the feelings generated by nature, and Sir Kenneth Clark noted that Wordsworth added the word 'moral' to the impressions he shared with Rousseau, perhaps his most well-known poetic reference being from 'The Tables Turned':

> One impulse from the vernal wood
> Will tell you more of man,
> Of moral evil and of good,
> Than all the sages can.

John Ruskin (English author, poet, artist and art critic. 1819 – 1900) considered that nature's beauty, its demonstrations of interdependence between species and between the component parts of each organism, had moralising effects on any who took the trouble to look and learn. Consequentially, and in the same way, Corbett's morality, knowledge and wisdom, were also present, but not on display, needing to be sought out by those who took the trouble to exercise interest and enquiry with due respect and humility – echoing the respect and humility by which they had been acquired. As the Japanese proverb has it 'The silent man is often worth listening to.'

In Corbett's case it appears we have the Viceroy Lord Linlithgow to thank for persuading Corbett to share something of what he knew. During the 1930's Corbett was requested to organise the Viceroy's hunting parties. John Christie was Deputy Private Secretary to the Viceroy and accompanied him on these hunts. He recalled Lord Linlithgow trying to persuade Corbett to write down his experiences. Corbett was unwilling at first and denied any literary abilities, saying he rarely wrote or read anything, except the Bible, John Bunyan and the Statesman newspaper. Luckily Lord Linlithgow persisted and we now know the treasure troves unearthed. (B15)

In our own cases we are each responsible for persuading nature (by our patience and persistence) to teach us some of her secrets. Too many of us have allowed ourselves to be distanced from nature and, consequently, our knowledge is predominantly academic and mostly, and merely, information. We (individuals, institutions and nations) and our knowledge are not, as yet, part of nature's unity. We may more fully appreciate our vast store of information, turn some into knowledge, and may even find some wisdom, if we can remember humility and respect for nature, and each other. Perhaps we can sense when people such as Corbett have this relationship with nature, and are closer to our common heritage, closer to an ideal, an ideal we lost long ago and far way away but which we begin to remember, and then recognise, when we stand closer to it. Such people are few and far between but we can go directly to the source by getting closer to nature ourselves. However, this is becoming more difficult as we destroy ever larger parts of it, which, in itself, further reduces our chances not only of access to it but also of being stimulated by it to recognise and remember. Without nature's guidance we have little chance of cultivating knowledge or wisdom, and therefore health and security, but every chance of going dangerously astray.

The Beginnings of the Environmental Movement

Those who looked at the past trail of human footprints and could see the direction in which humans were collectively heading were few, and those who took some sort of remedial action, fewer still. In the mid-nineteenth century the American George Perkins Marsh was an extremely rare individual who could see the damaging effects careless people were having on nature and who spoke out publicly about it. It seems that Swedish scientist Svante Arrhenius was the first to warn of global warming (as caused by carbon dioxide released from burning coal, oil and gas) in a paper published in 1896. The American president Theodore Roosevelt speaking before Congress in 1907 said "The conservation of our natural resources and their proper use constitute the fundamental problem which underlies almost every other problem of our national life."

Later in the twentieth century a few other notables took action to help the environment. Aldo Leopold, an American forester, published the Sand County Almanac in 1949 appealing for an ecological view of the earth and our relationship with it. The film maker Walt Disney was also an active conservationist: "You've probably heard people talk about conservation. Well, conservation isn't just the business of a few people. It's a matter that concerns all of us. It's a science whose principles are written in the oldest code in the world, the laws of nature. The natural resources of our vast continent are not inexhaustible. But if we will use our riches wisely, if we will protect our wildlife and preserve our lakes and streams, these things will last us for generations to come." (1950). A more recent stimulus to the environmental movement was Rachel Carson's book 'Silent Spring', of 1962 which particularly highlighted the dangers of DDT (she was ridiculed by the petrochemical industry making, and agriculturalists using the poison but subsequently shown to be correct).

The reader will know the movement has grown considerably since then but, sadly, not as extensively and rapidly as the abuse of nature, which assumed gargantuan proportions throughout and soon after WWII, using the technology developed during it, and the political, socio-economic situation resulting from it – most notably the rapid growth of multinational corporations. Wasteful and damaging consumption of natural resources by these corporations and pollution on global scales have literally imbalanced the world environmentally, and due to their excessive influence over governments, commercially and politically as well, as explored, for nothing less than our survival, in the following chapters.

By having studied nature with head and heart, Corbett's balanced appreciation enabled him also to see where human use and abuse of nature would lead. Among the first few pioneers of conservation, from the 1930's onward Corbett delivered film shows, public talks, published a conservation magazine and made prolonged efforts to found, what was later to be called, Corbett National Park (now Corbett Tiger Reserve). Living so closely to nature was an important part of Corbett's ability to be among those who could see furthest soonest – far beyond most of his contemporaries.

By the Light of Sun, Moon and Stars

A close contemporary of Corbett was Albert Einstein. Their lives and deaths were dovetailed beautifully by Corbett's first biographer, D.C. Kala, who wrote: 'Albert Einstein died on 18th April 1955 at Princeton, New Jersey, and Corbett the next day at Nyeri, Kenya…They both were unpretentious wizards, one of mathematics and physics and the other of junglecraft. They both spent a lifetime studying the laws of nature in their own light.' (B41) In chapter IV we will see that Einstein's insights were not restricted to physics and that he too could see further and sooner than most.

For much of his life, Corbett lived between stars above and dust under foot, using his senses to study the laws of nature by the light of sun, moon and stars. Einstein used his senses to study the laws of nature by the light of sun, moon and stars and the dust underfoot (the former in his General Relativity, the latter in his work on atoms).

These laws reveal to us a harmony, a correspondence, nothing less than a unity of all things – from the awesome scale of the universe to the scales of individual animals and all between and beyond. A complete expression for this unity still eludes us, hidden in Distant Deeps and Skies. However, Einstein's work did illustrate many aspects of the unity, one being that: "…the inertia of a given body derives from its interaction with all the masses in the universe, so that, say, a bowler overcoming the inertia of a bowling ball is solidly linked, in a physical sense, to the entire universe." (B27). This is the scientist's head later explaining what a poet's heart had sensed first, since poets see furthest soonest.

"…thou canst not stir a flower, without troubling of a star."

(Thompson 1859 – 1907)

So, as each bird, each insect flits through the sky, as a flower stirs to track the sun or a tiger its prey, from brightest star to least dust, each movement, affecting and affected by others, are variations on a theme in a universal symphony. Some of those movements can be heard or read on a jungle path or night sky.

Corbett and Einstein could read more of the score than most, and can still teach us, if we would listen and try to catch, then match, the pulse, the rhythm – learn to live and move in harmony with nature, just as Karen Blixen 'caught the rhythm of Africa' in the quote above. Concerned only with ourselves, convinced that we know all before we know anything, we do not listen to nature but strike our own notes as and when we please – our behaviour out of tune, out

of time, manifesting as imbalance, degradation and disease, within and around us. Worse still, some try to beat their drum louder than all other instruments in the orchestra in vulgar displays of volume. Yet symphonic music is made when we learn how and when to play our parts unobtrusively, each essential to, but lost as individuals within the beauty of the whole.

Nature's rhythms are easier to hear when we listen, in stillness and silence. Some of the precious few areas left where we can still listen to the music are National Parks and Tiger Reserves. Through Corbett Tiger Reserve Corbett is still giving us the chance to hear the music, re-awaken dormant, undeveloped senses, understand what he tried to tell us and see the light.

Corbett Tiger Reserve

Corbett's pioneering emphasis on conservation was born of knowledge combined with compassion, reason with feeling, head with heart. Einstein's head and heart were also well developed; the latter in his efforts for pacifism, campaigning against nuclear weapons, his various attempts to right social wrongs and his promotion of morality and virtue above all other considerations, including science. Although not religious in any orthodox sense, Einstein considered that "Humanity has every reason to place the proclaimers of high moral standards and values above the discovery of objective truth. What humanity owes to personalities like Buddha, Moses and Jesus ranks for me higher than all the achievements of the inquiring constructive mind."

In addition to knowing with his head and heart, Corbett, in the context of chapter I, also

Dawn over Dhikala (Corbett Tiger Reserve) casting off the blankets of mists, ready for the coming day

knew nature with his feet, literally with regard to his marathon walks to account for man-eaters, and in the senses suggested by Vivekananda, in that he knew the earth with his feet and, while he was standing on the dust of the earth, perhaps in ways we do not yet understand, the earth knew him, maybe via a 'sympathetic touch' as referred to by Red Indian Chief Seattle in the next chapter.

Corbett's legacy includes LifeForce Charitable Trust, a tiger conservation and environmental charity, some details of which are given in the last chapter. Corbett National Park was so named after his death but during his lifetime he did enjoy being officially given the 'freedom of the forests'. His elder brother had first introduced him to those forests but some inner qualities quickened in response and good seeds grew in fertile soil. These qualities and potentials are held in our earth and lie dormant until we grow them by providing the right nutrients. Corbett was standing with his feet firmly on good soil – literally and metaphorically – and this, with his other qualities of character, such as the well-balanced heart and head, appeal as much as his obvious integration with nature: which is cause and which effect?

The environment is showing us that the nutrients most of us are currently providing by our choices and resulting characters, need to change, if we would save the tiger and ourselves. Choices, experiences and character are mutually interdependent and are another of nature's cycles. From viewpoints in chapters IV and V the tiger represents qualities and potentials which we also hold, and which can be seen if and when we look into nature's mysterious mirrors. Some are best adopted; others best avoided. Which is which, will be considered in those chapters.

Buddhist Art and Nature

To help us with those choices and character development; to understand more of nature, and hence ourselves; to 'absorb' knowledge by letting heart work with head, stillness and silence are essential. Can it just be coincidence that stillness and silence are also essential for sadhus, gurus and other pious people, to meditate? Listening silently to nature without judgement, opinion or thought, has parallels with the discipline of meditation. Stillness and silence also help soothe, as Shakespeare put it, 'life's fitful fever'. Stillness and silence can also contribute to efforts toward self-effacement and, curiously, at the same time, an enhanced sense of self-awareness, in a similar paradoxical way to St. Francis of Assisi's observation that it is by forgetting self that one finds self.

Poets see furthest soonest, so is it only coincidence that many ancient scriptures are, in the original, poems? Regardless of personal views on deities and faiths, religious scriptures also offer healthy and sensible, unusual and refreshing insights to nature (some included in the LifeForce presentation to Forest Guards reproduced in chapter V). The same applies to religious art and the following photographs of Corbett Tiger Reserve seem to lend themselves to the art of Zen Buddhism.

'The idea of man as the conqueror and master of nature is not a typically Far Eastern idea. Chinese and Japanese painters were prone to depict man "at one" with the mysterious forces of the universe. Landscape was not used as a mere backdrop for a portrait of a man's head and shoulders as in Western Renaissance art, for instance. Instead the viewer has often to strain his eyes to see the tiny…figures going their indomitable way through a vast terrain of towering peaks and cliffs, lonely, misty valleys and rushing rivers.' (B55)

A solitary sambhar

Wild elephants, the largest tiny animals out of water

Wild elephants

Elephants with riders can just be made out in the centre foreground. Unknown to the riders, but known to the photographer, there is a tiger in the cover just to the immediate lower right of the elephants.

'An old pine tree preaches wisdom,
And a wild bird is crying out Truth.'

(ancient Zen poem)

Corbett told us that the book of nature has no beginning and no end, while Einstein told us that (with the speed of light as a universal constant) time passes at different rates for observers in relative motion, or at different positions in matter's gravitational field. Einstein joined time to matter and light to time. Although as yet unrecognised by physics, as time filters through the material framework of India it stretches into longer units than those of Western time...............

.................and so passes more slowly.

Usually, a rate of flow decreases as obstacles in its path increase. Curiously, time's rate of flow decreases the *fewer* the obstacles in its path and, flowing between a forest path below and stars above, uninterrupted by 'walls and all the little works of man', it flows at its slowest rate – and the wisdom that time brings seeps slowly into the soul.

When time runs slowly, patience can follow. In Franz Kafka's* view, impatience was the reason we were thrown out of Eden, and why we cannot return. Whether or not patience was necessary to live in Eden, it is surely necessary to live in India:

Now it is not good for the Christian's health to hurry the Aryan brown,
For the Christian riles, and the Aryan smiles and he weareth the Christian down;
And the end of the fight is a tombstone white with the name of the late deceased,
And the epitaph drear: "A Fool lies here who tried to hurry the East."

*(Kipling)***

The East...... India...... yin...... and time flows slowly. Yang, the West, and time runs rapidly. Nature's characters need to be balanced, and she awaits attentive pupils, but her patience, and her tigers, have almost gone. Tigers can teach us, in terms of symbols and potentials, something of ourselves via reflections in nature's mysterious mirrors. We look into these in the next chapter, and see vast regions of intellectual and spiritual territory, any one of which could fill many books. However, for our present purposes in these critical times, we will learn from them only what we need in order to further tiger conservation in particular, environmental health in general, and to face our responsibilities to both. We shall consider our reflections and, by their light, make our time matter.

*   Franz Kafka, Czech writer 1883 – 1924
** Kipling's 'hustle' has been replaced with 'hurry' as better representing his intended meaning, since 'hustle' has, in modern parlance, acquired extra meanings.

CHAPTER IV
DISTANT DEEPS AND SKIES
The Mystical and Mysterious

"Unless I can make you believe that there is something practically supernatural about tigers, that they are not just common flesh and bone and striped hide, but a kind of symbol of the jungle, of the cunning and the cruelty and ferocity and incredible strength and beauty of raw nature... there is no use in your going on with this tale."

(Edison Marshall)

We sense the truth of these lines but cannot define it, cannot capture it, and thereby, the tiger.
The tiger has captured us.
Confined in our cage of questions we watch the tiger but are free to wonder.

The secrets of tigers are held in their slow-blinking eyes, through which we see clearly the limits of our comprehension. The eyes have a glowing depth beyond which we cannot penetrate and it is in those distant deeps that hold what it is to be a tiger.

The fire of those eyes tempts us while warning us. As we look, we want to approach more closely, feel the glow, but hesitate for fear. Those of you who have read Corbett have approached a little closer and felt the warmth in his stories. Yet we want to get closer still, conquer our fear and seize the fire for ourselves. By some artificial and impudent bypass of nature's order, some people have been privileged to touch a living tiger – but still, it is not enough. We seek the non-physical, spiritual power of the tiger, its essential energy – which flickers and changes, making our search more difficult.

And it is 'energy' that is virtually synonymous with 'tiger' and appropriately so, since tigers represent highly concentrated energy. Although much of this chapter explores beyond the boundaries of science, on this point it agrees. The reader is probably familiar with triangular or 'pyramid' diagrams of hierarchical levels relating producers and consumers in an ecosystem (if not, please see Chapter V and diagram 1 of the Presentation to the Forest Guards). The broad base of the 'pyramid' includes vegetation capturing the energy of sunlight. The next level is formed by herbivores which, receiving little energy from each plant, have to eat most of the time to acquire sufficient energy to sustain their bodies. Herbivore bodies therefore represent energy concentrated (as compared to their plant food) into bones, muscle, tissue and tendon. Carnivores further concentrate that energy, and 'moving up' through hierarchical levels of carnivores represents an increasing concentration of energy into individual animals, as compared to their food, until at the apex, at the point of the pyramid, a 'super-predator' represents the most highly concentrated energy. Tigers live atop Asian pyramids.

To clarify: there are three types of pyramid diagram; numbers (of individual organisms), biomass (the total dry weight or energy in calories/joules of all organisms at each level) and energy flow. The energy-flow pyramid shows that (for each type of diagram and all ecosystems) the transition from a lower to an upper level tier always represents a decrease in overall energy (e.g. the total energy of, say, the biomass of all tigers is less than the total energy of the biomass of the prey species. Less cannot sustain more.) From the base to the point of the pyramid much energy is lost overall but what remains is concentrated in the fewer individuals of the upper tiers. Hence it can be technically accurate to see a tiger as a form of concentrated energy, which could be measured in joules or calories.

However, although we share its conclusions on this point (!), in this chapter we are not constrained by scientific orthodoxy and can measure that energy in any way we choose; by Blake's brightly burning fires if we like, since energy concentrated at a point, like sunlight through a magnifying glass, turns into flames. And it is the energy of sunlight, caught by green leaves on a global 'glass', flowing through herbivores and carnivores and concentrated at the point of the pyramid, which ignites the tiger's fire, the flames licking its flanks and glowing in its eyes; the very same starlight and energy burning in distant deeps and skies, the nearest by far at 93 million miles. Hence our comparison is more than metaphor since the tiger (and all terrestrial life) represents concentrated sunshine, concentrated starlight, a universal energy connecting all, no matter how distant or deep it may be.

Moreover, stars of various sizes, compressing lighter elements into heavier ones by nuclear fusion and distributing them into space by supernovae, also produce the elements composing our bodies. Hence it is scientifically accurate to say that we are stardust animated by starlight, representing a semi-scientific parallel to the ancient Hindu text of the Rig Veda, and to Plato, associating stars with souls.

In light of this, Walt Whitman's belief that 'a leaf of grass is no less than the journeywork of the stars…' may seem unremarkable, until we remember that the physical explanation of elements being created inside stars was discovered by science during the 20th century, and Walt Whitman died in 1892. Freud (1856 – 1939. Doctor and founder of psychoanalysis) remarked that 'Everywhere I go I find a poet has been there before me'. The poet's prescience sees further and sooner than most, and this, as referred to in chapter II, is something of wisdom.

Also concentrated at the pyramid's point, is our attention. Disturbing and unpleasant as it is to witness violent death, we tend to concentrate where nature concentrates its energies: predation; since the undying struggle between life and death, in order that Life continues, comes into sharp focus at the point of the kill. As predator closes on prey, their separation in distance and time diminishes until, at the point of the kill, predator and prey unite, no longer separated in space or time. At one place and one time, there is no space, no time, only energies concentrated here and now – one dying; one living; Life continuing: just as in Hinduism, Shiva (the destroyer of life), Brahma (the giver of life) and Vishnu (the preserver of life) are fused into one tripartite godhead.

Ultimate answers to our questions about life and death lie beyond our physical senses and beyond rational knowledge. However, in this chapter we can continue to explore beyond physical senses and pure reason by using our imagination, intuition and feelings and by learning from questions without definite answers, such as William Blake's.

Two hundred years after Blake asked his questions, a remarkable lady and author, by the name of Louise Hay, wrote what might be part of an answer. It is one that, most unusually, can be universally interpreted – scientifically, religiously, romantically, or simply by recognising the unity of life and nature:

'The power that created the universe beats in your heart.'

Within that unity the tiger's heart also beats and we seek the shoulder and art that could twist its sinews – and thereby understand why it makes ours beat faster. And it is our heart, much more than our mind, that's involved. However, Oscar Wilde knew that '…emotion lives in terror of ridicule and the imputation of weakness, and is never happy unless it has got hold of its big brother Intellect by the hand' (in a letter to Mary Anderson concerning his play The Duchess of Padua). This seems even more widely applicable these days, with the cold rationale of science being, it would seem, the only arbiter of truth, even though our feelings and spiritual qualities always play an equally, if not more important part in our lives, and quest for truth. The 'questions and answers' produced by feelings and spiritual qualities, like the lessons within them, cannot be definitively quantified or classified, nor do they always reveal themselves at first glance.

The word 'intellect' is now often used as Wilde used it, as a synonym for our powers of reasoning but its original meaning was summarised by Thomas Aquinas: 'Intellect and reason are not two powers, but distinct as the perfect from the imperfect…The intellect means, an immediate penetration of truth; the reason, enquiry and discourse.' In this sense 'intellect' operates independently of reason or emotion and relates to the instant, intuitive perception of truth.

Whilst reason rules over many aspects of the modern material world, reflection reveals that it is only our emotional response to our lives, our world and the other life we share it with that motivates, pleases, pains us or provides a sense of purpose – including the application of 'reason' – scientifically or otherwise. Scientific endeavour might initially seem an unlikely link with emotion but it too depends on feelings for its foundation and its maintenance. Few would deny that emotion can be provoked by great scientific achievement but it is also stimulated by the day-to-day application of reason: the solution sought and found for an equation, the precise logical progression that delivers a conclusion, the argument that makes sense, hi-tech that works like a wizard, deducing or discovering one of nature's secrets, all produce a good *feeling*, a sense of completion, agreement, fittingness.

Reason applied rigorously according to agreed criteria and tested empirically has developed into the discipline of science. However, experience teaches us that no proposition of reason, of the mind, is ever for certain. The mind can always challenge what the mind asserts; can always cast doubt on what is thought. Just like our being led by a street trickster to say under which cup certainty lies, we point at science but find we're mistaken. Experience teaches us that it is the heart's propositions which are for sure – nobody can prove to you that you are not feeling what you're feeling. As the old song has it 'something here inside cannot be denied.' (Agreed, nobody can prove you're not thinking what you're thinking – in the sense of conscious awareness of the thoughts – but the thoughts can always be challenged, in contrast to the heart's propositions (our feelings, such as love, wonder, fear or grief, which cannot be challenged)). 'The heart has its reasons which reason knows nothing of.' (Blaise Pascal 1623 – 1662 French mathematician, physicist and philosopher)

Steadying ourselves on our principle of balance, no recommendation is being made for a complete swing toward the emotional side of life, since freely indulged emotion is as dangerous as freely indulged reason – each must regulate the other and each must balance the other. Neither extreme is recommended. On the middle path, head and heart, reason and intuition, temper and discipline each other, and both should obey morality and practise virtue.

They also stimulate each other: reasoning stimulates, and is stimulated by, emotion and intuition. Few scientists remain unmoved by nature's beauties, spectacular displays and / or fascinating intricacies, available in all fields of study, and scientists will refer to the beauty of a theory or set of equations, both as an inherent property and as an indicator of their truth – millennia after Plato equated beauty and truth and years after various poets, Keats and Browning for examples, said the same (John Keats, English poet 1795 – 1821. Robert Browning, English poet and playwright 1812 – 1889). Many of the greatest scientists also attribute their most seminal ideas to intuition, not logical deduction. The idea occurs and is then usually followed by much labour to transform it into a logically coherent hypothesis. Intuition and emotion are also important for humans in general and scientists in particular to help us decide what is good or bad, right or wrong, important or unimportant.

'The same duality of approach – the rational and the intuitive – characterizes, as we saw, the scientific quest. It is therefore a perverse mistake to identify the religious need solely with intuition and emotion, science solely with the logical and the rational. Prophets and discoverers, painters and poets, all share this amphibial quality of living both on the contoured drylands and in the boundless ocean. In the history of the race as of the individual, both branches of the cosmic quest originate in the same source. The priests were the first astronomers; the medicine-men were both prophets and physicians; the techniques of hunting, fishing, sowing and reaping were imbued with religious magic and ritual. There was division of labour and diversity of method in the symbols and techniques, but unity of motive and purpose.' (B43 Excerpt from The Sleepwalkers (© 1959 The Estate of Arthur Koestler) is reproduced by permission of PFD (www.pfd.co.uk) on behalf of The Estate of Arthur Koestler.)

We saw in the previous chapter that this combination of intuition and reason characterises Corbett's jungle lore. Similarly it was a combination of intuition and reason that guided, for example, Edison, Marconi and the Wright brothers as referred to in chapter II.

Anyone who adopts the conceit of being a detached, 'purely rational being' does so because it gives them a good feeling – their position is falsified by their adoption of it! Even the denial of emotion depends on emotion!

However, for our present purposes, we are tracking our reactions to tigers – and it is reason that must live in terror of ridicule if it dare describe a tiger in terms of matter and mechanics and claim that all has been said!

Manimals

To harmonise with that universal heartbeat, play our part in the unity of life, the preceding paragraphs suggest we will need our hearts, and their intuitions, as much as our minds. However, let us begin with basics and our feet firmly on the ground.

At the lowest level of commonality, animals and Man are part of Earth, made of earth, and physically operate according to principles of matter and mechanics. All life on Earth, from bacteria to the blue whale, is physically based on DNA and its coding mechanisms. We share much else with animals: behavioural repertoires and strategies, care of young, mating rituals and displays of status being but a few examples. The ground is so common it passes underfoot unrecognised until our attention is brought to it.

One theme of this book is that of nature's mirrors and our reflections in animals (some as just described) are easily seen. However, in another sense, in the more formal terms of animal behaviour studies, the 'mirror test' demonstrates whether or not an animal can recognise itself in actual, physical mirrors and, if they can, it provides strong evidence that those animals are self-conscious i.e. aware of their own identity. Not all species have been tested but scientists are sure that orang-utans and chimpanzees can recognise themselves, and there is evidence to suggest that dolphins and elephants can too.

Recent research has also suggested that animals could experience feelings such as love and sympathy. Specialised neurons in the cerebral cortex of the brain called spindle cells (already identified in the brains of humans and the great apes) have now been found in the brains of humpback, fin, killer and sperm whales. These cells are a fascinating link between humans and animals, and the physical and emotional, since they are associated with intuition, empathy, speech, social skills and love. This research is supported by other studies revealing that whales form strong emotional bonds and social networks, have a language, are self-conscious and vary the songs they sing. We also know that many whales take hours to die after we have inserted explosive charges into their bodies, to get materials we do not need. As you may have guessed, whales have proportionally three times as many spindle cells as humans but, sadly, no harpoons.

Supposed limitations of animals' abilities, and their conscious experience, could well be reflections of our limitations. Rational knowledge is always incomplete, partial. At best, it is only probable (to a greater or lesser degree) and the answers provided often multiply the questions. Reason also has a curious ability to defeat its own quest for certainty by forever questioning its own findings; never still, never silent, never sure.

However, people *are* sure that they respond emotionally and spiritually to the tiger's aesthetic beauty, the proportions of its body, its power and grace of movement, the imperious and dignified demeanour, some indefinable mystique, or all of these combined. Such intuitive responses may be surer guides to truth than reason as recognised by Blake who told us that 'The tigers of wrath are wiser than the horses of instruction." Clark explained Blake's observation in his book 'Animals and Men': 'Spontaneous emotion and natural instinct, in other words, are more genuine guides than the intellect and man-made rules (*'intellect' used here in the sense of rationale – author*). The Romantics turned their backs on the cultivated garden of civilisation and strode into the jungle…Delacroix, like Barye, regarded animals as noble in themselves, and had particular sympathy with the great cats…Delacroix himself, says Gautier, "had tawny, feline eyes, with thick, arched brows, and a face of wild and disconcerting beauty; yet he could be as soft as velvet, and could be stroked and caressed like one of those tigers whose lithe and awesome grace he excelled in portraying."' (From 'Animals and Men' by Kenneth Clark. Text © 1977 by Kenneth Clark. Reprtinted by kind permission of Thames & Hudson Ltd., London (B16b)). We began with feet firmly on physical earth but if we want to continue tracking the tiger we will now need our hearts as much as our heads and physical senses.

Our emotional reactions to a tiger are often expressed by describing characteristics of a monarch, or other metaphors for power, beauty and dignity. These characteristics we admire or respect and this anthropomorphic view sometimes satisfies temporarily. Yet we also know how inappropriate it is to attribute human characteristics to animals which, while seeming to draw us closer at superficial levels, distance us at deeper levels. To more meaningfully gauge our relationship we must travel in our hearts and imaginations to more mysterious areas of life – to those distant deeps or skies, or 'womb of Time', where the fire of those eyes still burns and spears of starlight begin their journey (background and overleaf is an image of the aurora borealis).

In those depths where ancient texts tell us each star is associated with a soul, we see that a reflection of traditional anthropomorphism is more appropriate – by an attribution of animal characteristics to humans: "It is our conviction that if souls were visible to the eye we should distinctly see this strange fact that each individual of the human species corresponds to some one of the species of the animal creation; and we should clearly recognise the truth, hardly perceived by thinkers, that, from the oyster to the eagle, from the swine to the tiger, all animals are in man, and that each of them is in a man; sometimes even, several of them at a time. Animals are nothing but the forms of our virtues and vices wandering before our eyes, the visible phantoms of our souls. God shows them to us to make us reflect." (From the novel Les Miserables by Victor Hugo 1802 – 1885.)

Many years before Hugo, Nicolas de Cusa (1401? – 1464), an amazing scholar, philosopher, Bishop and Cardinal of the Holy Roman Empire living in what is now Germany, considered that the human soul assumes the capacities of all creatures within its own unity. Previously to Nicolas de Cusa, Socrates (469 – 399 B.C. Greek philosopher) had referred to '…the element of the lion and the snake in us…', Plato told us that animals were 'framed out of men', Aristotle (384 – 322 B.C. Greek philosopher) referred to the characteristics of plants and animals in humans and Genesis told us that man and animals are all produced from earth. For Hinduism, aspects of one almighty God are personified as different individual gods and many of these are associated with animals (e.g. Hanuman with the monkey, Ganesh with the elephant, Durga with the tiger. Individual gods can also have many names, such as the 1000 names of Rama, describing his various attributes). Other religions recognise a similar concept but differently named gods have become different 'names of God' (e.g. Islam recognising 99 names of Allah and the Bahai'i religion knowing 19 names for God). Just as with the gods of Hinduism, some of these 'names' can be embodied in animals, while man represents them all. This could correspond with the account in Genesis wherein Adam names the animals – he recognises those 'names', or characteristics, which each type of animal represents, as part of himself, while he 'contains' them all; relating to the Luther quote in Chapter III about our lost communication with animals – and hence ourselves. We, the collective Adam, have named the tiger, identified its qualities, but not lived up to their part of our identity. Worse, we have just about destroyed them, permanently impoverishing our freely chosen, self-formed identity.

If, despite this agreement between the erudite and renowned Victor Hugo, Socrates, Plato, Aristotle, a Bishop, the Bible and Martin Luther, all this is too religious or philosophical for you, science has found physical counterparts to the idea that characteristics of the natural order are common to all species. They are revealed in embryonic development, the stages of which are so alike, the same names can accurately be given to them whether they are, for examples, molluscs, crabs, worms, fish, reptiles, birds or mammals. Hence human embryos share all creatures' body plans at various stages in their development. So, from a scientific perspective we could say, in at least one sense, that all animals are in man, and elements of man within animals.

(This is not suggesting a revival of Haeckel's 'Biogenetic Law', according to which 'ontology recapitulates phylogeny' (i.e. development of the individual retraces the evolutionary development of the species). Before publication of 'The Origin of Species' (1859), biologists knew that, despite their obviously divergent appearance as adults, different species were similar as embryos. In 1828 Karl Ernst von Baer recognised that features common to a broader taxonomic group (e.g. Vertebrata) usually appear developmentally before specific characteristics of more specialised taxonomic groups (e.g. orders or families). This principle is known as Von Baer's Law (although it was anticipated by Aristotle). Darwin was aware of similarities between embryos of invertebrates (e.g. molluscs, crabs, worms) and vertebrates (e.g. fish, reptiles, birds, mammals) and their patterns of development such as the generation of organ systems. Haeckel (1834 – 1919), who was a supporter of Darwin's theory of evolution, exaggerated the similarities between embryos across a wide range of divergent species, such as the well-known 'gill slits' appearing in vertebrate embryos, claiming them as evidence for evolution. Haeckel's exaggerations have since been exposed and his law discredited. As a consequence there has been a danger of the pendulum swinging too far in the opposite direction and an over-emphasis being placed on dissimilarities between embryos. However, whether or not it is evidence for the theory of evolution, comparative embryology does reveal striking similarities between various and diverse species).

The recent discovery of 'homeobox' or 'hox' genes has revived recognition of the fundamental embryonic similarities shared between all animals. The body plans (the orientation of head, tail, positioning of limbs and the basic pattern of internal organs and other structures) of whales and humans, lambs and tigers are initiated using the same groups or 'families' of genes. Genetic and embryological similarities between all animals are such that humans can be scientifically said to share much commonality with all other animals.

'Animals in man' are no strangers to people practising Eastern religions. When interpreted spiritually and / or psychologically they help us, as Hugo suggested, understand what makes us who we are. For example, the multi-faceted significance of the tiger in Zen Buddhism teaches various life-lessons in stories collectively called 'the Tiger's Cave'.

'The tiger is instinctual nature, which is very powerful and not to be underestimated. Until this instinctual energy is well tamed, for want of a better word – brought into harmony with the rest of our being – it will be very hard for us to gain emotional stability or deep happiness. Sooner or later we have to confront the instinctual energies in ourselves and engage them in our quest for freedom, otherwise we can easily swing between extremes. Most of the time we stand well back from those energies and…remain at a safe distance from the tiger…

We…tend to have a part of ourselves that subtly uses power to manipulate others to do our bidding. Operating in this way we often manage to create what feels like a secure world for ourselves, in which we stand at a distance and keep everything under control. This is true of our relations with others. It is also true of our relations with our own deeper, more instinctual energies on the early stages of the path to freedom. Somehow we manage to ignore the roars of the tiger, which symbolise the parts of ourselves that we cannot control. Nonetheless, those roars and growls still register somewhere, and we know deep down that when we act in this way we are not finally secure. We can never feel safe if we have had to cage up part of ourselves…

The tiger…can take on other symbolic meanings. It can stand quite simply for whatever we avoid…When we find ourselves side-stepping in this way, we have to do our best, however falteringly, to take steps to face the tiger. I find it helpful to reflect on the maxim "If you do not deal with life, it will deal with you."…Facing tigers is not easy, and very often it is only when we see that we have no alternative, through experiencing the painful consequences of our avoidance, that we start moving towards the tiger's cage. Facing our own tiger, whatever it might be, is very often the fastest way to transform ourselves as human beings. It is easy to keep circling some crucial aspect of our life or character without addressing it. We may sometimes need to be strategic about setting up the right conditions for facing our tiger…We may be better off not giving ourselves too much time to think before facing situations we would rather avoid. As Mark Twain wrote, "If you have to swallow two frogs, swallow the big one first, and don't look at it too long."…

Imagine that in a remote part of the jungle there is a cave. If there happens to be a tiger in this cave, there might be many animal tracks, perhaps even human footprints, going into it, but none coming out…Thus the tiger's cave suggests an experience that many people enter and from which no-one returns (*i.e. the person is fundamentally changed or developed, so the original 'person' with their predicament, no longer exists – author*). In Zen, this becomes a symbol for insight into Reality, for understanding the true nature of yourself and your life. This insight into Reality…is the crucial point on the Buddhist path, the beginning of unending freedom…' (B69)

In summary, Zen Buddhism tells us that to face the tiger alone, and be within its reach, is to face our fears and, what is most frightening of all, ourselves.

Manmirrors

If we can accept that elements of nature, including those embodied in tigers, are within us, and elements of us are within nature, it is but a small step to also accept that the world, including tigers, can act as mirrors for us – if we would only look.

Once again, let us begin at ground level. It is obvious that our actions have a physical impact on the world and change it in ways that register on our senses. Hence, even at the most basic, physical level, we could call the world a mirror. This principle is both superficial and profound at the same time: it is superficial physically but, since our actions are governed by our thoughts, priorities, wishes, values, virtues, vices and morals etc., it applies to aspects of life lying far deeper than the physical, and directly relates to who we are.

The same theme is found in one of the most concise and profound pieces of advice ever given, written over the temple entrance at Delphi, the location of the oracle. It is to 'Know Thyself'. To this end, a reflection is essential for, without a reflection, how do we learn to recognise ourselves? Life is a process by which, if we exercise our interest and face our fears, we may learn at least part of the answer, since the reflections can frame for us some symmetries ('frame' in this context includes senses of 'selecting' and 'defining' – providing another angle on animals being 'framed out of men' as in the Plato reference above). If we choose not to exercise interest, we fail to know ourselves and, having no basis for development, risk falling into Socrates' category of the unexamined life which, he tells us, is not worth living. The Buddha also teaches the art of self-knowledge in all its aspects in 'The Setting-Up of Mindfulness'.

Zen Buddhism has pointed out some symmetries that might need taming or controlling, and the dangers of not doing so. Could it also be that one attraction of the tiger is that we see in it and dimly recognise some positive and magnificent elements of ourselves, or our potential selves? Could it be that we see, in what we refer to as the tiger's beauty, majesty or nobility, exhibited unsullied and unselfconsciously before us, characteristics that are sometimes evident, more often latent, in ourselves? If so, we can again adopt an anthropomorphic view but this time with a deeper understanding.

If this sounds far-fetched, consider quality cinema and theatre (and not films about vampires, werewolves or other semi-human creatures – although these in themselves give us 'paws' for thought!). Do we not go to the cinema or theatre to see characters play out our hidden or apparent selves? Or are we not at least provoked to consider how we might deal with, or react to, the situations portrayed? Is not Shakespeare the greatest playwright partly because he is universal, he knows us and we recognise ourselves 'so truly did he dwell amidst the elements constituting man in every age and clime'? (B36) Do we not watch a film or play as if it were a special type of mirror? Quality drama shows us ourselves, makes us ask questions about ourselves and how we are living our lives. Modern-day films with all-action thrills and 'special effects' but without plot or characters of depth and substance, are empty by comparison and will be forgotten when Shakespeare is entertaining new generations. Amongst others, T.S. Eliot (1888 – 1965. Poet and playwright) believed plays had the power and potential to redeem us morally.

If we are now an audience for man-made plays, we were first an audience for dramas and plays produced and presented by nature.

"All the World's a stage, and all the animals and people merely players…"

(not quite As You Like It, with apologies to Shakespeare)

Nature was our first and biggest theatre, which was, and still is, both educational and, long before the digital age, interactive, since it responds to and reflects our actions. In the modern world it is easy to imagine a hand-held electronic gadget with screens and buttons responding to our touch, perhaps with the ubiquitous bleep and / or light display. Our fingers follow our mental commands to execute some function and we can use, watch, speak or listen to the results. In comparison, let us consider an enormous and amazing entertainment system that also educates – by direct experience. Let your imagination transform the buttons and connections of the electronic gadget from silicon and silver metal into green organic tissue and other life-forms. Expand and 'morph' the hardware into a mixture of hard and soft materials, green plants, moving animals, patterns of light and sound…touched by your fingers, felt under your feet, tracked by your eyes and ears. The system responds to the thoughts which govern your fingers and feet. Your interaction with the system produces results which you can use, watch or listen to. It shows you how it responds to your mind touching it and in return, touches your mind – and often your heart. Obviously, the 'new' gadget or entertainment system is the natural world around us, fully interconnected with least dust, flowers, tigers, you, me and the very stars – our actions reach as far and determine whether or not they water heaven with their tears. While our actions are governed by our thoughts, our thoughts, as mentioned above, are influenced by our virtues and vices, and much more besides, but all of which can be summarised by – our characters. The results of our actions, of our characters, of our being who we are, are shown to us by the world and people around us. This is how we can follow the Oracle's advice to 'Know Thyself'; this is how we get to know our character, and its faults, and how to correct them.

However, it's not only trial and error, if it were, few of us would make it to spiritual self-sufficiency. Mother Nature provides lessons and models to imitate. When, even from purely practical perspectives, we model our activities according to nature's examples and work in harmony with those patterns and potentials, they give rise to harmonious, healthy developments (e.g. organic agriculture, recycling, optimal usage and hence, healthy bodies, mind and spirit). Where we ignore nature's lead or lessons we produce discordant or damaging developments (e.g. chemical farming, pollution, wasteful and excessive consumption, excess fat, sugar and salt, and hence, obesity, disease and depression). We can change these harmful results by changing our actions; our behaviour, and in so doing develop our characters in accordance with free tuition from nature's interactive theatre. So, even from practical, physical perspectives, we can immediately see a bridge between the outer world and our inner worlds of heart and mind, behaviour and character.

With careful observation we can follow the lessons incorporated into the system, interact with nature's entertainment / education system and, sometimes, manage to make an adjustment that harmonises with the system as a whole. Our adjustments may duplicate what we have seen, make some variation on a given theme or create something new. However, if we are only concerned with our own wants and wishes and ignore nature's lessons regarding connections and unity, we often damage or spoil the system in some way. Sadly, and ultimately dangerously, we are too often only concerned with what we want, or how clever we are, so full of ourselves we fail to see the greater unity of which we are a part. We play with tiny toys while we could be helping sustain the web of life, if not the very universe itself.

Could it be that the more we fail to be as we would ideally like to be, the greater we value (or resent) the missing qualities of character and the more motivated (or abashed) we are to see them, in films, plays, nature in general and animals in particular? If so, a deeper and disturbing meaning to our collectively threatening the tiger's continued existence is revealed: not only do we so often fail to achieve nobility, majesty or beauty in our own lives…we are going to sink so low as to destroy those characteristics where they still remain. We are going to damage and scribble over, if not destroy, the beautiful entertainment / education system of which we are part. Rather than frame the symmetry, we are destroying the symmetry and, since symmetry is a type of balance, we are destroying the balance – but balance is health and life, the principle of yin and yang, and to destroy that balance is to destroy ourselves.

Whilst we would like to identify with the nobility we see in the tiger, the world is telling us that our nobility is currently outweighed by selfishness, and the selections of vices it breeds (greed, weakness, dishonesty etc.) Selfishness also cultivates fear, which the tiger also represents, as in Zen, but in this case we cannot identify with or imitate the tiger, we have to confront it.

In addition to psychological fears (of rejection, ridicule, etc.), what are these fears, these tigers of Zen?

Jack London refers to '…the fear that is to life germane and that lies twisted about life's deepest roots.' (Short Story 'Love of Life'). Life is, for most independent people, a struggle. Struggles usually include uncertain outcomes and they can be a fearful experience. Life holds few certainties other than Benjamin Franklin's 'death and taxes' (and we may be fearful of those too!) and no security that we can guarantee, so even if we survive our current struggles there is always fear of future ones. These include not only the current array of terrifying global dangers but also local ones, where life is also full of perils and pitfalls. We fear for 'me' and 'my; life / family / health / job / security / status / material wealth'. Even in relatively secure surroundings, we may still be beset by 'fears' that we will not 'succeed' or cannot keep or have more, or bigger, or better. Fear can infect and then kill any and all pleasures, plans and purposes. All, ultimately, reduce to a fear for self and a fear of the unknown. The latter aspect underlies our inability to rest easily with doubt, our unease with those unanswered questions. There is an antidote to this as described by the poet Keats who referred to our 'irritable reaching after fact and certainty' but who also identified what he called a 'negative capability' – the capacity to be at peace in a state of doubt, to rest with uncertainty.

Are there any other antidotes to obsessive or excessive fears for self? The Hindu religious text of the Padma Purana tells us that 'Of all the gifts only one is supreme. It is the freedom from fear. For all the creatures of this universe, there is no other gift greater than this.' There are similar references in other religious scriptures but what if we have not been blessed with such a gift? At Mahatma Gandhi's ashram, one of the 'rules', or guides to conduct for spiritual development, was to 'meditate on and cultivate fearlessness', so we are capable of consciously developing fearlessness to some degree. Another antidote to fear is knowledge. As we proceed we will learn that exercising interest in life and nature grows knowledge, keeping fear in perspective and under control – in something of a parallel to both Corbett's jungle lore and his observation of wild animals living with danger but remaining joyful, and even benefitting from the stimulus it sometimes provides.

Due to the universality of fear we can all appreciate a hero – someone who risks their welfare for another's (not someone who wins a game of sport, and we see that misuse of language impoverishes not only language but also our values). Heroes need not necessarily appear Hollywood-style but in everyday scenarios such as mediaeval apothecaries tending those with the plague, 'ordinary' people who sheltered agents or escapees in occupied territories, or 'ordinary' people who break from the herd and endure ridicule to do what is right in terms of their life-styles and consumer spending.

In contrast to heroes, fear for self not only makes us unlikely to save others, it makes us more likely to harm others, if only inadvertently or indirectly, since we only use our faculties and resources to look after ourselves, or those who mean most to us (and even these, often only for selfish reasons!) Fear may also tell us that neighbours who were harmless yesterday might not be tomorrow, so we had best conquer them today. Fear for self also leads to selfishness since, to acquire security, we must get and keep as much as we can of money; land and other material items; status and contacts, even if it means others go without. With so many adopting this fearful focus on self we have produced for ourselves the most fearful situation: a corrupted and imbalanced world with an environmental crisis. The current state of the physical world reflects that, spiritually, we are fearful of facing up to our selfishness and character faults, and resolving to address them.

It is when we conquer these fears; face our innermost frightening tigers, that we achieve the nobility of the tiger.

Ironically, it is our fear that often prevents us achieving the very situation that would remove our fears: imagine for a moment that you are in some way guaranteed health, total financial security and physical safety indefinitely – never a material need or want ever denied, nor ever an injury or illness, for you or your family. Once this benefit had been fully absorbed and all fears had disappeared forever, it is possible, if not probable, that you might then consider how you could help other, less fortunate, people. You may make efforts and take time to ensure others had life's essentials and then, perhaps, education and healthcare. In doing so you might meet some wonderful characters and form firm friendships. The irony is that, in doing the latter (sharing with and caring for others) we all achieve the former (material security, health and comfort for all). It is fear (including fears that others will take advantage of us) that pushes us in the opposite direction and, as the balance tips further from equilibrium ever fewer get ever richer (once you have got something, it's easier to get more) while ever more get ever poorer (the downward spiral of increasing debts and decreasing abilities to meet them).

In a currently imbalanced British society people can even be ennobled for living a life of personal promotion and self-indulgence, or sometimes for financial donations to political parties – all of which are the opposite of nobility; the pendulum at the opposite extreme. This trend is also associated with a 'fear for self' since the acquisition of status and wealth bring a sense of security (albeit a false one), reducing or eliminating fear while promoting yet more self-indulgence and passing pleasures. Wealth also equates to power and the same spiritual insecurity may manifest as the pursuit of power exclusively, expressed collectively in the current Western obsession with yang, material, power – the power of wealth, of science, of arms, of economics – any of which can transform into the power of manipulation (associated with avoiding Zen's tiger). Out of all healthy proportion, the symmetry distorted horribly, it seeks dominance disguised as defence, and threatens yin, hence the whole, and hence itself. Spiritually speaking, those who seek and overtly display most wealth and power may actually be the most fearful, although disguised by every possible sign and symbol of the opposite.

Despite all the enormous complexity and variety of life it is possible (amazingly) to use the above considerations to find some simple rules: Actions, whether of an individual or a nation, that lead to hurt, harm or unhappiness can ultimately be traced to selfish motives. Actions that are noble and dignified, healing and healthy in the long-term for all, can be traced to unselfish motives. Pedants will immediately seek exceptions but exceptions will either be found in short-term minority perspectives or according to the letter of the law ('which killeth') but not its spirit (which 'giveth life'). The water may also be muddied by providence, accident or chance but, by examining our motives (which we always know for sure) we gain clarification and reflection.

So, in summary, we are attracted to the tiger's nobility but hesitate for fear. Yet we have to overcome our fears and approach our tigers to achieve nobility. We have to face our fearful selfishness, and the failures of character it fosters, seize the tiger's fire, letting it smelt and then temper our mettle, freeing our character from the dross and thereby achieving the nobility we see in the tiger.

We form our character for the better by denying self. The more we are able to deny self the more may our potential be realised. Each person has enormous potential, not necessarily in terms of scientific, artistic or any other sort of technical accomplishment, but as members of families, as friends and civilised, supportive members of small and large communities.

'Can you walk on water? You have done no better than a straw. Can you fly in the air? You have done no better than a blue-bottle. Conquer your heart; then you may become somebody.'

Ansari of Herat (1006 – 1088) Persian poet and Sufi

Developing ourselves and discovering others' true selves takes time, interest and effort. Socially there is a tendency for people to be defined by their occupation and, in some cases, this can be indicative of character. However, if circumstances permit, it is often more interesting to ask someone what they would be doing if unconstrained by their situation in life, or to ask about their hobbies and interests. Although he did an exemplary job for the Indian railways, think what would have been missed by only enquiring after Jim Corbett's paid occupation, or, having met William Blake, discovering only that he engraved metal for a living. Where, happily, occupations are also vocations, they are more direct manifestations of character and can be inspirational for those who have them, and those who witness them at work.

On the negative side, a person may use their occupation to define themselves and thereby avoid responsibility in the world: 'I'm an engineer; doctor; journalist; manager; manual worker; mechanic; scientist; solicitor; teacher etc. and have no business worrying about abuse of the environment, tigers, or people starving to death'. In addition to the demands of morality, nature's network of connections means all these issues are, ultimately, relevant and important to that person and their family. Nature's network will teach us that in the first and last analysis, we are human beings and, as such, must observe a sacrosanct set of values and morals essential for our survival, however we may earn our livelihood.

All of these reflections are variations on the theme of the world, nature in general, and tigers in particular, being a mirror in which to see ourselves and to which we are connected in an organic, dynamic and unified way – our own personal and collective 'inter-active', educational theatre and concert hall.

Losing the Light of Our Reflections

Sadly, many choose not to seize their tiger's fire and resign themselves, in a sort of spiritual parallel to nature's pyramid of biological levels, to herd behaviour, or lower still. In the modern, at least Western world we have, collectively speaking, 'lost the plot', lost our conscious connections with nature, our priorities, and the play called 'Life'. It is this 'separation' between nature and ourselves that makes the reflections, the symmetries, so distant and difficult to see, the imbalances unnoticed and therefore unidentified. Modern industrialised life easily compounds this problem by obscuring any reflections that remain visible. Natural scenery, natural processes, plants and animals become 'other than', apart from our daily lives, allowing their neglect, abuse or destruction. Yet these life forms are as guides to us along the way, since they are both lights in their own right and also reflected light, illuminating nature and nature's way, the fundamentals of life on which we all depend. Some animals, such as the tiger, burn brightly and we see more of nature by viewing it in their light (to study the tiger is to study its prey, and then the forest…as we study further connections and sense others, each bird, each insect flitting through the sky illuminates a little more). However, as the Liberal, Lord Grey is said to have remarked to a friend as the street lamps were being lit in London just before the outbreak of WWI "The lamps are going out all over Europe; we shall not see them lit again in our lifetime." Within a few more years the darkness grew deeper as other lights were, and still are, going out all over the world. As it is beyond our powers to re-light them, our lives are intimately linked with those lights we can keep lit.

Nature's concentrated energies, her brightest lights such as, to name but a few, tigers, dolphins, elephants, apes and whales make people (even those who choose to live with blinkers) concentrate, if only briefly. However, when nature's most concentrated energies, her brightest lights cannot pierce the gloom of self and wilful ignorance and these living lights are extinguished, the symmetries become more difficult to see in the ensuing darkness, and hence our path ever more dangerous.

John Seymour wrote many guides for people who want to live off the land self-sufficiently. He did so himself, tended his land and kept its lights lit and burning brightly. His light left us in 2004 but some of his reflections remain in his books:

'When you retire to the country and spend at least part of your life in simple and manual pursuits, you find yourself far better able to take stock of the way civilisation has gone in the great world beyond the boundary of your holding. Your holding itself becomes your real world, therefore you look at the other, lesser world beyond your fences with a dispassionate eye and can understand it better than you could when you were immersed in it yourself.

If I am not very mistaken you come to understand that that world out there is a very sad and sick world indeed. There you are, in your little kingdom, striving with all your strength to husband and nurture the life force – and out there you see vast human forces doing all that they can to destroy it. You see the napalm bombing of the Brazilian forests carried out to achieve financial profits for a few wicked men; the murder of the last of the world's great fish stocks to provide fish-meal for the feeding of battery hens and broiler chicks; the slaughter of the noble whale to provide perfume… and food for…pet dogs; the covering of the green surface of the earth with tarmac and concrete; the corruption of the world's peasants – the only people who have been leading lives which nurture and do not damage the life of the earth. You see the insatiable agribusinessmen striving to destroy every form of life on vast acreages in order to favour their one profit-making crop; you see apparently honest and sane scientists following lines of research that they *know* will probably lead to the destruction of all life; you see nuclear engineers and physicists who know perfectly well, deep down in some well-suppressed part of their minds, that what they are doing will maim and destroy future generations and yet they do it for salary and pension – they do it to pay their children's school fees at expensive schools knowing full well that their grand-children and great-grandchildren will have to pay the price in mutilation and misery; you see the 'civilised' nations engaging in an unseemly scramble to sell increasingly vicious weapons to the foolish leaders of the so-called 'Third World'.

The list goes on and is apparently endless. And you come to realise that post-industrial man has gone mad. Materialism; humanism (the worship of mankind) – these religions, for black religions they are, have led men down a dark and desperate path. Our leaders tell us we must have nuclear power because without it we will have to freeze in the dark. In other words we may, if we do not have it, have to put up with a little less warmth, a little less comfort, a little less 'growth'. Our governments are all committed to 'growth'. What is this 'growth'? Is it the growth of the human spirit, the growth of the true moral and spiritual stature of mankind? It is not. It is the growth of the proliferation of rubbish, and to proliferate the rubbish it is necessary to rape our mother, the earth.

Therefore we *drop-ins* – we who drop into a saner and less exploitive kind of life – have a terrifying responsibility: We must be content with nothing less than building a new civilisation – a new world order. It is when men are crammed into huge conurbations that they become sick and dangerous to the rest of the biosphere…Man becomes a destructive parasite on the earth. In all the truly golden ages of mankind towns and cities have been of a humane size – flowerings, as it were, of rural cultures. Townsmen have had their roots in the family acres not far away. It is when people are cut off from these roots and survive rootless in the great brick, tarmac and concrete jungles that they lose their way.

So the return to our birthright is…religious. This is the only word we have to describe it, whether we believe in a God or not. In pure urban materialism mankind has gone up a blind alley – an alley that will end up by destroying him if he persists in trying to follow its course. There is no way of telling how many other species of life he will take with him to destruction…through selfishness and greed… We have only one duty (and only one true pleasure, which lies in the performance of this duty), and that is to work to further the purposes of the life force. It may not always be easy to see in which way the performance of this duty lies. Often we may find ourselves perplexed. Pure reason – reason alone – is never enough to show us the right way. Reason must be reinforced and informed by something else, too…we who belong to small areas of the earth's surface have dominion over the animals and plants on them, at least up to a certain point. We are, to that extent, kings of our kingdoms. But the good king rules for the sake of his subjects. He is their servant. We must learn these two rules: it is the land which owns the husbandman, not the husbandman who owns the land; and the king is the servant of his subjects.

Man is part of nature just as a robin is. If man tries to 'conquer nature' he will destroy himself because it is something of which he is a part.

It is probably possible to persuade intelligent people that the above statements are true by reason alone. Reason alone will lead people to realise that it will not be possible to store radioactive material safely for a hundred thousand years (while adding to that store all the time); reason alone will tell anybody that it cannot be right to keep dousing our planet with hellish chemicals that poison life, and that any agent that harms one form of life will harm another. But, alas, reason alone will not cause us to act in the right manner and forego these things.

We who return to our birthright, the land, are in a position that is rapidly becoming rare on this planet in that we have time and space to cultivate that part of our brain that has been suppressed by materialism. We can cultivate our power of feeling and being as well as our power of knowing and reasoning. As we hoe our turnips the reasoning part of our minds takes a rest and we can allow our being to be truly aware of the fields around us, and the woods, and the marshes and the hills, and the life in these things, and to feel that we are part of this life, not a special part but just a part, and that our reason has been given to us so that we may play our part well and honestly to further the purposes of the life force.

Books, words, reasoning – these things can never develop this consciousness in us. Hoeing turnips, lovingly nurturing plants and animals (aye, and as lovingly killing and eating them occasionally – it's all part of the role of the true husband-man: the lion husbands the wild zebra and the bison husbands the prairie grass), watching and *feeling* the turn of the seasons, watching and feeling the life-and-death-and-life-and-death that goes on all around us, for ever and ever, and that we are part of it. These activities and non-activities can reawaken our hearts and spirits and enable us to see the universe with the inner eye. You think that the five senses of which you are mentally aware tell you the truth, nothing but the truth, and the whole truth? Do not believe it. Certain limited aspects of the truth, yes, but the whole truth – no! And until a large section of mankind becomes capable of perceiving the whole truth again and not just the less important aspects of it, we have every reason to despair of the hopes for the future of life on this planet. And we will not become capable just as long as we live insulated from the rest of nature by glass and concrete, plastic and tarmac, and our own insatiable materialistic greed…

So let us come back to our birthright: let us repair the ruined smallholdings and cottages, and build new ones, and bring such pressure to bear on our 'masters' – on the great know-all government – as will cause the release of the empty acres for the good purposes of nature and of mankind.

I do not advocate that we should all be self-sufficient small-holders. But let us practise our various skills and trades and professions not cut off entirely from the rest of nature, but affected by her throughout our lives…Imagine a land in which the towns and cities were the true flowerings of a fruitful and happy countryside, in which the countryside was husbanded as it should be husbanded – by men and women and not with huge machines and poisonous chemicals – in small plots, each bearing the imprint of some individual or small group of individuals – with gardens and orchards and arable land and pasture and woodland and wilderness all mixed in happy, fruitful confusion – with the homes of husbandmen forming a natural part of the landscape – with happy, free children laughing and playing, working…with their elders, and learning real things in a real way…

Why are our present conurbations (I cannot bring myself to call them by that beautiful word *city*) …so hideously ugly? – because they were built for ignoble ends. Every building in them was built for one reason only – to make a rich man richer. The humble cottages of peasants, the village churches, the great cathedrals, the majestic barns, the fine, timber-framed villages of the honest weavers, the splendid sailing ships – all these things were built, even though perhaps the builders didn't know it, for the glory of God.

You cannot have a noble artefact if it is created for an ignoble end.' (B60)

By losing the light of our reflections we may even lose the mirror. The following sub-sections remind us of the more obvious mirrors around us.

MIRRORS...

...of a Material World

"Greed shows quicker on the environment than on a man's face."

(ancient Chinese proverb)

Materialistic greed is a powerful weed and has infected many aspects of our lives. It's infection of agriculture, the most important of human activities, is most dangerous since all else is built upon agriculture. All life and wealth comes from soil. The soil is the basis of plant life and hence all terrestrial animals, including tigers and humans. In addition to food it also provides all the resources necessary for all human activities. What Man does to the earth he does to himself, and all other species, since all species are made of earth. Nothing is more important for terrestrial habitats than the soil, and we need to understand something of what we are doing to it if we are to save the tiger and ourselves.

Appendix II summarises the vital importance of soil. It explains how, in addition to ever-increasing amounts of poisonous chemicals being sprayed onto it, current agricultural techniques damage or destroy its life-sustaining properties, and how agriculture has become 'agribusiness'. Our indispensable topsoil is disappearing (into the oceans via streams and rivers) while forests (one of the few remaining areas generating the nutrients and micro-organisms which make topsoil) continue to be clear cut across areas which defy common, but not commercial, sense. Appendix II also reveals the darker shades of the 'green' revolution and examines world hunger, concluding that the majority of which is not due to food scarcity but financial poverty (which, in turn, provokes poaching and timber felling). It also describes the parallels between our soil as treated by the chemicals of agribusiness and our bodies as treated by the chemicals of pharmaceutical companies. Finally and most importantly, it appetisingly illustrates how healthy soil farmed organically grows healthy food, healthy bodies and healthy societies – simultaneously.

Appendix II also describes how humanity's obsession with a one-dimensional material world has dangerously reduced nature's mature and complex ecosystems to simple, and vulnerable, immaturity (vast acreages of one single crop). This immaturity mirrors our immaturity, illustrated by our failure to face responsibilities; putting ourselves first; manipulating others for personal advantage; and preference for the playground before the classroom (even sophisticated technology and scientific equipment are often just expensive toys – and all the better if their complexity allow their operators to 'blind with science' any who might question the priorities and values they display). Pre-occupied with constructions and toys we have made from nature's provisions, we forget about other people and nature hidden behind the artificial scenery these products represent.

"While civilization has been improving our houses, it has not equally improved the men who are to inhabit them. It has created palaces, but it was not so easy to create noblemen and kings."

(Henry David Thoreau)

Farmers who resisted the onslaught of industrialised chemical farming of mono-crops exhibited the kind of 'intuitive knowledge' referred to previously. They had absorbed knowledge through long years of first-hand personal experience, through their attentive proximity to nature. They understood what was best for the soil, their crops and their animals. They could not immediately 'prove' their view correct, write an equation or even necessarily articulate what they knew. Yet they resisted the seemingly irrefutable evidence of scientists' facts and figures, bigger, more abundant, 'pest-free' crops, the temptation of increased yields and higher profits, and the pressures of marketing, advertising and governments influenced by big business. Their wisdom saw beyond facts to truth. No doubt dismissed as 'old-fashioned' and / or their intelligence ridiculed, they could see further and sooner than most but couldn't see where they were wrong – this was mainly because they were right: completely, healthily, naturally and profoundly right.

The same, if not deeper understanding of the seasons, sowing and harvest was known to our ancient ancestors, who may now be thought of as primitive. Yet no matter how sophisticated we might think ourselves, we depend on nature in exactly the same way as they did and their knowledge, unknown to or forgotten by the majority of modern populations, is essential for our long-term healthy survival. Mr. or Ms. Modern Executive, trading stocks and shares by Internet on their mobile telephone from fast cars, are often associated, by commercial interests at least, with success and intelligence. Yet they and the rest of us still depend on little green leaves flourishing in the sunshine – which much of their trading is neglecting, if not poisoning, damaging or destroying. Is this success and intelligence? More worryingly, they may become role models for the young, the wrong sort of ideal to have in our current circumstances. More importantly, if our fragile systems of communications and commerce collapse due to our abuse of what they are built upon, we may be literally returned to earth for our survival, where few of these 'executives' can do anything useful at all. Most executives, without a telephone and something to sell at an inflated price, will be hungry and helpless.

If not presented with images of material 'success', we may be told that this is the 'information age', or the 'information economy' succeeding the industrial revolution which had previously succeeded the agricultural revolution. One index often used to illustrate this sequence is the numbers, or percentage, of workers in the respective industries. The number of people working in agriculture decreased as dramatically as those working in industry increased. The same pattern has repeated with workers moving from industry to 'information' and associated services. Somehow there is an implication that we are 'moving on' and anything associated with the previous industries – especially agricultural – is old-fashioned or plain primitive. Sometimes a documentary or article will refer to a 'primitive' society being based on agriculture. It is rarely acknowledged explicitly that all societies, past and present, are based on agriculture. All of us, whatever our occupation or the labels we attach to them, still depend on agriculture. One reason relatively few people now work in agriculture is due to agribusiness; chemicals, machines and mass production. As for the 'Information Age', it still depends on plumbers, electricians, mechanics and engineers in order to operate – and all depend on farmers.

Nature was, and still is, our first priority. The ancients knew this and lived accordingly. They had knowledge of animals, domestic and wild, and of the properties of herbs and other plants. By paying attention to sun, moon, stars and the dust underfoot the ancients learned laws and lessons, knowing exactly when to plant and when to harvest. Festivals, rituals and 'holi-days' marked our harmonisation with nature's cycles – read directly from a cosmic canvas on permanent, if occasionally obscured, display above us. The change between ancient and modern is that, despite still being dependent on nature and agriculture, we no longer respect or value this foundation and most of us are no longer able to read the cosmic canvas. The ancients and their knowledge are often portrayed as quaint and childlike as compared to modern man, who is the apex of sophistication and slick control of nature. Such a view is not a mark of their ignorance and immaturity, but ours. Moreover, it would be a good wager that their food was tastier and healthier, for them and the earth, than our modern chemical concoctions.

No longer able to read (or sometimes even see) the stars, we live more of our lives in fluorescently-lit darkness and, having lost sight of nature's path, trust in human institutions to guide us, although it is those very same institutions that have led us into various crises, culminating in the current environmental one. That we have lost our path and standards of both personal and professional behaviour cannot be disguised by media Newspeak telling us society is 'evolving' or that 'we are becoming more tolerant' and similar verbiage, no more than an incompetent navigator could convince the crew he has led into a life-threatening wilderness that their journey is 'evolving' or that they have become more tolerant. We must urgently re-harmonise with cosmic rhythms and patterns which provide guiding, cyclical paths, which we wander away from at our peril.

In chapter II we reminded ourselves of science's inability to pronounce on the existence of gods. Now we will consider a possibility of gods pronouncing on man. On Olympus, the gods, finding man wilfully running away from nature's guidance, and persistently choosing to be smaller than his potential, see the damaging if not disastrous consequences to all sentient creatures, and sit in council: 'To view man makes the head and heart ache together! He refuses to learn what he needs to for his own benefit, let alone others. So we shall make some unmistakeable lessons; living lessons of creatures – some similar to man; some to set smiles on the saddest face and some so impressive to his faculties that even he cannot fail to notice them. Several creatures shall combine beauty, grace and dignity, to remind man of his potential beauty, grace and dignity. Although one insect is more than man can fully account for, that takes a little effort to recognise and few men can be bothered to make effort for anything other than making money, so the creatures we shall make will be noticeable without effort. Yet, let there also be justice, and justice that man may understand and be in control of: let him be able to see clearly the effects of his behaviour; let him see health and abundance when he conforms to nature's laws and vice versa. He will see that nothing compels his demise, only his own choices. Nature's laws will allow some time in which he can, if he chooses, rectify his behaviour. By his behaviour in general and by his treatment of other creatures in particular he shall pass sentence on himself, since we will tie his life to these creatures and these lessons'.

Printed by kind permission of Bill Longshaw (porpoise), domdeen (elephant), Michael Elliott (gorilla) and nuttakit (tiger), all at FreeDigitalPhotos.net

And so man looked on apes, and dolphins, and elephants, and great cats – they could only be ignored by the dead – but they were noticed only insofar as they could provide interest, entertainment or adventure for man; their welfare, in general, was ignored. As man-made technology grew to provide other interests, entertainment and adventure, even these animals, except for a few to feature in exotic holidays or television documentaries, were ignored, and gradually wiped out by greed, selfishness and ignorance. And so the gods knew that it was best for greed, selfishness and ignorance to be wiped out.

Man has gradually surrounded himself with his man-made artificial world. The sophistication of computer networks, civil engineering and military capabilities create an illusion of human mastery over nature and natural resources. Yet all of them put together cannot compete with one green leaf; they cannot turn starlight into sugar and feed one hungry person; yet we trample, poison and otherwise abuse the leaf that can, undermining while simultaneously over-burdening our foundations – which must eventually destroy not only all we have built but also dramatically increase how many of us are hungry. It is true that scientists have made advances in developing artificial photosynthesis. Yet, even if current research into artificial photosynthesis bears fruit, the point still stands since, if needed as an emergency response to the environmental crisis, which our so often lauded intelligence allowed us to be led into, it will be part of another frantic effort to cure what could have been prevented. Moreover, it is ironic that artificial photosynthesis would, in and of itself, be hailed for the achievement it represents – yet from a broader perspective, we would have artificially re-created, at great expense, inferior examples of what we continue to cut down! More importantly, naturally photosynthetic organisms fulfil numerous other functions which maintain our life-support systems, probably including some we have not yet imagined, let alone discovered.

Research almost exclusively confirms the superiority of nature's processes to ours and that we are absolutely dependent on those natural processes – without question, demur or debate. In addition to being the source of our air, water and food, all our facilities, no matter how seemingly sophisticated, are standing directly upon the ever weakening and reducing foundation of the natural environment. As we remove elements in the chain of connections the breakdown of natural systems occurs more extensively and rapidly. For all our supposed sophistication, we can be reduced to savages (but sadly not noble ones) in a few turns of the earth.

Technology and science, unconstrained by selective funding and political / corporate influence, would be recommending a return to natural practices and processes and guiding us how best to achieve this. However, current circumstances mean that some scientists, also dependent on employment trends and funding, have been largely compelled to either stand idly by while nature is abused, or actually contribute to poisoning, damaging and destroying it.

...of Contaminated Agriculture growing more than Contaminated Food

If we poison our roots, all the stems, branches and leaves that grow from them can only carry the poison – from the root to the fruit. Similarly, when society, physically, culturally or spiritually, ingests poisons and adopts a diet of too much fat, sugar and salt with too little fibre, nutrition and trace elements, the imbalances will manifest in commerce, politics, science, art, architecture etc. just as they have in agriculture and medicine as referred to in Appendix II. Hence society as a whole is affected, which then influences the offspring of that society. Like physical food, cultural 'junk food' restricts taste, blunts discernment and promotes uniformity (just like the mono-crops of agribusiness), reducing variety and stability. Media is a worrying example, since it not only exhibits the symptoms itself but also has a powerful influence on the rest of society. Just as the predominance of fast food is a symptom of society's malaise, the majority of press or television menu items offer little nutrition and too much 'fat', 'sugar' and 'salt'; the sterilised contents are packaged in lightweight containers called papers or programmes. Feeding society a constant diet of media junk food dulls its faculties and makes it stodgy and prone to all manner of health problems, from localised boils of concentrated poison to obesity and systemic heart disease.

Since the recent and long overdue wake-up to the dangers of global warming, the media has (in the U.K. at least) added some healthier ingredients to their usual menus. Yet, even the new 'healthier' nutrition falls far short of what is required in quality and quantity if we are to thoroughly 'de-toxify' ourselves and our societies while ensuring healthy growth and practices henceforth. What there is of the healthier television diet is still only an extra 'choice'. A disembodied voice between programmes invites viewers to select between global health, if not survival, and a majority of trivia or junk. Some snippets heard include a reference to a programme featuring melting ice and permafrost 'that threaten us all' spoken with a syrupy tone of anticipated self-indulgent entertainment, as if introducing a film of fiction, as was another invitation to see a programme on whether or not we can 'save the planet'. Mmmm, what shall we choose? Especially since the planet is not under threat – only our tenancy on it. The scenario in which viewers choose comedy or melodrama in preference to the protection of life itself is almost beyond belief but is part of the modern world's distorted imbalances and evidence that the artificial world made by modern society – the media-moulded world inside the television – has become more 'real' than the real world. For some, the world is in the television, whilst at least some others remember that the television is in the world. For those in the former category, television has become part and parcel of the system of 'dumbing-down' and 'economies' with truth during decades of selective silence, which has made major contributions to the demise of the natural world (as well as, of course, numerous other problems).

Those who live in the television world will, in its defence and in the context of the environment, refer to the public 'awareness' of nature that the television has achieved and cite popular wildlife documentaries with their stunning images and claim these have 'raised awareness' of conservation and environmentalism. In themselves, perhaps so, but contemporaneously with their transmission, natural habitats suffered the greatest man-made devastation. There is no value to awareness that does not result in remedial action – which is rarely promoted, organised or featured on television. As written in a LifeForce newsletter; we are constantly told of the fire but not where the extinguishers are. Some symptoms (e.g. poaching, timber theft) are occasionally covered but the root causes never are nor, of course, the media's own cultural and socio-economic causal connections and unmet responsibilities. Being 'politically correct' or 'playing it safe' with regard to the environment is currently the most dangerous thing to do.

Without particular reference to wildlife documentaries, it could still be claimed that television has brought more of the world to its audiences than most would see for themselves and has therefore expanded viewers' perceptions. There is truth in this but the television also distances us from the world, since, beyond entertainment, it tells us of all the disasters and tragedies we can personally do little or nothing about and that, if anything can, it must be governments and / or massive corporations and / or organisations wielding elaborate technology. The individual is made to seem helpless because the television world, and the viewers' own real world, are rarely allowed to overlap in any meaningful way that could bring significant beneficial change for society. The individual's role in the world beyond their own backyard has generally been confined to the option of whether or not to donate money to 'organisations' in the world within television (supposedly the bigger the organisation the better, an impression fostered by 'big names' receiving most airtime, because most airtime make names 'big'). A trivial but telling example, and one consistent with the current theme of obesity, was a national news bulletin aired in the U.K. in 2007 reporting that, in a particular region, there was insufficient money to provide facilities and training to help obese people lose weight! Unless suffering from a medical condition, what about exercising more and eating less fatty, sugary and starchy food? The former is free and the latter would actually save money! Even though we have noted obesity in many forms as a characteristic of our current culture, and that our culture influences us in multiple subtle and not so subtle ways, we need not be slaves to it and by correctly exercising our individual choices we not only help ourselves but also our societies. The size and weight of society's problems have been reduced to the one-dimensional falsehood that 'if only we had enough money, we could cure all our problems'. Whereas if we cured our problems, we would realise that we have more than enough money.

Considering size, weight and individuals brings to mind Sir Kenneth Clark's comments on some early Renaissance architecture. The examples he considers are scaled in proportion to normal human capacities, he says their size and weight do not seem to crush the viewer but make each aware of their own intellectual and moral powers, thereby asserting the dignity of man. Today, Clark comments, this dignity is lost but below, and in chapter V, we will see how nature in general and the tiger in particular can help us recover some of that dignity and, moreover, do so in accordance with these observations of Clark's.

Television executives see the natural world in terms of audience appeal but not, due to the modern myopia, as that which also gives them life: television executives can see the television but cannot see what's on television, just as agribusiness-men cannot see soil as the source of their food, only as a source of profit. Businesspeople who focus exclusively on material assets make the same mistake as scientists who focus exclusively on material objects – they miss the broader perspective that gives meaning and purpose to their activities.

One small but relevant irony is that in the television world, credits of recent Western films or programmes often reassure the heightened sensitivities of modern audiences that 'no animals have been harmed in the making of this film' while innumerable animals, plants and people have been harmed in the making of the modern world – to which we all contribute. How we contribute and that we, as individuals, must rapidly and extensively contribute in healthier ways will be seen in the sub-section below: 'Reflections on…personal responsibilities'. However, firstly we need to understand the context within which we make any sort of contribution.

There is a factor common to contaminated agriculture, medicine, media and many other elements of our society. The common factor is that the overwhelming majority have become businesses (or dependent on businesses) exclusively pursuing maximum profit and power. In due course, this will help us form a diagnosis and decide treatment.

...of Capitalism

'...The time – which, looking back, seems so idyllic – is gone forever when individuals or relatively small groups could be completely self-sufficient. It is only a slight exaggeration to say that mankind constitutes even now a planetary community of production and consumption...I may indicate briefly what to me constitutes the essence of the crisis of our time. It concerns the relationship of the individual to society. The individual has become more conscious than ever of his dependence upon society. But he does not experience this dependence as a positive asset, as an organic tie, as a protective force, but rather as a threat to his natural rights, or even to his economic existence. Moreover, his position in society is such that the egotistical drives of his make-up are constantly being accentuated, while his social drives, which are by nature weaker, progressively deteriorate. All human beings, whatever their position in society, are suffering from this process of deterioration. Unknowingly prisoners of their own egotism, they feel insecure, lonely, and deprived of the naïve, simple, and unsophisticated enjoyment of life. Man can find meaning in life, short and perilous as it is, only through devoting himself to society.

The economic anarchy of capitalist society as it exists today is, in my opinion, the real source of the evil...it is important to realise that the means of production – that is to say, the entire productive capacity that is needed for producing consumer goods as well as additional capital goods – may legally be, and for the most part are, the private property of individuals...

Private capital tends to become concentrated in few hands, partly because of competition among the capitalists, and partly because technological development and the increasing division of labour encourage the foundation of larger units of production at the expense of the smaller ones. The result of these developments is an oligarchy of private capital the enormous power of which cannot be effectively checked even by a democratically organized political society. This is true since the members of legislative bodies are selected by political parties, largely financed or otherwise influenced by private capitalists who, for all practical purposes, separate the electorate from the legislature. The consequence is that the representatives of the people do not in fact sufficiently protect the interests of the underprivileged sections of the population. Moreover, under existing conditions, private capitalists inevitably control, directly or indirectly, the main sources of information (press, radio, education). It is thus extremely difficult, and indeed in most cases quite impossible, for the individual citizen to come to objective conclusions and to make intelligent use of his political rights...

Production is carried on for profit, not for use. There is no provision that all those able and willing to work will always be in a position to find employment; an "army of unemployed" almost always exists. The worker is constantly in fear of losing his job... Technological progress frequently results in more unemployment rather than in an easing of the burden of work for all. The profit motive, in conjunction with competition among capitalists, is responsible for an instability in the accumulation and utilisation of capital which leads to increasingly severe depressions. Unlimited competition leads to a huge waste of labour, and to that crippling of the social conscience of individuals...the worst evil of capitalism. Our whole educational system suffers from this evil. An exaggerated competitive attitude is inculcated into the student, who is trained to worship acquisitive success as a preparation for his future career...' (B25 reprinted by kind permission of Philosophical Library, New York USA)

Since Einstein wrote this overview, television has been added to media that were familiar to him and there has been a dramatic increase in the power of corporations, including the media itself. Corporate power has not only diminished governments' abilities to control them but also grown to an extent that allows corporations to wield controlling influences over governments. Media in general are not, as is sometimes naïvely thought, services, reporting on what is most important for society, they are businesses reporting on, and influencing, events that are most important to their proprietors, in terms of sales and / or their corporate and / or political affiliations. More worryingly, these trends have now developed to scales and resultant effects that might have surprised even Einstein since the consequent damage to and dismantling of the life-support system of the planet will remove any value to the profits and power so assiduously sought. Yet the madness continues and those responsible ignore or dispute what is obvious to all thinking people, while tigers, and much more besides, teeter on the brink of oblivion.

Considering the problems produced by improperly controlled capitalism is not meant to suggest that the pendulum at the other extreme is recommended – guaranteed employment for all can be as wasteful as an army of unemployed. For example, in Mao's communist China, workers could not be fired from their 'collectives', which were often inefficient and hardly productive. Such a system is obviously open to abuse by the unscrupulous and / or lazy. Provided means of preventing this sort of parasitism are in place, the majority can generate sufficient to support genuine cases of disability or disadvantage.

Communism and capitalism could be seen as yin and yang respectively – the former being (in theory at least!) more passive, caring, supportive, sharing and giving; the latter being more active, acquisitive, aggressive and taking. As usual, neither extreme is ideal. Mussolini promised an economic system that was neither capitalism nor communism but also imposed (by violence and intimidation) a political system of fascism (well before the alliance with Hitler) with aggressive expansionist policies (e.g. Libya, Ethiopia). It may be suggested that Socialism is such a middle path but communism sees it as only a transitional stage to full communism while capitalists never agree to land, business, industry and transport all being state owned. More recently the U.K. Labour government under Blair spoke of a 'Third Way' which was, supposedly, neither capitalist nor socialist. However, that big business was allowed to create an economic crisis so severe that it threatened, and still threatens, national and international economic stability for decades to come, proved that the way actually followed was as, if not more, capitalist orientated as any that might have been followed by a government openly declaring itself supportive of capitalism.

Perhaps a 'Capcomm party' could blend democracy and some state ownership with some private enterprise. Provided both state and capitalist enterprises were carefully monitored by *independent* government agencies to guard against sloth and waste in the former and greed and excess in the latter, such an arrangement might find the balance point and, perhaps, enthusiastic endorsement and commitment from both sides. Once again, success would depend on independent government and each individual's ethical decisions. Historically, capitalism, in theory and practice, is based on selfishness while communism, in practice, is often hijacked by selfish people who take control of it. As noted above, selfishness is the root from which all poisonous and harmful growths appear.

However, regardless of this speculation, what is generally referred to as capitalism is currently the overwhelmingly dominant socio-economic system globally, and will almost certainly be so for the time remaining to the tiger, so we can confine our reviews to the environmental effects of capitalism.

...of Corporate Contamination of Government

In an ideal democracy, the government governs the community while the community, or at least the electorate, governs the government, according to the will of the majority. Let us consider some of the pressures this ideal is subject to in practice.

Government is, obviously and inevitably, beset by human inefficiency and incompetence. Unfortunately, incompetence at government level affects millions of people. G. Robert Blakey was recruited as a young lawyer in 1960's America by the then Attorney General Robert Kennedy. In a filmed interview years later he said "You just can't know how inefficient, and complicated, and inept the government is unless it's held together in some way – by the force of somebody's personality. Robert Kennedy had that and did that." Perhaps Britain's best known example was Winston Churchill whose wartime memos bearing 'action this day' had civil servants hurrying along corridors to make sure essential work was completed. Unfortunately such individuals are exceptions rather than the rule.

All these difficulties are present even when members of government are models of moral rectitude and efficiency. Yet, equally obviously, by virtue of holding positions of power, members of government run the risk of corruption, either by being subjected to it or tempted to indulge in it. Corruption is not confined to collaboration with powerful vested interests. Politicians neglecting duties and / or taking advantage of privilege (especially privileges unavailable for inspection by the electorate) also detract from the overall health of society.

Having acknowledged inevitable inefficiencies, incompetence and the potential for corruption, it has also to be acknowledged that, even if government is highly efficient, responds promptly to the needs of its citizens, and beyond reproach in terms of right and honourable conduct, government by its very nature inevitably attracts the attention of other individuals and groups within society who only want to ensure their own welfare. By their very nature, the foremost of these must be the most self-orientated, manipulative and acquisitive. They attach as leeches that, by rights, should be prevented or, at least, regularly removed. If they are not removed, these leeches represent a constant drain on and irritation to their host, gradually weakening it.

Multinational corporations represent the largest and most dangerous leeches and they have sunk their jaws deeply into governments the world over. If there were any who might have doubted the degree of independent power wielded by corporations prior to 2007, irrefutable evidence was provided by the financial crash of that year. The banks, in addition to surviving penalty free, maintained practical autonomy and their senior staff still collected, and continue to collect (even while majority-owned by the public) lucrative salary and bonus packages while, due to bankers' incompetence and greed, thousands become unemployed, businesses collapse and numerous cuts are made in public spending. The crash proved that greed and incompetence (its only root causes) have greater control over events than the institutions founded to protect us from them. In terms of consumption of natural resources and pollution, the environment (the source of all commerce and economies) has also been disastrously affected by the same greed and incompetence (particularly during the financial boom preceding the bust) and we rapidly approach an ecological crash which will make the economic crash child's play by comparison. 'Recessions' and 'depressions' lend an academic air to economic disasters, allowing them to be talked about as if they are expressions of natural laws, over which we have no control. In reality, they are the products of mismanagement and nearly always driven by commercial greed and stupidity. There have been great financial crashes prior to the 20th century (also born of inadequate government control of commercial greed), but the purpose of this section is to examine our current environmental problems which became critical during the 20th century.

Even when the economy is relatively stable, multinationals have been responsible for multiple and varied abuses of their power and position. Just three out of many possible examples follow: In China, 'guolaosi' means death from overwork, which is killing c. 600,000 people in China every year, in human 'battery farm' factories making Western consumer items. Workers have endured extremely long shifts (some of 35 hours) and bad conditions. Unions are not allowed, but spontaneous solidarity has arisen and workers have refused to continue until better conditions are provided. In response, the authorities have granted some concessions but Western corporations are protesting and lobbying the authorities, claiming concessions create a 'negative investment environment' – Newspeak for falling profits (details from The Week 21/08/10 quoting the Independent). The environmental impacts of China's industrial expansion are considered below. There was justifiable outrage at the 2010 BP oil spill in the Gulf of Mexico where every effort was made to repair the leak. For 30 million inhabitants of Nigeria's oil producing Niger Delta the equivalent oil spill has been happening every year for five decades. People have to live with dead fish and numerous other ecological imbalances, continuous gas flares illuminating the night sky and washing and cooking with oily, polluted water. These people are poor, and powerless to mount opposition or law suits. Despite being well known to the oil companies responsible, the Nigerian government and, no doubt, the governments of nations in which the oil companies have their head offices, the situation continues (details from The Week 19/06/10 quoting the New York Times). Oil companies have also arranged for the export and illegal dumping of toxic waste in areas where people are poor and powerless, causing deaths and illness for hundreds of thousands of people, birds, fish and animals (most recently reported, to this author's knowledge, in the Daily Mail newspaper of 24/07/10).

To understand some of the most harmful connections between the environment and economics, we must examine the connections between corporations and governments.

To enter into political issues is to enter a jungle far more dangerous than any natural one. However, whilst there will probably never be universal agreement over all political questions, we should all be able to agree over the importance of the environment since we all breathe air, drink water and need food, and utilise its resources for all our activities, including commerce and politics. Since our environmental supplies and / or quality of these essentials are directly affected by government policies we are forced, for our survival, to enter political jungles. Politicians mentioned below may have achieved some political successes in their careers and be due credit and appreciation for those successes. However, for our current purposes we must focus on the adverse environmental effects of governments dominated by corporate power. The information presented here is not intended to approve or disapprove of any one particular political party. As the environment is fundamental to all else, Prime Ministers and Presidents, of whatever political party, are the very people who should be most conscious of it and hold it firmly as their first priority. To the extent that they have not done so, is the extent to which they have failed in their most important duty. Failure to protect and conserve the environment makes whatever else they may have achieved mere decoration, or some contribution to the band playing on while the ship sinks.

As we proceed, it will become clear that this book cannot be promoting any political agenda, hidden or otherwise, since the most important conclusion reached will be that big business now has a more powerful, longer term and more consistent effect on our world, and our lives, than any political party, in or out of office. Indeed, collaborations between multinational corporations are so extensive, elaborate and influential that even fundamental political ideologies, supposedly identifying nations as communist or capitalist have, in comparison, been reduced to issues of secondary importance.

So, regardless of your views on particular political parties and politicians, please assess the following only from the perspective of corporate influence over government (of any political type) and its consequences for the health of the planet, yourself, your family and your tigers. Any political or economic views expressed here relate to the environment, and the principles we need to practise in order to survive ecologically and economically (the two being inseparable). This brief survey does not seek to apportion 'blame', but identify the major milestones along our route into the environmental crisis, in order that they may help us find our way back to junctions with healthier alternative directions.

Withot doubt, the most enormous milestone, visible from any perspective, is big business, which has exploited limited natural resources excessively and wastefully while polluting the surroundings and hence been responsible for large scale abuse of the environment. Obviously, governments originally failed to protect the environment from such abuse but even subsequent environmentally protective legislation has been successfully ignored or manipulated due to corporate influence over governments, either directly or via organisations such as the WTO (some details below). Corporate power has also created socio-economic conditions forcing many people, especially those in the developing nations, to fall back on any natural resources remaining in order to survive (either by using them directly or selling them) and this includes all remaining tiger habitat.

The most extensive and critical damage to the environment can be traced to the technology developed during WWII and the political and corporate systems emerging immediately after it, hence we shall confine our review to the aftermath of WWII.

Considering the latter aspects firstly, it is possible to argue that WWII rescued capitalism from certain collapse. For examples, Germany's economic depression had begun with their defeat in WWI and Britain's began in the 1920's followed in 1929 by the Wall Street Stock Exchange crash in the U.S.A. where the depression was deepest (unemployment increased from 1.5 million to 12.8 million (25% unemployment)) causing economic repercussions beyond America. President Roosevelt's policies of 1933, his 'New Deal', and public works programme helped stimulate the economy but by 1939 and the eve of WWII, unemployment was still at 14% and economists predicted permanent stagnation. It looked as though capitalism had brought itself (and many people) to ruin. It was also German capitalists who financially backed Hitler and his National Socialists, fearful of German communist parties taking (their) power in Germany (Germany's post WWI Weimar Republic had built a brief period of economic stability after the worst of their depression but the Wall Street crash adversely affected this revival).

WWII brought full employment to the U.S.A., buoyant markets and many customers, which not only revived capitalism but ensured the U.S.A. emerged from the war as the wealthiest and most powerful capitalist nation. Whilst the need to rebuild after the war offered (and later produced) an economic boom, Europe was too impoverished to be customers of the world markets that wealthy American capitalists now wanted to establish. These capitalists could also see real possibilities of Japan tending toward China's communism and of Europe tending toward Soviet communism. So the U.S. Marshall Aid Plan to Western Europe, and other subsidies to Germany and Japan, provided loans to buy American goods and establish those world markets. Hence the U.S. benefited from both the sales and the subsequent repayment of the interest-bearing loans. Much of the 'American Dream' was funded by a 'European Nightmare'.

(This situation also provides a graphic example of corporate power influencing politics. Post-war American governments protected capitalism with various covert, and not so covert, interventions in other nations to de-stabilise any regime considered potentially or actually communist. The post-war period also saw the beginning of the campaign of public conditioning that led to the excesses of McCarthy-ism and the word 'communist' becoming a term of abuse. In the interests of a balanced argument it should be noted here that U.S. president Jimmy Carter opposed a foreign policy of uninvited intervention. He also promoted a much more equitable and morally superior alternative, including demands for improved records of human rights from those countries receiving U.S. aid.)

The Stock Exchanges of Wall Street and the City of London dominated the development of post WWII world economics. Hence, having already confined our review to the post WWII period we can now further confine it to these two nations as they were the capitals of international finance during that period. The patterns of development identified are now prevalent globally.

President Roosevelt's 'New Deal' of 1933 has already been referred to and a few details about it are essential to understand developments over the subsequent decades, up to and including our own. To counteract the previous government's lack of control over the Wall Street Stock Exchange, the newly-elected president brought in legislation to prevent a repeat occurrence of the crash. A central pillar of this protective legislation was the Glass-Steagall Act which, most importantly from our perspective, prohibited banks from trading on the stock market with mortgages.

Deregulation (an extensive relaxation of President Roosevelt's and other restrictive controls, in order to create a completely 'free market') began most extensively in the U.S. with the Reagan administration (two terms 1981-1989) and in the U.K. with the Thatcher government (almost three complete terms1979-90). Immediately on taking office in 1979, the Thatcher government abolished exchange rate controls (allowing money to be made by trading currencies) and numerous other drastic reforms followed thereafter, the most important of which, from our perspective, are referred to below. In the U.S.A. in 1999 President Clinton repealed the Glass-Steagall act and allowed banks to trade on the stock market with mortgage-backed securities. This is not so much evidence of disastrous political decisions as of the influence of big business on government. People's memories are short, and while political parties alternate in office, big business remains a constant, consistent and focussed force, continually pressurising and influencing for its own financial advantage. (A positive note of early 2010 was the U.S. Obama administration considering renewed legislation in the spirit of the Glass-Steagall act to control the banks and protect citizen's savings and mortgages).

Three organisations arising from the debris of WWII supported the rapid growth of enormous conglomerates and their ability to influence the development of the 'free market' and later to monopolise 'free trade': The World Bank, the International Monetary Fund (IMF) and The World Trade Organisation (WTO). The first two were founded at the Bretton Woods conference of 1944 and the latter was formed in 1995 to replace the General Agreement on Tariffs and Trade (GATT) founded in 1948 when 23 countries agreed to reduce customs tariffs to support free trade. Due to their influence over all aspects of national economies these groups wield enormous power over most aspects of daily life for billions of people, but none are elected bodies. The World Bank and IMF have no accountability to the public at all and the WTO's national representatives are civil servants and hence faceless and nameless to the public who pay their wages (in the U.K. at least, you can make an appointment with your M.P. but you will not be able to identify the government employee who represents such power over your life at the WTO).

The policies followed by the WTO, World Bank and IMF blatantly ensure that they, and those corporations they collaborate with, retain all commercial and legal advantages while imposing on 'developing countries' constraints they avoid themselves. The World Bank and IMF help to ensure that, whatever happens politically or socially, the wealth of Western multinationals is maintained or increased. Their record includes a complete reversal of principles previously applied when it was in their financial favour to do so, and manipulating / bullying weaker developing nations into 'agreements' which benefit their Western cartel but levy a terrible cost on those nations' economies, people, environment and wildlife (appendices III and IV have details). Due to such practices, and subsidies and tariffs, trade is anything but free, and certainly not fair.

Of course, neither incompetence, nor corruption, nor global commerce, nor even multinational companies and their influence, are new. In his informative book 'How Mumbo-jumbo Conquered the World' Francis Wheen reminds us of the wealth and power of the 'multinational' East India Company and reports that the global movement of capital was greater from 1870 to 1914 than at any time since. So what is new?

...of What is New

Francis Wheen's book also refers to a 1997 report from the Institute for Policy Studies in Washington DC claiming that fifty-one of the 100 largest economies in the world were corporations while only forty-nine were countries: General Motors, with annual sales of $148 billion, exceeded the GDP of Denmark or Thailand; the Ford Motor Company was 'bigger' than Turkey; Wal-Mart was 'bigger' than Greece. While it is pointed out that these figures are misleading insofar as they compare a company's turnover with a country's GDP (which does not measure sales alone but total added value), it is also conceded that the unprecedented size and power of modern multinationals are undeniable.

In the previous sub-section, technology was cited as another critical factor featuring in the development of the modern world's environmental problems. Whether or not WWII was the saviour of capitalism, it was definitely the stimulus for developing much modern technology, which allowed the rapid growth of multinationals in terms of transport and communications. Obviously, any empire or enterprise in history utilised the latest technology and say, clippers, provided the fastest overseas travel available in the mid-nineteenth century. So, utilisation of the latest technologies is nothing new in relative terms. However, in absolute terms, there is much that is new since modern technology is allowing abilities undreamed of by the trustees of the East India Company or any other 'multinational', or empire in history. In the modern world, technology allows unprecedented speeds and scales of effect including the consumption of natural resources at a rate far exceeding their rate of generation, and interference with nature for financial profit (e.g. agribusiness, GMO). Compounding these direct effects are the side effects of modern technology since machinery, transport, communications and computers have all been environmentally devastating both in terms of the destruction of natural habitat for resources and in terms of associated toxic industrial effluent and general pollution. Hence modern multinationals have unprecedented scope and abilities to damage the life-support system for all. This is what is new, and dangerously, probably fatally, new. Previous 'multinationals' and economic patterns of globalisation have contributed to, say, the consumption of natural resources but now the speed and scale of wasteful consumption increase evermore rapidly as the final remnants of resources decrease evermore rapidly.

Despite the enormous power wielded by multinationals, the World Bank, IMF and WTO, a few aspects of socio-economics are still controlled by governments, so the media, itself an example of big business, has developed powerful influences over which political parties and individuals gain power. Modern, media-made governments make many decisions based on how they and their decisions will 'appear', be reported, affect votes or virtually any other short-term consideration rather than what is fundamentally right, good and healthy for the community at large in the long-term. This overwhelming emphasis on the short-term is a factor which has helped us into the environmental crisis but it remains a powerful influence on government policies and decisions. In contrast, media and other big businesses, with long-term agendas extending well beyond four, eight or even twelve years (comparable to one, two or three terms of political office), continue to grow their influence over governments, political procedures, the world and its citizens.

One foundation stone of society still controlled by government is law. For all their power, big business cannot completely control legislation. It can avoid it, for example, in support of big business, the WTO might claim that various aspects of environmental legislation are barriers to 'free trade', allowing them to be ignored with impunity. However, neither corporations nor the WTO can actually pass legislation and make it law. Hence, via the law of the land, governments can be, and on some occasions still are, more powerful than 'market forces' or multinationals. Therefore business recognises the value of having a presence in government which can help moderate, negate or implement laws, or gain prior knowledge of how new laws relate to trade, taxation or criminality.

In the U.K. at least, gaining a presence in government is achieved by a variety of methods, for examples: via government 'lobbyists'. At time of writing, there is no way for the public to find out who these lobbyists are, who they are lobbying or what they're lobbying for. However, ministers who lobby on behalf of big business are either paid directly and / or can take a job with that business (currently a minimum of one year) after leaving office. In addition to lobbyists there are individuals who hold public office but who may also be paid to hold a position in a company (as 'consultants' or in positions with a token title but rarely associated with any real work). Politicians also recognise the value (to themselves) of having a presence in business; some sitting on boards of directors, or being promised a lucrative position with a company on leaving public office (provided, of course, they were of some value to the company whilst in office). In various guises, corporations have been gaining far more influence over government than the majority of decent citizens making up 'democratic' nations, who have diminishing voices, and increasingly fewer options, to create healthy change via official channels. The close relationship between business and politics produces serious conflicts of interest and, via a chain of connections, adversely affects economic balances and therefore the health of society. Via direct connections between commerce and government, natural resources (including forests and jungles) are exploited with scant regard for the future, adversely affecting ecological balances and therefore the health of the planet.

The enthusiastic supporter of capitalism as fostered by Reagan and Thatcher will claim economic and technological growth during the last two decades of the 20th century, particularly in all forms of communication, which have increased productivity globally and, supposedly, brought millions of people out of poverty. The implication is that we need only continue in the same way to spread these benefits to all. It is unnecessary to refute all these claims since the premise (the economic growth, on which the others rest) is false.

In 2002, as co-director of the Center for Economic and Policy Research in Washington, D.C., Mark Weisbrot presented irrefutable evidence that world economic growth between 1980 – 2000 slowed significantly, or actually reversed, as compared to the previous 20 years and also showed that, whatever their political or economic views, no-one could deny the expanding global gulf between rich and poor. He explains how the U.S. Treasury department precipitated the Asian financial crisis of 1997. He also explains how the IMF's subsequent 'remedial' actions actually worsened the crisis, which then spread to Russia and Brazil. More faulty reasoning and / or false arguments from the IMF and World Bank are identified and, although China and India are cited by the World Bank as countries profiting from globalization, he points out that this results from their not being subjected to the globalization polices which have devastated other countries economically. (Although not referred to in Weisbrot's article, it is relevant to mention here that China, having noted the economic disasters in the 'developing world' caused by Western fiscal policies, protected itself from them by loaning significant amounts of its growing income (of mainly Western money) to America, by buying American government bonds. This, and a few other economic developments, resulted in America's economy becoming increasingly dependent on China's.) Cutting through 'free-market' or 'free-trade' jargon, Weisbrot frankly and firmly identifies the underlying self-interest of the major Western economies as the culprit and identifies a 'creditors cartel', led by the IMF, controlling international fiscal policies. Weisbrot predicted that until this cartel is broken, or its policies revised, the economic failures of 1980 – 2000 will not be reversed (J30). This 2002 prediction was spectacularly verified five years later.

Even had there been real economic growth, growth cannot continue indefinitely. "Anyone who believes exponential growth can go on forever in a finite world is either a madman or an economist." (US economist K. Boulding, quoted in the Independent newspaper). This reminds us of fundamentals: whatever economic system is adopted, nature ultimately forces us to find the balance between consumption and regeneration (or she does it for us). Another fundamental, regardless of the economic system and amount of wealth generated, is distribution of that wealth. The quality of the future for all is determined by how wealth is distributed and invested. Top priority should be ensuring the environment is protected and nurtured. If, for example, agriculture is organised on sound and sustainable practices it automatically has healthy influences on all that grows upon it (biologically, economically and socially).

Weisbrot's work also showed that the environment suffered during both rapid and slow (if not reversed) growth. So, other than replacing the current global economic systems wholesale (and this is not a possibility in the time remaining to the tiger or, perhaps, humans) what solution can there be, if the environment appears to suffer in each possible scenario?

To answer this question we need to look at the history of multinational development. As they grew in size and number they learned, unlike political bodies within nations, how to co-operate to achieve their objectives: '...multinationals have extensive participations, partnerships and joint ventures with each other...in the petroleum...chemical, rubber, plastics, paper, electronic, nuclear and service industries...the multinational companies are...the core of modern capitalism and have replaced the Western nation state as the real political power centers of the age. This transfer of power to the multinationals has caused a profound structural reformation of the entire Western system and by the late fifties was already emerging as the critical element of industrial societies.' (Charles Levinson, author of 'Vodka-Cola'. This well-informed and detailed book reveals the awesome global extent of multinationals' influence politically, militarily and socio-economically. That the current state of the world must in large part be a direct consequence of this influence is an inescapable conclusion).

Now we can answer the question. While the economies of *nations* no longer bear any direct or simple relationship to environmental conditions, the economies of *corporations* do, and it is, with few exceptions, an inversely proportional one. While corporations prosper (in the short-term), the environment is impoverished, along with millions of people, partly as a result of environmental degradation, partly as a result of imposed economic systems which suit corporations but not nations (socially or environmentally) and partly due to the actual commercial practices themselves such as, for example, land owners choosing to grow highly profitable cash crops to be sold nationally and / or internationally (e.g. tobacco, soya, palm oil) but not food for locals. Many of these local people have previously been dispossessed of the land on which they had been self-sufficient for generations, but provided with no alternative employment options. In the hope of finding employment, the majority migrate to cities where they have no option but to form or join ghettoes.

Environmental and social securities are not compatible with the exclusive pursuit of maximum profit. Very well, but there are many people who are not obsessed with material wealth and profit, so why not let those who are, get on with their obsessions? Those who are obsessed in these ways engineer themselves into positions of power, ultimately exerting great influence over the lives of millions (and not just human lives) who or which have little or no influence over anything, including factors necessary for their own survival. The influence of corporations' unhampered pursuit of their own short-term prosperity at the expense of the majority, is now global, affecting everyone and everything. This has resulted in vast social inequalities which can be seen within and between nations, and ultimately in the environment (e.g. as direct damage, pollution and, as noted above, when people are forced to fall back on basics provided by nature). Hence, nature also acts as a guide toward optimal socio-economic systems.

Unlike nations, multinationals pursue only profit, observing no historical, traditional, religious, social or moral standards. Science fiction writers often portray horrific futures in which robots without compassion or pity have taken over the world – seemingly unaware that the world has already been taken over by pitiless beings programmed with a single, exclusive, robotic quest after profit, now laying waste the Earth and causing millions of helpless humans to struggle for survival.

Tedious as these political and socio-economic realities are (one reason so few people face their responsibilities toward them), they need to be addressed in order to find the root of our environmental problems. 'Free-market fundamentalism' gives rise, through social division and environmental damage, to other equally vigorous fundamentalisms in society and, like all extremisms; they do not help us toward a healthier balance. We have to pull out these poisoned roots and re-plant with seeds of something healthy (before nature makes the changes, without reference to us).

To find the poisoned socio-economic roots, we need to be clear about what we are looking for. Are we looking for either of what media may refer to as the old rivals of capitalism and communism? No. This simplistic description glosses over some features of crucial importance:

Firstly, it implies an on-going 'debate' between capitalists and communists to decide what is best and what we want. This is similar to the GMO 'debate': both 'capitalism' and GMO proceed apace, whether or not there might be any who are debating it.

Secondly, it is debatable as to how far the systems labelled communist during the 20th century resembled the work of Marx and Engels. It would be difficult to make a convincing case that this world has ever seen 'pure communism'.

Thirdly and similarly, for all the repeated and unqualified references to the current system being 'capitalism', it is questionable whether the world has ever seen 'pure' capitalism (at least on national and international scales). The 'capitalism' currently operating via multinationals, the IMF, World Bank and WTO, is maintained by biased laws and 'agreements', laws imposed unilaterally on weaker parties, disproportionate voting allocations, hindrance disguised as help, deceit and blatant, biased use of commercial or legal force. Appendix III and Weisbrot's article both refer to instances where the IMF has behaved as both a bully and 'con-man'.

Apologists may claim these are current distortions of the capitalist system and that capitalism itself is characterised by fundamental and worthwhile principles. Perhaps so, but a brief look at practical reality reveals too many significant mismatches between theory and practice: capitalism stresses the value of competition, but in practice capitalists make every effort to achieve monopolies, including underhand methods to sabotage the competition; capitalism stresses the value of free-trade and free-markets but in practice large capitalist industries are heavily subsidised by governments using tax-payers money (long before the banking crisis), which is the very antithesis of free market trading. Capitalists also manipulate the law and politicians to favour their business, making markets anything but 'free'; when capitalism is profitable we hear of social Darwinism and 'survival of the fittest' but when big business fails through greed and incompetence, it is happy to secure its survival via tax-payers' money. (Even if, after the current crisis, banks repay the money, they are only in a position to do so by having abandoned the 'rules of the game' when it suited them. If they do repay the tax-payer's money, can we say that all is well again? Well, we need to ask all the business proprietors whose good businesses had to close down, the unemployed, and those whose houses were repossessed in the resulting economic climate, and then to consider the scale of national debt over the coming decades). Again, apologists may claim it was not for the companies' sakes but for fear of the social consequences, nationally and internationally, that big businesses were rescued. This only prompts the question why national and international financial security has been allowed to depend on private greed. Public health should not be dependent on private sickness.

This is the true success of whatever we may call the current system; that it is not only rescued by government but allowed to continue without fundamental re-adjustment. The disease is not cured but actually sustained; every effort is made to keep the host alive – and the tumour. Those who commit the most serious economic crimes possible (which lead directly to so many other types of crime, including poaching and timber theft) are paid to recover, and continue in the same way that produced the crisis they have been rescued from. Far from being the public's servant, governments are now servants of a few powerful capitalist enterprises, which can do literally as they please with total impunity. The wealthiest capitalists keep their profits (all too frequently untaxed) when business is booming but receive tax-payers money *without penalty* when their businesses fail (and since the government allows big business and its senior employees to take billions, tax free, but chases and threatens hard working and law-abiding individuals for a few pounds, the government can also be seen as a type of bully in this context). That the system continues without complete and fundamental reform and re-adjustment is perhaps the most crucial evidence that, at the level of national and international economics, 'pure capitalism' does not exist. The wealthy and powerful have engineered it such that they can win, but never lose.

'Capitalism' might be thought a better label than 'big bullies rule' but capitalism – as a formally defined system operating under one set of fair rules *applicable to all participants* – does not exist. For brevity and the purposes of this essay, the current globally dominant socio-economic system will be referred to as 'capitalism', due to there being no commonly accepted alternative, but without withdrawing the reservations just given with regard to the accuracy of this label. Finally, while dealing with definitions; if 'pure' capitalism did exist we would need to decide whether it represented an economic system or a socio-economic and political system combined, or which of these we want it to be, if any.

Without taking into account such distortions and corruptions, 'capitalism' or 'anti-capitalism' debates, movements, protests and even government policies will remain misguided at best and useless at worst. Within the current, artificially sustained form of 'capitalism' it is, yet again, imbalances which are the main problem. If differentials were not so extreme (such as enormous wealth coexisting with grinding, hopeless poverty) much good could come from the current system. A more equitable distribution of profits could bring health and wealth for all. However, the few with most wealth want to keep it, and use the power it brings to ensure they do.

In practice, this is the only 'system' there has ever been. From the beginning of human communities in so-called civilisations, regardless of labels given to their political, social and economic systems, the rich and powerful ensure the maintenance of the status quo, agreeing to change only if it increases their wealth or power. (When Gandhi was asked what he thought of Western civilisation he replied that he thought it would be a good idea. On a more positive note in a different context he also said "There is nothing to prevent us from profiting by the light that may come from the West. Only we must take care that we are not overpowered by the glamour of the West. We must not mistake the glamour for true light.") A few notable and refreshing exceptions to this pattern are referred to below in the sub-section '…on Changing the Reflections'.

However, historically or currently, as touched on above, the poisonous root of most societies' environmental, political and economic problems is greed and / or vice acquiring power and using it to bully and / or manipulate public affairs to favour private interests. We are back to individuals, since only individuals can choose greed and / or vice. It is from these roots that all the tangle of poisoned growth appears. Physical poisons in the environment are associated with mental and spiritual poisons in the humans who create them. Hence environmental (and social, political and economic) 'illnesses' are manifestations of spiritual illnesses or spiritual immaturity in individuals. Symptoms may include physical disease or general ill health in individuals and, correlated with them, violence and crime, which are the diseases and / or general ill health of societies.

Old as this pattern is, it has now reached its most comprehensive and critical phase due to its global environmental effects; including the threats to tigers and many other species. The global grip of a few conglomerates, pursing self-interest while manipulating the law and governments into positions of helpless complicity, will bring about its own downfall due its environmental consequences but, in doing so, impose a hard lesson on all of us – the guilty and the innocent. Alternatively, we can start to dismantle greed as a socio-economic 'system' and thereby remove its pernicious influence over the environment, the government and hence over the community; we can retrace our steps along our currently suicidal path. To do so we need to follow in the footsteps of American President Abraham Lincoln (1809 – 1865), first knowing where we are, and 'whither we are tending' allowing us to 'better judge what to do, and how to do it.' Hence the need, as just referred to, for each of us to educate ourselves with regard to the enormous disparities between the theory and practice of socio-economic and political systems and act accordingly – most importantly with regard to our environmental situation. The latter part of this chapter, and the next, offer practical suggestions.

…of Complete Contamination

The previous two sub-sections briefly explored the corporate acquisition of unprecedented global power – practically due to technology and politically due to their influence over government. These two factors provided some answers to the question 'What is new?' The same factors have also produced new problems of their own. While 1929 was a deep depression with widespread ramifications, it occurred before globalisation which, as we have seen, developed after WWII. The 2007 crash of closely connected global markets had the potential to cause an unprecedented global depression (and we are not out of the woods yet). The greed is the same but its effects have been magnified by globalisation.

We have also noted that the Reagan and Thatcher governments began the deregulation that sowed the seeds of corporate controlled globalisation and, as one direct consequence, the current financial and environmental crises. Prior to Reagan and Thatcher, trade unions had wielded enormous power (sometimes to achieve political objectives, which is (and was then) also harmful to the nation) and productivity had been significantly reduced by 'wild cat' strikes, often over petty disputes between individuals. So the above comments are not intended to imply approval of Trade Unions using their power to de-stabilise economies. Had history occurred differently, this section may have been warning of the power of Trade Unions (traditionally the major sponsors of the U.K. Labour Party) and government collusion with them.

Unfortunately, the pendulum swung so rapidly and violently from an excessive influence of unions to an excessive influence of capitalists, citizens did not enjoy even a brief period of balance in between. Yet, achieving and maintaining this, amongst other balances, is one of governments' most important responsibilities. In the U.S.A., President Carter had been urging restraint and conservative use of resources, looking ahead and trying to ensure future security. He counselled against extravagance and self-indulgence, also warning that people had come to be defined, not by what they did, but by what they owned. He lost the election to Reagan who promoted and promised continued consumption and indulgence. In the U.K. the Thatcher government (her

Conservative party having been significantly funded by capitalists), despite claiming neutrality toward industry, passed numerous policies and legislation to break the power of unions while allowing and encouraging capitalism to thrive and prosper, not least of which was the privatisation of numerous publicly-owned utilities.

To ensure greater independence from funding agencies and individual donors, how else might political parties be funded? Perhaps individuals or groups donating to political parties could do so through a third party which must ensure the donors remain anonymous. Any self-identification results in the donation being returned. Or, maybe, if a party has a manifesto relevant to modern society and, say, a minimum number of members, it could be funded from the public purse – which would be vastly cheaper than bailing out failed banks (a situation which would never arise since the truly independent government would control the banks' attempted excesses). These suggestions may be naïve and the reader probably has better to offer but, whatever the source, some alternative needs to be found for the excessive influence over political parties wielded by funding agencies, financial donors and sponsors.

Regardless of these suggestions and whatever the source of their funding, it is government's responsibility to have prevented (but now try to reduce the effects of) climate change; to prevent even more species extinctions; wholesale de-forestation; enforce standards of clean and conservative use of natural resources, anti-pollution laws etc. However, when political institutions are hi-jacked by corporations which profit from these activities, governments are unable to effectively protect the environment. Hence, millions of people (and the few remaining tigers… forests…); nothing less than life itself, are all adversely affected including, ultimately, the corporations themselves and we see the stupidity of such short-term practices and policies.

Did even the most capitalist orientated governments not recognise this and therefore their responsibilities toward the environmental foundation of capitalism – and all other human systems and activities? Mrs. Thatcher did consult senior scientific advisers over the environmental situation and mentioned it in various public speeches. However, no significant actions were taken and, when one looks at the period of intense consumerism she fostered, there would have been little hope for any policies that promoted restraint, conservation and careful use of resources. In the U.S.A. consumerism increased and Reagan removed the solar panels from the White House which Carter had had installed.

Consumerism in the 'free market' could only increase significantly by freeing people from financial restriction (if only artificially) so the credit culture arose and borrowing money became a good and accepted norm, in contrast to Mrs. Thatcher's proclaimed value of thrift, and previous eras when borrowing was seen as a last ditch resort, and then for necessities only, to be repaid as soon as possible. Consumerism and credit provided the freedom to get into deep debt and deeper problems, while enormously increasing the power and profits of banks and credit companies. They also promote the culture wherein status, fulfilment, happiness, sophistication become identified (falsely) with buying things. Credit, whether on the scale of individuals, or nations (via the 'creditors cartel' referred to by Weisbrot above), financially enslaves people. No doubt Mrs. Thatcher's extolling of morals and virtues such as thrift, hard work, and the industry of individuals and nations etc. was completely sincere on her part but she was mistaken if she thought the capitalists she nurtured shared her values. Her policies and legislation favoured those whose every activity worked against the values she promoted. They paid lip service to such principles to maintain favour with her but overall and over time greed grew to be the most characteristic feature of British socio-economics (and, due to the similar policies of the Reagan government, so too in America). Indeed, it was during the 1980's that the slogan 'greed is good' was coined. Whilst Satan can cite scripture for his purpose, he has no need of such subtleties when people voluntarily adopt slogans such as these. Hence we can see that economic policies spawned by close collaboration between government and big business contribute not only to environmental degradation but also to a decline in morality and values within society. The human tendency to put oneself first appears to be an inherent characteristic and rarely needs encouragement to develop. What usually do need encouragement to develop are the characteristics of sharing and giving, considering others and cultivating respect and compassion for other lives. Hence it was with great sadness and apprehension that this author heard children at school during the Thatcher government say that they understood the recommendations of her government were to rank themselves as their top, and some said only, priority in their lives.

Another of history's basic lessons is that affluence breeds decadence. Hence, any significant increase in affluence would best be accompanied by tighter controls on social behaviour, customs and etiquettes, all with increased emphasis, both within the family and in formal education, on personal conduct, manners, morality and virtue. In practice, the exact opposite occurred and the trend toward consumerism amplified what had started in the West during the 1960s, when increasing wealth and leisure was accompanied by a rejection of traditional values of behaviour, sexual fidelity, the importance of healthy marriage for the growth of healthy children, and respect for others. (This is not to totally dismiss the philosophy which arose out of the 'counter culture' hippie movement of the 1960s. 'Libertarianism' emphasised the importance of free will choices and opposed the extreme materialism of the time. However, philosophical devotees were far fewer than those who merely jettisoned traditional values, replaced them with none at all, and simply took advantage of the social trends to gratify themselves sexually and / or with drug induced self-indulgence while spreading disease and producing illegitimate children).

In summary, self-interest and self-indulgence became many people's first priorities. The 1980's promotion of consumerism added frequent and extravagant material acquisition to the other modes of self-indulgence already well under-way. Both aspects were enthusiastically endorsed by those seeing their income increase significantly; the new stock market speculators, business owners, sales executives, bankers and investors etc. In consequence, the gap between the 'haves' and 'have-nots' grew wider still and crime increased amongst the latter group; stealing what they saw no chance of ever gaining by legitimate means, or stealing to buy the drugs to which they had become addicted. Others, who could not even acquire basic necessities, did not turn to crime but to the streets and, after decades of absence, the 1980s saw beggars and the homeless return to the streets of UK and US cities.

Before being refuted by Weisbrot, as noted above, many claims of global economic prosperity had been made (usually by those enjoying personal economic prosperity). So, could apologists for, say, the Thatcher government claim that since there was wealth, however it may have been distributed, it must mean her policies were effective? Much of that 'wealth' was the same as that claimed by banks prior to the 2007 crash – loans, interest and overvalued stock i.e. wealth on paper. A significant proportion of the U.K.'s real wealth during that period, was that provided by North Sea oil, which has been a significant economic bounty for all British governments in office since its discovery. However, regardless of particular governments' influence on economic performance, there is no dispute that, given the appropriate circumstances, capitalism can create economic wealth. The dispute is usually over the distribution of that wealth and whether the majority or the minority of the population are protected by government policies and the law. The environment is teaching us (if we would pay attention), that wealth produced via improperly controlled capitalism is (like all excess and imbalance) toxic to health and life.

Vigorous consumerism, stimulating uncontrolled consumption of natural resources while minimising cost and maximising profit, must spell disaster for the environment, and hence us. For example, its emphasis on sales and profit as opposed to workmanship, means that poor quality consumer goods are purposely produced in order to guarantee future sales of replacements. This feature alone guarantees vast wastage of natural resources but increases wastage still further by disposing of whole items when one component malfunctions – even though neighbouring components are functioning perfectly well. This also erodes knowledge since mechanics and engineers are reduced to swapping 'old' units for new. Such policies make governments and corporations complicit in wastage, pollution, destruction of natural habitats and the growth of ignorance.

Commerce without morality reduces all operations and activities to one question: 'Will it sell?' Questions concerning whether it is healthy for the environment or community, or right, or proper are not even asked. Commerce also promotes consumption in order to increase sales, and is therefore the antithesis of repair, re-use, thriftiness, economy, and conservation – ironically many of the virtues promoted in Mrs. Thatcher's speeches. This emphasis on 'selling' must also promote self-indulgence in the purchaser; putting 'what I want' and 'me and my wants, my pleasures' as paramount and therefore automatically the antithesis of giving or sharing, doing without, making do, or sacrifice. Due to the growing influence of corporations, especially the media, marketing and advertising agencies which promote these trends, they become dominant, and eventually consumerism and self-indulgence characterise society, and youngsters growing up in such societies consider these values and behaviour as the norm. Apart from adverse environmental effects, an increasing self-indulgence and selfishness in general can only mean a corresponding reduction in caring for, or helping others. In such a climate, it is easier for small discourtesies and rudeness to develop, and for more serious abuse of others' rights to follow, tending to fragment societies and increase crime rates still further.

Self-indulgence or selfishness is the fundamental social sickness that breeds all others and is manifest not only in corporate voraciousness and poor government but also in individuals' selfish and ignorant behaviour, since individuals and organisations within society affect each other reciprocally. Socrates saw that good grace and manners in individuals are small but significant indicators of healthy law and order within society as a whole (B32). When these fundamental laws, representing the true health and prosperity of a community, are lost, petty laws and their amendments will multiply (after taking office in 1997 the Labour government of the U.K. introduced 4200 new criminal offences (the Independent Feb 2010)) but '…with all their doctoring they accomplish nothing except to complicate and augment their maladies. And they are always hoping that someone will recommend a panacea that will restore their health.' (B32) Dr. Johnson (1709 –

1784) also noted that 'A corrupt society has many laws' and Socrates adds that the man who speaks the truth about this, and the decline due to self-indulgence taking priority over public duty, will be hated. So this author is obviously not seeking popularity, but he is seeking a way out of the current mess for all of us since, unlike ancient Athens or any other place or time in recorded history, the global scale of our decline and its effects, as reflected to us by animals, plants and our environment, is showing us that our situation is critical and, as we have nowhere else to go, that we must solve our problems here and now.

Political policies and debates, rational analyses of society's needs and ailments, social programmes and charitable work, conducted without recognition of the critical importance of the environment, are all merely re-arranging chairs on the deck of the Titanic, which is under full commercial steam ahead, although design and construction materials are not all as they should be; legal regulations are not keeping pace with developments; those on the bridge are not completely aware of all relevant information; the environment is producing conditions not previously considered possible; warnings are being ignored; there are too few lookouts; binoculars are available but not in the crow's nest and; in the event of a disaster, there is inadequate safety equipment for all passengers. 'Passengers' on Earth could make constructive contributions to the situation but choose to live in their own miniature and temporarily comfortable world while ignoring the real world around them. Make no mistake: nature is warning us for the last time to change our course, before she changes it for us. If you feel secure because you have money in the bank, or a pension to come, or know his Lordship, or the minister, or the butcher, baker or candlestick maker, know also what those poor souls sinking with the Titanic came to know too late: when nature overrules man's arrogance, money and contacts mean nothing.

Lest any reader be troubled as to how and where their views might relate to these issues, let us establish an absolute reference point: Nature. For whatever political debates may be had, for all the number and enormity of problems, for all the difficulty of finding accurate information and knowing who or what to believe: whatever system or systems are running the world, they must be seriously flawed because far too much of life on Earth is dying. Whatever one's own position in political and commercial jungles may be, a brief look at nature's jungles will confirm the situation – and not just jungles: in addition to tigers and numerous other animals being pushed to extinction, the oceans are being emptied of fish and mammals. Resources are plundered without thought for the future while the air, water and soil are laden with toxins. From the depths of the ocean to the edge of the atmosphere, man's activities are bringing degradation, damage and death to the natural systems that support life, including our own. There's the truth. There's the guide. There's the problem and there's the challenge. The recommendations in this book only promote health and life. By caring for nature, she will gradually teach us something of truth, independently of human selections or corruptions of it. By solving our environmental problems we'll be solving much more besides, since any human activities modelled on nature will be healthy new growth. (Please note that the contentious, 'debatable' issue of global warming has not even been mentioned. We might even debate that the debate is itself another smoke screen to obscure the real situation). Nothing else compares with the environment in importance, although nuclear energy is a close second – both civil and military.

Military budgets, whether for nuclear or conventional weaponry, and other aspects of 'defence', are enormous, and translate into enormous profits for manufacturers, highlighting a particularly dangerous form of corporate contamination of government. The enormous financial resources being allocated to the American military and the resulting social ills were noted and warned against by Einstein in 1950 (then a U.S. citizen) referring to the 'mechanistic, technical-military psychological attitude' and its inevitable consequences domestically and for foreign policy. He spoke of supervision of the loyalty of citizens, an increasingly conspicuous police force, indoctrination of people by radio, press and schools and the growing restrictions on information available to the public. The trend obviously continued in the wrong direction since, on leaving the White House in 1961, President Eisenhower felt it necessary to warn of the dangers of what he called the 'military-industrial complex' and the need to guard against its influence (Francis Wheen (B74) points out that Eisenhower's original phrase was the 'military-industrial-congressional' complex and notes the mutual interdependence of the three). This warning was also ignored. Moreover, 'military-industrial-political' complexes are no longer confined to America.

Whatever form of government is in office, industry must obviously be a feature of any modern society and, even if all corrupt, criminal or merely inappropriate effects of corporations on governments could be removed, it is true that governments have to take notice of corporations since they are now so large they have direct and politically relevant effects on employment, GDP and socio-economics in general. So governments are compelled to listen to corporations but, due to factors touched on above, they are now being dictated to, and nation states are becoming subservient to a few enormous conglomerates in the processes and procedures of globalisation.

The dominance of commercial globalisation can be reversed by its opposite – 'localisation'. Whilst this could eventually be applied to all aspects of economic life, agriculture should be the first priority. Agribusiness could be dismantled in favour of a return to more localised organic farms and to growing our own food in gardens and allotments. In addition to the benefits of locally grown, fresher foods, it may also be to our benefit to return to more seasonal foods, which probably had exactly what we require to suit our bodies to the season, so we would also gain in health and save money on medicine. In Jonathan Swift's novel 'Gulliver's Travels' the advanced and enlightened, yet simple beings, the 'Houyhnhnms' are bewildered by Gulliver's accounts of human behaviour in general. Among a variety of absurdities, Gulliver describes the culinary requirements of the wealthy classes amongst humans: 'I enumerated as many sorts (*of costly meats*) as came into my head, with the various methods of dressing them, which could not be done without sending vessels by sea to every part of the world, as well for liquors to drink, as for sauces, and innumerable other conveniences. I assured him that this whole globe of earth must be at least three times gone round, before one of our better females…could get her breakfast or a cup to put it in.' The world is still 'gone round' three times for that lady's breakfast but now we also manage to simultaneously burn tonnes of aviation fuel. In addition to transporting vast quantities of food internationally by air and sea, we unnecessarily deplete irreplaceable natural resources to grow it where nature would not normally allow it. If it really were so desirable to have all choices of food all year round, it would make more environmental sense to simply store and use home grown produce until the growing season returned. Even within nations, food is harvested or picked in one area, driven hundreds of miles to be processed in another, and then driven back hundreds of miles to be sold in the original geographical area. These absurd, and ultimately dangerous situations are produced by one criterion – an affirmative answer to the question 'Will it sell?'

Consider that in the U.K. (not that this trend is restricted to one nation) at the beginning of the 20th century there were hundreds, if not thousands, of places where one could buy fresh green groceries; the total probably being in four figures or more. At the end of the century four or five giant businesses account for the vast majority of sales. These retailers are therefore able to wield enormous power over what and how food is grown, and how and where it is distributed. They also maintain close links with agribusiness giants for their mutual financial benefit.

The same trend is found in politics and, for example, E.U. bureaucracy exhibits an ever-increasing centralisation of power, along with ever-decreasing accountability. The overall effect of too much power concentrating into too few hands produces the world we have, with the majority hardly able to survive while a minority exist in a brief, luxurious bubble blown out of fossil fuels, filled with gadgets. The principle and practice of what leads to globalisation can be stopped and reversed – if not by the disasters we are inviting – by 'localisation'. Localisation as a concept harmonises with Schumacher's concept of 'small is beautiful' (B59) and the philosophy and practices of his 'intermediate technology', particularly those concerned with providing people with the opportunity to work themselves out of poverty.

As alternatives become available, re-adjustments could be gradual, according to people's needs and socio-economic conditions. For those products and services that must, for the time being, remain centralised, it is surely not beyond the wit of man to devise a system of monopoly controls, management structures and taxation to prevent power and profits continually concentrating into fewer and fewer hands, as they do at present. The reader will know that some legislation affecting, for example, monopolies and mergers has been passed, at least in the U.K., but it has obviously not prevented the globalisation we see going on around us for reasons already discussed – those in power ensure as much by avoidance or manipulation of the law.

Allowing all profits to be drained out of communities and nations into a few companies produces the obese corporations currently dominating and damaging natural habitats, while their localised workers struggle to survive. Should not substantial proportions of profits be invested, by law, in those communities local to, and providing the labour for, the operation of those units? Other features of 'localisation' appear below in their appropriate contexts.

So, in summary and whatever one's political affiliations might be, it is apparent to all that while principled democratic processes are subject to

- loss of power
- competition rather than collaboration between political parties
- short-term agendas
- manipulation by the media

big business has no principle other than profit and

- grows in power
- practises collaboration
- plans according to long-term agendas and
- uses the media, which is itself big business.

Due to competition in finite markets and extensive market research, corporations represent finely focussed forces. We need governments with an independent, equal (or even more vigorous) single-minded determination to control them and enforce policies beneficial for the community in the long-term (and there can be no debates over what is beneficial when clean air, water and food grown in healthy soil are all seriously threatened). The abuse of the majority for the benefit of the minority who wield power has been with us since the world began but now, due to its environmental effects, unless we choose to change it, it will be the reason it ends. 'The end of the world is nigh' is no longer a message confined to 'sandwich board prophets' on street corners, it is now a probability, due to 'management board profits', and is backed by scientific evidence and well-informed common sense.

Consideration of the most important of natural resources, and some of the most dominant corporations, leads us to soil and oil.

...of Moving 'from Soil to Oil'
(Capra quoting farmer Wes Jackson in appendix II)

State funding for any significant attempts to find clean alternatives to fossil fuels have been (obviously!) negligible and one wonders to what extent corporate interests have played a part in such laxity. Those alternative, environmentally-friendly energy options we do have are mostly due to a precious, but all too few, private investors and researchers. For decades, oil companies have been, and still are, rich and powerful enough to have maintained their power and wealth *and* developed alternative, environmentally-friendly options for their customers, to ensure the planet's, and, hence, their own company's, future health. Yet throughout the latter part of the 20th century, by which time their products' polluting and poisonous environmental effects were well known, their decision makers chose to stick with these products.

Shakespeare's lines on lust of the flesh apply equally to lust for cash:

> What win I if I gain the thing I seek?
> A dream, a breath, a froth of fleeting joy.
> Who buys a minute's mirth to wail a week
> Or sells eternity to get a toy?
> For one sweet grape who will the vine destroy?

(The Rape of Lucrece)

Recent, slick advertisements from oil companies will tell you how their scientists are investigating solar or other natural energies, or carbon capture, with an eye to all our futures. Why was not such foresight employed decades ago? With the resources available to companies of their size they could have been among the vanguards of society, if only to safeguard their own future. Even at this eleventh hour, as those in the industry have remarked, there is approximately one trillion barrels of oil left in the world and if, on average, each sells at $100 a barrel, that's 100 trillion dollars of business remaining – which the oil companies still want and plan to get. From their perspective, their research into alternatives is advance planning for when the oil runs out. However, like so many others, they plan without considering nature / the environment. It is possible, if not probable that, by the time the oil runs out, suitable infrastructure for markets, maybe civilisation or even large societies will no longer exist, due in large part to their guarding their poisonous product for so long and scraping the last $100 trillion from the bottom of the barrel. Yes, members of Greenpeace or Friends of the Earth may now be invited to sit at some meetings of some oil companies but this and other measures are all fickle and pathetically late, while global warming is currently irreversible and right on time. Yes, attitudes are changing and some level of appropriate education and responsibility is gradually appearing amongst corporate decision-makers and all this is positive – just don't be lulled into a false sense of security by advertisements telling you that they're responding promptly to 'global' problems and dynamically directing their scientists to find philanthropic solutions.

Big business in general, including some oil companies, have not only neglected (for decades) to incorporate environmentally-friendly, clean alternatives as part of current and future business strategies, but they have also directly de-railed environmentally-friendly developments of others which represented competition. For example, General Motors (GM) bought the trolley car system in Los Angeles and destroyed it. After GM's R&D department produced both solar powered and electric vehicles, the Air Resources Board of the State of California devised legislation favouring the production of motor vehicles with zero emissions and GM began to produce electric cars commercially during the last decade of the 20th century. However, there are, obviously, close links between the oil industry and car manufacturers and so, soon after their launch and via a range of covert strategies, GM ensured poor sales of electric cars and ultimately opposed legislation by suing the Air Resources Board, supported by other vehicle manufacturers and, incredibly (until we remember the connections this chapter has been considering), the Federal government! Before the decade was out, GM's remaining electric cars had been decommissioned and destroyed. It is difficult to establish the exact details of allegations that oil companies bought the patents for newly invented clean fuels (not derived from oil) and then binned those patents, so we shall not include this example as 'evidence'. The few examples just cited are in the public domain. What don't we know about? We might be tempted to say 'anyone's guess' but actually it doesn't have to be a guess, anyone who bothers to look can see the effects all around the world and they're of the most worrying kind possible. Once again, nature is our reliable guide.

Ross Gelbspan, co-recipient of the Pulitzer Prize and author of two books on climate change (B29), recorded his personal reflections on the Montreal Summit of 2005 regarding carbon emissions: '…The range of emotions one encounters in Montreal is as varied as the morass of languages, costumes and street-theater performances.

The only emotion conspicuously absent here is courage.

People will leave here amidst a flurry of self-congratulatory handshakes and hugs. But as the frosty glitter of the Montreal moment melts into memory it will leave a sodden legacy of historical cowardice.

What the delegates will not acknowledge is their own arrogance: their assumption that the planet's operating systems will obey the open-ended timetable of their own procrastination rather than nature's immutable deadline.

There is another aspect to their denial. They pretend that with enough patience and understanding, they will succeed in bringing the world's largest carbon emitter (U.S.A.) in line with the rest of the world to address this unprecedented global threat.

They will not. In the U.S., the White House has become the east coast branch office of Exxon Mobil and Peabody coal – and climate change has become the pre-eminent case study of the contamination of politics by money.

What is missing from all these discussions is the sense of desperation and helplessness that is shared by all of us who are shaken by each new terrifying impact of our increasingly inflamed atmosphere.

When Tony Blair and Margaret Beckett wax optimistic over the potential of a new framework, they ignore ten long years of failed negotiations. U.S. negotiator Harlan Watson proclaims that America has done more to solve the climate crisis than most of the world's governments. Does he really believe nature can be finessed by a public relations scam?

Not far from Montreal, glaciers are melting, deep oceans are heating, violent weather is increasing, the timing of the seasons is changing and all over the world, birds, plants, insects, fish, animals and whole ecosystems are migrating toward the poles in search of temperature stability.

All because the world's diplomats are too cowardly to take on an American administration whose climate and energy policies are dictated by coal and oil executives -- men who, for their part, value their companies' quarterly earnings more than their own children.

There was a hopeful moment, not long before the Protocol was ratified, when officials from France, Switzerland and Canada confided how they would deal with their outlaw ally after Kyoto took effect. They were planning to sue the U.S. under the World Trade Organization on the ground that the WTO prohibits countries from subsidizing their products. Since the rest of the industrial world would be drawing down emissions according to the Kyoto schedule, they planned to charge the U.S. with "carbon subsidizing" its products – and bring suit within the WTO to impose prohibitively stiff taxes on U.S. exports.

That conversation, which took place more than a year ago, provided some of us a badly needed moment of hope. Almost as much hope as the prospect of all the nations of the world casting off the albatross of outdated nationalism and joining together in a common global project to rewire the planet with clean energy – and, in the process, creating a far wealthier, far more equitable and infinitely more secure world.

But the temporizing in Montreal has submerged that hope – even more quickly than the rising Pacific is submerging island nations.

To be sure, there is glitter in Montreal – and a sense of great moment.

But where, after all, is the will? Who, among the nations of the world, will call to account the real criminals against humanity? Where can one find people with the courage to put a stop to the carbon lobby and their political handmaidens who are dragging the rest of us straight to the bottom of climate hell?

Where, in this world, is the vision? And, absent the vision, where, in this world, is the rage?'
(reprinted by kind permission of Ross Gelbspan)

The poet Dylan Thomas told us to rage against the dying of the light but currently, as Ross Gelbspan reports, there are, collectively speaking, no raging, no heroes and no brave new world – only a cowardly, dying, one. In this author's experience it truly is cowardice that prevents some people facing the environmental crisis and all it bodes. Of course, it *is* frightening to contemplate, but will not go away because we ignore it. We need to remember Mark Twain's advice that courage is not absence of fear but mastery of fear. Characters, and ecosystems, decay from the top down and so, as the light is dying, our tigers are disappearing into night. Soon much else will follow, lest we decide to be a braver new world. There may even be bravery in recognising our collective immaturity; the bravery to recognise, admit that, collectively, we act like children in a playground: There are various sub-groups, most of whom can't or don't want to tackle the physical or economic bullies and just hope to survive. Few dare challenge the bigger, stronger ones but some may try to ingratiate themselves, hoping for personal advantage or at least safety. Some show off their toys and technologies for swapping or selling, while others swagger around with the biggest guns and bombs. Very few have the compassion or maturity to appreciate the food and security they all enjoy and receive from their mother – nature. Too intent on self and play, most of us are not listening to Mother Nature, or her warnings for our benefit. It looks like only a smart slap will get us to re-assess our priorities.

Some of us share Mother Nature's anger, but anger may seem at odds with the detachment associated with self-control and the Eastern disciplines of yoga and meditation referred to below and in the next chapter. The majority of sages throughout history warn of the dangers of anger. When examined, the advice of the sages refers to dangers arising from emotion overriding reason, from anger taking control. (A balance between extremes of behaviour was recommended by Aristotle who referred to the mean, a mid-way position between two extremes – each of which is a vice. For examples, with regard to anger, extremes are to be either irascible or spiritless, and gentleness is the ideal point between them. With regard to money, extremes are either extravagance or stinginess, with generosity at the mid-way position. Courage is the ideal between the extremes of foolhardiness and cowardice). In the context of this book, if not Eastern disciplines, the essential elements that allow anger and detachment to co-exist is, again, balance, and the self-control to maintain it. Detachment does not mean indifference. If one controls one's anger, its energy can be channelled into constructive, not destructive, uses (constructive uses are suggested in the next chapter). 'Temperate anger well becomes the wise' (Philemon 370 – 260 B.C. Athenian poet).

(Yet, could 'destructive' not be worthwhile? Would not the 'destruction' of multinationals as global giants seem to be beneficial for all (including the staff of multinationals)? If multinationals' activities, processes and products are adjusted to be environmentally-friendly and ethical; if they are compelled to abide by the law and prevented from influencing politicians; if they pay their taxes; if their corporate structure is revised to prevent too much power concentrating into too few hands, then business may continue as normal, not in the abnormal, grotesquely excessive ways they have to date. To be controlled is not to be destroyed – a concept valid in both spiritual and commercial contexts).

That our very survival is threatened by greed and stupidity, uncontrolled by the people paid to protect us from them, is a valid stimulus to anger (if you're not angry about this, what would make you angry?) By practising self-control you may remain detached (in the sense that you do not succumb to the emotion and either suffer impotent internal rage or physically attack multinationals' premises or people) and take peaceful action to directly affect multinational corporations. For example, you may deny them your money, and persuade others to do the same.

The enormous power of this option is explored more fully below and in the following chapter (some practical suggestions under the sub-section 'You can make a difference'). A few suggestions will suffice for now to illustrate the point: denying our money, for example, to oil companies, is extremely difficult in today's society, due to them engineering our dependence on their products, and the diversity of their influence, investments and businesses. However, the accumulation of sufficient individual actions can have cumulative beneficial effects e.g. eating organic food reduces the market for the pesticides and herbicides derived from oil (and is full of other benefits for you and the environment). In addition, acquiring alternative forms of household energy (e.g. solar, wind, geothermal – obviously, supplied by companies not owned by oil companies! It is also worth investigating the 'green tariffs' now available from energy companies); minimising or eliminating plastic from your life; identifying other capital investments of oil companies and not giving them your custom or making investments with them, all help to push the balance in the right direction and, collectively, will stimulate new options, unavailable at present due to insufficient people taking these simple preliminary actions. With regard to motoring, hybrid or, better still, electric cars are becoming more easily available. (If this is not feasible or desirable, drivers of conventional cars can donate to organisations (which provide personal carbon emissions calculators on their websites) to fund projects absorbing or reducing carbon such that they personally become 'carbon neutral' (admittedly this does not always directly impact on oil companies, but it does help the general trend toward healthier and sustainable living, while we think of other ways to control corporations)). Where multinationals have abused the environment or people, such as for example, illegally dumping toxic waste (even if thousands of miles away), you may also take action by supporting NGO's which either challenge them (e.g. Friends of the Earth and Greenpeace) and / or try to alleviate the consequent human suffering or environmental damage. If such an option is not available, you can practice environmental welfare and acts of charity locally – since all things are connected. This is a sort of spiritual version of the practical slogan 'Think globally, act locally' (various people are credited with its first use but perhaps a number of people did so independently as the insight occurred separately in response to environmental developments. Perhaps many who thought and spoke it never had a public audience as did those who are currently considered to be its author). This insightful phrase is referred to with regard to practical environmental actions in the next chapter.

While exercising these options in how we spend our money we may also practise moderation in all aspects of our lives. Even though, on global scales, each person's individual share seems insignificant, the recent social emphasis on excess, and each individual's responses to it, has had adverse global effects. By the same principle, each individual's emphasis on moderation will, ultimately, also have global effects – but beneficially so.

Above we looked at Blake's reference to the 'tigers of wrath' and a sceptic may point out that the line preceding this in Blake's 'Marriage of Heaven and Hell' is 'The road of excess leads to the palace of wisdom', whereas this book is suggesting balance or optimum as our wisest option. Yet there is no disagreement since Blake was saying that it is by experiencing excess that one realises one's folly and, by rejecting it, finds wisdom. Excess is experienced as part of the journey (the road) but on arrival at wisdom, one wants to stay (the palace). Spiritual development for a corporation only has validity in terms of the spiritual development of its human personnel. Usually the people deciding corporate policy are exclusively acquisitive, and even if some did balk at the never-ending pursuit of 'more', there are others ready to replace them. Moreover, most corporations are driven by shareholders demanding maximum share price and dividends, and so the combined effects are that corporations never learn wisdom from excess. The corporation never arrives; only takes more roads to excess.

We now see another aspect of wisdom which, along with foresight, includes right action (one of the eightfold paths of Buddhism). Without right action, wisdom has no more value than ignorance. It actually has less value: to live is to be compelled to act. If the wise fail to act in accordance with their knowledge and wisdom and, in this context, see approaching disaster but do nothing to help prevent it, they commit a worse offence than ignorance.

We also need to act at the right time (environmentally speaking – now!) and, as individuals, we have to act while we still have some youth and the necessary energy. 'He lacked the wisdom, and the only way for him to get it was to buy it with Youth, and when wisdom was his, Youth would have been spent in buying it.' (Jack London. Short Story: A Piece of Steak). Just as with youth and wisdom, many of our attributes are inversely related over time. The ideal position is to have some of both (another manifestation of balance). Hence middle-aged people offer some of the best chances for worthwhile change and / or to guide the energies of the young. This is lent further justification since many middle-aged people are parents and owe as much to their children.

With regard to what we can do as individuals, many suggestions are made in the next chapter, which include and elaborate on how selective spending can be a powerful stimulus for change. Demonstrate and protest peacefully if you wish, but the decision makers make their decisions regardless of you because they have the power to do so. As we have begun to see, and will see more clearly by the end of chapter V, it is possible, if not probable, that you contribute to that power; that, in effect, you pay them to ignore you, by not being selective in your spending. If you, and many others like you, reduce their profits sufficiently, they will listen to you. In fact, they'll do more than listen – they'll jump through hoops; save forests and tigers; find clean, alternative sources of energy; practise ethical trading and anything else humanly possible, because money is all they understand.

What if they now see our strategy? What if they adjust their values and priorities voluntarily? Good! The same purpose is achieved. When environmentally-friendly and ethical paths are followed, all lead to one and the same place – a healthy environment. Protecting nature and behaving ethically protects all, including those who are doing neither (obviously, we must ensure adequate checks on claims to be ethical and environmentally-friendly, which are where the law and the media could be so valuable).

Once we have secured our life-support system we can educate and develop those people who can see money but not sense. If waxing a little lyrically will be excused: those who still insist on greed, self and stupidity will be on view behind their own bars in their own zoo, where children can be taken to see such dangerous creatures, being told that if these creatures were ever allowed to roam freely they would turn our beautiful world into a poisoned and poisonous dustbin of commercial debris, just so that they had bigger, better and shinier toys than anyone else, and kill us all in the process. Cages will be empty of animals since we will be able to see them in their natural environment – in our brave new world, where such adventures will be part of a full and healthy education extending throughout one's whole life. If we ever achieve the maturity to establish such a society we will have freed ourselves from at least some of our cages of questions as referred to at the opening of this chapter, since we will have identified and tamed some of our inner tigers.

Society could let all big business, oil companies and otherwise, try to maximise profit by whatever means – provided we were sure of government to legislate appropriately and effectively; and of its agencies to actively monitor and protect us from those who would try to ignore or manipulate the law. We are, however, far from such a society. Taking just one example to illustrate: Greenpeace activists have in the past blocked effluent pipes from giant chemical companies to draw attention to the fact that the company was breaking the law on the toxicity and quantities of the effluent. Embarrassed at the exposé (if not the failure of official law enforcement?) the government is compelled to prosecute and fine the company. Justice done, nature and the community protected? The fines have been so small (relatively speaking) that the company was able to pay them while continuing to pump out the same effluent. Business and government remain in collusion while the media moves on and all is forgotten. However, nature does not forget and our compensation bill – impossible to meet with money – grows.

When one considers the scope of corporate influence and political failure, and in consequence, millions of lives condemned to grinding poverty and all that goes with it such as ill health, crime, innumerable personal tragedies, the disappearance of tigers and damage to our environment (the basis of all other human activities) it brings to mind Steinbeck's lines: 'There is a crime here that goes beyond denunciation. There is a sorrow here that weeping cannot symbolize. There is a failure here that topples all our success.' (B66 reprinted by kind permission of the Penguin Group)

...of New Environmental Legislation?

Despite all of the above socio-economic factors, are not governments now facing their responsibilities to environmental problems?

One response of recent governments' awakening to climate change has been the increased use of bio-fuels, but this has resulted in governments sponsoring the clear-cutting of mature forests to plant mono-crops of species providing bio-fuel! Politicians want to be able to say they're 'doing something' about global warming, the current environmental hot topic. Focussing only on carbon dioxide and not really understanding, or even being aware of nature's interconnections, one of the most important and beneficial natural features remaining – mature forests – are destroyed as part of supposedly remedial measures, by those who have allowed us to be put in peril in the first place. Moreover, deforestation is itself a major factor contributing to climate change. Governments' solutions are short-term – to solve problems produced by short-term policies. When not being clear cut for bio-fuel projects, forests are (despite existing protective legislation) still being clear cut for financial profit. Companies logging rainforests (particularly in S. America) have been implicated in the murders of people trying to protect the remaining trees. No government agencies have been successful in indicting, let alone convicting, those responsible. Business continues, unimpeded and unaffected by the law.

Forests, amongst other essential functions (please see next chapter), hold the water table in the land. This leads us to another set of government responsibilities, also as yet, unmet. Demand for freshwater is increasing (due to increasing populations and the increasing affluence of some of those populations) but planetary supplies are coming under threat since, amongst other environmental problems, rising sea levels are contaminating some freshwater supplies with salt water, while climate change is predicted to increase droughts (higher temperatures increase evaporation from the earth). Freshwater supplies subject to human use suffer high degrees of wastage and can be subject to contamination by faulty waste disposal, medical and industrial pollutants and fertiliser run-off. As supplies become limited costs will rise and, inevitably, the poor will be most vulnerable as well as, of course, plants and animals. Depending on the degree of water scarcity, starvation, disease, political instability and armed conflict can follow. Professor Peter Rogers is a senior adviser to the Global Water Partnership. He reports that, to a great extent, technologies and policy tools that can prevent a major water crisis already exist but that action is needed now from governments to agree and implement plans to avoid disaster for millions of people all around the world. (J25). While measures to address global warming are attempts to cure problems that could have been prevented, we still have a chance to prevent further serious problems; in this case a dangerous depletion of freshwater, but these opportunities are, at least at time of writing, still being ignored.

Freshwater for human populations does provide at least one positive example and one which also illustrates principles this book is attempting to emphasise and recommend – addressing causes and not effects, following nature's patterns, and the rejection of great financial expenditure as the only answer to our problems. New York City's supply of drinking water is piped from the Catskill Mountains many miles north of the city. During the early nineties, it was warned that, due to growing human activity and pollution in the mountains a £4bn water purification plant would have to be built. Instead, the authorities decided to purchase land in the Catskill region and persuaded local farmers to adopt more environmentally-friendly practices. Much money was saved and more importantly, clean water continued, courtesy of Mother Nature Inc. This Telegraph newspaper report was referred to in 'The Week' magazine (12/06/10), which also referred, in the same article, to a UN report which had tried to cost the services provided by nature, and arrived at a figure of £40 trillion. It is hoped that this may make some impression on those powerful decision makers who only understand money as a measure of value. It is also hoped that the exercise itself will be seen as indicative of the current social sickness – needing to estimate nature's services financially is one reason we are in such a dangerous situation in relation to her. What would you think of a child who economically evaluated their mother?

We have looked briefly at the most important of all nature's 'services' and human activities – agriculture, and appendix II refers to big business (mainly the oil companies) changing the basis of our existence from soil to oil. This is not only in terms of pesticides and herbicides (derivatives of oil), since Western farming, at least, is totally dependent on oil in terms of tractors, machinery and transport. Even if we ignore climate change and consider only physical supplies, oil production has peaked, or very soon will. Therefore future supply will decrease while demand will increase. This situation is unsustainable, not only in terms of being ecologically irresponsible but physically – it must and will stop, and soon. Farming has been neglected by successive governments and, whilst it is obvious that agriculture has dramatically reduced in terms of the number of people employed in it, those who remain are essential but relatively old, while too few new farmers are replacing them. Hence old knowledge and wisdom is dying with the old hands. All this has been known for decades and yet we find ourselves at the eleventh hour with no viable alternatives available. Note that all governments' specialists, scientists and advisers have proved inadequate to prevent our arrival at this point.

We have mentioned selective spending and environmental legislation as possible ways to influence our situation to everybody's benefit. A supremely dangerous development is manipulation of legislation by big business such that we are deprived of making our choices felt by selective spending or via the law. The U.S. government colluding with GM in a law suit against the state government of California has already been referred to. Other examples include the the 2010 European Union Food Supplements Directive and the U.S.A.'s Food and Drug Administration's (FDA) attempts to regulate (including bans on) natural alternatives to allopathic medicine such as minerals, herbs, homoeopathic medicines, essential oils and supplements (more details below). A few years ago (either in or around 2000) the British government's Company Law Review recognised that any environmentally harmful products and processes should be reported by the companies concerned. Such reporting was made voluntary on the part of the company directors! We have already noted the same with regard to making GMO food labelling 'voluntary' (more details below). Above Socrates reminded us that 'the true health and prosperity of a community' is enshrined within its laws and these few examples clearly illustrate the risks to our health by abuse of those laws.

...of What is News

When the law is avoided, manipulated or corrupted at the levels of organisation we are considering (government and multinationals), only media can form adequate safeguards to our political systems and our lives, as Pulitzer recognised when considering the U.S.A:

'We are a democracy and there is only one way to get a democracy on its feet in the matter of its individual, its social, its municipal, its state (and) national conduct, and that is by keeping the public informed about what is going on. There is not a crime, there is not a dodge, there is not a trick, there is not a swindle…not a vice which does not live by secrecy. Get these things out in the open, describe them, attack them, ridicule them in the press, and sooner or later public opinion will sweep them away.' (The truth in this quote accords with comments below on the power of 'social pressure').

This quote throws the misuse of power and the current failure of the media into even more stark relief. We supposedly have a free press but, as American journalist A. J. Liebling (1904 – 1963) said, 'freedom of the press is limited to those who own one'. Newspapers print selections of whatever will sell most newspapers and / or favour their corporate/political affiliations. Analysis of coverage reveals that while dramatic headlines will report, for examples, deaths due to terrorism or tragic accidents, other disasters such as some civil wars (causing deaths far in excess of those in the previous categories) are not even reported. Sensationalism sells. Even if the proprietors of a press agency were not business people but sincerely public spirited, papers selling millions of copies automatically take their owners into a world dominated by power, corporations and politics. Hence, their coverage becomes highly selective, often avoiding the root causes of the tragedies reported, since their livelihoods, life-style and status have become too closely connected with those causes. In the worst cases, banner headlines shout indignantly (but insincerely) what most of the public want to shout themselves, thereby guaranteeing sales, while the newspaper is a covert part of the system responsible for the injustice denounced in the headlines. The public might gain some sort of temporary comfort that truth and abuse have been exposed, but nothing happens as a result, and a fresh outrage is ready for tomorrow. However, pretending to be the public's friend is both lucrative and perpetuates that system. As Liebling also observed "People everywhere confuse what they read in newspapers with news."

The selection and bias involved renders even the various vulgar exposés (even if true) almost useless and rarely improves the health of society. Moreover, the 'dumbing down' of the population through the media means that the reader/viewer/listener is unaware of the report's implications (no wisdom) and relevant connections (no knowledge). Only information is transmitted which, unless it can be united with knowledge and wisdom, will result in no action and it is therefore of no value. Even when journalists sincerely write to promote justice, editors edit in accordance with the bias of the paper or other medium. Despite their questionable value, newspapers remain, for now, a very powerful influence within society. A description that, once again, could be applied to fast food, alcohol, drugs etc. emphasising the idea that we are seeing multiple symptoms of a few root causes.

A refreshing example of a press proprietor of the highest calibre who was not overwhelmed by power, politics and corporations and who produced a paper as tangible proof of Pultizer's vision was Ramnath Goenka (referred to in his lifetime, and hereafter, as RNG) who founded the

'Indian Express' newspaper. One of Gandhi's inner circle, RNG was charged by Gandhi to protect India's new-born democracy and his very effective response was to found the Indian Express.

The full story of his crusade and the battles he had to fight are told in 'Warrior of the Fourth Estate' by B.G. Verghese (published by Penguin / Viking 2005). The Express' motto is, appropriately, 'journalism of courage' and RNG had to be a courageous 'warrior' not only to win battles but often just to survive. For example, when Mrs. Gandhi declared the emergency and ruled almost as a dictator, out of all Indian newspapers, the Express was the only one to constantly and vigorously oppose her abandonment of democracy. This was a courageous stance to take since commercial and industrial strings were pulled and advertising revenue dried up. There was direct harassment from government and attempts to ruin his businesses with economic and legal strategies while, on various flimsy pretexts, raids and disruption by police made life very difficult for the Express. RNG withstood all these attacks and the Express still survives, run by his son who maintains the newspaper's reputation, continuing the same pursuit of fairness and concern for the man in the street, opposing corruption in government and the dominance of big business where it threatens democracy, justice or the environment. After exposing say, some corruption in political circles, the Express follows up the sequence of events until justice is served. This author talked to taxi drivers in Mumbai (where the Express has its headquarters) about the newspaper and heard that, apart from crusades for justice, when natural disaster strikes, emergency food kitchens, or shelters, or aid centres are set up – by the Express, proving that concern for the man in the street is not merely a ruse to sell papers.

RNG considered a newspaper as a 'peculiar amalgam of public service and public patronage. It is not a business and has its own special economics.' Sadly, in the West at least, newspapers and other forms of media have mostly become businesses and their content reflects this, albeit indirectly. However, the Indian Express is more than a newspaper chain. RNG envisioned it as a national institution, a custodian of the people's freedom and their right to know, an instrument for national service, not commerce: 'Because the Truth Involves Us All' (an Express motto).

Keeping in mind the mass of the people, RNG wanted, in news coverage, to promote what has been called herein 'localisation', while keeping an eye on national events. Reducing the space given to politics as a 'privileged game of a few chosen individuals' and in which the Indian people were relegated to be just spectators, would provide space in which other important areas of human activity involving large numbers of people could be covered. He wanted to include social, economic and cultural content in all coverage to bring 'all news nearer the people …and make it more meaningful…from the district level to the national capital.'

RNG did not use his newspapers for self-advertisement or aggrandisement. When the Express received a photograph of his granddaughter's wedding he withheld its being printed on the basis that weddings did not constitute news. In telling contrast, an elderly English gentleman of this author's acquaintance had read the London Times newspaper for over 60 years and commented that it had in recent years included more 'gossip' type information in its coverage – such as weddings, divorces and other aspects of the personal relationships of famous people, scandals and other 'fashionable' items. These elements are firstly effects, and then become causes, of changes to our culture, collective values and priorities.

On the 25th March 2009 a brief, national 'news' broadcast on English television included reports on three television light entertainment programmes and a pop band re-forming. This type of 'empty' information has increased at the same time that the seriousness of our problems has increased. Is there not some sort of distorted symmetry here – that increasing gravity of our global situation has accompanied increasingly meaningless, purposeless media coverage? (Such inversions remind us of over-protective legislation relating to trivia while the world spirals into ecological Armageddon, and of legislation which favours the criminal instead of their victim).

Out of many possible examples of connections between environmental dangers, business, consumers, and the media, we will refer to one which directly involves tigers as well – the extreme monsoon floods suffered by Bangladesh every year. As it occurs every year it is no longer 'news worthy' and usually receives no coverage. The cause of this annual flood is the commercially driven de-forestation of the Himalayas, removing the 'sponge' effect of the forests that held back much of the annual monsoon rains, releasing the excess slowly throughout the remainder and drier part of the year. Now the run-off is mostly unrestrained along vast areas of the mountain chain and, via innumerable tributaries, is delivered by the Ganges and Brahmaputra rivers to Bangladesh, situated in the Bay of Bengal, as an unstoppable torrent. Balpakram National Park sits on the Indian side of the border with Bangladesh. This park has plentiful tiger habitat but when this author spoke with the Forest Guards there in 1996 they could not remember the last time they had heard or seen evidence of a tiger's presence. One of the National Park's senior staff said that his armed guards will catch a man from Bangladesh cutting a tree on the Indian side of the border but that the man has been reduced to such circumstances he sincerely tells the guards to shoot him since without the tree he will die anyway. The director asked how to police such situations. The answers lie far away from forests, in boardrooms and government buildings.

Whilst most of us cannot completely see how we relate directly to many of the political and corporate connections listed above, we do know that we are consumers. We need to ensure that we are not among those who provide the incentive for felling millions of trees and hence be partly responsible for the man from Bangladesh not being able to take one. Mirrors are being held up to us by the environment, socio-economics, our neighbours (human and animal), and this and previous sub-sections have listed some of the more important, in which we have been losing the light of our reflections. Before they disappear completely we shall take a look at some reflections, identifying features for self-examination and, most importantly, actions to change the reflections, and thereby the world.

REFLECTIONS...

...on Personal Responsibilities

The end of a previous sub-section 'Contaminated Agriculture Grows More than Contaminated Food' referred to us all contributing to making the modern world. We might claim that most of us are not part of board or government meetings and hence not personally approving of, or investing in, ecologically disastrous schemes or perverting the course of justice or political policies, or putting poisonous chemicals into the soil, supporting 'profit first' projects and investments, or interfering with the genetic basis of life.

Yet is it not our apathy, our unexamined life-styles, consumerism and renunciation of personal responsibility that allows other people to do these things? Think of how many millions of us are contributing to dangerous and unethical practices by our life-styles. Even when awareness of immorality or danger dawns, few take any action to balance the effects of their activities. Think of how many people you know who are voluntarily involved with any community or social programme to promote the welfare of anything other than their own immediate families (and some do not even promote that). Think of how many people you know who challenge the stupidity of some political policies, or miscarriages of justice and the corruption of legislation. 'For evil to prosper requires only that good men do nothing' (Edmund Burke 1729 –1797. British statesman, author and philosopher), or 'To sin by silence when they should protest, makes cowards of men.' (Attributed to Abraham Lincoln).

As we know, the most important decisions are made in boardrooms and government buildings but, since we have influence over governments and businesses some responsibility must lie with us. Those of us who bank or invest unethically are directly funding ecologically disastrous schemes and / or human rights abuses. Those of us who buy the products made from those trees taken from the Himalayas help fund the flooding of Bangladesh. The chain of connections linking a consumer to a denuded mountainside is not long but there are still shorter chains of connection by which the future of trees and tigers are written on cheques in suburban banks. Tiger habitats in particular represent rich natural resources and within the last decade, three U.K. 'High Street' banks were funding the logging of the already seriously depleted Indonesian rainforests, which hold the last few remaining Sumatran tigers. These activities are not advertised or exposed by the media and one has to exercise some interest and responsibility even to discover them, let alone oppose them. If you have an account with those unethical banks you were helping to fund this logging. Choosing how we spend and invest our money can help the tiger and the man from Bangladesh. Provided sufficient people meet their responsibilities, it can also control corporations, since boardroom decisions will immediately comply with whatever and whoever ensures profits are maintained.

Obviously, no one individual person funds the abuse alone but collective funding is made up of individuals' funds. No one individual is responsible for, say, chemically poisoning food supplies and ground water, but the mass sales of agribusiness is made up of individual sales. As more and more people realise what has been done to their food and the environment, in the name of profit for a few, organic food sales are increasing significantly. If you buy non-organic food you contribute to making it financially profitable for others to poison the soil.

In this amazing, multi-dimensional world full of beauty and subtlety, offering us opportunities to develop some dignity, if not nobility, all is being reduced and restricted to the ugly, crude and exclusive pursuit of money – until we decide differently, (and thereby start to develop some dignity…) Anything not directly part of profit-making processes is literally being eliminated (including that which makes the attainment of profit worthwhile), and ultimately poisoning those who pursue them but still, those immediate profits take priority. Whilst the answer to the question 'When will they wake up?' is unknown, the answer to the question 'When will we wake up?' need not be. We can challenge and oppose this trend, personally in the first instance and then in ways suggested in the next chapter. It involves us in educating ourselves, acting accordingly and remaining vigilant to resulting developments. As U.S. President Thomas Jefferson told us 'The price of freedom is eternal vigilance.' Part of that vigilance is choosing to stop paying people to abuse or destroy parts of our life-support system, our families or our tigers. You can

…the future of trees and tigers is written on cheques in suburban banks…

choose not to support, endorse or tacitly approve such behaviour, by not lending or paying a single penny of your money to those who will use it in this way. Will you find yourself up against a determined and principled group who believe their way to be right? No, you will not, business will behave as you compel it to in order to get your penny.

This returns us to our theme of how we contribute to making the modern world, and we do so in ways more numerous and diverse than buying chemically-farmed food. We contribute when we buy detergents to wash clothes and dishes which, via drains, accumulate in lakes and waterways – natural habitats of algae. Detergents (invented in the 20th century) represent abnormally large amounts of nutrients (mainly phosphates) for algae, which grow to produce 'blooms', covering the upper regions of surface water, cutting off light to aquatic photosynthetic plants and killing the ecosystem dependent on them. This effect is called eutrophication and we shall refer to it again in chapter V. We contribute when we buy aerosols (some details on CFCs, HCFCs and HFCs in the next chapter). All our commercial and consumer activities contribute; both directly in terms of physical impact and indirectly, in terms of connections to national and global economics, and 'agreements' made on our behalves (Appendix III has details of 'agreements' of importance to us all, and tigers, and trees…)

Why can we even buy harmful cleaning products or aerosols? It would appear that the giant corporations manufacturing the harmful ingredients carry more influence than government legislation to protect the environment. Alternative and safe cleaning products are available and consumer choice can grow the sales of these, instead of algal blooms in ponds and waterways. All we have to do is reach for the healthier product on the shelf. Far too many of us are currently not doing so. The reason cannot always be to save money since we waste money, and energy, and contribute to increasing the greenhouse effect when we leave unused electrical appliances switched on and when we waste hot water (the need not to waste cold water has already been mentioned). All things are connected. Tigers, and most other species, depend on us (conservationists included) not funding (accidentally or ignorantly, directly or indirectly) logging, abuse or poisoning of their habitats. As the environmental crisis deepens and governments' remedial measures remain inadequate, it is increasingly important to think and act as individuals.

By doing so we need not, for example, be surprised at reports warning of more extensive damage caused by climate change 'than previously predicted' by 'surprised scientists'. Nor need we be surprised at another attempt to create impressions that we can only rely on 'scientists' and, if they can't get it right, all others are blameless. Similarly, in the current financial crisis, news reports regularly refer to the 'global recession' – which has some truth but helps foster the impression that, since it is everywhere, we can't blame our own system too severely, we can't point a finger easily; everybody's in the same boat. Actually we can point a finger, and at the only ones not in the same boat – the few who have caused the problems, who are on luxury yachts and liners. The effects are global but, both financially and environmentally, the causes are few and simple. So, environmentally speaking, we can also point a finger, but the difference is that those responsible, and all other lives, are in the same boat – called 'Earth'.

The dominance of big business is so all pervading, both directly and indirectly, it is of limited or no value to address the individual problems it gives rise to unless we also address it at root. Discussion of this or that abuse, this or that executive or politician, this or that harmful policy or perversion of justice only allows the same or similar to be repeated in the near future, since all sprout from the same root. The dominance of big business may even be well known to many of those debating the daily news crop of 'bad fruit' sprouting from 'poisoned branches' yet digging out the roots does not feature in their analysis, articles, conversation or actions. Particular problems or instances discussed may well be valid, interesting and important but, ultimately, they are not as important as that which gives rise to them, and to so many other poisonous but hidden developments which never even become public knowledge. We met Henry David Thoreau in the previous chapter and now we consider his advice that "There are a thousand hacking at the branches of evil to one who is striking at the root, and it may be that he who bestows the largest amount of time and money on the needy is doing the most by his mode of life to produce that misery which he strives in vain to relieve." Thoreau's philosophy of non-violent resistance to the root of problems influenced Mahatma Gandhi and Martin Luther King.

Socio-economics controlled by a few powerful and greedy corporations represent a critical common factor between corruption in and manipulation of governments and many aspects of social and environmental malaises. Would this qualify as a root Thoreau refers to? Practically speaking; yes, but it is not the entire root.

...on Maximum

To see another part of the root we need to look carefully and bravely into life's mirror. Does it not show us, in the image of business greed, our own priorities and, possibly, our personal greed? Do we not seek maximum profits on our investments? Most individual investors echo companies and select according to one criterion only: the investment that will yield maximum profit – regardless of any other consideration. However, ethical investments have shown performances as good as, if not better than, conventional investments. More importantly for the future or, perhaps, in order that we should have a future, is to demonstrate that we hold other criteria as dear, or more dearly, than profit and be prepared to receive less money if the investment benefits the bigger picture (of which we are all a part; not apart).

Do we say the best job is that with the 'best' (i.e. highest) salary, or do we try to do the best job we can, whatever our work or salary? All the familiar patterns of corporations striving for more, to eliminate competition, to manipulate the government and the law; are the result of individuals pursuing maximum – most significantly those in senior positions, but the corporate culture they generate, both within business and within society, influences staff and citizens to also continually seek maximum – sales, salaries, status, benefits. Optimum is never considered.

Do we also look for what we can take, rather than what we can give? Do we seek to do our duty or seek the elusive 'happiness'? (Which is actually a by-product of other processes, one of which is doing our duty!)

Obviously, we need money and materials to survive – and a little more to enjoy some of that survival. So where do the problems come from? At risk of repetition, problems are produced by imbalances. In a nutshell, our healthiest strategy is to seek balance, a sense of proportion, in all material aspects of our lives, individually and collectively, exercising self-control to achieve and maintain it. In the long-term it harms each and all of us to seek or acquire maximum profit, or the maximum of any material thing. If we must aspire to a maximum, let it be the development of our characters in terms of morality and virtue, while maintaining our lives in the material world with, and in, due proportion. To use a basic but natural example: while a person usually stops eating when they feel satisfied, this does not represent the maximum they could consume. Imagine them continuing to consume beyond a feeling of satisfaction, forcing, stretching their capacity as far as possible, and in order to do so, taking food from others who do not have enough for healthy survival. Such a person would not enjoy good health nor the respect or admiration of others, yet a person who behaves like this with money *is* often respected and admired.

Ironically, it is for a better quality of life that we seek a maximum – but in doing so we find minimum quality, partly because no time is left to enjoy it and partly because the process of acquiring maximum seriously damages our life-support systems (once again, externally and internally). Maximum material acquisition brings problems that, in the long-term, reduce or rob one completely of the benefits sought. From a global perspective, the pursuit of maximum profit has brought maximum peril for all.

As we pursue 'most', the results are also reflected in our artificial environments: Businesses making the most money become the most commonly occurring such that each city centre, town or 'high street' becomes virtually identical in terms of retail outlets since space on high streets or in shopping malls is also let for maximum rental, hence only those businesses generating the most money can afford to be there. The result is less diversity, less variation (echoing the same pattern in ecosystems (see chapter V) and the disappearance of seeds and species as referred to below). Even the stock within those retail outlets is often required to be identical since it is also selected for maximum sales. Any item that does not sell as much as another is replaced with the 'better seller' – there is no allowance for tastes other than the most common, lest any profit be lost. The curious or quaint, innovative or special, disappears – small might be beautiful, and healthy, but it's disappearing. Maximum eliminates the unusual and promotes uniformity, which is reflected in us, the consumers, who become as similar and as 'packaged' as the products we buy (the current commercial demographics) since we too want 'the most' (usually most money or material products). Ruskin predicted that the industrial revolution would distance people from nature and its moralising, healthy influences (referred to in the previous chapter), and turn them into slavish workers as identical to each other as the products their machines produced.

The trend extends beyond commerce and we find ourselves being treated by 'McMedicine' (no interest in or compassion for the individual as a person but only as a collection of physical symptoms requiring drugs from pharmaceutical companies – sometimes to counteract the effects of previously prescribed drugs!).

Above we briefly touched on lightweight 'cartons' of highly processed 'McTelevision' programmes. These are often reduced in nutritional ingredients but rich in questionable ones, since media and entertainment also seek maximum – in terms of audiences. Programmes which require effort from viewers in terms of self-control, self-discipline, concentration, responsibility and morality will not appeal to the majority and so receive little or no air time. To attract a maximum audience, television tends toward lowest common denominators and therefore lowest common behaviour, those appealing to basic impulses, multiple vices and ignorance. Merely displaying such behaviour tacitly approves of or even glamorises it, especially for fans of 'stars' who exhibit it. Standards slip down toward crudeness, vulgarity, conflict and extreme emotional displays (all examples of lack of self-discipline or self-development and least personal effort) helping to reduce or eliminate aspirations in the viewer to rise above what is most common or base, especially children, who model their behaviour on what they see around them. Worse still, children see 'stars' made by media and apparently adored by society for displays of vulgarity.

Films, plays and television could (and in some cases do) offer powerful guidance and influence for the health and welfare of society. There are even academic studies showing beneficial social effects of television. However, there are also studies showing the almost hypnotic influence of television and that it can even produce symptoms of drug addiction. Obviously a medium as rich and powerful as television must have a variety of effects. Whatever they are, selectivity and moderation in viewing it are the best options.

Actually living a modern technologically-driven life involves us in so many diverse activities we sometimes barely have time to reflect upon our journey through it – other than by material acquisition, sadly and currently the dominant mode. At times we are so busy surviving; we forget the purpose of surviving. Here, ironically, a potentially beneficial influence of television is as an antidote to the culture that has given rise to it since a play / film / television programme requires us to devote time exclusively to watching it. While we sit in stillness and silence, a programme may lay our lives before us and offer us an opportunity to reflect on and consider what we are doing, where we are going, how we are behaving; the values we are living by and where we could have done better and / or how we should, or did, act in similar circumstances. All this can be healthy, a teacher of virtue, a warning against wrong-doing etc. Whether or not this opportunity is afforded and this potential realised, reduces to the intent and quality of the production. Feeding people cultural junk has similar effects to feeding them junk food and, if maintained, means we are on the road to ruin. Quality productions offer us not only entertainment but also hope.

To set all these comments in perspective, it is necessary to recognise that, despite the convenience of the prefix, no particular fast food chain is being condemned in and of itself, nor any particular medical facility or television programme etc. Any one of these particular examples may serve a positive purpose in particular circumstances. The point being made is that it is less than healthy for society when these modes of medicine, nutrition, programming etc. become dominant, representing increasing corporate influences over our lives. Such dominance is clearly apparent in politics, medicine, science and the arts, cinema, television and sport.

Since sport has attracted 'big' money and big business, winning has become the only criterion by which to play (since it alone acquires most money). Hence, science and technology are employed to hone the player into a perfect mechanism of supreme fitness and tactical skill, foregoing all other aspects of the game. Sport used to be about building character but now any aspect of character not part of the training regime (e.g. creativity, fun, personality) is eliminated in order to achieve a 'mechanised product' (the player) with maximum potential to win.

Now the last refuge of the intelligentsia – books – has also been invaded. The market for books is being influenced both in terms of books about 'celebrities', forming a new and lucrative niche, and the tendency to print only mass market best-sellers, resulting in more eclectic titles being squeezed out of the market. To defend the trend we are told that each year there are more titles than the previous year. At first glance this seems to provide greater variety but, of course, it is only in terms of numbers of different titles – the contents will be a standard recipe, a repeat mix of similar themes high in sex and violence; sugar and salt. In the same way, Hollywood is possibly producing more films than ever before but they will also be endless variations of the same few ingredients. When money and profit become the primary focus, it is the kiss of death to all genuine forms of endeavour, art and expression – since the only expression, no matter how much sugar and salt, or sex and violence is mixed in to obscure the poison, is 'love of money'.

While the gulf between rich and poor widens, more people have to do more work in less time just to acquire sufficient money for survival. In addition to the resulting physical and mental stresses, little courtesies disappear and, later, larger ones. Forced into survival strategies, people have less time and little inclination for caring and courtesies. Life becomes less and less pleasant to live and social structures start to fragment and unravel. At the same time the associated environmental abuse decreases physical, mental and spiritual health, fragmenting and unravelling life-support systems, ultimately bringing about the demise of the community that allows itself to be organised on profit-first principles. In this we can see more links between morality and nature, as warned of by Wordsworth and Ruskin. The pursuit of maximum profit is incompatible with caring for others. Care costs something, but ensures that something remains worth caring about.

In addition to orchestrating the working and living conditions for the majority, corporations also try to ensure that we are subject to non-stop advertising which sells superficiality, ego, instant gratification, vulgarity and baseness. (Marketing and advertising is 'one-way' communication – a type of brainwashing – and therefore not true communication, which has to be 'two-way'). These powerful influences have also contributed to social decadence and, in the West at least, overwhelmed any and all government, religious, family and school controls. The dam has burst and these elements and associated vices have flooded all aspects of our society. Those ethical and environmentally-friendly individuals, organisations, companies and their products which have survived the poisonous inundation represent strong, healthy shoots of new growth. They and their activities thereby acquire a significance and importance out of all proportion to their size. We must nurture them as we should nurture the soil and new growth. Beware however, 'traditional' business people exploiting new markets. For example, some of the fruit from these 'new shoots' also carry the worm of greed and, whilst for example, organic food is currently more expensive than chemically contaminated food (appendix II explains why) the profit margins can still be excessive, since the company is owned by standard businesspeople exploiting a new market niche. Similarly, successful ethical or 'environmentally-friendly' companies might be bought by big conventional businesses which retain the name and reputation of the original. Hence the benefits are minimal (some ethical or environmentally-friendly activities remain) but the seed of new growth may die since the conventional company maintains its poisonous activities, just acquiring a new source of income via its now wider range of products. Unless we are careful, we still financially support that which is destroying our life-support system while thinking we are doing the right thing. The way we can keep the seed alive and grow it is to exclusively buy the healthy option. We thereby utilise business' obsession with maximising profit, but to the benefit of all – including business.

For instance, some manufacturers make only environmentally-friendly cleaning products, store them in environmentally-friendly containers and make all in environmentally-friendly factories. Other companies make some environmentally-friendly products but also poisonous products – they have no principle other than profit and will sell whatever you will buy. Hence we must identify and support the former and deny money to the latter – which, if sufficient consumers do the same, will change its products, virtually overnight. A new company was successful making and selling organic chocolate. It represented both (semi!) healthy products and healthy new seeds of growth. Sadly, from an environmental perspective, soon after its success, it was sold to a large conventional chocolate maker (which maintained its non-organic products), putting the 'new growth' at risk. Now only consumer choice can keep that seed alive, wholesome and growing while stifling the poisonous aspects of the bigger business at the same time. In the absence of appropriate government legislation and a new breed of businesspeople, consumer choice is currently the only mechanism remaining by which we can grow healthy changes.

However, consumer choice still has significant obstacles to overcome since big business also works to manipulate governments into subverting consumer choice. GMO is an example that holds two time-bombs for society: one is as an incentive for corporate manipulation of the law (as already referred to briefly above in the sub-section 'What is News'). The other is GMO itself and is so important for all our futures we shall consider this latter 'time-bomb' first.

Nature is the organic, interactive, educational life-support system that supplies air, water and food. This fantastically complex, yet flexible system has functioned for millennia. Even the damage we have caused and many of the man-made threats comprising the current environmental crisis can, if we change our ways, still be repaired and / or averted. Nature, given time, will recover. Usually we need only leave it alone for its self-healing properties to work.

So, figuratively speaking, as long as we have one healthy tree, a forest may eventually re-grow. If we tamper with what it means to be a tree, or a tomato, or a sheep, or a bison…we destroy any such guarantees. If we have more than one tree and genetically tamper with some we are still voluntarily risking all since we have no knowledge whatsoever of how the specimens tampered with will affect the natural remainder. GMO allows us a level of interference that (as far as we know) alters nature itself, possibly including nature's self-healing capacity (if there is a natural and still more fundamental principle of organisation than that represented by genetics, and to which we have no access, so much the better but, once again, we don't know, so why unnecessarily risk everything we depend on?) Our interference with nature via GMO is irreversible and 'experiments' are obviously not confined to laboratories – even though we have only one earth to experiment with. In England and with regard to GMO, a harried senior politician assured reporters and concerned crowds "Yes, we need to know it's safe" before hurrying away in a motor car. Well, apart from the fact that we cannot know this (until it's too late), it is also to deny democracy in that we do not need to know it is safe – if the majority do not want it, that's all there is to it. Clichés such as 'assurances of safety' and 'adequate testing' are all humbug.

Apologists for GMO say it is merely the latest form or extension of manipulating nature, just as we have done previously via, say, selective breeding. This is not correct. Selective breeding experiments are still subject to nature's controlling influence determining which experimental results will survive and which will not – just as the artificial big cat hybrids; leopons, ligers and tigons, mentioned in chapter II, are always sterile. Perhaps the most obvious selective breeding is that of cows for bigger udders and more milk. Man continued the process even when the udders became an obvious impediment to the cow. However, again, nature imposed a limit. Altering the genes of organisms may alter or remove nature's controlling influence.

During the early 20th century it became possible to mutate genomes by irradiation (usually X-rays) and other apologists for GMO cite the experiments in which the genomes of fruit flies were irradiated as evidence that the effects of GMO will be equally benign. As far as this author knows, all irradiation experiments were conducted on specimens strictly confined to the laboratory, with no intention of releasing experimental mutants into the world's gene pool. Even if they had been and the introduction of those mutant flies has not – to date and as far as we know – had deleterious effects, this is not as a result of any prescience or understanding on the part of the scientists concerned.

There may be great medicinal advantages in genetic engineering and valid cases for helping individuals by, for example, gene therapy (to cure congenital diseases) but beware of media covering such cases and using emotional bribery to sway public opinion towardf approval of genetic engineering *in general.* Otherwise, by helping a poignant case today, while not carefully controlling the general spread of altered genomes or the technology to do so, we may produce hundreds or thousands of poignant cases timorrow, due to our ignorance of what we are doing in the larger context. We would probably have no idea how to treat the new cases tomorrow, due to currently unknown interactions of the artificial genetic mix with the environment and other gene pools. Let us treat specific individual cases and / or diseases but employ the strictest controls on genetric engineering in general.

GMO must, by definition, alter the fantastically complex and flexible system called nature, since changing one part changes the whole. The one or two changes engineered for (plus changes and effects currently unforeseen) may have adverse or fatal consequences, of which we have no current conception. Corporate driven science is currently like a child taking a tin of sweets from the lowest tier of a pyramid of tins – and no-one can deny that the child achieves its immediate objective. Perhaps more pertinently it is akin to somebody standing immediately next to the wall of Chartres Cathedral who has no knowledge or perception of the building as a whole, its design or the subtle and esoteric knowledge manifest in its masonry. Nonetheless, this person has discovered how to remove individual bricks – and has already started to do so according to their own tiny perspective! GMO is a threat more serious than most other threats since it is to change the system that has been, and still is, our only reliable supplier of life, and guide to health and security; GMO has the potential to distort, damage or destroy that guide, our life-giving model. No person on the planet, nor all of us put together, can say otherwise for sure, so why risk it? Supporters of GMO will claim that much might be achieved, such as feeding the starving, but Appendix II explains that people starve due to poverty – not scarcity of food. It also explains how an economic system dominated by a few agribusiness companies (the sorts that now make or market GMO products) actually guarantee that people will starve. It is instructive to remember that the first successful cloning of the sheep 'Dolly' was produced by a commercial company and therefore by the profit motive, possibly combined with the personal agendas or egos of the scientists involved.

The threats posed by GMO are compounded still further by other man-made, self-imposed threats such as our interference with ecosystems. For example, as climate changes, moth and butterfly eggs are hatching earlier in the year than previously. However, since the environmental cues triggering bird migrations are not changing in the same ways, birds are not arriving in time to feed their young on these larvae. This has an impact on insect and bird populations, therefore pollination, plants, herbivores and then carnivores. The interconnections within and between ecosystems are largely unknown to, and probably too complex to be completely understood by, humans. Whilst we remain in ignorance both of the ecosystems we are interfering with, and how they are changing in response to that interference, we are also simultaneously interfering with the genes underlying the ecosystems and organisms themselves – compounding, beyond any hope of human comprehension or control, our effects on the natural world. As Schweitzer said 'Man is a clever animal who behaves like an imbecile.' (Albert Schweitzer 1875 – 1965 Franco-German theologian, musician, philosopher and physician).

Consider for yourself media coverage of GMO which reports the genetic manipulation of organisms accompanied perhaps by a brief quote from some representative of a group opposed to the work. The impression given is that 'both sides of the question' are being aired and reassures us that we live in a complex, but essentially fair, society. While the report is being transmitted or read, the damage is being done, the experiments are being conducted and 'man-made' or 'man-manipulated' organisms are now extant and part of the global gene pool. 'Both sides of the question' should be debated *before* humans were legally allowed to interfere with nature, without knowing what they are doing.

Also consider for yourself the standard, and seemingly plausible, arguments such as 'like all inventions or discoveries, they can be used beneficially or harmfully'. We may be benefited or harmed by, for examples, fire, the wheel, weapons or tools but whatever the results, our collective food supply and ecological balances maintaining life-support systems remain unaffected in other than localised ways. So GMO is *not* like any other invention or discovery since it is interfering, in a completely purblind way, with these fundamental essentials.

Due to the recent sanctification of science it has also been suggested that the commercial motivation for GMO research is irrelevant if the results are scientifically sound (reproducible, peer reviewed etc.) i.e. research results add to our knowledge and can therefore only be good. Yet, what good are research results when finding them causes serious threats to our crops and global ecosystems? Ridiculously distorted priorities such as these indicate how far we have travelled down the road of arrogance and conceit. That increasing our store of facts and information could be considered as more important than safe-guarding our life-support system is only possible in artificial worlds of 'ivory towers', laboratories and academic/corporate cliques where people congratulate themselves on their supposedly elevated view, before going off to a hearty lunch, which their activities are putting in peril.

In the real world, bee populations are declining rapidly in America and Europe. No single cause has been identified that explains all problem areas but all potential causes relate to human activities, with a cumulating concoction of pesticides being a strong candidate for at least one causative factor. Some studies have shown a direct relation between the decline of bees and GMO crops. Bees are the only pollinators for many fruit and vegetable species (e.g. broccoli, oranges and almonds) and if their decline leads to extinction, the immediate implications are obvious but there may be further and as yet unknown problems connected to more distant parts of nature's honeycombed networks. The reason we are so dependent on bees (and bee keepers) as pollinators is that we have removed wild pollinators by agricultural practices such as destroying hedgerows, repeatedly soaking the soil with poison, and favouring agribusiness' mono-crops (which not only lack diversity but only flower for a few months each year, leaving the area, from pollinators' perspectives, sterile for the remainder of the year). There are calls for more research and, of course, reliable information is valuable, but this approach is consistent with 'clever humans solving the problems nature presents us with'. Even the most intelligent people work on curing the 'next problem' without realising that *we are the problem*. Another element of nature now has to shout the message that we need to fundamentally change our activities to harmonise with nature. Currently we are continuing on the same path and trying to find another stopgap 'cure' to nullify that message. We need, with utmost urgency, to retrace our steps until we find the path that lets us walk with natural views and natural perspectives around us. Nature will not adapt itself to us – we must adapt ourselves to nature.

The agricultural techniques just mentioned, and closely confining domestic animals to small, single pens away from sunshine and fresh air, injecting them with hormones and antibiotics, are all in the name of maximising profit. When we stop interfering with and poisoning other life forms for profit, we might find that, for just one example, bee populations return to normal. (As this book was going to press, scientists identified both a virus and a fungus in all the collapsed colonies of bees examined (The Week 23/10/10). How the combined fungal-viral threat functions is as yet unclear but the point made above is that, if they prove to be the immediate causative agents of 'colony collapse disorder' a cure for the fungal-viral threat is likely to be the sole aim of our scientists, whereas it is suggested here that the whole situation (including the sudden proliferation of the fungal-viral combination) is nature's reaction to man-made interferences with natural balances.)

One of the great values of nature's creatures is that they show us when ecosystems are healthy

– which also means healthy food, fresh air and water for us. One of the self-defeating arguments for GMO, but rarely recognised as such, is that pest-resistant crops can be developed, meaning that less and fewer pesticides would be used, which is good for the environment. Within this argument is the tacit recognition that the last scientific wonder (i.e. pesticides) is harmful. Now we want to meddle further and once again the same old arguments are repeated whilst we still try to cope with the effects of their last application. Hidden behind the rational arguments and science are, of course, the same old motives of greed and power. Current research would be better directed to finding how we reverse the results of applying previous research. Nature is showing us, by the increasing dangers associated with scientific dabbling, that scientists can no longer pretend they work without personal accountabilities much wider than science. GMO has been referred to as 'Frankenstein food' and, appropriately since, in addition to the obvious parallel, the novel 'Frankenstein' (first published in 1818 and written by Mary Shelley) addresses the responsibilities of individual scientists beyond the boundaries of and general enthusiasm for science.

In this chapter and the next we are considering how we might change the world by changing ourselves according to morality, virtue and free will. GMO is already changing the world genetically according to commerce, vice and parliamentary bills. Those U.K. parliamentary bills reveal the other 'time-bomb' GMO represents: the dangers to democracy. The consumer response to GMO food was to leave it on the shelves – initially possible due to it being labelled as such. However, corporations would not let go of their potentially absolute control of future markets so easily. After a little time their response was to claim that the public's refusal to purchase GMO was a barrier to 'free trade' (whereas it is actually a demonstration of one element of it). The supposed bastion of democracy, in the U.K. at least, the houses of parliament (having already contravened its own stance of supposedly ensuring GMOs were 'safe' before allowing them to proliferate) allowed labelling of GMO ingredients to become voluntary on the part of the manufacturers! Big business can literally force feed us, with the co-operation of those paid to protect us. There could hardly be a clearer demonstration of the community's views than the failure of GMO products to sell, yet the very people who represent democracy legislate in favour of corporations. This situation stimulated much debate and controversy in the media over the GMO labelling issue (reminding us of G. K. Chesterton saying about a written work that it was "putting out the fire of truth with the fuel of information"). All of the discussions, all those intelligent comments from intelligent interviewees on radio programmes, consumer affairs agencies, consumer protection programmes, and our protective laws, all concentrated into the democratic process represented by the House of Lords and Houses of Parliament proved to be helpless and hopeless in the face of a few corporations which, with a huff and a puff, blew those houses down. The safeguards were all just a 'show'; more fragile stage props on another show called 'democracy' – often viewed as a comedy but actually a tragedy of tragedies.

Although science driven by vested interests produces such problems, is it not science that provides us with the only trustworthy information? Surely science itself is purely objective and totally reliable? As a product of humans, science is not only subject to all the fallibilities of humans but it is also influenced in the same way as its practitioners are influenced by social customs and cultural features from television, marketing and modern life in general (which itself is dominated more than at any other time in history by a few globally powerful organisations). Science is significantly influenced by commerce, the military and politics – it began in wonder but has become, and will no doubt end in, the pursuit of power; sometimes as money (e.g. chemicals for agribusiness, GMO, drugs) and sometimes as military power (e.g. nuclear weapons and space exploration, satellites and rocketry, all born of military agendas). Moreover, most scientists ultimately find themselves, along with the rest of us, either as employees and / or consumers, having to fit themselves and their work into 'cartons' defined by corporations' products and services and become identical, sanitised and lightweight people – 'McPeople' – unfortunately not to our, or our community's, best benefit.

The examples above are all different manifestations, different symptoms, of the pursuit of maximum profit or power or both, and the resulting influences on society. If 'maximum money' ultimately depraves and corrupts, those who pursue it and count the resulting profits, claim it is not their responsibility to regulate it. Talk of 'freedom', the 'public's intelligence' and 'right to choose' are the predictable but dubious defences – readily endorsed by those most susceptible to depravity and corruption, once again, usually youngsters. All of us, including businesspeople, have responsibilities in proportion to our power. When, in this instance, businessmen, neglect their responsibilities, they find themselves retreating behind locking gates, window grilles and alarms, too frightened to protect their cars or other property from that part of society poisoned partly by their neglect of communal responsibilities and partly by the aspirations to wealth and possessions they have helped create. Consumers neglect their responsibilities when they buy products or services without a care about where or how they are produced or sourced. The most poisoned part of society is largely formed by the upcoming generation which reflects the imbalance, the 'disease', most acutely since they have literally grown out of a poisoned society, without alternative personal experience for comparison. When we lament that our societies are increasingly under surveillance we are told that crime rates are increasing and surveillance catches criminals. This view ignores the original sequence of events which was that increasing crime prompted the installation of surveillance cameras. The latter are indicative of society already going in the wrong direction. More numerous cameras are more numerous symptoms. We need to treat causes.

Media and entertainment form strong influences on the young but the majority output is incessant promotion of 'celebrity', the cult of ego and self-indulgence, all linked inextricably with selling products and commerce in general. The 'fame factory', empty of any worthwhile product, then attracts youngsters who 'want to be famous' but when asked 'famous for doing what?' cannot answer, reflecting the emptiness of not only the 'fame factory' but those lives seduced by it. The traditional acme of an acting career was to play Shakespeare, to express the subtleties and power of those words while accommodating, but not being a slave to, the iambic pentameter – and maybe find something new within, for and to the delight of audiences. Now, instead of providing the value of drama's most accurate mirror, finding fame is sufficient in and of itself, even if this is via vacuous nonsense; the emphasis being, once again, on self, and not service.

This is all part of the 'dumbing-down' of people; occupying them with all sorts of celebrity, consumer and fashion emptiness instead of essential issues. New generations obliged to consume this cultural 'junk food' are unaware of anything better and try to assimilate it without understanding the vague sense of dissatisfaction and disquiet it brings. One result is that many people do not even have an opinion on environmental issues or, if pressed, decide that they don't care, so great has our distance from nature, healthy values and true education become. When the media covers environmental issues they might report 'greens' or 'environmentalists' as 'angered' or disappointed at the continuing abuse of nature, a technique which implies that there are other groups of people not totally dependent on nature, creating an illusion for the reader or viewer that they live in some neutral isolation. The practical importance of tiger conservation, the reasons why we should save the tiger, are illustrated in the next chapter. However, if asked about its practical importance, most 'normal' or 'average' people would be unable to answer – including many who consider themselves 'well educated'. The News may tell us that the tiger is facing extinction, allowing some to think 'pity, but it's not me, or us'. A more accurate report would tell us that *we* are facing the tiger's extinction, and all that that represents.

Too few real, admirable characters who might act as role models, ideals or inspirations for youngsters to rise above the baseness surrounding them, are offered by parents, schools or society. Too many of those parents, schools and societies will tell children that gaining most money is their most important goal. Media promotes characters who conform to its rules and continue to 'sell' (air-time, magazines, papers, marketing products), confining variety to narrow margins of format and style, shrinking the kaleidoscope of choices to a mono-crop of images and behaviour patterns from which only a few well-known repeats can be harvested. The pursuit of maximum produces other maxima: maximum conformity, boredom, discourtesies, depression…danger – and minimum individuality, creativity, subtlety, meaning…if variety is the spice of life, maximum means bland uniformity.

In addition to the identical products and people of the commercial demographic world, and dangers to democracy and decency, 'maximum' means factory farming and nature being turned into products as defined by categories of type, number and profit. It also means 'factory fishing' either with weighted 'bottom trawling' nets or with drift nets, which result in extremely intelligent, self-conscious, socially bonding and possibly loving dolphins, dying uselessly along with many other non-commercial species in those nets, since in reality the pursuit of maximum also means ignoring the rights or well-being of others.

The pursuit of maximum profit is also responsible for most of the adulterations to our food. As farming became centralised agribusiness the produce had to be transported over long distances so processes such as 'refining' developed along with chemical preservatives to increase 'shelf-life'. More chemicals, such as colourings, flavourings and flavour-enhancers, increase sales and profits but decrease health. Poisons have seeped not only into our bodies but also into our minds and cultures and we forget, or some have never known, the taste and smell of fresh, uncontaminated, healthy, nutritious food, the very bread of life itself.

Commercial developments (including modern food production) have built highly complex and interlocking systems of mechanised and computerised production, transport and communications. However, the pursuit of maximum puts even these creations at risk. The magazine New Scientist, by virtue of its subject matter, ranks as one of the most objective and sober journals currently available. Its issue of 5th April 2008 carried two major articles considering the collapse of civilisation ('The End of Civilisation?' pp. 28-31 and 'Are we Doomed?' pp 33-35 or at www.newscientist.com). Amongst factors contributing to the risks, environmental abuse and the vulnerability of complex networks are cited. It also reports that 'Globalisation is resulting in…tight coupling and the fine-tuning of our systems to a narrow range of conditions… Redundancy (*anything that is not strictly functional and necessary – author*) is being systematically eliminated as companies maximise profits. Some products are produced by only one factory worldwide. Financially, it makes sense, as mass production maximises efficiency. Unfortunately it also minimises resilience.' Again this echoes the principles exhibited by ecosystems (see chapter V) from which we can learn, and would best copy to build our own systems.

Commercial jargon such as 'globalisation, redundancy, efficiency' etc. might better be described as greed bringing about its own downfall. A thoughtful and concerned reader may wonder what is to be done since they might consider that they too pursue maximum money, profits and / or assets. Yet even ardently acquisitive people do observe some codes of conduct – but without necessarily being consciously aware of doing so. A moment's reflection reveals that if the majority of people really were only pursuing maximum profit they would knock down the first old lady they could and take her money. They do not do so due to their moral code and / or compassion or, if not these, fear of legal penalty. Moral codes or compassion do not feature in the decisions of big corporations and the law can be manipulated or ignored since profits also bring power, corrupting the very systems designed to protect people and the environment from the ruthless practices of corporations. Or to use the metaphor of being at table again, a person who consumes as much as possible without regard for the needs of others is likely to find themselves dining alone – except perhaps for other gluttons. This would be unappetising to witness since gluttons respect each other no more than they do non-gluttons. The scrabbling for bigger and bigger slices of business usually occurs behind closed doors without media coverage. The only bites that escape are sound bytes sanitised in lightweight cartons and delivered for our consumption. The majority of people only receive the results of scraps at the tables of big business. However, the amount of food, and nearly all other natural resources, is finite and, whilst sufficient, as Gandhi said, for everyone's need, it is insufficient for everyone's greed.

In multiple subtle and not so subtle ways, wanting, taking, believing in and pursuing maximum lead us into the situations and societies we have around us. These situations and societies in turn influence the characters of their citizens, and the decline of both is mutually reinforcing.

The opposite extreme i.e. minimum, can be equally harmful. Yet most of the world is forced to live on it – due to the practices of the few with maximum power and privilege. While it is true that each extreme can only move in one direction, the poverty trap is just that, and can only be opened, or movement allowed, with help from outside. Whilst material poverty can enrich one spiritually, physiology imposes limits on the depth or duration of material poverty that can be endured. At or near this limit a person may be spiritually rich but too materially impoverished, weak or disadvantaged to open the poverty trap. At the other end of the spectrum, the trappings of wealth are also appropriately labelled, since those with most material wealth are often spiritually impoverished, too weak and spiritually disadvantaged (selfish, fearful etc.) to open the trap for themselves. Although there are no physical constraints, it takes much spiritual strength to voluntarily walk away from wealth, to give up some or all of those trappings – the strength of a Siddartha Gautama who voluntarily gave up his life of privilege to begin his journey to enlightenment and Buddha-hood. However, such strength need not be confined to spiritual leaders; the 09/06/10 issue of the Week magazine summarised a report in the Guardian newspaper which told of two millionaires who, able to see the spiritual emptiness of their lives, voluntarily gave away their fortunes. For the present, such people remain a minority. It therefore falls to the Western world's 'middle class', those who are materially poor as compared to the wealthiest few, but rich as compared to two thirds of humanity, to try to bear the extra cost of buying what is right and healthy, for examples; fair trade and other ethically produced products, organic food and environmentally-friendly products. (Some of the Western world's 'middle classes' may claim that they cannot afford, say, organic food – and yet they have mobile phones, DVDs, computers, regular holidays abroad, luxury cars etc. displaying some dangerously disordered priorities). In addition, they may also choose to let someone out of the poverty trap, perhaps by supporting a chosen NGO.

Consumers can help manufacturers and retailers move away from maximum and toward health for all by questioning some of the excessive prices put on poor quality products; re-cultivating a sense of proportion in purchasing, with an eye for quality and durability, and teaching children not to be duped by ribbons tied around rubbish. Where there is obvious profiteering, we can politely tell the retailer why we are leaving the item on the shelf (and encourage our friends and family to do the same). Similarly, we can challenge excess 'administration charges' for, say, altering a date on a computer, passing an item of information and similar trivial activities which should be simple courtesies. Some consumers may save a few pennies by buying a supermarket's own branded version of a bought-in popular product. In due course the original and smaller manufacturer goes out of business while the power of the supermarket grows. The Western world's 'middle class' can also help by educating their children generally, and particularly about the value of the middle path and adopting many of the suggestions in the next chapter.

...on Optimum

When we let go of maximum in a material sense, the exhausting and never-ending chase relaxes, some free time returns, improving our quality of life and helping us remember, and then develop our characters; find and develop 'who we are' as individuals. Being satisfied with 'optimum' instead of 'maximum' allows more control of one's own life – you decide when to walk away, when to stop the chase.

The pursuit of 'maximum' is voluntary slavery since there is no choice: one can never stop, because there is always more to be had, and more to be done. Sometimes illness or stress stops us, which are nature's attempts to teach us physically what we will not learn mentally. Usually, if there is recovery, we repeat the same routine and sow another mono-crop: perhaps the final crop.

Those whose income represents more than they could use in a lifetime and those of the middle income groups who aspire to the same, together form an economic system that means the majority of the remainder must pursue 'maximum' for survival. Hence, the emphasis is on the first two groups to begin replacing maximum with optimum, in order that the last group is able to.

Replacing maximum with optimum begins to provide a little free time and free us from patterns of identically reproduced products and people. As mentioned in Chapter III, having a worthwhile ideal, someone or something to venerate, someone to emulate, helps provide a new direction and use for that free time. 'Without worship you shrink, it's as brutal as that…I shrank my own life. No one can do it for you. I settled for being pallid and provincial, out of my own eternal timidity. The old story of bluster and do bugger-all…(*I settled for*) the good Normal world where we're tethered…blinking our nights away in a non-stop drench of cathode-ray over our shrivelling heads!' (B57) As should be clear by now, what we 'worship' would best be a well-balanced ideal. The Karin Michaelis and Vivekenanda quotes in chapter III remind us of some benefits of having an ideal.

Materially speaking, optimum represents a balance point between maximum and minimum and this balance leads to health and real wealth. Our activities are all subject to limitations; our own and those of resources and time. Extremes in any one activity will cause other activities to disappear. Living and working within these limitations and having to operate in collective, communal situations, demands of us that we find how to divide and apportion our time and resources optimally. These enforced practical lessons also provide some spiritual lessons, since among all the decisions which have to be made are those which will have consequences for others and, to the degree by which we favour self or others in making them, determine the development of our character. Just as the location of this balance point was crucial in assessing Corbett's character, so it is with ours. Well-balanced characters form well-balanced communities, and then societies, with well-balanced approaches to economics, environmental utilisation and conservation, the material and spiritual etc. 'Extremes' do not; cannot, be sustained in the long-term. Nature's models show us a dynamic equilibrium.

Global imbalances such as 'globalisation' are produced by multinational corporations, themselves a physical manifestation of imbalance. Via their products, use of the media, and power over politicians, they introduce further imbalances into nations and communities. Consider also how corporate power over the consumer has grown over recent decades: We are continually being pressured (e.g. by poor quality products) and persuaded (e.g. by advertising and marketing) to purchase more, to be acquisitive whenever and wherever possible. We are also increasingly subject to corporations protecting their markets and ensuring a lucrative trade in maintenance and spares, by preventing the purchaser maintaining or repairing products for themselves (in days gone by, manufacturers might even include diagrams with their products to help the purchaser maintain it at home but now, whether it is a household machine or a car, we are faced with panels under panels, sealed units, screws that need specialist screwdrivers etc.) We are made increasingly helpless and useless, needing the corporate world to wipe our noses, tuck-in our shirts – and empty our pockets. The same pattern is apparent in what is now referred to as the 'nanny state'. However, corporate and state 'nannies' are not motivated by loving and giving but control and taking (or avoiding law suits and claims). The situation produces dependent, powerless citizens, increasingly forced into paying excessive prices for basics to increasingly powerful organisations.

Power has a unique and dangerous property – it is subject to no natural constraints. Vices to which we may succumb (debauchery, drunkenness, gluttony, vulgarity etc.) find limits imposed by our appetites or physiology. Power is not subject to such constraints and, once some has been acquired, it automatically supplies opportunities for further acquisitions. Rather than sickening by surfeit, as with physical indulgence, power feeds upon itself and (in the modern technological and capitalist world) rapidly exceeds the capacity of individuals, corporations and governments to properly control it – it begins to control them. Moreover, instead of seeing their increasing slavery to it, those in positions of great power may even convince themselves that it is they who are powerful, failing to see they are merely temporary custodians of something far in excess of their own feeble frame (like holding a tiger on a hand leash), pontificating or bragging for cameras and sycophants (as did some senior bankers prior to the 2007 crash) before the tiger decides to go in another direction.

By using our free will to curb our appetites for food, or drink, or debauchery…we prevent pleasure turning into vice. We have already looked at one of the inscriptions above the entrance to the temple at Delphi ('know thyself'). The other is 'nothing in excess' or 'everything in moderation' – expressions of balance, or optimum. Practice with these, where safety nets of surfeit prevent us going too far, is training for our free will struggle with power. Whilst many can see the dangers of excess, and the benefits of balance between two extremes with regard to, say, weight, work, exercise, alcohol, play etc., they forget or ignore all these lessons when their application is of most importance and value – in the acquisition of power, which, in the material world, may manifest as, perhaps, pursuit of status; or fame; or money; or manipulation of others.

As power is not subject to limits, it means we must set our own. We have to exercise the power we have over ourselves, the power of our free will. By setting limits to what is unlimited we become master of, and greater than, that which is unlimited. Just as in the pursuit of maximum money, where there is always more to be had, setting our own limits sets us free.

Those who have either not set limits or not been able to keep to them, become slaves to the power they gain. The resulting imbalances manifest as excesses, such as the vast accumulated assets held by a few people. This forces the majority (including even those who see the sense of 'optimum') to work for the maximum attainable, little though that may be. Consider what the world would be like if, instead of trying to give minimum and get maximum, all, or even the majority, were satisfied with receiving optimum while giving of their maximum.

Having adopted these principles ourselves, we need to apply them in ways suggested in this and the next chapter to help bring corporations into harmony with these, and other, principles of nature. Our personal and collective responsibilities in this context provide us with purpose, but this concept has, like others referred to in the previous chapter, become twisted and obscured over recent decades, and firstly we need to unravel the tangled skein.

...on Purpose

The attraction of maximum self-indulgence, profits and power, has gained momentum from the increasingly common conclusion that life is purposeless.

From a sufficiently distant human perspective in space or time, all and anything can appear to be pointless. So, let us, for a moment, grant that life is purposeless and the universe meaningless, both being a manifestation of mindless physical laws operating over aeons of time. It could still be argued that blind, purposeless, mechanical forces have produced purpose – in the human life forms created. Although apparently purposeless from a cosmic perspective, life can still be purposeful from our earthly perspective – and Earth is where we find ourselves, with enough challenges and problems to deal with while trying to survive and make our world healthy for individuals and nations, before solving, in imagi-nations, conundrums of the cosmos. Given life as we actually experience it, securing life's necessities by co-operation; sharing and celebrating when times are good; sharing with and assisting each other when they aren't, we find plenty of purpose without any textbook 'proof' being required. It is on this foundation that we build civilisation, the arts – and science. Those in ivory towers who dismiss or despise these foundations are, as described below with regard to the earth or soil, despising the ground on which they are standing. It is we who choose to distance ourselves so far from nature around us by studying nature so far from us, without seeking the unity that binds both together in practical ways that benefit all. 'O foolish one to roam so far in thine own mind away from home' (Walter de la Mare. 1873 – 1956 English poet and writer)

If we accept personal and collective (co-operative) survival purposes, do these lead to any further purposes beyond survival? For most of us, it is other people that provide a purpose beyond survival (if you doubt this, imagine living on Earth entirely alone). So, further purposes include healing, helping, teaching and contributing to the health of our communities and environment, improving the lives of others. The philosopher can argue the point – but only as a philosopher, not as a human being. A philosopher incapacitated by accident or illness will not need to debate the purpose, and more importantly the value, of a helping hand. Real life's most important lessons are quite simple and found without need of philosophy, science or other text books. As Shakespeare's Leonato says in **M**uch **A**do about **N**othing:

> For there was never yet philosopher
> That could endure the toothache patiently,
> However they have writ the style of gods
> And made a push at chance and sufferance.

A scientist, a philosopher, or any other occupation or discipline we care to name, is a 'subset' of a human being i.e. does not represent all that a human being is. Reason alone fails us if we use it to try to understand our total experience, especially life's complexities such as virtue, wisdom or love. Pascal's observation will bear repeating: 'The heart has its reasons which reason knows nothing of.' Moreover, it is often those complexities which we find so personally important and, in addition to sharing...teaching...and improving other lives, it is to and from other people that we also hope to give and receive love, acceptance and approval – including those who like acceptance and approval by pointing out pointlessness, which, according to them, is a pointless thing to do.

If other people prove so important for our lives, do not other life forms? The well-known passage by Chief Seattle and Ted Perry includes the following passage: 'What is man without the beasts? If all the beasts were gone man would die of a great loneliness of spirit. For whatever happens to the beasts, soon happens to man. All things are connected.' 'A great loneliness of spirit' translates, in physical terms, to isolating elements of our life-support systems from essential connections, distancing ourselves from nature, from functionality of the whole, from the flow of energy, by breaking cycles and travelling off on tangents to separation and imbalance. In truth we are all as one: 'that which befalleth the sons of men befalleth beasts; even one thing befalleth them; as the one dieth, so dieth the other; yea, they have all one breath; so that a man hath no pre-eminence above a beast...' (Ecclesiastes 3:19)

Given our dependence on and kinship with animals and the deeper waters just glimpsed beyond the surface appearances of mechanics studied by our physical senses, is our view of a tiger completely described as one genetic automaton observing another? Are there more things in tendon and earth than are dreamt of in Darwinian theories? Does not the living tiger and its mysteries transcend our definitions, theories, our egos and conceits? For, despite being subjected to all of these, it still holds its mysteries and still intrigues us. If you feel there is more in you than genes with a capacity to be moulded by experience and environment, can we claim with confidence that the tiger is devoid of anything similar? If not, what about the rest of nature? Perhaps we share something more than physical and behavioural similarities with our animal cousins. Some possibilities were touched on above with regard to whales and dolphins possibly experiencing emotions, including perhaps, love. For us, emotion, spirituality, morality and virtue bring meaning to our lives, which reason cannot reason away, so perhaps it is not unreasonable to wonder if some animals experience something similar?

Of what can we be sure? What can we know for certain? The deductions of reason are not included. Perhaps the world and our lives are more complex than reason can reason? Our conscious experience seems all that we can be sure of – even if all is ultimately illusion, we are sure of experiencing the illusion.

> ...I...could not sing at all,
> Believing me mere matter on a rotatory Ball.
> Such horrid thoughts confuse my mind, they fill my soul with woe;
> But when in meadows green I stray,
> And hear the lark's shrill roundelay,
> I *know* I KNOW I KNOW
>
> (Walter de la Mare)

If you still have an unreasonable faith in reason, remember that reason can always reason against its own propositions:

'The human brain is a physical organ – as such it is subject to the laws of physics and chemistry. And one of these laws is that physical causes always precede physical effects, and that teleological kinds of explanation – that is, explaining natural phenomena by reference to future goals – are inappropriate. But almost all human researchers think of their own work as responsible and goal-directed, and when a person presents a rational argument he or she is doing something more than simply giving a report on his or her own past brain states. When Jacques Monod declared that his goal in writing 'Chance and Necessity' (Collins 1971, p.30) was to show that there was no such thing as purpose, his argument depended on exempting himself from its remit. For purposive activity is basic to all rational argument, and genuinely purposive activity is incompatible with physically determined activity.' (With thanks to Prof. P. Badham for kind permission to quote this passage from his contributory chapter to 'Animals on the Agenda' Eds. Linzey and Yamamoto (B46))

'In the mechanical universe of indivisible hard little atoms, causality worked by impact, as on a billiard table; events were caused by the mechanical push of the past, not by any "pull" of the future. That is the reason why gravity and other forms of action-at-a-distance did not fit into the picture and were regarded with suspicion; why ethers and vortices had to be invented to replace that occult pull by a mechanical push. The mechanistic universe gradually disintegrated, but the mechanistic notion of causality survived until Heisenberg's indeterminacy principle proved its untenability. Today we know that on the sub-atomic level the fate of an electron or a whole atom is not determined by its past. But this discovery has not led to any basically new departure in the philosophy of nature, only to a state of bewildered embarrassment, a further retreat of physics into a language of even more abstract symbolism. Yet if causality has broken down and events are not rigidly governed by the pushes and pressures of the past, may they not be influenced in some manner by the "pull" of the future – which is a manner of saying that "purpose" may be a concrete physical factor in the evolution of the universe, both on the organic and unorganic levels…If time is treated in modern physics as a dimension almost on a par with the dimensions of space, why should we *a priori* exclude the possibility that we are pulled as well as pushed along its axis? The future has, after all, as much or as little reality as the past, and there is nothing logically inconceivable in introducing, as a working hypothesis, an element of finality, supplementary to the element of causality, into our equations. It betrays a great lack of imagination to believe that the concept of "purpose" must necessarily be associated with some anthropomorphic deity.'

(B43 Excerpt from The Sleepwalkers (© 1959 The Estate of Arthur Koestler) is reproduced by permission of PFD (www.pfd.co.uk) on behalf of The Estate of Arthur Koestler.)

The Eastern concept of karma also represents a 'pull of the future' by making experience an incentive to develop character. We experience the effects of our character in the world's reflections and, in response, we can change the cause. For each person, karma is the ultimate reflection and combines cause and effect with a 'pull' of the future. Physics' law of cause and effect may merely be the physical expression of karma's law of 'cause and reflect' – 'reflect' in both active and passive senses.

So far, we have traced various sorts of purpose from personal survival to sharing and co-operation for personal and collective survival, and on to other people and other life forms providing purposes additional to survival (love and acceptance), and perhaps (in terms of karma) beyond earthly survival. Along the way we found limitations to the deductions of reason. We have also seen that non-physical features of our lives, psychological aspects, priorities and values connect to, influence and change, via our physical body, the physical world in numerous ways i.e. the world reflects our mentality and morals.

So, as our mentality and morals affect the world, and that world is part of a greater *physical* setting (solar system, galaxy…universe), can we be so sure that our mentality and morals are not also part of a greater *non-physical* setting? We saw in Chapter III that science shows us how literally everything in the universe physically affects everything else. Who can say that our non-physical experiences (e.g. those just mentioned and, say, thoughts, feelings, compassion, love and a sense of purpose) are not also part of, and affect, a greater non-physical scheme? If we cannot discount or disprove the possibility, then nature, the world…the universe, interacting with us as mirrors and / or teachers, might be physical clues that purpose, and perhaps all other non-physical aspects of our experience, also extend meaningfully, and perhaps consequentially, beyond us.

'I firmly disbelieve, myself, that human experience is the highest form of experience extant in the universe. I believe rather that we stand in much the same relation to the whole of the universe as our canine and feline pets do to the whole of human life. They inhabit our drawing rooms and libraries. They take part in scenes of whose significance they have no inkling. They are merely tangent to curves of history, the beginnings and ends of which pass wholly beyond their ken. So we are tangent to the wider life of things.' (William James. Philosopher. 1842 – 1910). The author Jack London saw something similar through the eyes of a newly captured wild wolf cub: 'He could now see the man-animals driving back the dogs with clubs and stones…Unlike any animals he had ever encountered, they did not bite nor claw. They enforced their live strength with the power of dead things. Dead things did their bidding. Thus, sticks and stones, directed by these strange creatures, leaped through the air like living things, inflicting grievous hurts upon the dogs…(*the cub looks in wonder at men and*) their capacity to communicate motion to unmoving things; their capacity to change the very face of the world…To his mind this was power unusual, power inconceivable and beyond the natural, power that was godlike…the wonder and awe that he had of these man-animals in ways resembled what would be the wonder and awe of man at sight of some celestial creature, on a mountain top, hurling thunderbolts from either hand at an astonished world.' (B47c)

'Man–animals' certainly change the very face of the world and therefore, physics tells us, the universe, and since they do so according to their choices and purposes – motive meets matter; locally and universally. Hence our concept can be expanded to one of complete unity. If connections, no matter how deep or distant, are traced far enough, everything has cosmic perspective, hence cosmic significance and therefore, perhaps, cosmic purpose – and we began, it now seems hastily, by assuming blind purposeless matter in motion in bags of chemicals (i.e. us!).

Amongst others, the ancient Greeks had considered the possibility that the Earth orbited the sun (a heliocentric system). However the view that gained general acceptance for centuries was that the sun and planets orbited the Earth (a geocentric system). Copernicus (1473 – 1543) is credited with changing this view, although the system he proposed is not exactly what we now believe. (Copernicus' system proposed that planets orbited the sun, but still included circular orbits, epicycles and other complications. Enormous contributions to our current understanding were made by Johannes Kepler (1571 – 1630) and Isaac Newton (1642 – 1727). We now believe (with good evidence) in a heliocentric system of planets orbiting the sun at the centre of its 'solar system').

The earlier geocentric view was not, contrary to some modern views, equivalent to an egocentric view! Assuming ourselves to be the centre of the known universe was not seen then as astronomical conceit. Nature was seen as God's creation and man was duly humble in the face of the vastness and majesty above him. The geocentric view was simply in keeping with peoples' direct experience and unaided perception (and still today, even though we believe differently, we are happy to talk of the sun rising, moving across the sky, and going down). Nowadays our direct, immediate, personal views (i.e. that accepted by us without involved analysis of many recorded observations) have been replaced by a rational, scientific view (sometimes enhanced or supplemented by instruments which extend our perception). This scientific view is now accepted as the correct and only view.

However, it *need not be the only* view. The positive benefits of learning to understand the factual information of the heliocentric system can, in this author's view, be offset to a degree by assuming that 'Now we know.'; 'Previous generations were wrong.'; 'We have found the only truth'. Does the acceptance of heliocentricity mean we must reject all aspects of previous viewpoints? There is a spiritual counterpart to the earth-centred view, to seeing ourselves as the centre of the universe and it provides an alternative, and maybe more practically useful view. The geocentric view, due to its immediacy and directness, and being available to all, whatever education or equipment may be available, must be accompanied by a focus on ourselves. Thinking of our location as significant lends us a significance, and a consequent sense of responsibility to live up to that significance, in how we are living our lives, how we are treating our home – the Earth and our personal home upon it – which necessarily includes our neighbours, human and animal.

The heliocentric system provides us with interest, wonder and learning opportunities. However, if we accept the scientific explanation, and *only* the scientific explanation, shorn of and sterilised from all other connections, we allow facts and figures, information, to lead us away from other truths – such as that of the geocentric view. Knowing that the Earth orbits the sun is interesting in an academic way but makes no difference to how we live our lives, except perhaps in a negative way, since such knowledge is also linked with knowing our tiny insignificance, not only as a planet, but also as a solar system, and even as a galaxy, in the vastness of space.

Physics tells us that by influencing the Earth, we influence the universe, so we could say that the universe is showing us ourselves and is therefore (in more than one sense!) all about us. Hence each person could consider themselves the centre of their universe – all of us at the same time! This sort of geocentric view also harmonises with themes explored above; that the Earth around us, even the people we meet, reflect aspects of ourselves, and hence can be influenced by us. If, as some claim, the universe is in the mind (and even if physically 'real' and external to us, our perception and concepts of it are still in the mind), the same applies. The universe is considered to be isotropic (much the same in every direction) so again we could say we are at the centre of our universe and, as the universe reflects us, here is more evidence that we can only change the universe by changing ourselves. If this sense, we can say that for as long as each individual refuses to improve themselves, they are a universal problem.

In contrast to the meaninglessness so often attributed to our individual lives, especially by mechanical views and rational 'explanations' of the universe, the concepts considered here suggest a universal significance for each and every one of us. Brace yourself, since the enormity of the solar system, the galaxies, the universe and life within it, are being condensed and compressed to bear on your shoulder, and your art. Perhaps this could be an interpretation of Greek mythology's Atlas who, for opposing Zeus, was charged with holding the heavens on his head and hands. Viewed from perspectives offered herein, the reader will understand that it is our head *and heart*, correctly balanced, which guides our hands to do this work.

Is this too much to bear? Surely we will be crushed beneath its size and weight? Yes, we surely will, if we only assess matters physically. Not, however, spiritually, in which we see the complement to the Kenneth Clark comments referred to above: it is when each individual is conscious of their powers, as a complete moral and intellectual being, that everything may be adjusted to scales of human capacities and personal proportions – through which we may rediscover our dignity. In our universe, we can exercise those moral and intellectual powers, live with compassion for and interest in Life, improve our character and do our duties diligently, however simple and mundane they may seem. Whether we are delivering a letter or a lecture, writing a cheque or a symphony, conducting a 'bus or an orchestra, all things are connected, so the consequences of our best efforts, in accordance with our purpose and duties, will help sustain the universe, just as our neglect of them will let it down. The greater weight we bear, the stronger the character.

We are all Atlas. The most powerful man on Earth is the man who can control himself and successfully carry all his responsibilities. Moreover, by keeping them balanced, he can avoid staggering around unsteadily, and risking a fall. We are on the Earth, and under the heavens, but hold both in our head and hands. Change your head and heart, and you change the action of your hand, and hence the universe.

The blindness attributed to nature, matter in motion, or the universe in general, might be a reflection of our blindness. Moreover, it is not so much that we cannot see, as will not see – since blindness frees us from personal responsibility. Therefore personal responsibility is surely a clue to our purpose. Many of us try to shirk our duty and pass it to someone else, just as Atlas passed his to Heracles but, also like Atlas, we find it returns to us by tricks similar to those we used to pass it on.

...on Mechanical Mirrors

Provided we do not allow our purposes and personal responsibilities to be displaced by them, we may enthuse about the mechanisms and matter in motion of modern Western science. However, science might seduce us with its clean, clear precision and mechanical certainty. It can give us a sort of confidence, by which we may sneer at the messy world of human opinions and emotions.

Confidence in science can grow into arrogance and may continue far beyond what science can actually support. How can this occur? Nature's mechanical components and principles are not always immediately apparent and require study, instruments and clever people who can tell us more than our unaided senses do. Study, instruments and clever people also provide information about everything from sub-atomic particles to galaxies and deliver it to us in rapid succession, often accompanied by stunning images. Meanwhile, scientific and / or technological applications

have radically changed material, physical aspects of our lives, and bedazzled us with a display of technical and practical achievement. Hence, there is a tendency to think that the source of this, in one sense, deeper knowledge must hold further and, in other senses, deeper answers. The old stories of explorers impressing 'primitive' peoples by predicting the darkening of the sun or burning matches, and their consequently being treated as gods, are being repeated with us as the astounded audience, viewing eclipses and burning DVD's, and consequently, but equally inappropriately, treating science as a god, or at least an oracle.

Although science has never pretended to be either, nor claimed to reveal absolute truth, some set it up as a god or an oracle, and appeal to it, asking all sorts of questions that are not concerned with physical mechanisms – but it cannot deliver any answers on these topics. Science is the current golden calf or graven image…and we are worshipping it, like 'primitives' asking the stranger with an almanac and box of matches for ultimate answers about life. Some of the 'explorers' have even begun to imagine they can answer these questions on the basis of science. Like those who gain any sort of power, such as those with great financial wealth whom we considered above, they assume that in acquiring it they simultaneously acquire the wisdom to wield it. Rather than realise their ignorance, and carefully use some of the newly acquired knowledge, wealth or power to improve themselves, while exercising humility and restraint, many assume they are now in control of that power and become the sorcerer's apprentice, to the devastation of the surroundings. (Not only scientists but, for example, people who win massive lottery prizes might experience the 'sorcerer's apprentice effect'. Suddenly acquiring great wealth and therefore power, but wielding it without wisdom, little knowledge and no experience, control can rapidly be lost and a mess made of their life and surroundings). The same, of course, is happening to us collectively in terms of the environment, where we are using technological power to make the most dangerous mess but here the analogy fails us, since there is no sorcerer to return and restore order. Sadly, it is usually the least-developed, most immature characters who most assiduously seek power – not to develop themselves and serve others, but to dominate them. In this sense, we might say, minimal character seeks maximum power.

Turning to science for truth is folly since it can only provide facts (sometimes it cannot even provide those – some distinctions given below) not the answers we seek. For facts and figures to be useful they need to be combined with other knowledge, feeling and purpose, as also explored further below. However, when science (correctly and factually) offers us nothing in answer to our deeper questions, people who have faith in science as a god or an oracle, conclude that their deeper questions must mean nothing. Yet in truth, science only provides some extra detail (sometimes interesting, educational and useful, sometimes boring, bewildering and dangerous details) about materials and mechanics. Science can also, as Chesterton observed about that article, put out the fire of truth with the fuel of information. Yet descriptions of scientific mechanisms have come to be thought of as the 'correct' or 'best' way of investigating our experiences. However, it is just one way, and tells us more about matter, which, without purpose, doesn't really matter.

Forgetting, ignoring or simply failing to consider the wealth of life experience from, and within which, science was agreed as a limited, constrained investigative tool, proclamations are made from that restricted scientific viewpoint about all of life and all of our experience. From a narrow vista (without even consistently explaining all that falls within that vista), confident proclamations are made about the whole panorama. Can all the mysteries of this world and beyond, through all recorded and unrecorded time, be fitted into a Western scientific paradigm a few centuries or, depending on definitions, even a few millennia old? Orthodox science can only reflect the material world. However, due to its undoubted success in understanding mechanisms, science brings power and has become powerful itself, intimidating some people into agreeing that, as our bodies exhibit mechanisms obeying apparently purposeless physical laws, we must be purposeless mechanisms too, and we lose our senses.

Ignoring, or trying to eliminate elements other than mechanics takes us further away from real life – since it is those other elements which bring all elements to life. Feeding the starving, educating the illiterate, healing the sick, saving the tiger, sculpting La Pieta, building the Taj Mahal, writing Hamlet or the Marriage of Figaro, can all be given a mechanical description, as can science itself, which might well be accurate – while missing all that's important about those endeavours at the same time. The last two examples prompt thoughts of Shakespeare and music which provide, perhaps, the most persuasive example of all – the almost universal appeal and emotional power of music, which no physical description can capture. In Shakespeare's day the strings of stringed instruments were made of sheep gut and physical descriptions of their music fail to answer his question as to why 'sheep's guts should hail souls out of men's bodies' (Much Ado About Nothing Act II Sc. III)

Just as a dictionary definition of a tiger as 'A large carnivorous feline mammal of Asia, having a tawny coat with transverse black stripes', is accurate and covers essential details, in the context of this chapter, it is also inaccurate and misses all essential details! Invoking science to 'explain' non-material aspects of life is often inappropriate and always unscientific. Yet somehow, we forego common sense and listen to, invite and often believe scientists opinions (and they are only opinions) on a variety of topics which the scientists themselves should either decline to answer as a scientist or specify that they are giving their views as lay people, since science has no authority in the area under discussion. For example, on a national radio programme in the U.K. in 2006, a scientist was asked for information regarding the moon. He delivered the information requested. The interviewer then asked whether any basis had been discovered for the mysterious, if not magical, effects of the moon and its influence on people in general, and poets and lovers in particular, throughout history. His answer was negative but taken, by the interviewer, as the definitive answer. The scientist would not know of these aspects by virtue of being a scientist, since science does not study them, and he should have said so. In this area his opinion has no more validity than anyone else's. The reply should have been that there is no scientific evidence. However, there is other evidence, proved by the question being asked – that people respond emotionally to the moon is evidence of the moon's power to provoke emotion. As to why this might be, is another unanswered question, from which we can learn. The radio interviewer made a comment regretting that our emotional and / or romantic notions have been falsified or revealed as empty or in some other way dismissed as unreal by science – but they haven't, nor can be. Science can't even comment on them, let alone falsify them. There are questions science cannot answer nor even legitimately ask. It can only seem to do so via a collective blindness to science's limitations by both lay-people and some scientists. Science can no more find a mechanism for the moon's magic than it can find a mechanism for love or poetry.

Moon over Madhai, Satpura Tiger Reserve

...on Common Sense, Compassion and Science

Currently science is held to be, and conducted as, 'value-free'. So, for example, scientists can claim that Boyle's Law relating the temperature, pressure and volume of a gas, remains the same regardless of ethics and they might well be right, but the crucial importance of all knowledge is the use to which it is put. Science may be value free but life isn't – and real life is where we decide what science will study and how it will be used. Our mortal hand and eye often create artificial pressures, temperatures and volumes in which other people have to live and in doing so they discover relationships not described by Boyle's, or any other, scientific law.

The Renaissance, Reformation and Enlightenment, were three major European cultural developments subsequently affecting most of the rest of the world. Many interesting volumes have been written on them and Appendix IV looks briefly at some of their rarely studied side effects, such as the divorce of ethics from commerce and science, and the swing of the pendulum to an extreme rationalism. Commerce conducted without morality is as dangerous as science conducted without morality, the former following the Reformation and the latter following the Enlightenment. To help modify the effects of these developments, we can create our own personal Renaissance, Reformation and Enlightenment (when our footprints will lead into, but not out of, the tiger's cave).

The imbalances introduced by the exclusive employment of reason, and amplified by military, commercial and political interests, made science a major factor in tilting the cultural balance so far toward the material side of life. Science, and all other manifestations of yang, are now over-emphasised in the extreme. Partly in consequence, a misguided cultural undercurrent is growing that development of intelligence is the ideal and science represents humans at their highest stage of development.

A related and additional danger is science being seen as the only answer to our problems. 'The scientists will find a cure / solve / repair it': 'it' being anything from sub-atomic particles to the environment. Yet there are dozens, if not hundreds, of scientists stating publicly that science cannot deal with impending environmental catastrophes and that we must change our life styles to avoid disaster. This is ultimately dependent on individuals facing their responsibilities – the very thing avoided by adopting the 'scientists will save us' attitude. The illusion of a scientific panacea is at best misguided; at worst, it is fostered by authorities and media to quell increasingly concerned populations (few of whom would feel confident challenging science). The media often employ the generic term 'scientists', implying a consensus amongst a collective intelligentsia. Due to necessary specialisation, most scientists are not even 'experts' across the full range of even their own discipline, let alone science as a whole. Therefore, like many politicians in relation to socio-economics, few see vital connections between their research and the whole of science, and fewer still the broader connections to nature's life-support systems and life itself.

Yet, are we not helpless without scientific advice / procedures / experiments and analysis? Well, useful though science can be, we may remember from chapter II some examples of scientists proclaiming impossible what practitioners subsequently (or had already!) achieved. A more environmentally relevant answer to this question is provided by the rate of melting of the polar ice caps: some years ago available data were plotted against time and a 'line of best fit' drawn through the data and then extrapolated to predict the situation over the coming years. However, the ice melted faster than this model predicted due in part to the previously unknown factor that vast, white ice sheets reflected sunlight and thereby contributed to cooling effects. As the ice melted, this effect decreased, so the rate of melting increased. At time of writing, the ice has 'startled scientists' (BBC television 07/10/07) by disappearing further and faster than any models predicted (even later ones incorporating the reflection or albedo factor) for reasons as yet unknown. Conservationists and other concerned people don't know the reasons either but most were not 'startled', knowing that 'facts' often fail to capture what is most important about the environmental situation. Their understanding and intuition that all and everything needs to be done as rapidly as possible to remedy environmental abuse is more useful than pondering our lack of technical understanding. People who care for life and the planet were taking action while scientists plotted inaccurate graphs and also, possibly, continued to live life-styles aggravating the situation. Individuals concerned about the environmental situation might not be able to write an equation or even necessarily articulate what they sensed, but they were sceptical of the seemingly irrefutable evidence of scientists' facts and figures. They knew nature is too complex to be fully represented by *any* diagrams, models or equations. Perhaps they keep in mind that logic is the 'art of going wrong with confidence.' (Joseph Wood Krutch. 1893 – 1970. American naturalist and writer). It might be unscientific, but taking action to respect and care for nature is a better policy than discussing and debating data which turns out to be useless and the time considering it wasted, while waters rise around us. Many conservationists were adapting their life-styles to minimise their impact on the environment long before science even began to produce wrong results. Yet science is increasingly promoted as the only source of truth and governments and media use it as the definitive source of information. Few people dare question it and even fewer are listened to if they do. Yet here is a real example of the original scientific model being worse than useless – since in addition to being wrong it could have encouraged complacency by suggesting we had longer to rectify problems than we do. This may be heresy from a scientific perspective and / or it may not be 'politically correct'. However, if we climb down to earth (before we're shaken down) from our man-made platforms, we may recognise dear old common sense, often invisible from the heights of our artificial constructions. Respecting nature and living according to her lessons still applies even when there are reports of the Arctic ice cap growing in size (relative to recent reductions). (Sunday Times newspaper April 2010)

Nonetheless, is it not science that tells us the best action to take? Well, out of re-cycling; using natural resources modestly while minimising waste; eating organic food; not killing or damaging anything unnecessarily; caring for living things and educating oneself practically; learning from those who work with nature in the field; earning and banking / investing money ethically; contributing to conservation projects; purchasing environmentally-friendly and fair-trade products – none require science or scientific endorsement. We are guided by common sense, compassion and our inner senses of proportion, humility, consideration for others and the necessity to work with, not against, nature. Care, compassion and common sense are of more value in this context than science, and all of the actions just referred to are bringing greater benefits to the environment, people and animals than any scientific work currently known to this author (with the possible exception of research which will help us utilise clean and renewable sources of energy. Other environmental abuse can be rectified by our behaviour).

Other recent reports (in 2008) have referred to highly complex and expensive equipment required for investigations of various layers of the atmosphere to enhance our investigations of global warming. The situation is so complex as to require bigger and better computers to model the changing climate. If this work finds funding what will be found? More information, cautiously presented with provisos about the limitations of the study, conclusions of which we cannot be 100% sure and, perhaps, recommendations for further study and expense – endless research, and then perhaps, adjustments, attempted repairs and 'cures' to enable us to continue in our same old ways, reinforcing the impression that scientists will help heroic humans overcome all of nature's attempts to thwart us. Just as with the example of declining honeybee populations, when will we learn that we and our ways are the problem? We are currently benefiting from nature's 'patience' – the allowance within her laws for us to accommodate ourselves to those laws. Nature can be seen as trying to teach us, not thwart us. Ultimately we must, and will, comply with nature's laws. The actions required of us are already known (some just referred to and others listed in chapter V). Further research to model what will be seen out of the window (if the window is still in place and the house not flooded) will be expensive (salaries, equipment, utilities etc.) but not contribute anything to the healthy, simple actions recommended above and in the next chapter. Far from contributing, many scientific studies detract from these healthy efforts by generating big 'carbon footprints' (while other scientific studies warn against the same) and do nothing to remind us of our personal responsibilities to change our life-styles. We may learn the most abstruse scientific theories but when will we learn the obvious?

We must find our way back to a closer and more harmonious relationship with nature, reduce our distance from our life-support system – which removes the need for expensive scientific equipment, saves money, time and effort; all of which can be used to heal our world more quickly. Dependency on science and technology is dangerous (which science itself identifies by the vulnerability of highly complex networks). Having travelled too far down this tangential path, we need to find our way back to nature's cyclical paths, on which science can educate, help and fascinate us.

In a well-balanced society, science can be seen as a useful contributor, providing some data for a community to work with, while allowing for other inputs. However, society is not well-balanced (which is why we have the crisis in the first place) and science is used as the only source of 'truth'; intimidating and dismissing non-scientific individuals and their possibly useful knowledge and suggestions. With regard to the conservation of species, this author has direct knowledge of workers 'on the ground' drawing accurate conclusions years before science caught up, and sometimes with it still not catching up. Science needs to be used in conjunction with other disciplines and ways of knowing, without being allowed to become dominant and / or 'blind us with science' to our personal responsibilities.

Science has obviously contributed greatly to our knowledge of what is happening to our environment but, being science, it passes no comment on its findings. Silence from *science* in this context is as it should be, but silence from *scientists* is not, since they have responsibilities as people extending far beyond science. All credit to those relatively few who have done their best to both broadcast warnings and take remedial action.

With regard to conservation, much of it is practical and economic common sense, following nature's path or model, while caring for other people and animals. What is most required in the current crises of imminent extinctions is for people to take action, make sacrifices and put in time, effort and (for the immediate future) money to support already established, but under-resourced, conservation programmes: not necessarily those with the biggest budgets or media profile but those which will tell you where and why the money is spent and / or supply sufficient detail for you to make your own assessments of how best to contribute. Species survival and in consequence, our own survival, depends on demoting ourselves from top priority and helping, caring for others – people, tigers and other animals, rivers, forests and the environment in general. In doing so, we provide ourselves with the best security; ensuring supplies of air, water, food and establishing health in body, mind and mutually supportive relationships – with nature and each other. We do what is ultimately best for self by *not* being selfish. However, this can only be seen from a long-term perspective while selfishness works with short-term agendas, taking 'what I want, now.'

'We know that the white man does not understand our ways. One portion of land is the same to him as the next, for he is a stranger who comes in the night and takes from the land whatever he needs. The earth is…his enemy, and when he has conquered it, he moves on. He leaves his fathers' graves behind, and he does not care. He kidnaps the earth from his children, and he does not care. His father's grave and his children's birthright are forgotten. He treats his mother, the earth, and his brother, the sky, as things to be bought, plundered, sold like sheep or bright beads. His appetite will devour the earth and leave behind only a desert.' (J22)

'The tenant pondered. "Funny thing how it is. If a man owns a little property…it's part of him, and it's like him. If he owns property only so he can walk on it and handle it and be sad when it isn't going well, and feel fine when the rain falls on it, that property is him, and some way he's bigger because he owns it. Even if he isn't successful he's big with his property. That is so." And the tenant pondered more. "But let a man get property he doesn't see, or can't take time to get his fingers in, or can't be there to walk on it"' then, Steinbeck tells us, 'the property is the man' again, but in a different sense. 'He can't do what he wants, he can't think what he wants. The property is the man, stronger than he is. And he is small, not big – and he's the servant of his property. That is so too.' (B66 reprinted by kind permission of the Penguin Group)

This is another way to view optimum as preferable to maximum. In the sub-section above (on Optimum) we saw that in setting limits we are set free. Perhaps as a parallel with this passage of Steinbeck's, we could also say that science takes on too much 'intellectual property', vast scales of matter, time and space. We are dwarfed by them, crushed into insignificance and meaninglessness by the associated facts and figures. Focussing so far away, we can no longer see what is immediately around us; life and our purposes and responsibilities in relation to it. Even the facts themselves, such as the mind-boggling distances to the stars, become as meaningless as science has made our lives and take us light years away into deep space seeking deep answers – which it may well hold – but which it is folly to seek when we have not found answers to fundamental questions such as how to properly protect our observation platform; our earth, which is in great danger. We, of the 'most intelligent' species, leave it on the point of collapse, while we continue observations, reminding us of Thales, one of Pythagoras' teachers, who was once supposedly so intent on his observations of the heavens that he fell into a well. By Chaucer's time (1342 – 1400) the same lesson had still to be learned, by some at least, since a student of astronomy was unwise enough to 'stare upwards while he crossed a field, Busy foreseeing what the stars revealed; And what should happen but he fell down flat, Into a marl-pit. He didn't foresee that!' (Canterbury Tales. Marl is a fertiliser mix of various compounds but mainly clay). Have we learned it now? As the French saying has it; the more things change, the more they stay the same.

Science has enabled us to look at the universe but to do so we have to look away from the Earth – which is our first priority and our main mirror. Our most important business is about us; ensuring the health and prosperity of life on earth; life immediately around us; our tigers and other creatures and hence ourselves and our children. The welfare of our Earthly neighbours should be the subjects of our first and most important questions, before asking about life on other planets. We are reminded of the value of a geocentric view. Let us study the stars and heliocentricity but live geocentrically. Earthly scales and possibilities do not seem to crush us by their size and weight, reminding us of Sir Kenneth Clark's comments above. They can be adjusted to scales of normal human capacities, in proportion to each person's intellectual and moral powers.

Space travel and exploration is exciting and fascinating. Who could not be impressed by the associated technology, the practical achievement and the courage of astronauts? The danger is that it diverts us from other more urgent areas in need of exploration – in order that we may continue many of our current activities, including space exploration. Is the possibility of extraterrestrial life not interesting? Of course it is; but not when life on Earth is in jeopardy.

Yet, other planets may hold strange life forms – in addition to some beyond our imaginations, some may have more than two legs, perhaps with bodies covered in scales or fur. They may not be able to communicate directly with us nor have our technology, but we are eager to demonstrate our respect for their needs and way of life.

How can this possibly be true?

We do not respect creatures like these that we live next to, grew up with and actually depend on! Any such claims are astronomical hypocrisy. Of the possible life forms that scientists speculate could be 'out there', killing them, skinning them, draining any gall bladders they may have, crushing into powder any bones they may have etc. has, as far as this author knows, not been suggested and, if they were would, presumably, provoke outrage. Similarly, potential space explorers would presumably be insulted if it was suggested they would stand idly by while other humans arrived to do these things to the newly discovered life forms. Why then do they stand idly by while other humans do these things to life forms on Earth? We seek new friends in space while treating neighbouring life-forms as aliens. We try to understand deep space while failing to see that all life is one – which brings an understanding deeper than space.

The undesirable possibility that neighbouring interstellar life-forms might be as violent and dangerous as we are, and the results of our contacting them needs no explanation – except perhaps from an earthly perspective that a privileged handful of people take that risk on all our behalves without reference to us, the vast majority, including tax payers funding some of their work.

However, let us suppose newly discovered life-forms have similar capabilities to us but are not as violent and dangerous. They must soon learn that millions of our fellow humans are neglected, poisoned, starved or murdered whilst we collectively damage or destroy our life-support system. More importantly from the aliens' perspective, why should they receive any better treatment from us than our fellow humans? If there was any life form with which/whom we might communicate, what could we possibly say – that would not immediately alienate us?

"Although, collectively speaking, we have just emerged from the most destructive century in our recorded history during which millions of innocent people, including those just born, were massacred and, while massacres continue and we destroy other species while degrading and damaging our planet, we thought we'd say 'Hello' and knew you'd be just thrilled to meet us. Despite all the greed, selfishness and additional abominations born of apathy and ignorance, there is a positive side – outstanding individuals have contributed to a periodic flowering of 'civilisation' and, as you can see, we are so intelligent, we have been able to contact you. We are clever, exceptional humans not to be measured by standards applicable to most other humans. We are neither typical of our brothers nor their keepers."

"You must indeed be intelligent beyond our understanding. To you we must be in the primitive condition you call 'savage' since we do not understand how intelligent it is for you to contact us while you are dying from self-inflicted ailments. Whilst you claim to be an intelligent sub-group, do you not depend on air, water and food? If so, you study communication with us while resources essential for your own life are being degraded and destroyed. We do not understand such intelligence. However, we will, nonetheless, consider why you have contacted us. Have you come to give to, or share with, us? If so, what would you give to or share with us that you will not give to or share with your own species, or other species, on Earth – and why? If you will not help your brothers and sisters why would you help aliens? Or perhaps your motive is not to give but to take – knowledge; resources; labour? If so, you now see your fatal problem. The only other motive we can imagine is that you aspire to be part of something greater than yourself – in itself a potentially noble aspiration. Yet you are already part of something greater than yourself, and the majority of it is degraded or dying, while your greater family is underfed, un-housed, unclothed and uneducated. You are not contributing properly to the welfare of what you are already a small part of, yet seek greater responsibilities.

Let us leave you with a gift from us: you cannot collectively exhibit healthy moral maturity until each individual does so. Society cannot make individuals moral but individuals can make society moral. Individuals behaving socially must contribute to society behaving socially, which, in turn, moulds society's values and the social behaviour of its current and future citizens. Society's approval or disapproval forms powerful influences on its citizens, sometimes more powerful than the law. Nonetheless, whether or not they are influenced by social pressure, the law, intuition, intelligence or conscience, it is only individuals who ultimately decide their own behaviour. You 'intelligent' ones, who can communicate with us, are able to do so by having chosen a restricted perspective of life – in ironic contrast to exploring the enormity of the physical universe – and by following that narrow, specialised path you avoid unpleasant scenery. This allows, in time and in combination with so many others doing the same in their own way, the abominations you mention with embarrassment but seem to think are eclipsed by purely rational and technological achievements. Yet you know for certain and for yourself, without need of 'proof', that if you or yours suffered as many of your fellow humans do, rational and technological achievements, your own or others', are a sorry substitute for practical aid so desperately needed. Healthy growth cannot be achieved by ignoring fundamental parts of humanity, or by ignoring fundamental parts of your humanity. Only by incorporating them in a balanced and harmonious unity within, can you become part of a greater balanced and harmonious unity without. While some of your species developed space rockets, which were born of military agendas, children of your species were being burned alive by napalm. Your collective priorities and values must change before you would be welcomed anywhere beyond Earth.

Currently it would seem one portion of space is the same to you as the next, you seem a stranger who would come in the night and take from space whatever you need, and when you had conquered it, you would move on. You would leave your fathers' graves behind and you would not care. You would treat your sister planets as things to be bought, plundered, sold like bright jewels. Your appetite would devour all planetary environments and leave behind only a vacuum.

Collective priorities depend on personal priorities, so each must arrange theirs in order and face their responsibilities toward them, without waiting for others to face theirs, or for guarantees, or rewards."

If alien life-forms are more intelligent than us they would most likely ensure we cannot contact them. Would you be eager to meet neighbours who polluted their own accommodation and others'; poisoned their own and others' food supplies; killed anything that could make a financial profit – and anything that couldn't? We are not currently fit, even by our own standards, to introduce ourselves to other life forms.

Ah, but if they are more intelligent, could they not help us develop? What can they possibly tell us that we don't already know about our problems? We do not require more intelligence but more morality, kindness, compassion and the courage to face our personal responsibilities. It is only we who can, and must, choose to change our characters in that regard before the world can change, and before anything else can help us.

More importantly, by looking longer and more deeply, we can see that the supposed choice between humanitarianism / conservation and technological advance is a false premise for argument. There need be no choice since, if we controlled self and greed (the real choice involved) there is enough for all and, when the disadvantaged receive their due, their abilities will help us achieve more than has been already by the tiny privileged percentage of human talent currently employed on projects such as space exploration.

The courage of astronauts and the technological achievement of space travel are truly impressive but surely these qualities have many more urgent applications awaiting them at home, on Earth? We left Earth on a tangent at Cape Canaveral. It is an exciting, impressive and interesting tangent but, nonetheless, a tangent. We currently need to stay within nature's cycles and orbits of effect here on Earth. As Schweitzer said 'In the hope of reaching the moon men fail to see the flowers that blossom at their feet.' We might say on looking at this photograph that in reaching for the moon men fail to see the sun at their feet…

"Now I know why I am here. Not for a closer look at the moon, but to look back at our home. The Earth." U.S. Astronaut Alfred Worden.

"The first day or so we all pointed to our countries. The third or fourth day we were all pointing to our continents. By the fifth day we were aware of only one Earth." Saudi Arabian Astronaut Sultan Bin Salman al-Saud.

In an interview, U.S. astronaut Eugene Cernam of the Apollo programme said that he knew it was due to science and technology that he was standing on the moon but when he looked at the Earth he knew that science and technology had no answers.

Reason practised alone, head without heart, has no ultimate answers. Solely relying on reason will lead us astray since science is neither our sole guide nor our soul guide.

Current scientific aspirations to 'know where we came from' reduce to discovering each link in a mechanistic chain. Let us imagine it is completed. The achievement may be impressive but it can only be descriptive, with explanations limited to details 'within that chain'. How, why and when the chain itself arose remains a mystery and, while we have fascinating and useful knowledge of nature's mechanisms, the same fundamental questions our ancestors asked remain unanswered. We can no more answer fundamental questions now than could Job (in the Biblical Book of).

We have considered that personal experience, combined with active interest and a growing maturity, is the surest knowledge, and that wisdom cannot be taught or learned from books. Let us imagine a young person, well-educated and perhaps in their first employment. Not necessarily arrogant, just confident in their recent qualifications and themselves. They might (hopefully only privately) dismiss the not so well-educated, but experienced elder. In so doing, they reveal their greater ignorance and also, perhaps, a lack of respect. Most of us play both roles at different times in our lives. However, as a class, and in the way their role is presented to society, science or scientists might sometimes play the role of the well-informed but massively ignorant youngster.

The Upanishads are part of ancient scriptures known as the Vedas and we have already referred to the Rig Veda (Vedas mean 'knowledge' and they were written by poets, as hymns or songs). They pre-date recorded history and form the first foundations of Hindu philosophy. These scriptures refer to the ultimate unity as the Self…

'This Self is not realisable by study, nor even by intelligence and learning. The Self reveals its essence only to him who applies himself to the Self. He who has not given up the ways of vice, who cannot control himself, who is not at peace within, whose mind is distracted, can never realise the Self, though full of all the learning in the world.'

Katha Upanishad

'…always learning but never able to acknowledge the truth.'

The Bible (2 Timothy 3:7)

The extraordinary Hindu priest, sage and mystic, Ramakrishna (1836 – 1886) lived through the most dramatic, near-death, direct visions and religious experiences. He had received very little formal education and only spoke his native Bengali, with its earthy symbolism of farm and field. Although not able to use the language of the well-educated, he was visited by many scholars, pundits, preachers and teachers, who heard, they said, the wisdoms of Hinduism expressed with a purity and simplicity only possible to genius.

Reason has asked many questions of nature, found some answers (in terms of mechanics) – and more questions, which we then ask, about the remotest sub-atomic particle or galaxy without asking why our children's futures are threatened, our neighbours starving, or tigers are dying. Some do, such as you who are reading this book, but you are in a minority, which is why tigers are still dying, people starving and the future threatened. When will we collectively remember the Earth?

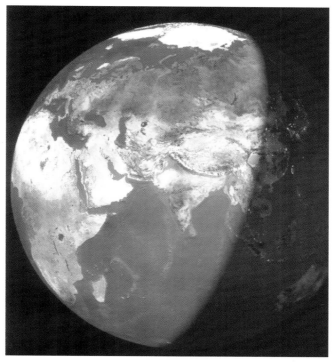

With thanks to NASA for placing satellite images in the public domain

Probably when it is too late. We have to convince others to try our viewpoints and not let reason (and other associated mechanistic, material and commercial factors) rule our lives exclusively. Much of our imbalanced world does not share our viewpoint and currently sees only material – scientifically, economically, financially, professionally, personally, socially (for status), nationally and even artistically (which is measured by the money it might sell for – reminding us of Oscar Wilde's comment about people who know the price of everything and the value of nothing. Similarly, we might say that science measures everything and values nothing – which is correct for science, but not for scientists).

These assessments are not restricted to space exploration. In our current global circumstances, any highly specialised, expensive and labour-intensive programme, not directly relating to maintenance of our life-support system, may be an example of great intelligence but no common sense or compassion. The environmental situation is so critical that what we call civilisation is in peril. Environmental disasters will not only claim health and lives directly but through economic and social repercussions. When civilisation, which has only ever been a thin veneer, is peeled away, comforts also disappear, food must be fought for and bullies rule. When the air is thin, the animals gone forever and waters lap around the lowlands (Pacific islands are already disappearing), let all those specialists prepare their answers – for questions about their discipline? No, for children's questions about what they did practically for Earth and life; how they can be so intelligent and so stupid at the same time; how they could see so much and do so little of real value. Specialism, extreme or otherwise, is legitimate for as long as the foundations that support them are maintained. This is currently not the case. More amazingly, much of the specialism is actually contributing to damaging those foundations (and often revered for the intelligence supposedly associated with them!)

John Seymour could see that we have to adjust our perspective and actions to literally change the world. However, to do so we must not allow reason to work alone. Due to our current imbalances, the rational is powerful and tries to convince us that it alone holds truth. "Science is not powerful because it's true. It is true because it is powerful" (Hilary Lawson, contemporary philosopher and broadcaster). Perhaps there is a time factor hidden within this quote: maybe science became powerful because it was true (within its limits, as already mentioned) but has now become so powerful (due to our imbalance), it is allowed to dictate what is true, aided and abetted by those who benefit by using science for personal, political and military advantages, profits and / or careers, to silence detractors or control others.

Just as with our earlier examples, instead of practising restraint, behaving 'proportionately' or settling for an optimum, the incessant strive for more power, more profit, more control, more information, is the disturbing force that keeps the pendulum moving. Our pendulum swings to a maximum due to a minimum of self-control, individually and hence, collectively. We are now at one extreme end of the swing in an imbalanced state – which is why a backlash against science, a swing to the other extreme, is the last thing we need. We must utilise and harmonise our efforts across all sincere fields of investigation, treating them with equal respect to find what is healthy and sustainable for all of us. A scientist who dismisses other disciplines (and / or aspects of life not accessible to science) is as foolish as practitioners of other disciplines who dismiss science. We have to co-operate, work together and mature beyond 'my team is better than your team'. An open mind is the only justifiable position – both rationally and intuitively.

Healthy environments and healthy people are mutually interdependent. One of the very few things that most people can agree on is that children are innocent of their situation (even if concepts of karma have validity, they involve much about which we cannot be certain. The only certainties are the children, their condition, our responsibilities, and our choices to face or ignore them). The situation for the majority of children is that education is not available to most of them…nor homes…nor clothes…nor food…nor clean water. We have worked out how to feed and clothe men in space but not worked out how to feed and clothe children on Earth – and that's not rocket science. We also know, and can tell those children about, that star in the sky, or tiny atomic particles that make up food, that they cannot see.

We may not find ourselves personally in this situation but, from a global perspective, this situation actually prevails. The distance between these choices, between compassion and computing physical distances, is astronomical, and we are in danger of losing ourselves completely between them, with no recognisable reference mark by which to find our way back. We either travel great distances from our connections to life, and from nature's lessons, or hide beneath layer upon layer of insulation. Both can be descriptions of over-specialisation, imbalance, or collective dis-ease. Given the opportunity to earn both their share of the Earth's resources and an education, many of the under-privileged would then be able to use the human talent they already possess to answer the academic questions confounding many comfortable, well-fed, privileged people. The appearance of hungry, illiterate children is often directly associated with the disappearance of tigers and trees (see chapter V). Exploring space and atoms is wonderful and intriguing, provided we first respect and care for others' space and atoms. In doing so we must avoid tangents and ensure man's cycles copy nature's, with a better balanced distribution of resources.

...on Reflecting Telescopes

The preceding sub-section suggested space exploration should not, in our current environmental circumstances, be a high priority for state funding. Some supporters of space programmes claim these are the very circumstances which make space exploration a priority, as we may find alternative planets to colonise. It is true that amongst a vast and beautiful arrangement of stars as revealed by optical and radio telescopes, some stars have been found with orbiting planets. None of these planets have so far shown anything approaching Earth-like conditions, but the search has only just begun.

For the moment, we will ignore the mind-boggling scales of space and time separating solar systems, even within our own galaxy; we will ignore Earth's ecosystems being poisoned and degraded as you read; and we will ignore that there is currently no remotely feasible way of establishing life support systems for 7000, let alone 7 billion, people anywhere but on Earth, and certainly not on the journey to Earth II, assuming 7 billion people agreed this was the correct solution (there will always be one who disagrees!).

The current fashion for colonising the 'final frontier' is fuelled by television sci-fi series and novels, with spacecraft commanded by body-suited, military-minded, new-colonial style space travellers. What if we find a paradise planet but it is not vacant? Will there be wars, conquests and colonies made anew? Oh no, we say, we are much more mature than that, we can spread love and health. Then shouldn't we establish these on this planet first? (Which would remove the need to colonise a new planet). How else can we take them to other worlds? Looking around us shows that we have not only failed to foster love and health, but are at the other extreme, perilously close to killing our own life-support systems.

However, exploring the unknown is always exciting so, in one sense, this is a stimulating idea. Yet, in another sense, it is pedestrian and boring, since it equates to eternal travel onward and outward – without ever venturing inward. Some consider it will be those new planets which might provide answers to our problems, new wealth and / or sources of energy, full health, or perhaps a means by which we don't have to work any more and new, currently unimaginable prospects.

Although we shall not be going anywhere beyond our immediate vicinity (in terms of space travel) for the foreseeable future, this idea has taken root in some modern minds as a real possibility, so let us look at these points in turn: By the end of the final chapter (in more senses than one!) we should see that we are the answer to our problems, since we are the authors of our problems. That we recognise this and deal with it is consistent with the clues above regarding our 'cosmic purpose' and, perhaps, indicates why the scales of the cosmos confine us to Earth. The Earth has all the wealth and energy we require, it just has to be harnessed cleanly, in a sustainable way and distributed fairly. Living in harmony with, and not poisoning nature, and hence ourselves, would cure most of our health problems. Seeking a 'magic bullet', or 'instant cure' is, from spiritual perspectives, weakness, lack of personal responsibility and a childish wish for a magic wand to change the world in accordance with our will, while it is we who must learn to comply with nature, and ill health is one of the guides to realising this. Whilst work can indeed be onerous and excessive when the system is exploitative and controlled by the few and greedy, at the other extreme, people do not respond or develop well without the discipline of work and its rewards, a process that develops healthy values and standards. As for unimaginable prospects, we currently can neither cope with nor realise most of our imaginable and achievable prospects (e.g. a healthy world for all).

Hence talk of technology to open new worlds is sophisticated blindness as great as any attributed to nature and life, and when examined, when really thought through, proves truly purposeless – unless accompanied by virtue and morality, in which case we can heal ourselves before spreading our imbalances to other worlds. Even if, after unimaginably long aeons of travelling onward and outward rather than inward, we completely 'explored' the universe, 'conquered' or 'settled' it, what value has it unless we are able to conduct ourselves with respect and regard for each other and other life forms? The astronomical scales that are part of our space travel delusions might actually be a better measure of our reluctance, our fear, to face ourselves and explore our inner universe, with its inner worlds, and their inner tigers. When we explore inwardly we discover meaning and purpose in our lives, all associated with character development and personal responsibility. We continually vaunt our intelligence as our greatest attribute while knowing that it can only bring benefit when married to morality – one mark of maturing character. Yet we now scan the skies with radio receivers seeking life as clever as we think we are. Our misguided over-emphasis on 'intelligence' has replaced personal purpose with technology, looking for neighbours to disturb and endless travel. 'Roaming so far in our own minds from home', we find eternal vagrancy dressed-up as adventure and heroism in the style of television science *fiction*, whereas in *reality* we can, and must, make our home healthy – healing our earth by working on internal navigation – the first and final frontier.

Some suggest that contact with alien life forms will help us 'develop' but 'develop' is not defined (it might rather be that it is when we develop, we will make contact – firstly with each other and life on Earth, and then with extraterrestrial life). Or, does it mean we gain more information about mechanics? Perhaps we shall be pointed toward solving one of our current major academic puzzles; reconciling quantum physics with Relativity and this would be a truly fascinating and profound advance. Yet, to discover it while life dies around us would be a magnificent conceit. If we continue with our inverted priorities and live to see the results, imagine trying to trade those new and profound equations for bread to feed empty bellies. Any sincere, well-balanced attempt to define 'development' leads us back to harmonising with nature, morality and virtue, not the pursuit of more information. (Einstein was a founder of quantum physics and solely responsible for Relativity. Could we say that these achievements were also magnificent conceits? No, at that time (1905 - 1918) global environmental perspectives were far from clear. As we have noted, the major, critical dangers arose after, and largely as a consequence of, WWII. We have also noted that Einstein was among the first to speak out about these dangers and their political, military and socio-economic effects. He not only used his fame to make his voice heard but also, where he could, to contribute to rectifying social wrongs, while repeatedly proclaiming morality as more important that intellectual endeavour). Reconciling quantum physics and Relativity is currently the topmost intellectual leaf we can see. To spend time, energy and resources grasping it, while the tree is dying from moral decay, would be, at the same time, both the height of intelligence and the depth of stupidity.

Due to our imbalances; our illness; we have used science without regard to morality or compassion and in our feverish state, are hallucinating, imagining that science or technology will take us to other places where 'everything will be fine'. Yet, in reality, we have no alternative but to make 'everything fine' where we are. Science cannot solve our problems. Only by working on ourselves as much, if not more than, the external world (where science may help us) can we heal ourselves and then our world. Paradise is always somewhere else because it allows us to look for solutions anywhere but where they are – inside. So we set off to find a physical paradise while we have the ability to realise a spiritual one where we are, and when we do, the external physical world will reflect it – as a paradise!

Returning to our reflections on telescopes and, for that matter, microscopes, it is, in summary, accepted that scientific observations of atoms, stars and planets are astounding and fascinating. At the same time, it is a mistake to invest so much in collecting them while the viewing platform is collapsing. Excessive attention to minutiae or over specialisation would be as if Corbett over-emphasised the physical aspects of his knowledge e.g. while he measured and re-measured micrometer differences in pug depth or, perhaps, variations in gunpowder composition of each cartridge, people would be killed and eaten and his own life put at greater risk. Such absurd imbalances and excesses help us see how we now collectively fuss over the nth degree of the nth degree while losing our perspectives, purpose and value to others, ultimately falling down the well shaft since we are too absorbed in our personal specialisation to see where we are going.

It is another mistake to see science as the only possible path to the stars. A wealth of wisdom is available to us in other ways and from other viewpoints, which might include philosophical analysis; their disguise in Greek mythology; or simply by watching and receiving, in stillness and silence, and 'absorbing' knowledge. Just as we may see above that there is more to the moon than science can tell us, similarly with the stars, and to live without these other elements would cause us to water heaven with our tears.

If science is lost in space (between stars and within atoms), we are lost with it, looking everywhere but where we should – at our earth and our responsibilities to it. Moreover, explorations of early wildernesses on earth – a history of exploitation of other people and resources – are now re-focussed on space exploration, but without our having learned the lessons of earth-bound exploration. We are already imbalanced by looking so intently into the furthest reaches of space and, by doing so, cannot see our earthly significance, disorientating ourselves still further. To find our significance and our balance we have to look around us. At his inauguration, John F. Kennedy paraphrased a passage of Kahlil Gibran's (1883 – 1931 Lebanese poet, author and artist) when he said 'Ask not what your country can do for you: Ask what you can do for your country.' Even more urgently now, we must substitute 'world' for 'country' and act upon the advice.

There are simple ways to do this, and without leaving one's neighbourhood. Later in this chapter and in chapter V we will see that adjusting our life styles to be ethical and environmentally-friendly are powerful ways to bring good, healthy change to our world, nations and each other.

...on Technology

'Trans-humanism' is a recently coined term describing abilities we either now, or soon will have, to genetically engineer children prior to their birth. This raises innumerable questions, to which there are no universally acceptable answers. Nonetheless, we know that if people are prepared to pay for this 'service', it will become available, legally or illegally.

Interference with nature's designs does not stop at the level of genes but reaches further to atomic and sub-atomic levels. Atomic and sub atomic distances may be measured in nanometres. A nanometre is one billionth (thousand millionth) of a metre and nature has been working at these levels since creation, but now we can as well, and are already at work. Nanotechnology promises a future where, for examples, microscopic silicon chips, driven by the flagella of bacterial cells swim through our capillaries to target and destroy fat cells, while other nano-robots will be able to deliver drugs to specific cellular sites. Who would not be impressed by such technology or the skills of the scientists and engineers? Yet, could such fantastic inventions also represent an over-emphasis on intelligence and technology, out of balance with other considerations? Could it almost have obscene, comic, even farcical aspects? Destroying fat cells with nano-robots is only one story the court jester is telling us and there are many more examples of how science will control all of nature and make machines to fabricate whatever we want... but some are taking the jester seriously. Apart from some medical conditions, fat cells mean more food is being consumed than is needed. The solution is to review one's life-style and change it – which brings health in a variety of ways (healthier diet, useful exercise, self discipline and the resulting character development by making these adjustments). 'Health' achieved via nano-robots means profits can be made, and excess consumption can continue while others continue to starve.

Some inventions are so far removed from what is most urgently required by the Earth and its inhabitants that they would be comic if they were not tragic. Even where inventions are relevant to current needs, too many scientists, supposedly our best bet for brains, continue to consider cures but not prevention and the childishly appealing idea that the world can be 'what we want' it to be. Elsewhere, much money and resources are plied into researching the possibilities of technology which, in many ways, is part of a fantasy world. Science fiction and fact blur together. This has especially been the case in the fantasy worlds of the film industry, which fuel our obsession with special effects, fabrication and falsehood. All is well while such amusements are kept in perspective and due proportion. Yet, these aspects of our societies grow out of all proportion, both in terms of money invested in them and the importance attributed to them by the media and other money-making concerns – which influences people and hence society. The cost is enormous: not only financially but also in terms of the values and priorities paraded in front of people, in particular children. Meanwhile, all that's real, worthwhile and of substance is being degraded and destroyed for want of a tiny fraction of the money spent on illusion, emptiness, falsehood and a 'celebrity culture' of endless puff and nothingness.

Even if we are able to temporarily continue gluttony, lying on sofas watching fantasy films while miniature robots kill fat cells, some currently unknown complication or side-effect will arise that interferes with our man-made 'heaven'. Will we learn then? Or will more commercially employed scientists develop more technology to meet the new market to overcome the new problem...? Technology extends our depth of influence but not depth of character, just as in the Koestler quote in Appendix IV regarding telescopes magnifying our sight but leaving us as moral dwarfs.

Telescopes and other technologies have also managed to magnify the budgets allocated to them. The Mars Climate spacecraft of 1998 was an impressive achievement. It is understandable that an all too human situation occurred in which, unknown to each other, one team working on the project used metric units while another used imperial units. The resulting mismatch rendered the spacecraft un-navigable and it disappeared forever somewhere near Mars. Harsh lessons have been learned but one wonders if the 'lesson behind the lesson' has also been learned i.e. that $125 million thrown into space has made no appreciable difference to space and told us nothing of Mars' climate but could have helped tell us something of, and made an appreciable difference to, Earth's climate. The scale of waste is put into some perspective by considering that a small NGO struggles to acquire even 1/100000th of this amount to help protect nature. Yet, admittedly, we must face facts; this is the real world and we just have to accept that a tiny NGO and a government-directed NASA make no real comparison and one is far more important than the other. That's right, the NGO protecting Earth's life-support system is far more important than government-directed NASA projects investigating if Mars has a life-support system. Some years ago a well-known U.K. television commercial for ready-made mashed potato showed mechanical Martians using that product and bouncing with electronically synthesised laughter at humans' alternative but labour-intensive, and therefore supposedly primitive, preparation of potatoes for mashing. Our antics trying to examine the Martian climate, while adversely affecting our own, would surely stimulate even more vigorous Martian laughter.

Although the whole imbalanced system is anything but healthy, ironically it is 'health' most often held up as the benefit of specialisation and hi-tech research. Yet it also seems to be the 'add-on' justification for what is now found to be possible and commercially viable. In few, if any, cases was the alleviation of particular problems the original goal or guiding light for the research. Personal promotion, publications, profit, prestige, publicity are usually the prime motivating factors. Once a result is achieved and the designers are asked "why?" answers take a second or two ("…oh…oh yes…to help people / feed people / cure disease") and, while they lack conviction, the answers suffice to deflect further enquiry. Even when sincere, similar claims have been made before – drugs were a technological miracle that would supposedly end disease but brought dangerous side effects which have brought, in many cases, as serious problems as they have 'cured'. The 'Green Revolution' (please see Appendix II) not only failed to banish hunger but has also had dangerous side effects on the environment. To balance this reference it should be noted that there were genuine advances made and millions of people fed by cross fertilising different strains of wheat and re-planting programmes (e.g. as in the sincerely philanthropic work of botanist Norman Borlaug. However, this exception is still in keeping with our principles; a) man experimented with new strains of wheat, but nature determined which would survive and thrive and; b) sincere and worthwhile work developed new mass markets, and these attracted those who only sought profit and so, when harnessed to agribusiness and chemicals, the Green Revolution became another Greed Revolution).

When prompted, scientists can always find benefits for humanity in their work, just as in Mary Shelley's novel, Victor Frankenstein is entirely focussed on science and its supposed benefits while ignoring basic balancing aspects of life (mostly elements of yin), which would set his work in a healthier, broader context. In the real world too, despite many claims that scientific discoveries will alleviate people's suffering, two thirds of humanity remain impoverished while the gap between rich and poor widens. No discovery or invention has, nor ever will, solve our problems on their own, since they cannot improve human character, which has to happen internally and by personal choice. Frankenstein's flaw was in his character, as it is in many characters of literature and, maybe, for many of us too. However, the modern emphasis on image and the excessive value placed on intelligence makes this ever harder to identify. The misplaced emphasis is itself evidence of our reluctance to meet the challenges of personal character development.

Beyond military and commercial objectives there appears to be little, if any, overall direction or even co-ordinated plan for research. Whilst modern developments are profoundly affecting society, society is never asked what developments it would like to see. In the U.K., government ministers need never have worked in the field they take responsibility for. Hence for eight years in the U.K. the science minister was a former chairman of a supermarket chain who had made significant financial donations to the Labour Party. He mainly allowed academia to decide their own developments and, almost inevitably, with each stage of research following on from the previous one, further steps are taken down ever-narrowing paths, ever further removed from daily life. Specialists become more of a law unto themselves and impervious to concerns of the tax payer, or other, private sponsors, that what is being funded can be justified from any but the narrowest of perspectives. The only measure of the calibre of academic staff, or their suitability for receiving grants, seems to have been reduced to the one-dimensional 'number of publications' authored.

The potential for devastatingly dangerous results from our abusing and destroying nature and tinkering with what remains, are recognised by some scientific pundits but also usually dismissed by them to justify their own research, with unscientific opinions that benefits outweigh risks and tired platitudes about man never shrinking from challenges etc. It is true that throughout history Man has bravely faced ever bigger challenges – to 'conquer' nature, achieve power, profits or fame, invent and construct, but always (collectively speaking) cravenly failed the challenge to become a bigger man, which nearly always means subordinating self. History records great advances in practical achievement for 'me' or 'my', matched only by retreats from responsibilities to other lives. Being a bigger person, growing as a character, is not found in conquering but in serving, in helping and healing other parts of the local or global community, human or otherwise. Choice also applies to challenges: protect the life-support system of the Earth; clean water for the thirsty; food for the hungry; education for underprivileged people; save the awesome and magnificent tiger from oblivion; or target and destroy fat cells in the obese? This is not an unrealistic comparison since the money spent on hi-tech research could achieve the other goals just listed. Just as our personal history helps us know who we are, History tells us who we are collectively. If we make real progress – develop our characters – History will tell us who we *were*.

The community can only reflect the values and goals its members adopt. In the West particularly, personal gain and development is often the top, and sometimes only, priority. This is manifested materially, physically and therefore bodily. It is common to find people 'pumping iron' or generally getting fit in expensive gyms (paying money to expend energy is a curious reversal of traditional principles). The energy expended does nobody else any good while, for example, elderly or infirm people (philosophers included) might need some groceries carried or the garden worked. It's a problem most able-bodied people can solve for them easily and those who exercised in this way would do so for free and find more than physical rewards. A single person can change an invalid's or pensioner's world, and hence their own world and, since all things are connected, *the* world by a scale that is known from within but cannot be measured by instruments. We are as insulated from our neighbours as from our environment. We search for new planets but don't know who our neighbours are; seeking 'new' life in space without discovering life next door, while billions of dollars are spent on creating false images and values. We have inter-planetary and sub-atomic sophistication but haven't safeguarded Earth's tiny percentage of fresh water, or the atmosphere, or our tigers…sophisticatedly ignorant, scientifically stupid, seduced by toys and playtime, we are conditioned and packaged physically and mentally, just like the products we buy.

…of Panoramic Views

The specialisation referred to above obviously applies to far more disciplines than science alone: the economist knows little or nothing of ecosystems and the biologist knows little or nothing of economics. Most politicians, carrying both responsibility and power, may know little or nothing of any discipline – this is thought to be unnecessary since they can call on experts and advisers. Yet, as in the example above, advisers were no doubt called with regard to bio-fuels, but these advisers either did not understand the importance of mature forests or, if they did, their advice was ignored.

Even the deregulation by the Reagan and Thatcher governments referred to above was influenced by specialist theories. One fundamental principle underlying their economic policies was Adam Smith's 'invisible hand' which supposedly regulates markets automatically, even though each individual person or business pursues their own selfish goals (Adam Smith 1723 – 1790. Scottish moral philosopher who developed a theory of political economy. He wrote the first modern work on economics, known usually by its abbreviated title 'The Wealth of Nations'). However, whilst it is true that all enterprises are initially subject to market forces, over which they have no control, once an enterprise has become transnational or multinational, it acquires profit and power on a scale that can be used to influence those previously independent market forces; to change them in their own favour. In practice, corporate commerce not only can, but actively and vigorously does manipulate economic laws; civil legislation; consumers by media, marketing, advertising; and uses every advantage of cheap labour in some countries, fiscal policies of others, and keeping profits in tax-free havens elsewhere. Once a corporation extends beyond national boundaries it is free of national laws. The most recent example of 2007 shows us that without proper regulation, selfishness, greed and stupidity can override any 'market forces' and distort and imbalance markets until they crash. Adam Smith's invisible hand transpired to be only a product of his visible hand but millions now suffer the consequences of governments' slavish adherence to his, and other economic theories (e.g. monetarism), despite the repeated lessons of common sense, history and nature. The invisible hands that ultimately control our systems, economic or otherwise, are those of nature, morality and virtue.

Although particular corporations, nations and politicians have been referred to, no implication is intended that many other corporations, nations and their premiers would not have behaved similarly in similar circumstances. Given the opportunity, few people are able to resist seizing wealth and power and, as will become increasingly clear, the main thrust of this book is that it is human nature itself that needs examining and improving, most importantly, our own

The power of big business is compounded by their influence through the media on millions of people and by their role as employers to hundreds of thousands of people, most of whose time is taken earning sufficient for survival. The working population needs to find some time after work for family and home, and is too tired and ill-informed to investigate socio-economics, abuse of power, corruption, environmental science etc. or even why they cannot rely on their elected representatives to do their duty with regard to these issues. Hence the status quo is not only perpetuated but reinforced. Due to the global reach and effects of modern multinationals, these factors have consequences for all life on the planet. Wider perspectives than making money, on the part of corporations and individual citizens, are now essential for our future health or, perhaps, just a future:

In business, it means looking beyond immediate short-term financial profit and protecting the source of all profit by curing the obsession with endless growth. Nothing in healthy nature grows without limit. That which does is cancerous. Yet, if a business is trading well and making some percentage profit, it appears to be an unquestioned law that true success means getting bigger...and bigger...If a business found a level of trading at which its customers were well-satisfied and its employees well-rewarded (corresponding to optimum, not maximum, profit), maintaining that position, by repeating its processes and procedures, would mimic nature's cyclical and guiding pattern, and the business would form a healthy part of its community. The modern incessant quest for more, means launching off on a tangent of endless and increasing acquisition. Even tangents do not satisfy all businessmen and some seek to ride exponential curves of compounded interest, sales and production. Exponential growth (of anything) cannot be sustained indefinitely and hence, in the case of commerce, requires us to impose our own limits, which will still leave us with plenty (and some time to enjoy it). If we do not, nature will impose her own limits – and take everything away by brief and drastic means, leaving us with little or nothing.

Breaking or unbalancing cycles leads to illness and ultimately collapse. Uncontrolled capitalism can be seen as cancerous because its units, like the cancerous cells of tumours, reproduce rapidly according to their own limited set of instructions, and at the expense of their host, eventually killing the host, and the tumours. It was mentioned above that healthy growth could be achieved by reproduction of smaller units connected physically and economically to their local communities (localisation). In contrast, today's banks, for example, have become 'too large to fail' since these tumours contain too much of society's life blood. A healthier principle and practice would be to sub-divide conglomerates ('localisation' economically, operationally and structurally). Organising our society such that business units (of any type) can only grow to a particular size (which may be measured in terms of people and / or profits and / or resources etc., depending on particular circumstances and situations) before a new but separate unit is produced (separate from the parent company in the sense of being compelled by law to be socio-economically related, and permanently connected, to a local community) means growth can be achieved without becoming cancerous.

Yet, in this book it is repeatedly suggested that nature should be our model, and if nature changes in order to stay the same, could 'maintenance of capitalism' be considered a natural or 'healthy' example? No, the critical word is, again, 'balance', nature changes to remain the same in a balanced, cyclical way, whereas capitalism represents extreme imbalances in terms of power, distribution of resources, unfair advantage, manipulation, coercion and control. It also promotes imbalance by breaking cyclical patterns in preference for tangential or exponential growth.

Localisation provides healthier patterns than globalisation – if only because other members of the community can watch developments and can communicate directly with those responsible to rectify imbalances or abuse. Localisation would also mean that local features – of geography, geology, climate or culture – become manifestations of character in the products made, and we see in communities what can be seen in individuals. As we free ourselves from being 'McPeople', 'mass produced' like manufactured products, so our communities exhibit their collective characters, in stark contrast to the majority of uniform and 'mass produced' modern city centres.

Mass production produces massive profits for a few. When commercial schemes are profitable all profits go to the owners / shareholders. If big businesses fail, governments allow the losses to filter back down the hierarchy to all working men and women, including those who earn average and below average salaries. This was an established pattern before the financial crash of 2007 made a larger proportion of the public aware of it. Despite smoke screens of jargon and images of 'executives' who 'understand high finance', analyses of failed schemes reveal little foresight and professionalism but much incompetence and greed. Such 'executives', surrounded by the most expensive cars, clothes and accessories, acquire a glamorous image others aspire to or fantasise about. Yet no credit worthy aspect to them or their schemes can be found. It cannot even be said that they play a 'high risk game'; there is no risk, only gain; on the backs of others' hard work. Natural parallels once again suggest parasites, leeches or cancers and they should be dealt with in the same way – treated astringently until they open their jaws and let go, or be surgically removed from society.

In medicine, panoramic views include getting to know people as individual characters and not simply as a set of symptoms; keeping open minds with regard to alternative treatments while ensuring healthy people take priority over healthy profits for pharmaceutical companies. Oswald Croll (c. 1563 - 1609) was known as the German Paracelsus. He recommended treating a patient by first comforting their heart and then dealing with the disease. Appendix II describes ways in which some doctors can be made comfortable when dealing with drug companies. Other examples were provided by a report in the Sunday Times magazine (31/07/05) which advised the reader that if they needed to know the driving force behind modern allopathic medicine they should turn to the business pages. The same report quoted figures of possibly up to 20 000 deaths per year, in the UK alone, due to adverse side effects or 'adverse drug reactions' (ADRs). Numbers of deaths are a curious index since one would be one too many – if it is our own or that of a loved one. As clinical trials are unlikely to identify ADRs which occur over the long-term, post-marketing studies are required and these can also hide a manipulation of patients for profits. Hidden behind 'post-marketing surveillance', some doctors are duped into thinking they are contributing to research and receive money to prescribe new drugs on standard NHS prescription forms. Patients do not volunteer to be test cases and no explanation may accompany the change of treatment. Various successive British governments have failed to control such practices but, on a positive note, in 2009 the new U.S. Obama administration fined a pharmaceutical giant $2.3 bn for putting profits before patient welfare by selling officially unapproved drugs and entertaining doctors at luxury locations as part of its sales tactics.

Relying on their own experience and thinking for themselves, many people have found alternatives to drugs in minerals, massage oils, herbs, flowers and dietary supplements which can have as beneficial effects as drugs (if not more so) and without side effects. It appears that sufficient numbers of people now use these alternatives as to represent a serious loss of profits for the pharmaceutical companies. Since 2007 the Food and Drug Administration (FDA) of the USA has been trying to gain legal control over these alternatives by having them classified as 'medical devices' and hence determine if, how and where they will be available. There have been various protests by U.S. citizens who see the pharmaceutical companies manipulating the law for their own ends. Similarly, in the U.K., since smaller businesses cannot compete with giant chemical companies and their advertising and marketing campaigns, it has become increasingly difficult to buy old-fashioned homely remedies (e.g. commercial Epsom salts, liniments and particular natural oils). This sort of market manipulation contributes to society forgetting traditional remedies and wisdoms. A few corporations prosper but society as a whole (including corporations) is ultimately impoverished. Echoing the developments in the USA, the 2010 EU Food Supplements Directive (if it becomes law) will result in many food supplements, such as minerals and vitamins, being removed from sale in the European market, which could result in the closure of a large number of health food stores.

In politics, panoramas mean looking beyond four or so years (even if a party is only in power for four years): The most important feature of which must be the environment, which is more fundamental and more important than politics, and therefore should be independent of it, enshrined in law such that any present or future government or business infringing those laws is accountable to the judicial system. In theory this is the situation now but existing environmental legislation is flouted by big business with the complicity of government (as in the examples given above of Greenpeace blocking effluent pipes or WTO's support and practice of 'free trade' riding roughshod over all else). Inextricably linked with the environment is agriculture, which should be the next priority of all governments everywhere. Largely responsible for the fate of the nation, governments should see furthest soonest, employing long-term agendas with wide scope for the future – and none are more important than environmental protection and agriculture. In practice, short-term views and policies prevail. Even within their limited period of administration, the individuals comprising a government have even shorter term perspectives concerned with their personal roles and responsibilities.

In academia, panoramic views would include more inter-disciplinary collaboration, allowing the results of various specialities to be related and co-ordinated. They also include the ability to keep a truly open mind allowing consideration of ideas that do not fit the current orthodoxy (some suggestions in the next chapter). Research should also be organised and driven with purposes beyond personal or institutional promotion; military or commercial agendas. Speaking to students at the California Institute of Technology in 1931 Einstein told them not to get lost amidst their diagrams and equations since all creations of the mind should be a blessing, and not a curse, to mankind. Governments could utilise academia in numerous practical ways to help the environmental situation in general, reducing the emphasis on 'research', 'monitoring' or 'measuring' while increasing the emphasis on practical remedial action (some suggestions in the next chapter). All things are connected. Science driven by community requirements could be the blessing Einstein referred to and not a curse, as it is when dominated by military or commercial agendas. If, as and when we start to face our responsibilities to the environment, other connections, be they scientific, political, commercial or personal, start to become healthier and better balanced – automatically. Eventually, by following nature's models and patterns we will find very little that is controversial, and that which is, will not be life-threatening.

Even now, some things remain uncontroversial, and for our present purposes, the most obvious example is saving the tiger from extinction. No nations, no corporations and no individuals (least of all poachers) are advocating its extinction – but it is happening, and the tiger is fading fast.

Similarly, every sane person values a healthy environment but it continues to suffer extreme abuse. So there must be a serious and dangerous dislocation between the will of the people and the will of governments. The dislocation is caused by the tiny but extremely powerful percentage of people whose corporations gain materially, in the short-term, from environmental abuse. If we refocus on tigers dying out, despite nobody wanting them to, we find factors include a lack of education and a lack of enforced legislation; and these in turn lead back to a lack of political commitment and corporate responsibility. So the world and the tiger are dying of the same malaise; socio-economics controlled by purblind vested interests, and we see that tigers disappearing (and other environmental deterioration) must directly mirror incompetence and / or corruption in our institutions and businesses. As the tiger disappears, so do the noble virtues the tiger symbolises and we see again the equivalence of the spiritual and the physical, inner and outer, the latter recording the former.

No doubt politicians and businessmen could quote millions spent on this or that community programme or community benefits, corporate compliance with the law etc. Yet even if such statistics are the truth, the whole truth and nothing but the truth, the environment is telling us that they are, as yet, inadequate and the prevailing socio-economics lethal to the majority of species, including our own.

Schumacher (B59) pointed out the dangers of giant corporations and fundamental errors in orthodox economics, both as practised in the real world and taught in universities (e.g. treating natural resources as unlimited and ignoring environmental health). During their time of plenty, too many corporations made too few efforts to clean up their operation and / or find healthier, more conservative alternatives. For decades corporate responsibility to the community and the Earth has been neglected in favour of profits. The very concept of corporate responsibility was only formed in the late 20th century in response to public outrage at the vast profit-driven abuses being inflicted on the environment and its inhabitants. Consider, for examples, the following features of the modern world; the vast mono-crops of agribusiness; their continual drenching in poisonous chemicals of increasing potency; consumption of natural resources more rapidly than they can be generated by nature; constant brain washing by advertising and media; the inversion of traditional values (e.g. credit or debt is good, greed is good); the trivialisation of major issues and the aggrandisement of trivia; ineffective control by legislation or government policies. Each of the features just listed is a result of powerful corporations manipulating people, nations and the Earth for their own restricted short-term objectives. For a healthy and sustainable future (if only commercially), consumers and governments must now compel corporations to re-model economics on nature, such that it become 'eco-nomics'.

What are the obstacles to panoramic views and 'eco-nomics' being adopted? Regardless of laws that may be passed and policed, any corporate, commercial, political or other type of organisation, can only be thoroughly and effectively changed by its senior members personally adopting priorities that are to the community's (and hence ultimately their own) long-term benefits. The 'root of the root' is still human free will decisions, obeying or disobeying standards of virtue and morality. The difficulties resulting from opposing the majority of senior management or even a group of one's peers, and the knowledge that others can easily be found to comply with them, is fully recognised. Yet, no matter how difficult it may be, the only way group mentality can be altered is for individuals to alter their own. However, at the present time, let us not be overly concerned about the number of executives struggling with their consciences or peer pressure. Today the pendulum is so far over to one side that the vast majority are happily counting the profits of compliance, exercising their sheep-like, if not lower, life forms. Their tiger looks askance at being laid so low.

Those with most power are failing to frame the symmetry and are killing tigers – metaphorically and literally.

Weakness of will is compounded by another problem captured in an old saying that 'the senators are good men but the senate is an evil beast'. In our current context we could refer to the obvious parallel with modern government; or say that doctors are good people but Medicine has become an evil beast; or that scientists are good people but Science has become an evil beast. Amongst some subtle and interesting truths in this old saying, the common thread running through the examples given is, again, that of money becoming first priority. This reminds us of the often misquoted Biblical reference that does *not* say 'money is the root of all evil' but that '*love* of money is the root of all evil'.

Of course, many individuals staffing say, big banks and other multinationals, are decent, hard-working, caring individuals who, by circumstance, have found themselves working in organisations which may not be contributing to the world in positive ways. The control or influence of big business is so ubiquitous it would be difficult, wherever one went, to avoid playing some part in the current socio-economic system of the world. No disparagement is intended here toward any person who, say, works in a standard (i.e. unethical) bank. It is understood that they are most likely trying to pay their bills and probably raise a family and are thus compelled to be part of something controlled by people to whom they would not, in other circumstances, offer allegiance. Similarly, the work of community-minded journalists is subject to editorial review and what may have begun as an honest, worthwhile article is transformed into another advertisement for the particular paper's corporate or political bias. Some people may start work understanding their new company makes less than ideal contributions to the larger community and may also start with high ideals and determination to make a positive difference to that situation. With time, they acquire some knowledge, experience, maybe a professional reputation, a family, mortgage and other financial commitments. All these factors lock them into their occupation for their financial, and often psychological, security, making it too dangerous and uncomfortable to 'rock the boat' – even though collectively sailing toward the greater dangers of an environmental abyss. However, unpopular as it may be, we do, at some point (and the environmental crisis is telling us that this is now) all have responsibilities to trace connections between our work, society and the world, and then face those responsibilities to ensure we are trying to influence events and other people to husband and nurture the life force – even if only slowly and from within an organisation. This may be as simple as organising re-cycling schemes, organic food in the restaurant and environmentally-friendly cleaning products. Personnel in senior positions can question investment strategies and examine the environmental impacts of their company's products and processes.

In addition to weakness of will and the pressure to conform there are, of course, other psychological factors. Suddenly subjected to question, many people will immediately defend their occupations – without considering what they would really and truly think, if they were entirely independent of them. Many will convince themselves that what they do is right – simply because they do it. In addition to wanting to keep a clear conscience, the power of authority, the group, one's employment, status and means of livelihood are powerful influences for all of us. These factors, in addition to socio-economic conditions (imposed by the system producing the environmental crisis), influence many people to continue buying harmful products, eating chemically-contaminated food and banking unethically. Few bother and / or have time to investigate aspects of their lives beyond what is immediately apparent. The influence of the majority is great, even for intelligent people, and even if the majority are all moving toward oblivion.

Are there still further factors allowing intelligent people to be herded in these ways? The reader will already know two parts of the answer as offered in this book: they consider only short-term time-scales (although many are parents); and their hearts are not as actively exercised as their minds. They simply do not care about other lives sufficiently to make the necessary efforts: firstly to inform themselves and secondly to take action in accordance with their findings. They fight neither for justice nor do they have mercy on other lives – reminding us of those whom Dante sees and hears in the Inferno (*Canto III*). Virgil explains that they were neither bad, nor good, but for themselves only. Now their 'blind life so meanly passes, that all other lots they envy.' Both 'mercy and justice scorn them.'

Although we are all sitting in the same tree, it appears that most of us only care about our own little leaf, that which is immediately accessible to us and which feeds us. Other leaves can be seen and their use and / or beauty may even be appreciated. Some leaves on the other side of the tree are not even known about. No-one is responsible for the whole tree or even the trunk which supports all else. We thought the government was but many individuals within government have only been feathering their own nests. Those with most power to bring change (either as senior personnel and / or the wealthiest consumers) are too comfortable in homes with full fridges, garages full of luxury cars and holidays booked, to make changes, even though all and everything that supports that life-style is unravelling around them. As Virgil advises Dante, on seeing the fate of those people who think only of themselves, 'let us think no more about them, but look once and pass on.'

Let us move on to make a difference. Since all sensible, well-informed people can agree on the importance of the environment, each must be able to answer satisfactorily when they ask themselves what they are doing toward a healthy environment, toward keeping the whole tree healthy – if only to preserve their own little leaf. Each and everyone must choose. Those tempted to choose selfishness must remember this only works for the short-term because, by choosing not to care for other lives, the systems that support one's own necessities and comforts are gradually weakened and damaged, until they collapse.

The majority of individuals are not directly to blame for the current crisis, but they are to blame if they now fail, in the face of it, to educate themselves and, more importantly, take actions to redress the situation. We cannot rely on political action, which is dangerously inadequate. Who can doubt this after the failure of the Copenhagen meeting in December 2009? The overall reflection from nature shows too much that is degraded or damaged and too many species dying. Without repairing this damage, any other progress (e.g. human rights and world development) is of no real importance or consequence. Nature is the absolute scale and it is showing that we are sick, very sick. That's how we know 'who we are' collectively, 'where we are' and 'what to do'. The only thing left is to do it. The Copenhagen delegates' strategy of waiting for all to agree and / or for others to match or exceed their own commitments is the road to ruin. We must do everything we can now – unilaterally, as a nation and as individuals, regardless of what the rest of the world may be doing. There's just one lesson, one duty, one thing to do – can we do it?

A sufficient number of individuals changing their life-styles side-steps governments' failures and directly compels corporations to respond. Although the powerful can influence us, community behaviour must still, to a degree, reflect the values and freely chosen behaviour of its component parts i.e. individuals. Society can only be as obsessed with toys, pleasure and self as are the individuals who comprise it, which is why it is only individuals who can re-shape society. It is tempting to identify the directors, chairmen or C.E.O.'s of multinational corporations as having most responsibility but many are at the mercy of shareholders and all are at the mercy of customers and consumers. Hence we see again the importance of connections, and of individuals facing their own responsibilities to bring change to their world and hence, in time, the world.

It is understood that people want and need to relax and / or have some fun after long hours at work. This is all well and good when those hours at work have, in the majority of cases, contributed to the health and protection of our society and life-support system, a healthy environment. The reality is that the majority of human work abuses nature and wastes resources. So our task is the most difficult of all: in addition to work that is, for many, already onerous, we need to find the strength, time and commitment to protect our life-support systems by assessing the environmental impact of our work and lifestyle, while positively influencing our employers/employees and government. By not having monitored and corrected government activities previously, we now find ourselves having to take on those government responsibilities. However, while the electorate has been lax, governments have increasingly centralised power, making our additional work even more difficult. Just as with the environment, we find that by initially choosing what seemed to be the easier option – neglecting smaller responsibilities – greater responsibilities arrive in consequence.

In the James Bond genre of films the hero has to prevent a renegade individual from dooming the world to destruction, allowing the establishment to reassert justice, law and morality for the benefit of all. This is fiction. The current reality is that renegade individuals are trying to reassert justice, law and morality for the benefit of all and prevent the establishment from dooming the world to destruction. Of course, not only the James Bond type of film but others from swords and sorcery to sci-fi, repeatedly play out the theme of heroes averting world devastation. Move from fiction to fact and multiply the villain from one to a number, the threat from a single event to a combination (developing over more than ninety minutes), and the majority of the audience, who previously identified with the screen hero, are rendered helpless and hopeless, content to watch the frightening *reality* of world devastation unfold, without lifting a finger to oppose it. A film of most of us playing our current roles would make for dismal viewing.

To face our responsibilities to the environment we don't, thankfully, have to go to the extremes of Hollywood-style heroes and can create real and rapid change simply by spending our money selectively. If we can't make our voice heard by those who make decisions affecting us all, we can make the impact of our money felt in the right places and, better still, not felt at all in the wrong places (see chapter V). By being carefully selective in how we spend our money, we can create healthy change. We can also (where our economic circumstances allow) reject maximum and accept optimum. It is the greedy who make others needy and when we reject maximum and aim for optimum, there is enough for everybody's optimum. As these actions take effect, more people will be able to adopt the same strategy, freeing themselves from the trappings of wealth and others from the trap of poverty. Such scenes would provide some inspiring viewing – and include some roaring tigers!

…on Natural and Human Currencies

Panoramic views help us see more. In terms of human currencies, capitalism, like other economic systems, can create wealth. It is the distribution of wealth, whatever the economic system, which is usually the more important factor. (On this point, Einstein's reference above to capitalism creating 'an army of unemployed' may seem to be in conflict with modern media referring to capitalism as the creator of jobs. The apparent conflict is resolved in Appendix IV). However, any and all wealth of all man-made systems is ultimately derived from natural wealth (natural 'currencies'). Not only does nature provide the raw materials needed to make our products but it also provides the air, water and food required by the makers. Ignoring this truth produces the illusion that man-made economic systems 'create' wealth. Moreover, economic wealth made by the pursuit of maximum profit in minimum time means damaging, polluting and wasting real wealth – natural resources (which are 'owned' by all of us, or none of us), eventually to the point of threatening the continuation of that economy, and many forms of life.

In the absence of properly enforced environmental laws, environmental charities are trying, for the benefit of all (including business and businessmen), to reduce or reverse the damage to nature, and push commercial and community processes toward a sustainable use of natural resources – until a healthy, balanced system will remove the need for charities. Charities may use money from industry and / or its employees to do so and therefore their work might be seen as dependent on industrial wealth; either directly, through funding from businesses, or indirectly, via donations from its employees. A broader perspective reveals the dependence of all on nature. Redistributing some wealth generated by unhealthy minorities to deprived majorities, to ensure healthy, on-going community life (human and non-human), is a service to all, business included. All and any money contributing to healthy environments are not donations but investments.

Yet money and self interest is so strong a cultural mode that industry is considered generous if it gives anything toward campaigns that it too ultimately benefits from. Donations treat symptoms but, until causes are addressed, those symptoms of environmental abuse and associated extreme poverty will continue to appear. Addressing causes involves a re-evaluation of our individual, and hence collective, priorities and these will be gradually manifested in our surroundings – just as our current priorities are currently displayed around us – and not only by the natural environment e.g. the Greco-Roman architecture of temples built to worship gods, is now displayed, usually in major cities, by buildings owned by the wealthiest corporations including banks, where, of course, they are still used for worship. Yet, for those who have made money their god, what shall it mean to gain a profit but lose the world?

So, environmental charities are trying to conserve 'natural currencies' (natural materials and resources) for the benefit of all. Until some significant success is achieved, they will continue to need human currencies to do so. For charities, money, for its own sake, is not the top priority, but it is sought to safeguard the real top priority, nature – the source of all wealth.

When distance is put between greed and its results, when connections between the two are covered up, it allows the effects of a 'money first' policy (personal or professional) to pass unnoticed and unidentified. The community sees only what the rich and powerful choose to display. This can be a splendid show of the best mankind can craft (buildings, clothes, cars…) and who would not be impressed by such trappings of wealth? However, tracing connections reveals all the waste and exploitation, the poisoned rivers and forests, hungry, dispossessed and diseased people and many other casualties, including dead tigers, associated with them. More openness, identification of and accountability for those connections would reveal the true cost of wealth as acquired by current capitalist methods. One consequence of this transparency would be that decency, common sense and social pressure exert a controlling influence on those exclusively pursuing profit and, for a trivial but nonetheless telling example, instead of being assured a table even though the restaurant is full, they wouldn't get a table even if it were half empty – and if they did, the restaurant would empty completely as a result. Alas, most restaurateurs also seek maximum money and some diners, especially when greed is disguised as dignity, have been culturally trained to gush over and defer to it. Social approval or disapproval is a powerful force for all of us and, again, the media plays an influential role in shaping society's values by the bias it gives particular issues. Too often they make the most sound about empty vessels; bad behaviour is given tacit approval; and wholesome, healthy developments are ridiculed.

From our perspective of optimum we can see that many, maybe the majority, of people are happy with optimum and neither crave maximum nor covet what others have. However, a proportion does and, even if small in number, they necessarily acquire positions of wealth and power, thereby having effects and acquiring significance out of all proportion to their size. As a consequence, the questionable values and priorities of these people gain increasing influence over societies and ultimately the planet as a whole, and therefore all our lives and those of other species, including tigers. Yet the very characteristics that stimulate them to seek such positions are those least likely to result in beneficial effects for the larger community. As the power of large profit-making enterprises becomes national and then global, they create social trends with which all people (including those not motivated by money) find themselves having to comply. In basic terms, life becomes the hectic and / or arduous chase after increasingly expensive, but poor quality, supplies because society is significantly influenced, if not controlled by, the greedy.

Above we met a tribal man who needed to take a tree. He was arrested and counted his losses. A corporation takes a whole forest (which it does not need) and counts its profits. Moreover, it is the latter, along with the IMF, World Bank and WTO, which often create the hunger and poverty compelling individuals such as our tribal man to attempt taking one tree. The vast appetites, consumption and power of corporations greatly imbalance the distribution of wealth (in terms of money, products and resources) such that millions of individuals face poverty, or are caught up in corruption or crime. Again we see that all things are connected and criminal acts in the forest are caused by criminal acts (morally if not legally) in corporate board rooms and high government offices, sometimes half a world away. The greedy make the needy, and then turn the needy into beggars or criminals – little of which is reported by media except for an occasional comment or article, but never with associated or invited action, campaign launched or pursuit of those responsible. Next day the article is forgotten. The imbalances produced by both corporate power, and the spiritual immaturity of many who seek power, also lead to corruption in public bodies. A 2010 national newspaper report in the U.K. identified corruption as a bigger killer than either terrorism or drugs, due to its numerous and multi-layered, direct and indirect, effects on communities. As we shall see in the next chapter, protection of the last remaining tigers is obviously of critical importance and is, or should be, the first priority of conservation strategies. However, it would remain necessary for as long as we fail to address the socio-economic imbalances that produce the majoity of criminal threats to tigers. Protection is not a long-term solution since it is not always effective, can disturb much of what it attempts to protect, and is treating symptoms rather than causes.

How can we, as individuals, influence society to improve it? We have to influence our part of society which, in the first instance, is ourselves, examining our own personal values and behaviour. By adjusting them for the better we may influence our families and friends, workplace and local community. When everyone urges everyone else to make or take as much as possible as quickly as possible, unbridled greed and lust for power is given social approval. If more people urged and observed compassion, restraint, morality and moderation, the effects spread automatically throughout the community. Without these personal commitments, any and every scheme that can be devised to oppose the effects of excess power and / or greed and the corruption they lead to, can and will eventually be worked around or manipulated. Individuals' moral and virtuous conduct, and their behaviour with a social conscience, is the only complete and absolute solution to our problems – since there is no other 'unit' of conscious free will, which collectively produce the character of the community. It may sound, or be, naïve, impractical, a long time coming, idealistic, or any of a host of other adjectives but, however persistently we want to ridicule or run away from it, it is the only ultimate solution. It can only be completely achieved by each of us starting with changing ourselves for the better. Spiritual pioneers must be the most courageous, because they will be lonely individuals, rejected and ridiculed by a seemingly confident but actually fearful majority. We need individuals who decide to be a hero in the film of their own life – not the spot lit, muscle-bound, toy-town type but those with self-possessed and quiet dignity, nurturing healthy life despite all odds and opposition (and the harsh but apparent fact in this world, that no good act goes unpunished!).

As indicated above, providing good service, pride in one's work, professional finesse, courtesy and care do ultimately translate into good business – but only in the long-term. The focus on maximum must always translate into short-term selfishness ('getting all I want' and 'getting it now'). Even if a business were willing to adopt a long-term strategy, the competition will not, and so, commercially, all participants are compelled to operate according to minimum time and maximum speed. Meanwhile, technology's labour-saving devices seem to increase the speed of life by allowing more to be packed into each unit of time, for both industry and individuals, and all these factors alternate between cause and effect to produce ever-accelerating life-styles.

...on Timely Topics

David Orr (Professor of Environmental Studies at Oberlin College, Ohio USA) has written on this topic revealing connections to several themes considered in this book:

'Several years ago the college where I teach created an electronic "quick mail" system to reduce paper use and to increase our efficiency. Electronic communication is now standard throughout most organizations. The results, however, are mixed at best. The most obvious is a large increase in the sheer volume of stuff communicated, much of which is utterly trivial. There is also a manifest decline in the grammar, literary style and civility of communication. People stroll down the hall or across campus to converse less frequently. Students remain transfixed before computer screens for hours, often doing no more than playing computer games. Our conversations, thought patterns and institutional clock-speed are increasingly shaped to fit the imperatives of technology. Not surprisingly, more and more people feel overloaded by the demands of incessant "communication", but to say so publicly is to run foul of the technological fundamentalism now dominant virtually everywhere. By default and without much thought it has been decided for us that communication ought to be cheap, easy and quick. Accordingly, more and more of us are instantly wired to the global nervous system with cell phones, beepers, pagers, fax machines and e-mail. If useful in real emergencies, the overall result is to homogenize the important with the trivial, making everything an emergency and an already frenetic civilization even more so. We are drowning in unassimilated information, most of which fits no meaningful picture of the world. In our public affairs and in our private lives we are increasingly muddle-headed because we have mistaken volume and speed of information for substance and clarity.

On my desk I have the three volumes of correspondence between Thomas Jefferson and James Madison written with quill pen by candlelight and delivered by horse. The style is mostly impeccable. Even when they wrote about mundane things, they did so with clarity and insight. Their disagreements were expressed with civility and felicity. The entire body of letters can be read for both pleasure and instruction. Assuming people still read two centuries hence, will they read the correspondence of, say, Newt Gingrich or Bill Clinton for either pleasure or instruction? In contrast to our own, Jefferson and Madison were part of a culture that, whatever its other flaws, had time to take words and what they meant seriously. They knew, intuitively perhaps, that information and knowledge were not the same thing and that neither was to be confused with wisdom. In large part the difference, whether they thought about it or not, was the speed of the society…

Water moving too quickly through a landscape does not recharge underground aquifers. The results are floods in wet weather and droughts in the summer. Money moving too quickly through an economy does not recharge the local wellsprings of prosperity, whatever else it does for the great scam called the global economy. The result is an economy polarized between those few who do well in a high-velocity economy and those left behind. Information moving too quickly to become knowledge and grow into wisdom does not recharge moral aquifers on which families, communities and entire nations depend. The result is moral atrophy and public confusion. The common thread between all three is velocity. And they are tied together in a complex system of cause and effect that we have mostly overlooked.

There is an appropriate velocity for water set by geology, soils, vegetation and ecological relationships in a given landscape. There is an appropriate velocity for money that corresponds to long-term needs of communities rooted in particular places and to the necessity of preserving ecological capital. There is an appropriate velocity for information, set by the assimilative capacity of the mind and by the collective learning rate of communities and entire societies.

Having exceeded the speed limits, we are vulnerable to ecological degradation, economic arrangements that are unjust and unsustainable and, in the face of great and complex problems, to befuddlement that comes with information overload.

The ecological effects of the increased velocity of water are easy to comprehend. We can see floods and, with a bit of effort, we can discern how human actions can amplify droughts.

But it is harder to comprehend the social, political, economic and ecological effects of increasing the velocity of money and information, which are often indirect and hidden. Increasing the velocity of commerce, information and transport, however, requires more administration and regulation of human affairs to ameliorate congestion and other problems. More administration means that there are fewer productive people, higher overheads, and higher taxes to pay for more infrastructure necessitated by the speed of people and things and problems of congestion.

Increasing velocity and scale tends to increase the complexity of social and ecological arrangements and reduce the time available to recognize and avoid problems. Cures for problems caused by increasing velocity often set in motion a cascading series of other problems. As a result we

Background image: A langur monkey takes a dangerous drink

stumble through a succession of escalating crises with diminishing capacity to foresee and forestall.

Other examples fit the same pattern, such as the velocity of transportation, material flows, extraction of non-renewable resources, introduction of new chemicals, and human reproduction. At the local scale the effect is widening circles of disintegration and social disorder…The increasing velocity of the global culture is no accident. It is the foundation of the corporate-dominated global economy that requires quick returns on investment and rapid economic growth. It is the crux of the consumer economy that feeds on impulse, obsession and instant gratification.

The velocity of water in our landscape is a direct result of too many cars, too much pavement, sprawling development, deforestation, and a food system that cannot be sustained in any decent or safe manner. The speed of information is driven by something that more and more resembles addiction. But, above all, increasing speed is driven by minds unaware of the irony that the race has never been to the swift…

Yet the same forces that have combined to give us a high-velocity economy and society reform themselves at a glacial speed…Thirty-five years after *Silent Spring*, we use more synthetic chemicals than ever. Twenty-five years after *The Limits to Growth*, economic obesity is still the goal of governments everywhere. Twenty-two years after Amory Lovins' prophetic and, as it turns out, understated projections about the potential for energy efficiency and solar energy, we are still using two to three times more fossil fuel than we need. Twenty years after Wendell Berry's devastating critique of American agriculture, sustainable agriculture is still a distant dream. Nearly a decade has passed since a scientific consensus began to form about the seriousness of global warming, yet we dawdle. I could go on, but the point is clear. Things that need to happen rapidly, such as the preservation of biological diversity, the transition to a solar society, the widespread application of sustainable agriculture and forestry, population limits, the protection of basic human rights, and democratic reform, occur slowly, if at all, while ecological ruin and economic dislocation race ahead. What can be done?

First, we need an absolutely clear analysis of the huge inefficiencies of high-speed "efficiency". We have contrived a high-technology, high-speed economy that is neither sustainable nor capable of sustaining what is best in human cultures. On close examination, many of the alleged benefits of ever-rising affluence are fraudulent claims. Thoughtful analysis reveals that our economy often works like a kind of Rube Goldberg device to do with great expense, complication and waste, things that could be done more simply, elegantly and harmoniously, or in some cases things that should not be done at all. Most of our mistakes have been a result of hurry in the name of economic competition, national security, or "progress".

Now many must be undone at great expense or written off as a permanent loss. The speed   of the industrial economy must be reset to take account of…natural rhythms and genuine   human needs. That means recalibrating public policies and taxation to promote a more durable prosperity.

Next, we need a more robust idea of time and scale that takes the health of people and communities seriously. In Leopold Kohr's words, "The only way that can induce us to reduce our speed of movements is a return to a spatially more contracted, leisurely, and largely pedestrian mode of life that makes high speeds not only unnecessary but as uneconomic as a Concorde would be for crossing the English Channel…In other words, slow is beautiful in an appropriately contracted small social environment of beehive density…"

Background image: A gharial (narrow snouted, fish-eating crocodile) in Corbett Tiger Reserve.

Our assumptions about time are crystallized in community design and architecture. Sprawling cities, economic dependency and the long-distance transportation of food and materials require high-velocity transport and high-speed communication, and they result in higher costs, community disintegration and ecological deformation.

Rethinking velocity and time will require rethinking our relationship to the land as well. Here too we have options for increasing density through development of open space and smarter planning that creates proximity between housing, employment, shopping, culture, public spaces, recreation and health-care – what is now being called the "new urbanism"

…We must learn to take time to study nature as the standard for much of what we need to do. We must take time and make the effort to preserve both cultural and biological diversity. We must take time to calculate the full costs of what we do. We must take time to make things durable, repairable, useful and beautiful. We must take the time not just to recycle but rather to eliminate the very concept of waste.

In most things, timeliness and regularity, not speed, are important. Genuine charity, good parenting, true neighbourliness, good lives, decent communities, conviviality, democratic deliberation, real prosperity, mental health and the exercise of true intelligence have a certain pace and rhythm that can only be harmed by being accelerated. The means to control velocity can be designed into daily life like speed bumps designed to slow traffic. Holidays, festivals, celebrations, sabbaticals, Sabbaths, prayer, good conversation, story-telling, music-making, the practice of fallowing, shared meals, a high degree of self-reliance, craftwork, walking and shared physical work are speed-control devices used by every healthy culture.[1] (reprinted by kind permission of Prof. Orr)

As Gandhi said "There is more to life than making it faster." We saw above the importance of festivals, rituals and 'holi-days' arranged according to nature's rhythms, by which we may set our clocks. We are healthier and happier when our lives are in tune with daily, monthly, yearly rhythms. With some independence from technology's artificial lights, our lives run at a more comfortable pace, harmonising more easily with other lives (human and non-human) by which we may find our earthly rhythms and cosmic keys.

…of the Cosmos Close to Hand

Of the cosmos close to hand, evidence is all around, as for the Indian potter.

'In the centre of a spinning wheel, a golden lump of clay slowly assumes the shape of a pot. At the instant when the pot is taking form, the hands of the potter are feather-light and firm. They cup the sides of the pot, guiding it, holding it, and for an instant, one feels the life force urging out of the clay into the space within, guided by those golden hands. In that instant, potter and clay are one. "Pots have a life," potters believe. The perfect shape of a clay pot is more than just a piece of good craftsmanship, it is an act of creation, which is why in the Bhagavad-Gita the human body is compared to a clay pot, and human beings are seen to be made out of clay. When the pot breaks, what it contains is reunited with the outside…at one level (the clay pot) is found in villages all over India, a humble object of everyday use, and on the other, an object of tremendous philosophical weight…a metaphor for life itself…the shock of recognition, a piece of knowledge, a memory found and brought alive…

For if there is one thing that is very deeply rooted in the Indian subcontinent, it is the belief that philosophy is central to both material and spiritual life, and that man cannot go through life without asking why he or she exists. But the answer to this question, according to the Indian way of looking at things, cannot be found through the mind. Hence, philosophy cannot exist on its own, cut off from the everyday experience of life; it is a search to find the meaning and purpose of life as it is experienced and must therefore include the emotions, the senses, and the material world as well. Thus philosophy and mysticism blend into one another, mixing sacred and profane…

Across India, plastic pots, lighter to carry and more durable, are rapidly replacing these same clay pots…Nothing keeps water cool like a clay pot. Trace minerals in the clay filter into the water, giving the water a sweet taste. And yet, in village after village, the arrival of steel and plastic pots made in factories far away is putting potters out of business, forcing them to leave their villages and go to the towns in search of employment. And across India, water now has the uniform taste of plastic…For, implicitly and explicitly…as human beings learn to control the environment through technology, they get further and further removed from the world. As human relationships become more a question of choice than of necessity, conflicts are more likely to be resolved through separation rather than communication. This is why, in the highly technological world of the future, the first casualty could very well be human relationships – with each other and with the natural world. In India, on the other hand, a billion people cling to the skin of the world, eat it, use it, fight it and worship it. Here human beings are tightly connected to each other and to the natural world, coexisting with nature and with each other, not just at the level of the material but also at the level of the spiritual.' (B28)

Herein we see the contrast to the conventional view that technology is linking us all together since, while we are linking globally, we are separating from those next to us, who have a far more immediate and greater impact on our lives than most of our contacts (a misnomer in itself) on the other side of the world. This distancing of the individual from their neighbours and nature, accords with the deteriorating relationship between individuals and society as identified in the Einstein quote on capitalism above.

No other country is more deeply spiritual or religious than India. No other religion is as intimately connected with the natural world and animals as Hinduism. In India, the connections between the world, its people, the universe and the gods are refreshed daily in countless rituals, prayer and meditation, habits and practices, personally and collectively, inwardly and outwardly, on large and small scales..

'As important…to the Indian psyche is stillness, and the mountains are the embodiment of stillness. This is why there is the old saying: The gods live in the mountains. To know the mountains is to meet God.' (B28)

Mountains, and men in meditation, are still and silent, reminding us of Corbett in the jungle. It is by our stillness, silence and self-effacement that we may receive from nature. Nature's fastnesses are the antidote to self, and in them we can begin re-connecting to our cosmos. The vast uninhabited 'snow-scapes' of northernmost North America said the same to Jack London and he called them the 'White Silence'. 'Nature has many tricks wherewith she convinces man of his finity – the ceaseless flow of the tides, the fury of the storm, the shock of the earthquake, the long roll of heaven's artillery – but the most tremendous, the most stupefying of all, is the passive phase of the White Silence. All movement ceases, the sky clears, the heavens are as brass; the slightest whisper seems sacrilege, and man becomes timid, affrighted at the sound of his own voice. Sole speck of life journeying across the ghostly wastes of a dead world, he trembles at his audacity, realizes that his is a maggot's life, nothing more. Strange thoughts arise unsummoned, and the mystery of all things strives for utterance. And the fear of death, of God, of the universe, comes over him – the hope of the Resurrection and the Life, the yearning for immortality, the vain striving of the imprisoned essence – it is then, if ever, man walks alone with God.' (short story 'The White Silence')

The following quote is from a letter sent to a friend from Eritrea by D. Pugh, Asst. Superintendent of Police in February 1952:

> '…out here, when one leaves the city behind and heads into the bush-country, you step back in time a thousand years or more…As a result, many things which confuse the so-called civilised world are simplified. A better perspective prevails. Take an oil painting – created, perhaps, by one of the old masters – stand with your nose almost on top of it and all you can see is a meaningless blur of jumbled colours and crude brush strokes. A few paces away, what a transformation takes place. The canvas is seen as a whole; the details fall into place and assume their correct relation with one another. Only then can one understand the message the painter intended to convey to those who view his work.
>
> To my mind, too many people today stand with their noses pressed against the canvas. Their outlook is cramped into tiny individualistic circles. They have no wish to look at – much less understand – the grand pattern of affairs.
>
> Out here, on the other hand, one has time to think. The vast, lonely spaces of desert and mountain clean the mind of petty thoughts of self and a slow realisation of greater things is borne within one…'

(with thanks to Mr. S. Gordon for permission to print this excerpt)

Aldo Leopold (1887 – 1948 American ecologist, forester and environmentalist responsible for the beginnings of official wildlife management in the U.S.A.) said that 'wilderness is a rejection of the arrogance of humans.' Pugh, Leopold and London would have understood each other well. A wonderful realisation is that by exercising interest, balancing head and heart, we too can be part of a universal understanding.

Nature is a universal solvent that can dissolve distance, including that separating two people living completely different lives, such as C.G. Jung (Carl Gustav Jung 1875 – 1961. Pioneering psychiatrist) and Ochwiay Biano, chief of the Taos Pueblo Indians of New Mexico. Together they were sitting on a roof as the sun rose higher and higher. The chief said, pointing to the sun: "Is not he who moves there our father? How can anyone say differently? How can there be another god? Nothing can be without the sun…what would a man do alone in the mountains?"

The sun was central to the belief systems of pagan cults and past civilisations, such as the Egyptians and the ancient Greeks who referred to the sun-god as Apollo. Just as for those cultures, Jung understood that the Indians' conceptions were not 'theories' to them but active, fundamental parts of their life.

'"Our religion…we do not only for ourselves…we do it for the whole world. Everyone benefits by it…" I therefore asked him: "You think, then, that what you do in your religion benefits the whole world?" He replied with great animation, "Of course. If we did not do it, what would become of the world?" And with a significant gesture he pointed to the sun…"we are the sons of the Father Sun, and with our religion we daily help our father to go across the sky. We do this not only for ourselves, but for the whole world. If we were to cease practising our religion, in ten years the sun would no longer rise. Then it would be night for ever."

I then realised on what the "dignity," the tranquil composure of the individual Indian, was founded. It springs from his being a son of the sun; his life is cosmologically meaningful, for he helps the father and preserver of all life in his daily rise and descent. If we set against this our own self-justifications, the meaning of our own lives as it is formulated by our reason, we cannot help but see our poverty. Out of sheer envy we are obliged to smile at the Indians' naïveté and so plume ourselves on our cleverness; for otherwise we would discover how impoverished and down at the heels we are. Knowledge does not enrich us; it removes us more and more from the mythic world in which we were once at home by right of birth.' (B40 pp. 235 – 236 reprinted by kind permission of Taylor and Francis)

Whether we accept, share, smile or shed tears at the various implications, for a people who never left their locale, the Pueblos showed a selflessness and global vision, while minding their own business and seeking no power over others, rarely, if ever, found amongst other modern 'chiefs'. Our modern 'chiefs', compared to the Pueblo Indians, are very powerful and well-travelled and many of them would probably consider themselves noble and the Pueblo Indian a savage, whereas the Indian is both and they are neither.

Nature, India, potters, poets such as Thompson and Whitman, ancient Egypt and modern physics, and much between such as Ochwiay Biano, tell us that, despite our 'finity', we have cosmic connections and our life on earth reflects cosmic principles. Science has also revealed a vast cosmos to us (the advances in the 20th century alone being literally astronomical) but the amount of information that comes with it is so vast that we can only hope to understand a little – and that only by extreme specialisation. Hence science can also make us 'hold our nose against the canvas' and lose sight of a cosmos which can teach us without technology.

'Human knowledge had become unmanageably vast; every science had begotten a dozen more, each subtler than the rest; the telescope revealed stars and systems beyond the mind of man to number or to name; geology spoke in terms of millions of years, where men before had thought in terms of thousands; physics found a universe in the atom, and biology found a microcosm in the cell; physiology discovered inexhaustible mystery in every organ, and psychology in every dream; anthropology reconstructed the unsuspected antiquity of man, archaeology unearthed buried cities and forgotten states, history proved all history false, and painted a canvas which only a Spengler or an Eduard Meyer could vision as a whole; theology crumbled, and political theory cracked; invention complicated life and war, and economic creeds overturned governments and inflamed the world; philosophy itself, which had once summoned all sciences to its aid in making a coherent image of the world and an alluring picture of the good, found its task of co-ordination too stupendous for its courage, ran away from all these battlefronts of truth, and hid itself in recondite and narrow lanes, timidly secure from the issues and responsibilities of life. Human knowledge had become too great for the human mind.

All that remained was the scientific specialist, who knew "more and more about less and less," and the philosophical speculator, who knew less and less about more and more. The specialist put on blinders in order to shut out from his vision all the world but one little spot, to which he glued his nose. Perspective was lost. "Facts" replaced understanding; and knowledge, split into a thousand isolated fragments, no longer generated wisdom. Every science, and every branch of philosophy, developed a technical terminology intelligible only to its exclusive devotees; as men learned more about the world, they found themselves ever less capable of expressing to their educated fellow-men what it was that they had learned. The gap between life and knowledge grew wider and wider; those who governed could not understand those who thought, and those who wanted to know could not understand those who knew. In the midst of unprecedented learning popular ignorance flourished, and chose its exemplars to rule the great cities of the world; in the midst of sciences endowed and enthroned as never before, new religions were born every day, and old superstitions recaptured the ground they had lost. The common man found himself forced to choose between a scientific priesthood mumbling unintelligible pessimism, and a theological priesthood mumbling incredible hopes.'

We need to draw these fragmented extremes together (which have diverged even further since this was written), from a perspective of the fundamental *purpose* of each. This purpose must be relevant to current and pressing problems in the context of a healthier planet for all. Today the exact opposite applies and billions are spent on sub-atomic exploration, space travel or a host of completely unnecessary tangents while agriculture and the environment are being degraded and destroyed. The incessant gathering of facts and information has been made synonymous with progress, regardless of relevance or necessity.

A rejection of scientific specialism and / or technology is not being recommended. What is being recommended is; a rejection of science and technology as the only source of knowledge and route to truth; and a re-evaluation of our priorities such that spending millions of pounds and many years on any abstruse specialism while our daily bread is at risk is also rejected. Science used properly is an amazing and potentially useful discipline. This book and this chapter has referred to scientific facts and fascinating scientific insights, and even considered some scientific parallels to a few spiritual aspects of nature. Danger arises when we become imbalanced and consider science (yang) the only arbiter of truth, rejecting other (yin) experiences because they do not (nor ever will) comply with current scientific orthodoxy. We need to combine our scientific results with our findings in other areas of life. We have to find how to combine East and West, female and male, yin and yang, religion and science. When each discipline is allowed equal status, the scales are balanced, the pendulum is brought to rest.

Without balance there is no rest. From ancient to modern times the pattern is the same oscillation between extremes and currently '…our minds are overwhelmed with sciences breeding and multiplying into specialistic chaos for want of synthetic thought and a unifying philosophy. We are all mere fragments of what a man might be…

There is a pleasure in philosophy, and a lure even in the mirages of metaphysics, which every student feels until the coarse necessities of physical existence drag him from the heights of thought into the mart of economic strife and gain. Most of us have known some golden days in the June of life when philosophy was in fact what Plato calls it, "that dear delight"; when the love of a modestly elusive Truth seemed more glorious, incomparably, than the lust for the ways of the flesh and the dross of the world. And there is always some wistful remnant in us of that early wooing of wisdom. "Life has meaning," we feel with Browning – "to find its meaning is my meat and drink." So much of our lives is meaningless, a self-cancelling vacillation and futility; we strive with the chaos about us and within; but we would believe all the while that there is something vital and significant in us, could we but decipher our own souls. We want to understand …we are like Mitya in *The Brothers Karamazov* – "one of those who don't want millions, but an answer to their questions"; we want to seize the value and perspective of passing things, and so to pull ourselves up out of the maelstrom of daily circumstance…We want to be whole, to co-ordinate our energies by criticizing and harmonizing our desires; for co-ordinated energy is the last word in ethics and politics, and perhaps in logic and metaphysics too…We may be sure that if we can but find wisdom, all things else will be added unto us…Truth will not make us rich, but it will make us free…'

In addition to over-specialisation representing chaos and philosophy's current inability to unify it, over-specialisation can actively contribute to the chaos. The author knows academics who do not understand the importance of saving the tiger, or other species, from extinction. They can discuss arcane and abstruse intellectual concepts but don't understand where their air, water and food come from, other than in the most simplistic way. They know everything about a leaf they can see but not touch, yet know nothing about the branch they are sitting on to view it. Such over-specialisation, and the resulting ignorance of basics, allow ecosystems to break down and helps create chaos – environmentally, economically and intellectually.

Without understanding the fundamental importance of the natural environment, no one can be truly well-educated. They may have other specialised knowledge, but of what relevance is it when life-support systems collapse? Even if complete rational knowledge were available, in itself it can only ever be half the truth. For complete unity we need to combine it with intuition, compassion and other aspects of yin.

Durant referred to our wish to find wisdom which, from this chapter's perspective, requires rational and intuitive knowledge to be combined. When they are, they allow developments to be anticipated, allowing us to see further and sooner. Durant also refers to truth, some of which can be seen, as the preceding chapter suggested, in the stars above, (star)dust underfoot, or heard – cried out by a wild bird, while an old pine tree preaches wisdom. Our imbalance is revealed in our obsession with the dust itself, not what it records; or with the physical properties of the stars; or the value of the bird in an oven or a cage, and the price of pine timber. We are obsessed with the score itself (the materials it's written on), rather than its music. It is as if we pay attention to the pugmarks just as pugmarks, not as a record of where the tiger came from, and where it is going to. Due to this same, overly specialised obsession with physical minutiae, we don't know where we came from, or are going to, or why.

We have studied light but cannot see the picture it reveals. Above we considered perspectives on an old master but our obsession with material means we are always up against the canvas studying texture, colour or its composition. Someone finds a new colour and calls attention to it; someone else breaks through to canvas and finds that colours are not truly 'real'; another breaks through the canvas and finds nothing to be the ultimate reality. Few look at the painting as a whole, and thereby miss everything of importance. Worse still, those who spend their life looking at one blob of colour find that blob of colour meaningless in itself, but then conclude (without looking at it) that the whole painting must therefore be meaningless.

We have studied sound but cannot hear nature's message. This is partly due to the cacophony of man-made noise surrounding us. 'There is no quiet place in the white man's cities. No place to hear the unfurling of leaves in spring or the rustle of an insect's wings…The clatter only seems to insult the ears, and what is there to life if a man cannot hear the lonely cry of the whippoorwill or the arguments of the frogs around a pond at night?... The Indian prefers the soft sound of the wind darting over the face of a pond, and the smell of the wind itself, cleansed by a mid-day rain, or scented with the pinon pine.' (J22) Aldous Huxley (1894 – 1963 English author) refers to the 20th century being the noisiest in history, physically and mentally, due in no small part to technology's contribution to the modern 'assault on silence' (B34).

In the meantime other technology, itself a result of the obsession with the material and mechanical, is invading the genetic basis of life, with potential practical and moral dilemmas so enormous it is as if nature herself develops counterbalances in proportion to our wilful obsessions, in an attempt to shake us out of our self-imposed blinkers. A few, self-satisfied scientists, trapped in microscopic worlds within Petri dishes, are growing a new world, encoding corporate agendas and / or their own purblind intelligence, egos and conceits into their new creations, which will manifest at birth as congenital defects.

When we look at the bigger picture and assess where we are going, open our minds and hearts to more than material, to life, to other people, to other creatures, even the dust can be viewed differently "…the rocks, which seem to be dumb and dead as they swelter in the sun along the silent shore, thrill with memories of stirring events connected with the lives of my people, and the very dust upon which you now stand responds more lovingly to their footsteps than yours, because it is rich with the blood of our ancestors, and our bare feet are conscious of the sympathetic touch.' (J26).

Something of the relation between the foot and the soil was mentioned in chapter I, and in the previous chapter with regard to Corbett. The world's dust also records the trail humanity has followed, collectively and individually. In the context of the above quotes – Life is recording our life. It records our actions and, if we look, if we will be our own detectives, find connections and clues, piece together the story of our actions, of our lives, we can connect past events in sequence to help lead us forward. The world shows us our footprints and thereby indicates the direction in which we are heading. That our footprints have led to an environmental crisis is incontrovertible proof that we are on the wrong path. We still have some options to change direction but those options are rapidly diminishing. To see the directions still available to us we need to readjust our viewpoints from specialisation to generalisation, vistas to panoramas, stand back from the canvas and appreciate the stunning beauty of nature's artistry, appreciating wider perspectives and therefore wider reflections than those of our own day to day routines, those confined to our work and family, and those packaged in lightweight containers for our consumption.

...on Changing the Reflections and the World

Lifting our eyelids to see beyond our own daily lives and face the world as it is, we can see 'specialistic chaos' in science and elsewhere, alienation of people from nature and each other; the global dominance of corporate power and corruption in politics, and the need to change it.

The standard record of world changes is usually called history and the changes wrought by wars, inventions, engineering, political ideologies, commerce and empires are undeniable. These physical, man-made changes have, so far, been most rapid and extensive during the 20th century due to technology loaning human activity a scope and scale greater than any previously known to history. At the beginning of the 20th century a world map showed fewer than 80 countries and passports, as we know them now, did not exist (appearing with WWI). During that century the colonial empires disappeared, there was a proliferation of nation states and dramatic advances toward universal suffrage. The demise of the imperial powers was accompanied by the rise of communism and fascism which were, ideologically, opposite extremes (we might even speculate that they were a yin and yang pair). In practice, however, despite differing ideologies, both used totalitarian methods to impose political policies and ignored any form of accountability. Fascism was destroyed by WWII and Soviet communism survived only because it had fought with the allies against fascism (after its non-aggression pact with Nazi Germany had been violated by Hitler). Even so, its survival was not certain, as Churchill wanted to crush Soviet communism immediately the fascist threat was overcome. As events actually unfolded, Soviet communism's survival into the decades following WWII produced the 'Cold War' but, before the end of the 20th century, it too passed into history. All of these developments were accompanied by profound human suffering; including the deaths of millions of people (even if we exclude the horrific death toll of 20th century wars, Stalin and China's Mao Zedong were responsible for the deaths of millions of their own people). Chinese communism arose with Mao Zedong after the Chinese civil war in 1949 but increasingly appears to be so in name only since it now shares many features with capitalism and maintains extensive capitalist collaborations with the West. Nonetheless, at the opening of the 21st century, China still operates under a single party system as do the other communist countries of Cuba, Laos, Vietnam and North Korea while other multi-party nations have communist parties (with some of these exercising significant political power) such as India, Nepal, South Africa and Cyprus.

However, by the end of the 20th century, globally speaking, the retreat of imperialism and colonialism had been replaced by a colonialism of 'capitalism'. Dominance over, and impositions on nations could now be exerted by monetary, instead of military, force (please see Appendix III for examples) largely as a consequence, as touched on above, of nation states having been replaced, in economic terms, by multinational corporations. Levinson's book 'Vodka-Cola' details how, even prior to the break up of the Soviet Union, a nexus of industrial collaborations had been formed between the West and the Eastern Bloc countries. Despite being generally concealed at that time, it was so economically significant as to reduce the political ideologies and identities of nation states to the status of window dressing – and totally unrepresentative window dressing. Since then such collaboration has increased and played a significant part in the political re-structuring of various nations.

From an environmental perspective, the 20th century's political and socio-economic systems, its wars and technology, have been responsible for the greatest abuse and physical destruction of nature in recorded history.

All these rapid and enormous changes have influenced our perceptions of what global change means. They may also make us wonder how all this could possibly relate to each of us as individuals.

Firstly, let us see if, amongst that kaleidoscope of recorded history and myriad events, we can identify any factors which have remained constant. Some may point to the fact that social organisation, however it may be labelled and whatever culture or technology may accompany it, reduces *in practice* to a few ruling elite exploiting the majority to varying degrees while preserving the status quo (unless changing it will provide more power and privilege for themselves). Others may point to the equally indisputable constant recurrence of armed conflict with all its associated barbarity and brutality (usually engineered by the ruling 'elite' to acquire more power and privilege).Yet, are there still more fundamental factors common to these political and military features, and all the other variety of human activities and events as well?

It is suggested here that during this immense panorama of history, humans, in terms of character, have remained much the same. Lives change, roles change and particular details of cultures and commerce change but, in the vast majority of cases, people's characters do not change. The repetition of the same historical themes, but with different people in the same roles, actually testifies, amazingly and in complete contrast to the immensity of change we have just considered, to no change! Hence, for example, plays from the dawn of civilisation such as those of Sophocles, Aeschylus or Euripides, through Mystery or Miracle plays to mediaeval Morality plays, on to Marlow or Shakespeare, right up to today, all remain relevant because human characters have remained the same, whether they are dressed in tunic and sandals and holding a stylus; doublet and hose, holding a quill; or in collar and tie, talking into a mobile telephone. Had we developed significantly, we would be as bewildered when reading or watching ancient plays as were the enlightened Houyhnhnms listening to Gulliver describe the behaviour and culture of humans. We would wander too far from our current path to examine this idea in detail, however, it possible to construct an argument that, in terms of human character, the world has changed little throughout recorded history.

This is a sobering thought but rarely considered. It is much easier and more comfortable to consider what is often casually accepted as 'progress'. However, progress does not equate to the passage of time. The freedom that allows progress must also allow regress, or it is not really freedom. Cases could be made that societies have become more knowledgeable, sophisticated, fairer and tolerant – it is heartening to think of examples such as the abolition of slavery or the 20th century's progress toward universal suffrage and human rights as well as advances in knowledge, science and medicine. Cases could also be made that societies have become more ignorant, sophisticatedly stupid, sheep-like and undiscriminating. It would be difficult to establish an unassailable position for either viewpoint. Even undeniable technological developments start to crumble as exclusive examples of 'progress' as we examine them, not only in terms of their environmental costs, but also in terms of all the knowledge and wisdom lost in exchange for technical toys and / or information and / or convenience e.g. we can mass produce millions of loaves of white bread but they are almost devoid of nutritional value (after this became generally known, one or two elements or vitamins replaced during manufacture are trumpeted by advertising as 'selling points'!) Some may consider that we have advanced because, for example, we no longer stage 'entertainment' such as that provided in the Roman Colosseum, or publicly execute criminals, or send children into mines and factories (although identical or similar situations to all of these can still occur somewhere in the modern world. With regard to children, they no longer work in factories or mines in the West at least, although they do in factories of the East (and often for Western corporations of the 'developed' world) and in mines in South America). However, even if we agree that some progress in some countries has been made, it is also true that, in the modern world, more people, and animals, suffer daily than all the victims of ancient empires and previous generations put together (i.e. those suffering today c. 4 billion people (two thirds of humanity) + ? billion animals, exceed the whole world's population of humans for millennia past).

In Greek Mythology, Sisyphus was condemned by Zeus to roll a rock up a mountainside and, as he approaches the summit, be unable to prevent the rock rolling all the way back to the base, from where he would have to begin again, for eternity. Durant sees Sisyphus as representing successive cycles of human communities following the same path of arduous cultural and economic progress, re-births of arts and sciences but, before reaching the summit, destroying civilisation and returning to baseness. He comments that man's tedious repetition is due to his not mastering the earth. Our speculations would suggest that it is due to him not mastering himself. This mere outline of the myth provides a valid comparison but, interestingly, there is more; Sisyphus was associated with commerce, he was also greedy and deceitful, even committing murder to maintain his privileged position and, by these vices he, in one sense, condemns himself to eternally wasted progress.

The quality of our characters, collectively speaking, has remained much the same. If anything, sadly and worryingly, recent trends indicate an increasing selfishness. Collectively and generally speaking, our behaviour, values and priorities, are virtually the same as any humans known to us in history, hardly developing spiritually, hardly maturing, over thousands of years. Part of a message Einstein wrote for posterity reads: 'If you have not become more just, more peaceful, and in general more sensible than we are (or were) today, then may the Devil take you!'

So, it is human character, selfishness and selflessness, and its struggle with right and wrong, which provides at least one constant factor underlying all the variety of events referred to above. This may be obvious, but so obvious it rarely, if ever, is considered. History usually records personal or national advantage, money, love, lust, status etc. as the usual motivating factors by which decisions were made, and for which action was taken – if it even bothers to identify them, knowing the reader will immediately understand the motives without explanation because they are still so prevalent today. Historical analysis concentrates on the resulting physical events, the material effects only, whereas history's true value is the opportunity for us to learn from the character who, and characteristics which, created those events, and thereby develop our own character (the law of cause and reflect) which then influences future decisions (the law of cause and effect; each law alternating with the other). We have arrived at the crucial causative factor inextricably linked to all the range of global history just considered – the individual's power to decide, to choose between options, to favour self or others, self or duty, self or society, self or environment. In truth, all are the same in the long-term, but the self is always seduced by short-term perspectives, and thereby destroys its own and others' long-term health. 'The true value of a human being is determined primarily by the measure and the sense in which he has attained liberation from the self.' (On this occasion the quote is not of an Eastern mystic but of Albert Einstein).

It was noted above that society can influence individuals to become moral, but *cannot make* it happen, while in contrast, moral individuals *can make* society moral. Sufficient individuals observing moral and virtuous values not only create a climate wherein young people's behaviour is automatically cultivated in like manner but also influences adults to consciously comply in order to gain social approval, or at least avoid disapproval (perhaps a sub-conscious effect operates as well, in relation to Jung's 'collective subconscious'). The promotion of healthy spiritual change / growth / development of individuals is a fundamental aim of religion, yet because even the devout often fail to achieve (or even recognise) this, its history is, more often than not, a record of barbarity.

The invention of the sword undoubtedly changed the world, as did the invention of the gun. Yet, in another sense, they are the same and actually testify to no change at all in the mentality and make-up of Man. Einstein saw this clearly in the light of the truly unprecedented and unique dangers of nuclear weapons and commented in 1946 "The unleashed power of the atom bomb has changed everything except our modes of thinking, and thus we drift toward unparalleled catastrophes." Some months later he elaborated a little "Science has brought forth this danger, but the real problem is in the minds and hearts of men. We will change the hearts of other men (only) by changing our own hearts and speaking bravely…When we are clear in heart and mind, only then shall we find courage to surmount the fear which haunts the world." A truly great scientist is not confined by science. In these quotes we see Einstein's understanding of the need to conquer self, balance head and heart, and face personal responsibilities to society. The examples of the sword, gun and nuclear weapons are obvious but it is also true of the wheel or iron tools, since these too are only beneficial for as long as they are used to harmonise healthily with nature and morality. Otherwise, technology is of mixed blessings; brings more problems than it solves; or is downright dangerous.

So we could say that history's record is mostly one of 'mechanical' or physical change driven mainly by the attempt (successful or otherwise) to acquire power over others. History hardly ever records 'real' or significant change, which only occurs when people acquire power over themselves, conquer themselves, achieving character development in accordance with morality and virtue.

Perhaps Solomon's kingdom was an example of such a triumph (as a perfect example of balanced yin and yang, what Solomon asks of God, in order that he may govern well, is an 'understanding heart', appearing in other Biblical translations as 'wisdom'). Pericles' Athens may be another (confining our view to its uncorrupted, peaceful democracy – albeit for a restricted electorate – and within Athens itself, since Pericles was often at war with other communities and enslavement was common practice) or perhaps Lydia in Asia Minor (largely modern day Turkey), ruled by King Croesus (he whose name is synonymous with fabulous wealth), where the inhabitants lived in a freedom and luxury which gave rise to a cultural and scientific renaissance. The kings of the Persian Empire, from Cyrus the Great to his successors, Xerxes and Darius the Great, practised conquest but not always bloody conquest, unlike those of other contemporary cultures, notably Rome. Rome divided the world into Roman and non-Roman and looked down on all who were non-Roman, even when their cultural achievements were superior to anything Rome had ever achieved. In contrast, there is good evidence to show that the Persian Kings (who successfully repulsed all Roman invasions and against whom the Romans never prevailed) celebrated the cultural diversity within their empire and supported religious tolerance, even re-building temples for the gods of other religions (one notable exception appears to be their oppression of Jewish people).

Frederick the Great of Prussia should also be mentioned as an enlightened monarch (indeed one who actually contributed to the Enlightenment itself). As a young man under the tutelage of Voltaire he wrote the 'Anti-Machiavel' defining kingship in terms of state welfare and the happiness of its subjects, in contrast to Machiavelli's 'Prince' with its emphasis on wealth and glory. Frederick's ideal prince is humane, gracious, virtuous and wise, all of which contribute to true Statecraft. On becoming king, he laboured long and hard to establish in practice what he had described in theory, implementing many social and legal reforms, abolishing torture, encouraging religious tolerance and being personally involved in all aspects of the state – agriculture, public education, civil service, the law, trade and industry. He also wrote a Code of Law which established the relationship between monarchy and state, both of which were to be bound by law and all with a view to justice for free citizens.

Perhaps other examples of ideal societies include India as ruled by Akbar the Great, or the Costa Rica of José Figueres from 1948 to 1974. Two features of the post WWII (1945 – 1951) Labour government of Britain stand out as some of the highest achievements of civilisation – in principle if not always in practice – the National Health Service and the Welfare State. It was also that government's economic planning which allowed the nation's recovery from post war austerity and sowed the seeds of the much improved national welfare, which came to fruition during the term of the succeeding Conservative government (1951 – 1964). Wilson's Labour government (1964 – 1970) also established the Open University, which offers part-time, distance-learning degree courses regardless of qualifications already held (if any), enormously expanding the availability of tertiary education.

It is easy to see how character development in Kings, Prime Ministers and Presidents can bring beneficial change to the world but how can character development in ordinary people achieve the same? As the possibility of making changes that affect millions, or even thousands of people, virtually overnight, is beyond most of us, our good intentions of making the world a better place usually end there. A few move on to realise that they can change themselves but generally consider this a poor second option. Yet it is in the latter that we achieve the former. If we change, the world must change – it has too, by definition, since we are part of it. The usual response to this point is that the change must be negligible. Yet Mahatma Gandhi advised us that 'You must see in yourself the change you want to see in the world.' How can this make sense? The world is surely so vast as to make the individual, and their efforts, insignificant? The world's enormous scales seem to crush by size and weight. We think they cannot be adjusted to scales of human capacities and that they surely rob us of our powers as moral and intellectual individuals. We considered some aspects of this above with regard to Atlas. Yet we may still wonder how individual efforts, on behalf of oneself and others, could possibly have any effect on the Earth at large. Happily, the Earth, large though it is, does respond to us both collectively and individually (no gardener would doubt it, nor any biologist, geologist, climatologist or Eastern mystic). Can small actions really achieve big effects, far beyond our own little lives? Yes, they can, and sceptical or cynical views need to be adjusted in light of the following.

Thomas Schelling, an economist at Harvard, examined how small quantitative changes in behaviour lead to enormous qualitative changes. The sensitive point, at which a small change produces a very large effect, Schelling called the 'Tipping point'. Malcolm Gladwell wrote a book with this title and described New York's plummeting crime rate (previously unaccounted for) as an example of the 'tipping point'. The violent crime rate, once among the highest in the world, suddenly fell so rapidly that New York dropped to 136th among cities of the U.S.A. For years the city had developed various programmes including improved methods of policing and graffiti removal, with few visible results. No single cause, action or programme could explain the huge scale of change. Small increments of effort produced a sudden and big effect. 'Tipping points' have been found in numerous situations where minorities are outnumbered e.g. racial segregation and epidemiology. Tipping points show that causes and effects do not have simple relationships. At a critical point small change can have a huge effect. Before that critical threshold, even relatively

With thanks to the photographer Tormod who has placed this image of the Parthenon in the public domain, free of copyright.

large changes seem to have small effects. (For all the intellectual analysis, the proverbial 'straw that broke the camel's back' seems to sum up this concept nicely).

This principle might also, obviously, work to our detriment in that the massive damage being inflicted environmentally could be approaching a critical 'tipping point'. However, just as the action of innumerable individuals constitute the damage, so the very same individuals can start pushing the tipping point in the other direction by changing their life-styles – perhaps by following some of the suggestions in this book. In fact it is only the action of individuals that push the balance toward the tipping point. Hence changes in individuals have more 'real' significance than mass movements, albeit that the latter create more physical change. The 'new' individual, whose 'old' footprints led into the tiger's cave but do not come out, brings 'real' change both to themselves and their environment. We might say that sincere change in one person internally, has more significance for the world than 'external change' as manifested by many people such as, for an obvious but indisputable example, thousands raising their arms in Nazi salute to Hitler. Nazism brought undeniable 'mechanical' change for millions upon millions of people but was actually new uniforms and equipment for a repeat performance of violence, exploitation and brutality. The new element of that tragedy was that it was performed on scales previously unknown. These are the changes which most often make history – a cascade of slightly different horror scenes in one constant kaleidoscope of violence and exploitation. Hence, one person's sincere spiritual development has a significance out of all proportion to their 'size'; to their being a single individual.

We might be more enthusiastic about our personal challenges if, perhaps, we could find just one nation which might set an example, living by good principle and practice, exhibiting the beauty of justice and peaceful progress in healthy harmony with nature. Could there be such a country… or maybe a city…perhaps just one household? Ultimately, we realise that it would be more realistic to seek an individual human being who at least aspired to such a description, and start looking for that person, until we find them in the mirror. We are the only entity over which we have complete control, and with which we can deal in the time scales remaining to us. Nonetheless, this is the very unit we need to work on since, although physically small, it is one of the units of conscious choice that comprises all others. Above we saw that space travel is unable to solve our environmental problems and that we have nowhere else other than Earth to go. Having just seen that our only real option is to work on ourselves, we could say that, spiritually speaking, we have nowhere else other than our own 'earth' to go. Again we see the equivalence of the natural and spiritual environments. We are compelled to deal with our world and with ourselves.

'Households, cities, countries and nations have enjoyed great happiness, when a single individual has taken heed of the Good and Beautiful…'
(Philo Judaeus of Alexandria (20 BC – 50 AD). Hellenistic Jewish philosopher)

'One of the things I learnt when I was negotiating was that until I changed myself I could not change others.'
(Nelson Mandela, quoted in The Independent newspaper)

Some consider individual efforts to, say, reduce contributions to the greenhouse effect, to be negligible as compared to the scale of current greenhouse gas emissions from the U.S.A., China and India (the practical effects which individuals may exert on, for example, China, are given in the next chapter). Such negative and dismissive views ignore 'tipping points'; the value of increasing environmental awareness; the value of individuals facing their personal responsibilities (and if more had done so sooner we wouldn't have the current problems, either with governments or the environment); and the network of connections to commerce and profits which are part and parcel of this (and so many other) problems. Moreover, those who decry such efforts don't have any certain knowledge or better suggestions to offer us.

In contrast to what cynics would have us believe, we do know of individuals who have created global change by their own efforts (and in doing so, the humble and the meek actually have a greater spiritual opportunity than Kings, Prime Ministers and Presidents since, by wielding less power, their challenge is greater). Obvious examples would include religious teachers such as Siddartha Gautama and Jesus of Nazareth and others, in recent history, include Henry David Thoreau, Mahatma Gandhi and Dr. Martin Luther King. All of these people have inspired others to look at themselves, correct faults and develop as characters, while also, in some cases, changing the world. Other individuals whose influence and efforts eventually reached out to millions include Jean Henri Dunant (1828 – 1910) who, in 1859, witnessed the aftermath of the Battle of Solferino (in what is now Italy) and wrote a book 'A Memory of Solferino' which inspired the creation of the International Committee of the Red Cross in 1863. Or Mrs. Sarah Hale (1788 – 1879) who thought that Thanksgiving (first established by the Puritan settlers in the Plymouth Colony of North America in the autumn of 1621) should become a recognised holiday throughout the U.S.A. For nigh on thirty years she wrote letters to presidents, governors, and other influential people, and published magazine articles urging the recognition of this celebration as a holiday (thereby raising the consciousness of the public and politicians). President Abraham Lincoln finally listened to Mrs. Hale and, in 1863, declared Thanksgiving Day as a national holiday for the U.S.A. on the last Thursday of November. More recently and relevantly we can think of Greenpeace and Friends of the Earth which began with just a few concerned citizens. In addition to many other famous cases, there are innumerable anonymous persons who have contributed, and are still contributing to communities for the benefit of all, and some may not even be aware of their contributions or their value. Amongst the anonymous are numerous humanitarian, wildlife and environmental charity workers (including many volunteers) who make precious contributions to – for just a few examples – health and education, ecology, clearance of land mines, and establishing, and guarding human rights. These people change the world every day, but do not necessarily appear in the headlines. One illness healed, one tiger saved from being poisoned or poached, one mine removed, one person for whom justice is won in the face of corruption... one act of kindness, one smile given... and the world is different to what it would otherwise be. We are part of one grand unity, and so each and every part has significance for the whole, since each and every part changes the whole.

We have found some philosophical and practical evidence that the world can be changed for the better by changing ourselves for the better. Whatever the results, you have done your best in the prevailing circumstances and no one can do more. You have a clear conscience and your answer to the question 'What did you do for the greater good?' if and when it is asked of you by your peers, yourself or, potentially most telling of all, your children.

'Noble savages' have not been included since they needed no change to establish healthy, peaceful, self-sufficient communities. Their societies were already in harmony with nature and each other – until other societies 'explored'. The reader may contend that some recent research has suggested that this is a romanticised view and that 'primitive' peoples did abuse their environment and merely moved on when it could no longer sustain them. The implication is that the human condition is fixed, and we now happen to be at the stage where population growth has resulted in there being nowhere else to move on to. Since we only have limited information on 'primitive' societies, we may wonder which of these two scenarios is correct. The position adopted here, and which is critical to many, if not all, the major themes of this book, is that the truth includes both scenarios and all the variations in between. Each scenario was / is dependent on human choices. Treating nature with care and respect, actively exercising interest and willingness to learn, balancing head with heart, leads to a life that is sustainable, which is nature's feedback that we have found the correct balance between rates of consumption and regeneration. It is suggested here that, whether it is 'noble savages' or modern technological man, each has the capacity to harmonise with that part of nature which gives rise to him. Whilst 'savages' are physically and spiritually closer to raw nature than technological man, the latter can only sustain his technology by ensuring that each preceding stage is maintained i.e. as noted above, the Information age depends on the Industrial age which depends on the Agricultural age. Our problem now is that we spend too much time, energy and money playing with technological toys while our foundations are crumbling. No doubt some primitive societies did abuse their environment (and many of their descendants are still with us!) but they disappeared as societies. With regard to those who were/are willing to learn from, and harmonise with nature (individuals and societies), perhaps there are various possibilities constituting 'sustainable', depending on the prevailing conditions and the people involved, and this is one reason why 'sustainable' is so hard to define. Whilst you may remain undecided about the academic debate, it is difficult to be undecided about practicalities (which should not need debating) since, in our current circumstances, we rapidly need to discover what is sustainable.

Whatever practical problems we consider, sooner or later we discover the common thread running through most of their solutions is the conquering of self by individuals. No matter how large or complex a problem may be, the ultimate causative agents reduce to 'conscious units' of free will choice i.e. people! This single factor changes the world, so changing the world depends on this single factor – and each of us is in control of one of these units. Power over oneself would be the best qualification for having power over others. Unfortunately, those wielding power over others in this world are, in this way (if not others) usually least suitably qualified. Even worse, as Francis Bacon warns us in his essay 'Of Great Place', seeking power over others is to lose power over oneself (Francis Bacon 1561 - 1626 1st Viscount Saint Alban KC English statesman, author, philosopher, scientist and architect of the scientific method).

In the face of the latest (and due to its environmental effects, the last) form of global dominance – corporate dominance – how can we, as individuals, even if we accept the relevant philosophy and tipping points, change the world in practical ways? As so often in nature, the problem provides the answer – big business' obsession with money and power provides the very salt or astringent needed to loosen its jaws. Rich and powerful corporations, and the people who run them, are no islands: they are linked to you and your choices – most importantly to what you buy, to your priorities, values and what you aspire to.

Firstly, let's check these with a quick look in our personal mirror. If we 'respect' or admire the rich and powerful simply because they are rich and powerful, or aspire to be the same without further qualification or reason, we fuel and sustain this imbalanced, unhealthy system, which is reflecting our own personal imbalances and less than healthy values. If we buy magazines which promote (because we buy them!) the rich and famous; the empty and meaningless celebrity 'culture' etc. our disordered priorities promote these lucrative but dangerous excesses, helping to produce obesity in the few, and emaciation in the many. Even so-called 'celebrities' do not always want or welcome the attention of the 'media machine' and, in the context of self-development, we are reminded again of Bacon's essay 'Of Great Place' in which he comments that 'It is a sad fate for a man to die too well known to everybody else, and still unknown to himself.'

Through chains of connection, the powerful make their decisions in response to the decisions you make. Admittedly, advertising, marketing and media have ways of influencing our decisions but it is our responsibility to think for ourselves, educate ourselves, order our priorities and decide our actions accordingly. As individuals are of such importance, both as the problem and the solution, are there individuals whom we can encourage toward better ideals? Where can we find individuals to contribute small changes toward a healthy tipping point? Again, and this time practically, we need to look in the mirror! It's you. It's me. Only we can ensure that our practical actions are in harmony with our spiritual and mental priorities. These principles and practices incorporate another important character-building process; by looking into our own mirror we are automatically prevented from looking at others. Prevented from criticising others, we are compelled to face ourselves.

It may be valid to talk of collective or community behaviour (or even 'will') yet it does not exist as an entity that can be accessed or addressed in anyway – other than through the individuals who comprise that community. Hence it can only be healthy individual character development that leads to healthy community development, which underlines why each person is not only relevant but essential in order to change the world. Damaged spiritual health / damaged mental health / damaged physical health / damaged natural environments, form a circular path. We may start at any one of them and follow around the sequence. We may also start at any one of them to replace 'damaged' with 'healthy'.

The part of society under your direct control is you. Internal revolution ultimately brings external revolution – but without bloodshed. Revolution without an 'inner revolution' merely equates to repetition. Chief Seattle, and numerous other 'savages', knew we were part of the unity of life, the web of life, and that changing even one part changes the whole – which is another way of seeing how our individual character development is essential for solving global problems. Any one of those global problems is beyond any one individual to solve – alone. Yet the group that can solve those problems will be comprised of individuals.

By changing personally to make the world a healthier place, if only in terms of purchasing patterns, we actually achieve what was thought impossible – the world does change; not only by definition in microcosm but also in macrocosm because each person's actions cannot help but influence others, even though we may not be able to follow all the chains of connections. The next chapter considers the changes we can make to our personal activities, in particular as a customer and consumer. The resulting changes may not be globally extensive and immediate as perceived by our physical senses and from our tiny perspective, but changes there will be. From nature's perspective, each action and event *must* and *does* change the whole world, and immediately, but not on scales of time and space that register instantly on individual human beings – reminding us of seeds planted, and time needed, before developments register on our senses. Such changes are difficult to measure and assess, and we may not always be sure of the sequence of connections. However, we may be sure of the converse: that while individuals will not change for the better, the world will not change in any worthwhile way.

Perhaps you only make a small impact on the planet, use a tiny fraction of the Earth's resources. That is probably so, but the concepts of unity and 'tipping points' means you cannot be freed from personal responsibility in the larger context. If you only have control over a tiny fraction of Earth's resources, your individual responsibility may also be viewed from a different, but equally valid, perspective: what have you done with the small amount entrusted to your care? How have you treated that part of the Earth under your influence, under your control? For far too many of us the answers would have to include waste and abuse. Your actions are the examples you set for family, friends, colleagues and, most importantly, children. You are only in complete control of you and hence, if you have not mastered your own limited impact, greater power is best avoided until you do.

The next chapter includes many easily adopted suggestions by which you can make significantly healthy changes to your life style. By doing so, we help the Earth and every living thing on it and cannot help but begin to expand our viewpoints, beyond self to oceans, forests and onward up to mountains and other worldly fastnesses, and then beyond, to achieve cosmic perspectives. William Blake knew that 'great things are done when men and mountains meet' and, looking with Pugh from mountains and deserts, and with Biano's cosmic vision, we see that greater perspectives liberate one from self. It works in reverse too: selflessness brings broader perspectives. Which is cause and which effect? Greater perspectives are the antithesis of self, since obsession with self is to suffer the most microscopic of perspectives – unless it's to develop self into a worthwhile contributor to the greater vision (and even this should not become an obsession, since this too speaks of imprisonment in self).

> "There's only one corner of the universe you can be certain of improving,
> and that's your own self."
>
> *(Aldous Huxley)*

The increasing promotion of 'self' in the shallowest and narrowest of ways; fame for nothing of note; inflation of egos; 'achievements' of questionable value (all linked with commercial profits) have accompanied a decreasing respect for each other, other species, nature and the environment, along with ever smaller perspectives in time and space generally, as reflected in the short-term views of commerce and politics. From tiny individual perspectives in space and time, too many of us think about what we can know of, expect or want from the universe, yet never give a thought as to what the universe might be expecting or wanting from us. In this sense, many individual egos are bigger than the universe – but contain more of a vacuum. The more we hear of science's scales for the universe, the more meaningless we, and our personal significance, seem to become. For some people this sense of insignificance can reinforce short-term egoism and the attitude to 'take what you can while you can'. These imbalances could all be classified as examples of disproportion, and so it is in finding a sense of proportion that we find our balance.

...on Balance

Regaining our balance as individuals and communities is a delicate operation since our balance, once disturbed, cannot help but move off in a wrong direction. Overcompensating, we then find ourselves moving too far in the opposite direction. Energetic efforts to regain our balance pushes the pendulum into wider arcs and we swing between wider extremes of maxima and minima, no longer sure where the mid-point, our reference point, is located. Hence, for examples; some businesses become global, tyrannical giants while smaller businesses disappear; food has no fibre or nutrition but excess sugar and salt; some children are spoiled while others starve (and not only for want of food); citizens become servants of bureaucracies; teachers become subordinate to pupils; and parents to their children; criminals become more important than their victims; entertainment becomes synonymous with sex and violence and / or special effects and falsehood; while (as in the excerpt from Prof. Orr's article) desirable changes proceed at glacial pace and undesirable changes race ahead etc. Extremes take more time and energy to maintain and so life becomes more hectic and draining.

How do we find more time? Reject maximum and seek optimum. How do we find more energy? Consume selected, quality, uncontaminated materials physically, mentally and spiritually and adjust one's timetable as closely to nature's as possible, allocating time for physical, mental and spiritual exercise – and rest. When these various correct proportions result in a balance, how can we keep it? How do we stop the pendulum? It is through the development of our character that we find a firm foundation. By defining our personal boundaries or guides to our behaviour we define our character and stabilise ourselves in the ever-changing sea of circumstance in which we live. When we discover and decide who we are (both passive and active elements forming another essential yin, yang pair) we find constancy. Adhering to morality, practising virtue, exercising our interest and compassion i.e. behaving according to a set of healthy values, provides us with boundaries, or 'frames', within which we can define ourselves, choosing and building our character. Whatever situations present themselves to us, we have decided on those actions we will, and will not, allow ourselves. Hence we define ourselves consistently, establish a constancy amidst, but unaffected by, uninvited promptings and unceasing change. Without self-imposed rules and guides, without 'knowing who we are', we are pushed and pulled by inner impulses and innumerable external stimuli. With our self-imposed limits and laws we find balance and stability, and stop the pendulum.

When we bring the pendulum to rest, time, in one sense, stands still, marking the middle path. Time standing still can represent a sort of death, but the death of the old self, the one that walks into the tiger's cave but does not come out. Hence the pendulum at mid-point represents a new time, a new life. Once we walk the middle path we feel the comfort of balance – between time allocated to work, to home and family, to nature, to others less fortunate than ourselves and to our interests, and well being. We know better who we are, why we choose to act in the way we do, and feel more confident when facing life's uncertainties, since we no longer fear surprising others (or ourselves!) by our responses to circumstance, or disappointing ourselves by following the crowd, or succumbing to temptation.

Translating this back into terms of motion, we might say that the pendulum can now rotate about, but very closely to its mid-point, according to our judgement. The regularity of these patterns was marked for millennia by divisions of the year, month and week into allocated activities, regularly marked by seasons, Sabbaths, festivals and holy-days. Our cycles moved in harmony with nature's – our lives moved with the rhythm of the Earth's rotations and orbits. Nature's cycles allow us to move, to change, in order to stay the same, just as nature does. Marks on this clock help us with 'recollectedness' (B34) (knowing where we stand in relation to nature and other lives and hence helping us to know who we are) and remind us of 'truth momentarily forgotten in the turmoil of worldly distractions' (B34). Respect and appreciation for these festivals, the seasons and other natural patterns, follow naturally, since we see their value and importance, and treasure them, as we treasure life. Moving in a circle is always easier when we are balanced. Observance of optimum and nature's cycles sustains health (another manifestation of balance) in spirit, mind and body – our 'earth' moves in harmony with the Earth.

From such perspectives we may see and share Ochwiay Biano's cosmic awareness and understand it as healthier, more realistic and purposeful, than any brought back by spacecraft or other hi-tech extravagances, fascinating though the latter may be. Ochwiay Biano saw the stars and the significance of humans as one. Modern Westerners let scientists see the stars on their behalf, and see humans as cosmically insignificant. Which is the greater vision? Which sees further and sooner into distant deeps and skies?

Nature's metaphorical mirrors might reflect more to us than mirrors in reflecting telescopes, and poems tell us more than particle accelerators. That mirrors and poems help us see further and sooner are recurrent themes in this book, particularly Blake's poem. If we look for reflections in Blake's poem, what can be seen? Firstly, another recurrent theme: yin and yang, the lamb and the tiger. Some interpretations see in the poem questions of good and evil and wonder whether the tiger is a creature of God or the devil. A deeper analysis can suggest that the tiger in the poem contains elements of both, while other interpretations see God as creating something that becomes independent of His will. All of these can be included, to varying degrees, in another theme; which sees the tiger, and the lamb, reflecting contrasting characteristics of our human free will and our ability to oppose God's purposes. As Blake was a devout, if unorthodox, Christian we can also recognise the Lamb of God and its principle of sacrifice in atonement for those characteristics of the tiger we choose to manifest.

As already suggested, nature is our model, and one of the most fundamental principles recurring in this book is that of yin and yang, which we have to combine harmoniously to achieve health. We can begin our combination of yin and yang firstly by trying to view the world from each viewpoint, without allowing one to dismiss the other. Science may listen to religion as a husband may listen to his wife. Consideration of Chief Seattle's or Blake's views broadens our perspective toward the panoramic but, for any and all lessons revealed by our expanded viewpoints, the question remains as to whether and if so, when, we will *learn* those lessons. When will we listen to tigers within and without? The most important lesson is to respect and care for nature. Even if we reject our exploration of more mystical, mysterious viewpoints, our practical environmental situation and the importance of personal choice is undeniable. In a physically real sense alone, we shall not avoid a settling of accounts and pay a heavy and frightening price for our abuse of nature, including those making short-term 'profits' from environmental abuse, who are currently insulated and distanced from the results of their behaviour, but rapidly moving closer to meet them.

For as long as we continue to distance ourselves from nature, imbalances, obesity and unhealthy growths will continue to appear. Obvious examples would include enormous concentrations of material assets or money into the hands of a few people, or concentrations of excess energy stored as fat in individual bodies but another and less obvious example is the vast amounts of information we have accumulated (along with, curiously, vast ignorance) and this wealth, like all excessive wealth, breeds arrogance.

In contrast, recognition that any wealth we have is but a part of nature's wealth, and that by sharing we stimulate others to share, and thereby receive what we were previously unaware of, builds knowledge and wisdom. Lessons learned are seeds nurtured healthily to bring forth good fruit.

Humans may follow and learn from nature; footprints may follow pugs. Tracking of pugmarks has been referred to on a number of occasions above and may give an impression that the tracker somehow holds superior knowledge to the animal being tracked. Tracking by use of one's head only can lead to arrogance. Tracking with head and heart leads to humility. Corbett tracked his man-eaters but did so with a healthy respect and humility, seeking the next sign from which he could learn, in order to take appropriate action. In a forest, he would be our best guide, since nature was his guide. This reminds us of Francis Bacon (1561 – 1626) telling us 'Knowledge and human power come to the same thing for nature cannot be conquered except by obeying her.'

Viewed from practical perspectives alone, we are still dependent on the natural world the tiger represents and there is really only one lesson, 'to husband and nurture' that natural world. This view point can be seen from scientific, socio-economic, mystical and spiritual perspectives, thereby ensuring its availability to all humans. However, it seems likely as I write, that our failure to learn that lesson, our failure to meet personal responsibilities promoting and protecting life in both local and wider communities, our imbalances, selfishness, ignorance and apathy will, to our everlasting disgrace, allow greed and corruption to take our tigers from us forever. We are going to destroy beauty, majesty and nobility and, as we destroy manifestations of these pure principles externally, we shall destroy them internally.

Our anthropomorphic views and 'nature as a mirror', each have their own validity, and point to natural physical manifestations of our set of values, virtues and morals; the quality of our characters. In more prosaic terms, our character governs our actions, yet we rarely let the results of our actions govern, or even adjust, our character. We thereby lose the value of the mirror, do not see the reflection, fail to 'know ourselves' and repeat the patterns that produce the problems, failing to frame the symmetry – with fearful consequences. Throughout history various maxims have described our failure to learn from history. One or two of the following may appeal to the reader. 'History repeats itself because we do not learn'. Or what could be called the school version 'If you do not learn your history, it will be repeated' or 'The most important lesson of history is that nobody learns history's lesson', or finally, the version by George Bernard Shaw (1856 – 1950 Irish author, playwright and critic), 'We learn from history that we learn nothing from history.'

Reflection, and action in response, forms another of nature's cycles. Correction is part of nature's cycles. For example, the earth returns to us in our food, water and air the poisons and pollution we 'throw away', contributing to physical illness, impaired senses and abilities. Another example referred to above was our incredibly slow recognition of the need to recycle instead of continuing to consume resources. We have, at least in part, recently woken up to this aspect. The same failure to learn lessons also appears in our own man-made disasters: despite archaeological evidence for disastrous man-made abuse of natural environments from Mesopotamia to Rome, the 20th century still produced, for just two examples, the Oklahoma dust bowl and Madagascar's rivers running red with eroded topsoil (the latter due to deforestation and over-grazing) and visible as red 'ribbons' from the space shuttle.

However, if it is left as a simple and collective 'we fail to learn our lessons' a very important point would be missed. Whilst individual humans often fail in this way, as pointed out above, the very institutions set up to protect us from this fallibility are failing because they are manipulated by a few individuals who personally benefit in the short-term from doing so. We cannot collectively learn our lessons while a few executive pirates waylay and plunder our economic, political and legal systems at the massive expense of the majority. Whilst this is possible in man-made systems, the resulting and directly connected damage to nature's systems will correct the imbalances but include all, or the majority of humans in its remedial effects. While there is still time we must improve man-made systems from 'grass roots' upward. Practical suggestions are made in the next chapter.

Let there be no mistake; changes are coming, and if we make the right ones personally and today, those imposed by nature may be modified. Our repetition of mistakes, whether individually or collectively, may also be thought of as cycles and, in addition to circular repetition, another perspective reveals that we also travel around a spiral, which adds a third spatial dimension, down which we plummet, spiralling into disaster. The length or duration of the downward spiral might well represent the span of History's, or Nature's, or God's patience…we will only repeat mistakes so many times until their increasing gravity prevents further learning opportunities. 'Always remember what you have learnt. Your education is your life – guard it well.' (Proverbs 4:13). Hence, we must apply our lessons and make those changes nature is showing us to be immediately necessary. We must correct the imbalances, dare to frame the symmetries, now, today, and deal with our fears before fearful symmetries deal with us.

...on Truth

To frame symmetries accurately we need to know when we are looking at the truth.

Facts are information, finding connections between those facts is knowledge and, as those connections of knowledge grow, wisdom sees where knowledge will lead – often by including elements of intuition, and taking into account the character of those who know. Remembering the examples given in chapter II, we might say that it is a fact that some particular address details are printed in a directory. Knowledge is aware that the occupant has recently re-located, and wisdom would discretely say as much to a third party, but within earshot of the person proclaiming that facts are all we need.

The relationship between information, knowledge and wisdom, as we would expect from the principles considered in this chapter, needs to be balanced. Imbalance leads to T.S. Eliot's questions: "Where is the wisdom we have lost in knowledge? Where is the knowledge we have lost in information?" Facts are parts (often dead parts) and can therefore only offer biased perspectives, incomplete views. Dickens lampooned his own Mr. Gradgrind who says in Hard Times: 'Now, what I want is, Facts. Teach these boys and girls nothing but Facts. Facts alone are wanted in life. Plant nothing else, and root out everything else. You can only form the minds of reasoning animals upon Facts, nothing else will ever be of any service to them. This is the principle on which I bring up these children. Stick to Facts, Sir!' The American historian Henry Brooks Adams commented "Nothing in education is so astonishing as the amount of ignorance it accumulates in the form of inert facts" and we have already referred to Chesterton remarking on the fire of truth being extinguished by too much information.

Facts can help us find truth but facts must not be mistaken for truth. In a film called 'Spring and Port Wine', a father tells his adolescent children "There is probably not one thing in this book (the Bible) which is not an undisputed fact, yet it is full of God's truth." Sir Henry Jones (1852 – 1922 Welsh philosopher and academic) told us that '…the poets…though they teach only by hints and parables, they nevertheless reflect the concrete truth of life, as it is half revealed and half concealed in facts.' (B36)

Today, due to technology, more information is available to people at the touch of button than ever before in recorded history, yet few have any real knowledge (including highly educated, intelligent people) and a glance at the world shows that wisdom is long since lost. We may alter the truth of this situation by our choices and actions. Exploring such profound concepts as facts, knowledge, wisdom and truth could fill many books but here we are concerned with their immediate practical importance for helping us find a healthier future, or perhaps just a future. Hence the following few remarks are offered in that context.

One of the dangers of concentrating solely on facts is that, due to practical and intellectual constraints, we never have them all. What, possibly critical, facts are missing? Even if we had them all they do not, of themselves, reveal their relationships. Now we see how knowledge can help us, since tracing connections between facts (or information) usually reveals relationships, providing a pattern or patterns. Patterns suggest where we have a complete or partial set or where facts may be missing and point to where we should seek them. Having found some knowledge we may use history (which shows how those patterns will develop), intuition and experience to see where we are going, which is something of wisdom.

What of truth?

Pilate asked Christ 'What is truth?' and did not wait for an answer. Can we find in our considerations anything that he might have heard had he waited? The Indian Express watchwords are 'Because the Truth Involves Us All' – and this is true in the sense of the Express printing the truth because decisions made by the powerful affect us all. However, it is also true in the broader sense that all of us participate in creating it i.e. all our decisions affect all. The truth Pilate asked about involves Pilate. It also involves us, and all that is involved in us; not only facts and physics but also morality, virtue, spirituality and, crucially, our choices involving all of these factors. In all these ways and more, we write part of the truth and, at the same time, part of the future (which creates additional facts, knowledge and truth). Therefore truth also lives and grows. The deepest Truth is in the unification of all human activity and, of course, much else besides – because the Truth involves All, in a unity connecting all things. Our involvement is critical and unavoidable, much as we may sometimes wish it was not, which is possibly why Pilate did not wait for an answer. We sometimes wish we could wash our hands of the whole affair. However, inaction may have as many consequences as action. Once we recognise our powers of choice and action, we realise that those actions may as well be for health as for harm (and ultimately, we only heal or harm ourselves). How do we know which is which? Nature, morality and virtue are our guides. Neglecting these guides will lead us into danger and, ultimately, disaster.

We considered above the possibilities of changing the world for the better by changing ourselves. Some might imagine that they may choose whether or not to make the effort – think that they may opt out, stay neutral, and carry on with lives that may not be ideal, but which feel familiar and safe. Our consideration of truth shows us that there is no neutrality, no-one can opt out, we are, all of us, already 'in it'; it's called life. We are already creating effects, even when we think we are just minding our own business, or 'keeping our heads down' or going through our own little routine. All of your actions, and inactions, have effects and then consequences. Some of your inactions may be allowing corporate pirates to waylay and plunder your civil rights, socio-economic security and environmental life-support systems, without the least opposition from you. Some, due to their circumstances, might be forgiven for not wielding a cutlass, but what can be said for those who could not find the time, energy or commitment to wield even a pen, or a shopping trolley, in the right way?

Due to too many of us washing our hands and avoiding personal responsibilities there is no time left to discuss philosophy, since tigers, and much else of our life support systems, are dying. We have to get our hands dirty, and dirty as never before, since we have allowed so much mess to accumulate. We have to grasp and apply the practical manifestations of these concepts as they occur in our daily lives (in how we spend our time and money, the values we teach our children etc.) and, as far as we are able, see that the same applies to local and national communities, commerce, corporations and governments. We may wash our hands when we have done our work, not to avoid our work.

Whether we wish it or not, we all create effects. Whether we wish it or not, all things are connected. Whatever your personal beliefs about the individuals involved, Pilate's decision affected your life, as did the decisions of butchers, bakers and candlestick makers – those living at the time, all those living before and all those living since, but these mostly pass unknown. Yet, no matter how mundane, or how convoluted the connections, connections there are. We have already referred above to conducting a 'bus or an orchestra with our best efforts, but even seemingly inconsequential duties, when done diligently, with courtesy and a smile or, alternatively, incompetently, rudely and with a scowl can, either directly, or via chains of connections, ultimately influence the moods and decisions of the powerful, and thereby the fate of nations. Even if all decisions and actions were known, their effects are too numerous and subtle for the mind of man to trace or record – but effects there are, so we had best be diligent, courteous and practise our smiles, to promote what is healthiest for all, including ourselves. Thinking of how past lives have influenced present ones, reminds us that we are all creating effects now, today, for our contemporaries and posterity, laying more emphasis on the importance of every individual's contributions. Each person, affecting and affected by others, make variations on a theme in a universal symphony and we are each responsible for playing our part and checking it is in harmony with other lives.

The environment is nature's way of telling us that we are currently producing a cacophony, out of tune and out of time.

...on Unity

We, especially in the West, cannot see much of the truth, partly because we have forgotten so much of the past that connects us to nature and each other (since unity is a concept that can apply to time as well as space). Having recently isolated ourselves in 'brick cages', glass, steel and plastic, we have, within a generation or two, distanced ourselves so far from the mirror as to lose our reflection and forget the part we should be playing.

Hamlet remarks that man has the ability to see 'before and after' (Act IV Sc. IV). If we call 'before' forethought or something of wisdom, and 'after' history, we can see that learning from history is also something of wisdom since the past predicts the future. The past has immense importance and potential value. 'The past is never dead. It's not even past.' (William Faulkner American author 1897 – 1962) History's repetitive account shows us that our civilisations collapse due to decadence and corruption. We can change this. When we have harmonised with nature's healthy patterns and rhythms, the past may still predict the future, but in wholesome, healthy and harmonious ways.

Too often we choose to forget or deny our origins. Like Pip in Dickens' 'Great Expectations' when good, sincere, country yokel Joe visits him in his newly acquired gentleman's life in London; we find we are embarrassed at our heritage. Isolated in our brick cages, we look down on the good earth. Yet that earth makes the brick cages, our bread and our bodies; makes all we make and, when our cycles are complete, receives us all, to make more cycles. Like Joe, it is the good earth that holds the true and quiet dignity, while we are with Pip, upstarts without our own foundation. No matter how apparently independent we may seem or how hard working we may be, ultimately we are all beggars in borrowed finery, since we do not have to look far to find where we need and use nature's bounties, but do not earn them. We have not only forgotten our origins but also our continuing need for, and dependency on nature and the soil. We tread underfoot, abuse and poison that which gives us life.

'You must teach your children that the ground beneath their feet is the ashes of our grandfathers. So that they will respect the land, tell your children that the earth is rich with the lives of our kin. Teach your children what we have taught our children, that the earth is our mother. Whatever befalls the earth befalls the sons of the earth. If men spit upon the ground they spit upon themselves.' In this same 'letter' Chief Seattle refers to himself as a savage and suggests his concerns arise because he doesn't understand the ways of the White man. If 'savage' is appropriate then he is truly a noble one and one who understood more than the self-proclaimed 'civilised' White man who, as such, should already have known of Socrates saying "…the earth may be truly called mother" and Plato's advice that "…the woman in her conception and generation is but the imitation of the earth, and not the earth of the woman" and that the first priority for a new community is to treat, "the soil you are now settling with all religious care…" (B32)

As the embryo in the mother contains all the potentials of the adult, so the green landscape, the Earth's soil, holds us, and our cathedrals and computers, indeed all of our potentials and all possible products, in addition to our sustenance and education. Nature provides food for body, mind and soul. Yet, having realised some of those potentials, we become impressed with ourselves and our products, forgetting what they and we are standing on and where we, and those abilities, come from.

What we build may hide natural scenery, helping us to either forget our heritage or consider it alien. We know modern stories of children who think food comes from supermarkets and have no understanding of sowing and planting, harvest, animals (other than pets) or breathing fresh, scented, sunlit air flowing between a forest path and skies above. No simple pleasures from simple games, running and rolling in grass and hay, getting knees dirty for washing in the stream, while bare feet and toes try to grip slippery stones. Today's situation is as if children had already attended the 'nature nausea' courses of Aldous Huxley's 'Brave New World' although these would now seem unnecessary since, after a certain age, some children, having only known 'brick cages', artificial lights and television, react with disgust to the reality of farm animals, mud or work in the fields. Computer games and videos viewed in sunless, airless rooms render the local farmer's field remote, let alone the jungle.

Today we are even warned against sunshine. Of course, a depleted ozone layer makes it sensible to seek more shade than one would normally do and to carefully monitor one's skin condition (the more important warnings should be about the corporate and political stupidity which allowed the ozone layer to be depleted in the first place. This would be something of knowledge in addition to information or 'facts'). Health warnings should include a wider 'wake-up' call regarding our treatment of nature in general and also be telling us what environmentally remedial measures are being taken (something of wisdom). Yet warning information is presented as another of nature's deadly dangers which clever, caring scientists have saved us from by inventing creams and lotions (with as yet unknown side effects) of which we can purchase a few ounces for many pounds. Glory be, sunshine has grown a new market! For those of us living in temperate climates, hiding from the sun is to hide from life, and to deny something that's inherently joyous about living. For however many thousands of years humans have walked the planet, they have done so walking in sunshine (even on cloudy days). In more than one sense we are now walking into darkness. We are consciously choosing to become H.G. Wells' Morlocks of the future (a fictional future cave-dwelling species, supposedly descended from humans, but without the skin pigment melanin). We currently accept over-priced creams and lotions in exchange for literal and metaphorical sunshine! Skin protection will soon be achieved by our behaviour, since it indicates we will soon be growing natural, woolly coats. Vitamin D is primarily generated in skin exposed to sunlight. The British Medical Journal (Pearce and Cheetham January 2010) reports that rickets, and other serious diseases due to vitamin D deficiency, are reappearing in children, at least in the U.K. Factors include so many children staying indoors to play computer games and / or, if children do play outside, parents' too frequent and / or excess application of sun-block lotions to their children's skin.

Not only do we isolate ourselves from nature in our 'settlements' but the darkness of our 'settlements' also produces alternative, artificial scenery and every form of vice and corruption to lead us still further from healthy balances. As our distance from nature's mirror increases, so does our ignorance of who we are. Moreover, increasing distance encourages decreasing care, and lack of care for living things leads to lack of care for each other.

"The old Lakota was wise. He knew that man's heart away from nature becomes hard; he knew that lack of respect for growing, living things soon led to lack of respect for humans too… For the Lakota (*one of the three branches of the Sioux tribe of Red Indians – author*), mountains, lakes, rivers, springs, valleys, and the woods were all in finished beauty. Winds, rain, snow, sunshine, day, night, and change of seasons were endlessly fascinating. Birds, insects, and animals filled the world with knowledge that defied the comprehension of man.

The character of the Indian's emotion left little room in his heart for antagonism toward his fellow creatures… the Lakota was a true naturalist – a lover of Nature. He loved the earth and all things of the earth, and the attachment grew with age. The old people came literally to love the soil and they sat or reclined on the ground with a feeling of being close to a mothering power…It was good for the skin to touch the earth, and the old people liked to remove their moccasins and walk with bare feet on the sacred earth…Their tipis were built upon the earth and their altars were made of earth. The birds that flew in the air came to rest upon the earth, and it was the final abiding place of all things that lived and grew. The soil was soothing, strengthening, cleansing, and healing…This is why the old Indian still sits upon the earth instead of propping himself up and away from its life giving forces. For him, to sit or lie upon the ground is to be able to think more deeply and to feel more keenly; he can see more clearly into the mysteries of life and come closer in kinship to other lives about him…In talking to children, the old Lakota would place a hand on the ground and explain: 'We sit in the lap of our Mother. From her we, and all other living things, come.' … Sometimes we boys would sit motionless and watch the swallows, the tiny ants, or perhaps some small animal at its work and ponder its industry and ingenuity; or we lay on our backs and looked long at the sky, and when the stars came out made shapes from the various groups.

…Everything was possessed of personality, only differing from us in form. Knowledge was inherent in all things. The world was a library and its books were the stones, leaves, grass, brooks, and the birds and animals that shared, alike with us, the storms and blessings of earth. We learned to do what only the student of nature learns, and that was to feel beauty. We never railed at the storms, the furious winds, and the biting frosts and snows. To do so intensified human futility, so whatever came we adjusted ourselves, by more effort and energy if necessary, but without complaint.

…Even the lightning did us no harm, for whenever it came too close, mothers and grandmothers in every tipi put cedar leaves on the coals and their magic kept danger away. Bright days and dark days were both expressions of the Great Mystery, and the Indian reveled in being close to the Great Holiness.

…Observation was certain to have its rewards. Interest, wonder, admiration grew, and the fact was appreciated that life was more than mere human manifestation; it was expressed in a multitude of forms…From the Great Spirit, there came a great unifying life force that flowed in and through all things – the flowers of the plains, blowing winds, rocks, trees, birds, animals – and was the same force that had been breathed into the first man. Thus all things were kindred, and were brought together by the same Great Mystery…Kinship with all creatures of the earth, sky, and water was a real and active principle. In the animal and bird world there existed a brotherly feeling that kept the Lakota safe among them. And so close did some of the Lakotas come to their feathered and furred friends that in true brotherhood they spoke a common tongue…The animals had rights – the right of a man's protection, the right to live, the right to multiply, the right to freedom, and the right to man's indebtedness – and in recognition of these rights the Lakota never enslaved an animal, and spared all life that was not needed for food and clothing…This concept of life…gave to the Lakota an abiding love. It filled his being with joy and mystery of living; it gave him reverence for all life; it made a place for all things in the scheme of existence with equal importance to all…The Lakota could not despise any creature, for all were of one blood, made by the same hand, and filled with the essence of the Great Mystery. In spirit, the Lakota were humble and meek…from the earth they inherited secrets long since forgotten. Their religion was sane, natural, and human.

…for the Lakota there was no wilderness, because nature was not dangerous but hospitable, not forbidding but friendly, Lakota philosophy was healthy – free from fear and dogmatism. And here I find the great distinction between the faith of the Indian and the white man. Indian faith sought the harmony of man with his surroundings; the other sought the dominance of surroundings…In sharing, in loving all and everything, one people naturally found a due portion of the thing they sought, while, in fearing, the other found the need of conquest.

…The American Indian is of the soil, whether it be the region of forests, plains, pueblos, or mesas. He fits into the landscape, for the hand that fashioned the continent also fashioned the man for his surroundings. He once grew as naturally as the wild sunflowers, he belongs just as the buffalo belonged…Out of the Indian approach to life there came a great freedom, an intense and absorbing respect for life, enriching faith in a Supreme Power, and principles of truth, honesty, generosity, equity, and brotherhood as a guide to mundane relations." (Reprinted from 'Land of the Spotted Eagle' by Luther Standing Bear (an American Indian Chief), by kind permission of the University of Nebraska Press.)

Chief Standing Bear's comments summarise much that we have seen from our path through these chapters and something of the chapter to come: the Earth as mother, unity, knowledge all around us and available to those who look with interest and wonder. Morality and virtue as guides for our relationships, love, joy, humility and meekness, communication with animals, the fear that inhibits sharing and stimulates conquest, lack of love for nature leading to lack of love for people. In the Lakota's stoic indifference to nature's caprice we are also reminded of the serene detachment of the advanced yogi or religious ascetic. Yet detachment does not indicate a lack of love or concern; does not indicate distance. Detachment from events in this little life is actually born of intimacy and humility in the lap of that which is so much greater. When we are self absorbed distance from nature increases, and we lose intimacy and humility in the same measure as we are distanced.

The distance between nature and ourselves has become so vast; nature has become so remote, it appears to be insignificant, and we mistakenly think we can destroy it without compassion, consideration or practical penalty. We behave in ways we would describe as acting like animals! Moreover, because our reflection has become so distant we fail to see that, as we destroy nature, we are destroying ourselves. Distance allows us to separate 'Life' into 'us' and 'them', other life-forms. Intimacy is lost, which allows us to exploit, damage or destroy 'them'. In this way we have not advanced from the Romans dividing the world into Roman and non-Roman. 'Life' is 'One' and when one part harms another, the whole is harmed.

We need to re-connect with nature; watching, touching, connecting, caring.

From childhood, Corbett's constant acquaintance with the forest nurtured a deep, first-hand knowledge of jungle lore. When staying at Kaladhungi he would sleep outside to be aware of what was happening in the surrounding forest. From a modern perspective and in modern parlance Corbett might be called an 'expert' – able to answer questions, knowing names of animals, plants, and his subject 'in depth'. No doubt this is true, but it misses an important point: the above description applies even when the 'expert' remains 'separate' from what he studies; it is one thing and he is another. Corbett and his knowledge were a part of, at one with, nature. Academic knowledge is mostly second-hand and there is a distance between the academic 'expert's' knowledge and their subject. When Corbett slept outside at Kaladhungi he was not merely listening to, but participating consciously and sub-consciously in the events of the forest, literally the life *of* the forest as well as life *in* the forest and that life incorporated him as well. He was aware of temperature, light, humidity, the 'four winds of heaven', mating calls, foot falls and alarm calls – what was happening and what was about to happen (he acquired information, and then knowledge, and then wisdom). Moreover, in ways we probably still cannot understand, his presence influenced the whole due to his conscious and sub-conscious awareness and participation.

It is the difference between someone who goes to interview a community and someone who lives in the community – no amount of questions or 'knowledge' can substitute for living life in the community. It is the difference between 'attending' a social party and being part of its life and soul. It is the difference between observing and experiencing. It is the difference between watching a play or film in a detached way and actually becoming part of it due to one's conscious involvement (there is, of course, a limit to one's involvement in a man-made play or film – but none in nature's productions). Nature's play includes any and all meanings, plots and potentials. Insofar as art apes nature, Shakespeare sounds the depths of our souls more deeply than most. Hence, unsurprisingly, there are similarities between nature's and Shakespeare's productions: on first viewing, some aspects can be of immediate appeal – scenery, spectacle, drama – but not all meanings or actions are immediately understood, they do not reveal themselves at first glance but require study, or at least familiarity, patience and, while we sit in stillness and silence, deeper meanings and significance are revealed and connections grow.

Our participation in these minor unities hints at the grander unity of which we, and everything else, are a part. Once we see and act upon this principle in a co-operative way, we play a part, firstly, in the healing process, and later, if we succeed, in the maintenance process – and all of us have a part to play, with humility and attentive awareness. We looked above at geo- and ego-centric views of the solar system. While the geocentric view prevailed, the study of nature was, in general, marked by a great humility. Dislodging the Earth and Man from our self-appointed pride of place is often referred to in modern texts as healthy humility. Yet, in curious contrast, the adoption of the heliocentric view, far from defeating arrogance, has actually stimulated its astronomical growth. The modern attitude to nature, particularly of some scientists, is not one of intellectual and / or practical submission but a domineering one, with intent to 'conquer' – a characteristic of those who have not conquered themselves. Yet we learn most in submission to nature and, paradoxically, gain some temporary mastery. With regard to Corbett, Seymour and others, including noble savages, their happy submission to nature leads to their consequent integration with nature, their participation in the unity and then, nature serves the servant, allowing them to utilise and adjust it to their needs, completing the cycle – since we must submit to our needs, as imposed by nature. 'It is by obedience to her that nature is conquered' (Bacon). Paradoxically, nature serves for as long as she is obeyed. Which is cause and which is effect?

In the chapter on Corbett we considered the superiority of first-hand experience over second-hand information – which is usually translated into written or spoken words. This is true for both the mundane and for life's most poignant moments. In the latter moments, the weakness of words is most keenly felt. Not only is our 'tool-set' of words limited but also, for most of us, our ability to use that tool set, and this author well knows the frustration of trying to convey subtlety sensed experiences. Even when communication is face to face, and supplemented with question and answer, one person's experience cannot be fully conveyed to another. All we can hope for is that sudden flash of insight to see, understand and appreciate, to fully receive all that is being transmitted (this is more likely when the experience being communicated relates to something the listener/viewer has already experienced themselves). Authors can only hope for the reader's active interest which, with luck, provides the flash of insight to fill in the dry black sticks of text with real meaning. Like dry sticks laid on the forest floor by the tracker who has gone before, letters are only signs by which the follower may find the way for themselves. Unfortunately, there is always a 'gap' between our experiences. Is there any way to encourage these flashes of insight, is there any way we can reduce the gap, or generate some sort of conducting medium that might allow that gap to be bridged? Exerting some interest, imagination and empathy will act as both the medium and reduce the distances between us, letting us get closer to each other, and other life. We may get close enough for the gap to be bridged by a flash of insight. Insights to the unity gradually draw one into the unity.

Chapter I referred to my arrival in Chitwan. Even when standing at the edge of the jungle, I knew I was still distant from it. 'Standing at the edge', despite a few faltering steps forward, is still literally and metaphorically true for me. I believe such a description also fits most modern 'experts' including many scientists, who are also in that same sense, standing at the edge of, or some steps further than me into nature's unspoiled habitats, looking in. What they see can generate interesting and wonderful information, both for them, and people like me on the edge, or outside of the forest. However, there is a more unified knowledge of nature, possessed by those who can live within the forest – our 'noble savages', John Seymour and 'his' peasants, or people such as Corbett, and it cannot always be communicated to others. They can only be encouraged to look for themselves.

What is found often depends on what is sought and it would be difficult to determine whether science or wood-craft provides the deeper understanding. Both seek and note connections, use tracks, signs and evidence to build an integrated system of knowledge. Wood-craft can generate theories, but not the abstract theories of science. Perhaps the element of 'abstraction' is the essential distinction: orthodox science is forever limited by its objectivity. It has value, but a limited value, since it is forever 'separate' from what it studies. Complete knowledge, in order to be complete, must include the observer. Even though 20th century physics discovered this for itself, it will not be able to fully explore the consequences since the observer includes much that is not subject to orthodox scientific analysis. Wood-craft also involves the observer (sometimes, to the point of survival); it contains a visceral component and is first-hand 'experience' rather than 'observation'. We can fully explore consequences since no artificial boundaries are imposed upon us. As noted above, 'the truth involves us all' and, we might add, all that is in us. Acquiring the skills of wood-craft balances head and heart, since 'absorbed knowledge' comprises both yin and yang. It also pre-dates science – the growth of science depended on previous successes with, and survival due to, wood-craft. Knowledge, other than experience, is second-hand, third-hand… and has been subject to selection and interpretation. One aspect of scientific knowledge is that it is held to be repeatable by others i.e. that it can become first-hand knowledge for anyone who cares to repeat a given experiment. Yet the experiment itself already involves, by virtue of being an experiment, selection and interpretation, which may or may not be valid in the context of what is investigated (if we knew, from a broader perspective, what was or was not valid, there would be little or no need to conduct the experiment! 'Prudens quaestio dimidium scientiae' – to know what to ask is already to know half). Wood-craft, jungle lore or any knowledge absorbed directly from nature, relieves us from the burden of making such selections in the semi or complete darkness of our ignorance. Nature provides the right apparatus in the right context at the right time and requires only interest, which it repays, and which appears in our account of knowledge. As has been referred to in chapter I with regard to spending time with nature and, as will be referred to in the next chapter with regard to meditation, both practices provide answers – before we know what to ask.

Without wood-craft one is forever standing at the edge of the forest. Neither I, nor most scientists, could live self-sufficiently within the forest, as part of it; we are not integrated, not unified with it, in contrast to Corbett and his like. Yet the modern trend is to consider science and scientists superior to them and their knowledge. Maybe in a few ways they are, but in many others, they are inferior. In the forest, our 'noble savages', John Seymour's peasants or people like Corbett would leave me and scientists standing, and probably starving, since survival without tools or technology, for many people, is now no longer an option. If you had to travel safely, man-eaters or not, and needed a guide, Corbett and his like would be a better bet than a scientist. A scientist might understand the academic principles of vegetative growth, weather patterns, friction and fire but few scientists would be able to keep us warm around a fire that they could light, without matches, in a cold and wet forest. Yet this sort of knowledge can keep us warm, even alive – to later learn the academic principles involved. The reverse scenario would not keep us alive to learn the application of practical knowledge.

It is not suggested that, with sufficient tuition and practise, other human beings could not acquire such abilities (they are probably latent in all of us – to varying degrees). It is suggested that these neglected abilities are not inferior to abstract theoretical accounts, which are confined to extremely narrow margins of study and forever 'separate'. Moreover, science, by current definition, and many scientists by choice, rarely recognise responsibilities beyond academic ones, whereas wood-craft or knowledge 'absorbed' directly from nature, awakens concern and care for what is studied and stimulates action to protect it. Any scientists (usually field scientists not insulated in laboratories) who have made sincere, prolonged and self-sacrificial efforts toward conserving what they study represent, in this respect at least, a well-balanced, healthy ideal.

After some years exhausting work at his hospital in Lambarene (located in what was then French Equatorial Africa, now Gabon), Albert Schweitzer and his wife were loaned a house near the seaside by a kind friend, in which they could spend the hot and rainy months. The friend's business at that location no longer operated and the staff huts near the house were disused and in disrepair. Schweitzer explored and in the last hut saw a man lying on the sand, head almost buried, with ants running all over him. He was a victim of sleeping sickness and had probably been left to die by his companions as they had passed by a few days before. Although past recovery, he still breathed, so Schweitzer tried to help him and says 'While I busied with him I could see through the door of the hut the bright blue waters of the bay in their frame of green woods, a scene of almost magic beauty, looking still more enchanting in the flood of golden light poured over it by the setting sun. To be shown in a single glance such a paradise and such helpless, hopeless misery, was overwhelming…but it was a symbol of the conditions of Africa.' ('On the Edge of the Primeval Forest' Schweitzer. A&C Black London 1953).

Schweitzer's meaning is clear and, sadly, the same could be said of other places within and out of Africa. In another sense, it is true of most of us, collectively and individually. We are standing at the edge of the primeval forest and have not learned how to fully integrate with nature's beauty and balances. Many of us remain confined to our huts, bewildered by fears and the diseases that still beset us, despite doctors such as Schweitzer. Some of us have a different sort of sleeping sickness to that of the poor man dying in the hut – those living in the largest and finest 'huts' money can buy, in numerous locations globally, have a type of sleeping sickness. Its symptoms include more pleasure than pain, and may be accompanied by severe bouts of boredom. The disease is terminal because it represents an extreme imbalance, albeit that they are at the other extreme to Schweitzer's patient. An extreme of wealth for one individual – beyond what could be used in many lifetimes – is only possible due to depriving so many others who, in consequence, represent the other extreme, with insufficient for one lifetime, even in terms of basic survival. Remember also that this is not some tragic accident or unforeseen calamity but fully understood, planned for and maintained by the dominant commercial forces currently organising global socio-economics. Hence the whole system is unbalanced, and therefore unhealthy, and therefore temporary. We would best be physicians who heal ourselves, before nature removes the possibility and provides her own stringent and uncompromising curative treatment. The easier path toward environmental and social health depends on us responding to nature's invitation to prevent disease and disaster. We must awake and move through the man-made frame and boundary of the doorway, leaving behind the exaggerated importance attached to all artificial constructions and status symbols; leaving behind our sickness, moving toward a healthy, harmonious, natural beauty and balance.

The knowledge of woodsmen, farmers, gardeners, naturalists and fieldworkers, and the knowledge of previous generations, is knowledge gained directly from nature by personal experience. Nowadays it is all too common to hear, especially in the media, that we must (conservationists included) have good 'scientific data' to make progress. We noted above that much of conservation is common sense, which can be enhanced by experience. Practical conservation

Background image: Satpura Tiger Reserve

strategies are described in the next chapter. Even if science could refine some of the techniques involved, the disappearance of tigers is too rapid to allow for the analysis. Threats posed by socio-economics have to be met with socio-economic solutions.

Although science could be useful in the long-term to help manage properly protected Reserves in countries with fair and stable socio-economic conditions, of the scientific research projects on the wild tiger to date, none (to this author's knowledge) have discovered new or additional conservation initiatives or even suggested what might have issued directly from that research; for example, the structured and managed re-introduction of prey species and/or re-planting of indigenous plant and tree species, as recommended herein. Moreover, the findings of the different wild tiger studies so far have drawn different conclusions on fundamental aspects of tiger biology. This is mentioned not to disparage science but counter the modern trend fostered by television that science is part of the vanguard of species conservation. Research projects often provide material for television programmes and, to gain a current legitimacy, television usually sets them in a context of conservation. Such programmes can create an impression that science is virtually synonymous with conservation yet, in the case of tigers, rarely, if ever, can science have any effect on the immediate and critical threats they face. Viewers of such programmes might also see reasons to neglect their own responsibilities, since it seems that 'scientists' are 'out there' saving species.

Moreover, in contexts broader than conservation, we need to remember that scientific data is never complete. It is often over-specialised, may be biased by overt or disguised political / commercial agendas, or work 'against' nature.

Following nature as closely as possible provides us with our healthiest path. To travel it safely we need to use our hearts and heads to guide our feet, keeping a healthy distance from over-specialised man-made artefacts created according to commercial or military agendas. On our current path the scenery is dominated by modern man-made gadgetry leading further away from nature. We need to reverse direction rapidly and one way of doing so is to begin caring about other lives as much as we do for our own.

Without care and concern for other lives, without morality, so much of our life, and so many of our activities, is simply self-indulgence or vanity, which never, ultimately, really satisfies. The worlds of entertainment and celebrity are obvious areas for self promotion and vanity but in art and science also, where the emphasis is on the artist and not the art, or the scientist and not the science, these disciplines may also be corrupted. In this context we may note that some of the greatest artists and scientists are characterised by their modesty. Their focus was not on how clever or talented they were but on their work, how it could be improved, and what value it may have for the community. Without these perspectives 'All is vanity' (Ecclesiastes 3:19).

One of Darwin's books was entitled 'The Descent of Man'. Probably as a play on this title, a 1970's television series, written and presented by Jacob Bronowski, explored human cultural achievements and was called 'The Ascent of Man'. How can our collective ascent be achieved without individuals indulging their vanity? The essential distinction is that the individual is important but not 'self', in terms of attitude and priorities i.e. the ideal is to serve others, not oneself. Individuals who have made great contributions are part players in the ascent of Man – the collective and collaborative progress; the process which is civilisation and life.

Jacob Bronowski was a rare species himself as he was accomplished not only in the sciences but also in the arts. As far as this author knows, it was Adrian Malone, the director of the series, who quoted and summarised Bronowski's view (using 'intellectual' in the sense of rational) that it is '…the intellectual commitment, and the emotional commitment, working together as one, which has made the ascent of man… (*which*) is vested in any one person and in any one person's life…It is not the business of science to inherit the earth, but to inherit the moral imagination, because without that, man and beliefs and science will perish together.' (This can complete our references to Mary Shelley's novel since Frankenstein is intellectually gifted but lacks essential balance, seeing science as our only enlightenment and, in its exclusive pursuit, he casts aside all other considerations such as human relationships, family and home. He achieves his goal, is revolted and disgusted by it, but finds it beyond his power to control. An over-emphasis on science brings disaster. (Selfishness and ego also play a part and, in seeking to elevate himself, he finds abasement to the same degree). Bronowski clearly recognised the essential importance of the balance between head and heart, of the individual as part of a greater whole, of morality, and that all are indissolubly linked with science (and any other human discipline).

So what is the value of science, or wood-craft, or any investigation of nature? To understand something of nature in order that we may more closely harmonise with it, copy it in our constructions, utilise its lessons, apply them in accordance with morality and virtue; all with the purpose of making the world a healthier, happier place.

…on Responsibilities to the Unity

For anyone in the modern world, trying to meet their responsibilities to the world is extremely difficult since one has to work against the system causing the problems – powerful, dominant commercial interests (some directly bulldozing the last forests); poor (or worse) governments, and the consumerism, socio-economics, ignorance, corruption and incompetence created by these factors. The people that comprise these groups are too comfortable (only temporarily, if they did but know it) and, being too fearful to confront their image in nature's mirror, are currently choosing to destroy the mirror, rather than look into it. We cannot, of course, destroy the mirror without destroying ourselves. For those who wake up to this reality, the choice is whether to learn quickly and easily, or slowly and painfully – and that's the only choice. Conservation promotes the quicker and easier route, and is marked out by individual and collective responsibilities

Ironically, trying to conserve forests actually keeps one out of those forests, in order to use 'phones, facsimile machines and lots of paperwork (to prevent trees being cut!), find funding and attend meetings. In a physical analogue to some concepts employed in this chapter, saving forests requires us to roam far beyond them. Hence further steps into the forest, literally and metaphorically, are prevented not only by limitations of knowledge but also by practicalities. Decreasing fragments of forest result in increasing rules and regulations relating to them, and make 'freedom of the forests' an extinct privilege in any real terms. However, other feet take many more literal and illegal steps into the forests, since the diminishing resource automatically concentrates every form of disturbance in terms of domestic stock, poachers and timber thieves and because the law of supply and demand increases the value of the diminishing resource. Hence, for forests and all natural environments, the situation approaches critical status very rapidly.

As time runs out and options diminish, a wider human appreciation of the crisis is, painfully and slowly, growing. However, despite being critical in the most serious sense of the word, a worrying feature of both recent media coverage of, and responses from the public to, the environmental crisis, is the stress put on human preferences and life-styles that should, it is claimed, be taken into consideration when planning remedial measures. The stark truth is that no human perspectives, nor any individual, nor the whole human race put together, has any importance whatsoever from nature's perspective. For example, recent flood waters surging into people's homes did so regardless of human perspectives or whose home was flooded. The same applies to the consequences of any other extreme weather conditions we may experience, rising sea levels, or the results of pollution, loss of topsoil, species extinctions, deforestation or depleted ozone. Our obsession with ourselves and human priorities has brought about the environmental crisis in the first place. Implacable laws determine our fates and our only hope is to comply with them, whether or not it is convenient, fashionable, or in accordance with human legislation, politics or preferences. The sooner we start doing so, the better for all of us – and other life forms, including tigers. Nature's laws first, our preferences next.

Akbar the Great of India (reigned 1556 A.D. – 1605 A.D.) was appropriately named. Under Akbar the judicial system was reorganised, as were the systems of finance and currency (compare with details in Appendix III). Unfair and / or prohibitive taxes were abolished. Under his rule he gradually established a tolerance and unity amongst his people. In so doing he showed that unity is not achieved by uniformity but by tolerance of diversity (which could also be a description of nature). Of course, tolerance is best balanced by being two-way. If, for example, a relatively small group of foreigners live within another community, tolerance is required by the majority 'host' population. However, the smaller group can also exercise tolerance in the sense of trying to adapt to, or at least not offend, the customs of the larger group (when in Rome…). The more they ignore the culture they live within and promote their own, the less tolerance is likely to be generated in the host community, whereas the more they try to adapt, the more willing the host will be to accept them. When this author spent long periods in India, he tried to observe local customs and adapt himself accordingly. Visitors were advised on dress code and various other cultural aspects to ensure respect was shown to the host community.

Akbar had built a 'House of Argument' for that purpose alone (remembering that arguing is not quarrelling. A 'House of Discussion' would be, perhaps, a better description in modern parlance). Night after night he could be found 'listening while doctors of the law, Brahmins, Jews, Jesuits, Sufis – God only knows what sects and creeds – discussed truth from their varying standpoints…the unbiased readers of Akbar's life cannot avoid the conviction that in dealing with him, they are dealing with a man of imagination, of genius…Between the lines, as it were, of bare fact, the unconventional, the unexpected crops up perpetually, making the mind start and wonder…' (B65)

Yet, what have these attributes to do with our current environmental crisis? By their light we may see that truly civilised government can co-exist with, may even be defined by, an enlightened treatment of nature since 'On an occasion which proved to be a turning point, Akbar "gave orders for a (*great*) hunt, and that the nobles and officers should according to excellent methods enclose the wild beasts…But, when it had almost come about that the two sides were come together, suddenly, all at once a strange state and strong frenzy came upon the Emperor…to such an extent as cannot be accounted for. And everyone attributed it to some cause or other…some thought that the beasts of the forest had with a tongueless tongue unfurled divine secrets to him. At this time he ordered the hunting to be abandoned. Active men made every endeavour that no one should even touch the feather of a finch."

Now whether the legend which lingers in India be true or not, that it was the sight of a chinkara fawn which brought about the Emperor's swift change of front, apparently (*these events*) were incomprehensible and but vaguely praiseworthy…Viewed, however, by the wider sympathies of today, the fact stands forth indubitably that the "extraordinary access of rage such as none had ever seen the like in him before" with which Akbar was seized, was…a sudden over-mastering perception of the relations between God's creatures, the swift realisation of the Unity which binds the whole world together; for it seems certain that he never again countenanced a (*hunt*).' (B65)

With time and patience, in the right meditative mood, one can sometimes begin to grasp the unutterable magnificence of nature's exquisitely intricate, complex, self-sustaining, ever-changing to be ever-constant, beauteous grandeur. Meditative mood over, the stark, shocking contrast of the wasteland we have made of the wonders we were given, the damage we have done to what remains, the suffering we have inflicted on countless lives that had the temerity to offer us beauty and interest, comes violently to mind and we see the almost unbelievably purblind, selfish, spiteful immaturity of our collective human behaviour – and Akbar's anger is our anger.

Anger eventually gives way to shame and allows, even makes us eager, to accept retribution, to pay compensation in full. We seek justice and, finally, as understanding dawns, we realise that nature's laws incorporate justice and that correction is created as damage is done – for all the wanton, wasteful damage; for all the pain and suffering we inflict, we ultimately inflict it on ourselves, but with a slight time delay. The English poet and preacher John Donne (1572 – 1631) who became Dean of St Paul's Cathedral in London told us 'No man is an island…Any man's death diminishes me, because I am involved in mankind…therefore never send to know for whom the bell tolls: it tolls for thee'. The principle is not only applicable to us as individuals but as a species, since Man is no island. We are involved with life on Earth. Ask not for which species the bell tolls, it tolls for thee. Choosing a viewpoint to include non-human life allows an expanded view of both Donne's and (as above) Shakespeare's vision, and reveals a greater unity. Some examples were given above with regard to man-made poisons which, having harmed other lives, are returned to us in air, water and food. However, the current context is much larger and refers to an all-embracing natural cycle. We can now see symmetry's deeper significance, it being both reflecting and correcting. The mirror is not passive but active. The mirror is alive. Hence, we shall be paying the price, every penny, in every sense. Nature's all-embracing cycles are physical manifestations of the karmic wheel – ensuring people will 'go in bondage to their own acts. Just and sure is the Wheel, swerving not a hair!' (B42c)

Our responsibilities to the unity are inescapable. 'The justice of the gods who dwell on Olympus' was referred to by Homer to tell us that no damage to that unity, no wrong doing, is ever forgotten. As Plato put it: 'This justice of heaven be sure neither thyself nor any other that has fallen on ill ways shall ever claim to have escaped; 'tis that which the fashioners of justice have established before all others and that which should be shunned with utter dread. It will never leave thee forgotten. Though thou make thyself ever so small and creep into the depths of earth, or exalt thyself and mount up to heaven, yet shalt thou pay them the due penalty'.

As we shall be paying the price, every penny, in every sense, we had best consider carefully, in every sense, literally and metaphorically, how each of our pennies is spent. We have ignored our personal responsibilities at each junction along the path where new directions pointed toward community; morality; loving kindness; environmental and economic security. We have repeatedly chosen to continue on the same old path of immediate short-term self interest, material wealth in preference to spiritual wealth, and now find ourselves in this dangerous and desolate position. Many cannot see the edge of the abyss since it is obscured by man-made scenery and the glare of artificial lights. However, any serious effort to understand our position will leave one in no doubt of how close we are to the edge of the abyss, which is too deep to see where the fall will end. Will we now, for our very lives, voluntarily make our way back to those junctions and take the safer, more secure routes, by facing our responsibilities in relatively easy and comfortable ways? If we do not do so voluntarily, the environmental crisis will force us to face those responsibilities in the few remaining ways left, none of which will be easy or comfortable. In facing our responsibilities we finally face ourselves, but for as long as we will not look into the mirror, our conduct deteriorates further, and the reflection, like Dorian Gray's portrait, becomes uglier and harder to view ('The Picture of Dorian Gray': a novel by Oscar Wilde published in 1891in which Dorian Gray magically retains his youth and handsome features while the effects of his immoral conduct appear on his portrait, which he hides from view). However, we will, ultimately, be compelled to look and to comply with nature's laws. As referred to above, the only choice is whether we learn quickly and less painfully or slowly and very painfully.

Living alone for two years and two months in a log cabin he built next to Walden Lake in Concord, Massachusetts U.S.A., Thoreau recorded his experiences in his book 'Walden' and above we have referred to some of his observations. A similar experience was recorded by the naturalist and writer Henry Beston (1888 – 1968) who lived alone for a year in a tiny, wooden house located on a remote beach of Cape Cod, Massachusetts, U.S.A., where it faced the Atlantic Ocean. Beston wrote of his experiences in his book 'The Outermost House'. His solitary routine was occasionally broken by a visit from a coastguard or fisherman. 'It was not this touch with my fellows, however, which alone sustained me. Dwelling thus upon the dunes, I lived in the midst of an abundance of natural life which manifested itself every hour of the day, and from being thus surrounded, thus enclosed within a great whirl of what one may call the life force, I felt that I drew a secret and sustaining energy. There were times, on the threshold of spring, when the force seemed as real as heat from the sun. A sceptic may smile and ask me to come to his laboratory and demonstrate; he may talk as he will of the secret workings of my own isolated and uninfluenced flesh and blood, but I think that those who have lived in nature, and tried to open their doors rather than close them on her energies, will understand well enough what I mean.'

Pithoragarh is situated in the Himalayan foothills, at an altitude ensuring very cold nights, even during summer. Visiting Pithoragarh during one winter, I stayed alone in a little old bungalow, going to bed quite early in the evening and curling up to conserve what warmth I could, and never looking forward to washing my body in icy cold water each morning. Across from the bungalow was a narrow path, which led through trees to a clearing, perched on the top edge of a well-wooded mountain, overlooking an enormous and beautiful gorge, with a river flowing far, far down below. After washing each morning, I would walk to a little wooden seat in this clearing and sit there as the sun crested the opposite mountain, literally absorbing warmth, peace and life into body, mind and soul. Hinduism refers to 'Prana', an energy or 'life force', in sunshine.

At the time, I didn't know it by this name. However, had I failed to learn lessons in Pithoragarh I would have learned them later at the LifeForce base in Pachmarhi (situated in the smaller Mahadeo mountains) since there is no heating there either and, after washing in the bathroom on winter mornings, my escape to the sun outside confirmed to me that it brings more than warmth and light. Prana can also be felt amidst an abundance of healthy life, especially wildlife, and it is surely Prana that Henry Beston describes above. Prana is, as yet, unrecognised by Western science and, like Henry Beston, I can't demonstrate it in a laboratory but, also like him, I know it when I feel it. Moreover, I am sure that, sitting with a scientist (on holiday!) fresh from a winter's bathroom and content to simply be at one with nature, they too would sense it in the sunshine – and shared smiles, through which it also shines.

Just as there is Prana in sunshine, so there is sunshine in the Indian smile, and it is literally life-giving. It is made mostly with the eyes but also by the mouth (as it is said in India, a smile is a curve which sets many things straight). Without exaggeration or sentimentality, it has been smiles from Indian people, often strangers and unaccompanied by any word or conversation, which have, on occasion, literally refreshed and energised me to overcome days of deep frustration and exasperation, and continue the conservation work.

After his journey through the seasons, Beston's view of animals aligns well with those of this chapter: 'We need another and a wiser and perhaps a more mystical concept of animals. Remote from universal nature and living by complicated artifice, man in civilisation surveys the creature through the glass of his knowledge and sees thereby the whole image in distortion. We patronise them for the incompleteness, for their tragic fate of having taken form so far below ourselves. And therein do we err. For the animal shall not be measured by man. In a world older and more complete than ours they move finished and complete, gifted with extensions of the senses we have lost or never attained, living by voices we shall never hear. They are not brethren, they are not underlings; they are other nations, caught with ourselves in the net of life and time, fellow-prisoners of the splendour and travail of the earth.' (B6)

Consciousness of the unity leads to improved communications with it. Could that include communication with the animals? Luther Standing Bear found that it did for the Lakota. It is said that King Solomon could understand the language of birds, other animals, and even the whispering of the grasses. Apparently Pythagoras could communicate directly with animals and Orpheus could with music he made on his lyre (given him by Apollo). Similar stories say the same of Buddhist monks living alone deep within jungles and, amongst many stories about him and communication with animals, St. Francis of Assisi persuading a large wolf to stop preying on men, is well known (St. Francis of Assisi 1181/1182 (?) – 1226 Catholic patron saint of animals and the environment, and founder of the Franciscan Order). For the majority of us who have separated from nature, we find our languages confused, and the writer Michel de Montaigne (1533 – 1592) may speak for us all: '"The defect that hinders communication betwixt them and us, why may it not be on our part as well as theirs? 'Tis yet to determine where the fault lies that we understand not one another; for we understand them no more than they do us" (Another of Montaigne's unanswerable points relates to references above – "by the same reason they may think us to be beasts as we think them" and could be applied to another question that goes closer to the bone: "What evidence do whales have that *we* know the difference between right and wrong?")' (Essais, trs. Charles Cotton, 1693 (B46)).

In terms of animal/human communication it might be we who are the poorer party; a fascinating insight was given me by R, a long-term guide at Kanha Tiger Reserve who related his experience sitting on the back of an elephant, talking to the mahout. They were taking a rest from ferrying tourists to and fro, in a little clearing in the forest and nearby, a hat lay on the ground. The mahout was speaking to R and, as he spoke, he interspersed "pick up the hat" in the continuous flow of words directed at R. The elephant reached out its trunk and delivered the hat to the mahout. R was immediately struck by the implications and interrupted the mahout: "Wait a minute… how is it possible that the elephant distinguished a particular sequence of words for its attention, from others that were not, without you giving any other signal of voice, hand or foot?" Now it was the mahout's turn to look surprised; he replied, "The elephant understands everything I say."

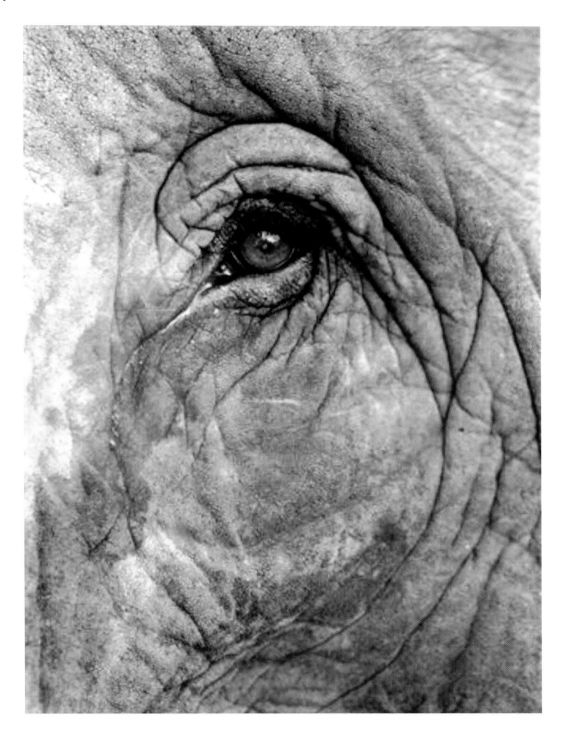

As Luther told us (quoted in chapter III) we have, in the modern world, largely lost our abilities to understand and communicate with animals (and lost much of our ability to understand ourselves). Most particularly we cannot hear or see what they are telling us and, partly as a direct consequence, the unprecedented and perilous state of the planet we share with them means we need to re-cultivate that ability with great urgency. Whilst direct two-way communication seems to be no longer an option, we can still watch and listen to animals. They have their language (without words) and can teach us without questions and answers, provided we practise silence, stillness and patience.

In chapter III we saw some ways in which we could learn from nature in general and animals is particular but now let us extend those possibilities in the company of author Barry Lopez: 'The idea that animals can convey meaning, and thereby offer an attentive human being illumination, is a commonly held belief the world over. The view is disparaged and disputed only by modern cultures with an allegiance to science as the sole arbiter of truth. The price of this conceit, to my way of thinking, is enormous.' Barry Lopez grew up in a farming valley and speaks of discovering his wild animal neighbours: 'These creatures seemed more vital than domestic animals. They seemed to tremble in the aura of their own light…Holding their gaze, I saw the intensity and clarity I associated with the presence of a soul…the rational mind (to which many of us acquiesce) posits that there is little to be learned from animals unless we discover a common language and can converse. This puts the emphasis, I think, in the wrong place. The idea shouldn't be for us to converse, to enter into some sort of Socratic dialogue with animals. It would be to listen to what is already being communicated. To insist on a conversation with the unknown is to demonstrate impatience, and it is to imply that any such encounter must include your being heard…The eloquence of animals is in their behaviour not their speech…In daily conversation in many parts of the American West today, wild animals are given credit for conveying ideas to people, for "speaking". To some degree this is a result of the pervasive influence of Native American culture in certain parts of the West. It doesn't contradict the notion of human intelligence to believe, in these quarters, that wild animals represent repositories of knowledge we've abandoned in our efforts to build civilizations and support ideas like progress and improvement. To "hear" wild animals is not to leave the realm of the human; it's to expand this realm to include voices other than our own. It's a technique for the accomplishment of wisdom. To attend to the language of animals means to give yourself over to a more complicated, less analytic awareness of a place. It's to realize that some of the so-called equations of life are not meant to be solved, that it takes as much intelligence not to solve them as it does to find the putative answers.' (J18)

Perhaps the greatest lesson wild animals provide for us passes, like so much of nature, unnoticed unless we exercise our interest, or our attention is drawn to it. In fact it is so common an occurrence, the reader is requested to pause and think about it – and not just from the obvious viewpoints of hunting, commerce or diet. The lesson is that, with rare exception, *they run from us on sight* (if trees were not tethered by their roots no doubt they would do the same. Animals reactions fulfil the prophecy God makes to Noah: 'And the fear of you and the dread of you shall be upon every beast of the earth, and upon every fowl of the air, upon all that moveth upon the earth, and upon all the fishes of the sea…' (Genesis 9:2)). Equating behaviour to language, this is a stark message; an indication of the level to which we have reduced communications – by our behaviour. That animals run away from us is not an innate safety mechanism but a learned response to us, as proved on those increasingly rare occasions when people venture into unexplored territory and find the animals curious but unafraid, allowing humans to approach and mix with them and their offspring. It is fully acknowledged that many people will voluntarily help trapped, wounded or sick animals and demonstrate much enthusiasm, effort and sincere care in doing so, but we are considering our collective behaviour. Those wonderful, warm-hearted people who help stricken animals would be the first to agree that our behaviour as a species, toward almost all others, is disgraceful.

If full communication with animals were possible, what could we possibly say to them – that would not stick in our throats? Worse still, consider what they could say to us. The phrase from Edwin Arnold's 'Pearls of the Faith' might summarise the situation: 'By these dumb mouths be ye forgiven, ere ye are heard pleading with heaven.' The Bahá'i scriptures record God speaking through the founder of that faith; Bahá'u'lláh: "…ye walk on My earth complacent and self-satisfied, heedless that My earth is weary of you and everything within it shunneth you." The truth of these lines is apparent whatever one's views on God may be. The greater the sense of shame we feel in the face of it, the greater hope there is for us, and the other species with which we share the earth.

Isolating ourselves from nature, imprisoned by our fears, self-obsession or greed, we can no longer hear or see that of which we are part and, prompted by our prison perspective, believing ourselves to be separated, we abuse nature; abuse that which is a greater part of ourselves. Some people in physical, mental or spiritual prisons, or even modern 'brick cages', may have inflicted harm on the society of which they are part and / or harmed themselves, possibly by self-mutilation, in another reflection between inner and outer. Individuals who harm themselves and / or their society, present to us in microcosm what in macrocosm is sometimes too large for us to see immediately, since we too, as a species, are doing exactly the same – harming our communities and ourselves. They are interchangeable as cause and effect (society / individual) yet both stem from the same root.

Jean-Jacques Rousseau knew that only nature can fully restore our health and spirits. In 1765, after three years of extreme stress and strain, Rousseau retreated to the little island of St. Pierre in the region of Bern, Switzerland, where he surrendered to nature: 'I used to sit on the beach by the lakeside in some hidden refuge. There, the sound of the waves and the stirring of the water held my senses still, drove out of my mind all other kinds of agitation, and immersed it in a delightful reverie. Night often crept upon me without my noticing.'

Modern therapeutic techniques treating neuroses and psychoses have successfully included re-connecting people to nature through contact with animals, including dolphins and even domestic cats (care workers report that the cats know when they are being held by patients with, for example, severe learning difficulties). When we no longer feel separated, isolated, alien, and see ourselves as a functional part of the whole, the larger life force, we no longer wish to harm either.

We have considered much commonality between animals and humans yet we are also, of course, distinct. Humanity undeniably exhibits unique features, such as our culture, including the arts and sciences, and our ability to record information, which enormously enriches that culture. Our practice of cooking food is another unique characteristic and reminds us of yet another; our ability to make and use fire for our own benefit. Fire provides heat and light independently of the sun (although what is burned originally acquired its combustible energy from the sun) and enabled us to unlock natural resources, such as metals, and to develop technology, arts and sciences. Perhaps our breadth and depth of moral awareness, and our flexibility of behaviour associated with it are other distinguishing features (humans have been called the moral animal) since it does appear that the majority of other species are more tightly confined to behavioural repertoires necessary for physical survival. We cannot entirely discount that some of the higher mammals also share some sense of morality (and we looked at a few examples of dolphin behaviour in this context in the previous chapter) but our unique cultural abilities such as our science and technology, combined with our morality (or lack of it), give us another unique capacity – to dramatically affect the lives of so many, if not all, other species.

Perhaps the unique characteristics of our culture and use of fire combine to provide the physical, mental and spiritual 'environment' by or in which we exercise our most important unique feature – our moral capacity. This truly unique morality is obscured by the old proverb that tells us 'a leopard cannot change its spots' which compares features fixed by nature to people, supposedly, being bound inflexibly to 'who they are'. However, our considerations in this chapter suggest that the most distinctive characteristic of being human is that *we can 'change our spots' – at least in terms of morals and virtues and, thereby, our character*. Having 'changed our spots' in these regards, our behaviour changes too – toward leopards…and tigers…other people…and the rest of creation. We can see that animals' options are, relative to ours, tightly constrained (and, in consequence, help maintain the life-support systems for all). Humans have many more options available to them, including options to bend or break nature's laws (this concept is summarised by the Islamic concept of 'Tasleem', referred to in the presentation to Forest Guards reproduced in the next chapter). In bending or breaking 'local' laws, we find 'broader or deeper' laws, which allow us to revise our behaviour, and voluntarily comply with 'local laws'. Collectively we are currently bending and breaking laws as if, and thereby ensuring, there is no tomorrow. We are utilising all our options but not learning from them. We do not even ensure that those put in positions of power have learned these critical laws. Nature provides for second chances, and maybe more, but whatever the number, there is a limit – which we need to avoid finding.

Even having suffered abuse, animals and humans can, given sufficient time, learn to trust again. Luther told us how well Adam understood the animals, and we have heard of Pythagoras' abilities, and others', to communicate with them. Such abilities appear to us now as miraculous, but they are a measure of how far we have distanced ourselves from animals, from nature, and hence from knowledge of ourselves. When we harmonise with nature, when we 'vibrate' with it on the same or harmonious wavelengths, communication is created naturally, but without words (and no pet owner, horse rider or animal keeper would deny it).

With regard to relationships between humans, such wordless communication is confined, for many of us, to that special someone whom we love, and this mutual but unspoken understanding, may be a factor initiating the relationship or developing during it. If love is the common factor in both possibilities, could lack of love for nature explain our lost communication with her? Love may even be a language of its own; all others, including written and spoken words, being but crude shovels in comparison with love's delicate scalpel, which may heal or cut deeply, create or destroy, just like nature, in response to the love we choose to give or deny. Love locked in between the lines of Corbett's accounts has been referred to above and love is implicit in Seymour's writing and Seattle's speeches, and explicit in the book by Chief Luther Standing Bear. 'If music be the food of love, play on' (Twelfth Night Act I Sc. I) and we remember that it was the musical vibrations of Orpheus' lyre which could communicate with animals, and influence other parts of nature such as rocks and trees. Perhaps 'influence' hardly says it since his music charmed and enchanted all creation. After his love, Eurydice, dies from a poisonous snake bite, his musical laments melted the hardest hearts and were so beautiful the gods themselves advised him to travel to the Underworld and request its rulers to restore her to life. The rulers, Hades and Persephone, are so moved by his music they grant his request. Orpheus, and the Orphic cult which grew around him, was closely associated with a 'philosophy of love' and poetic expression. Huxley (B34) identifies 'lovelessness' as the factor common to many aspects of modern society at which we have looked (abuse of the environment, decline in art and architecture, collaboration between business and politics, mass production). A love of self often accompanies a lack of love for others and above we considered selfishness as the offspring of fear. The cycle is complete since fear often springs from lack of love (both given and received) and hence selfishness can also be a consequence of 'lovelessness'. The Presentation to the Forest Guards reproduced in the next chapter quotes from Hosea 4: 1-3 "...Listen to what (God) says: 'There is no faithfulness or love in the land… And so the land will dry up, and everything that lives on it will die. All the animals and birds, and even the fish will die'." As the pop song says 'All you need is love' and so, from the Bible to the Beatles, the message is the same; love is all we need. Cosmic accounting ensures we receive the same as we give, but not always immediately, nor necessarily in the same form.

For communication, community, and unity, love is the surest foundation, especially since it is not restricted to the fireworks of romantic passion, and may manifest as compassion, care, kindness, concern, courtesy, sacrifice and suffering (sometimes voluntarily, sometimes not). William Blake was a Christian (albeit an unorthodox one) and Christ's ultimate sacrifice for the greatest love prompted Blake to write that '...every kindness to another is a little Death' since even the smallest courtesy or favour usually involves some small sacrifice; of time, effort, convenience, money etc. and is prompted by some form or aspect of love.

Love, communication with animals, the unity of all and Virgil's advice that "Love conquers all things; let us too surrender to Love" (Virgil. Roman epic poet 70 BC – 19 BC) is unified for us in one painting of Aphrodite, the goddess of love, by Briton Riviere (British artist 1840 – 1920) shown here as background and overleaf.

Whether or not love or music is involved, many people can agree that, at some conceptual and practical levels, we are part of nature and nature is part of us. Pythagoras considered all of nature alive, just as did Chief Seattle and many other 'savages' – that unity of heartbeats we began to explore above – and exactly where life starts and stops is probably beyond our ability to tell. Yet it remains our responsibility to husband and nurture the life force wherever and whenever we recognise it. It is another sad symptom of our condition that people's own dependence on it must be continually emphasised to stimulate any serious collective interest in doing so (and we find ourselves returned to love since, being so imbalanced, we have to appeal to self-love in order to survive long enough to develop real love). When real love prevails, children are born into the healthiest possible environment.

Yet, we have squandered our birthrights for a mess of cruelty and those birthrights have now been bastardised by big business. For example, modern 'agribusiness' does not let a field lie fallow for a year (to naturally regenerate the soil's nutrients) since that would mean a year without produce and hence, profits. The soil is impregnated with chemicals, some of which promote an artificial type of 'fertility' – once the plant assimilates artificial nitrogen-based fertiliser it loses the ability to assimilate nitrogen naturally – and guarantees a continuing market for the manufacturer. Other

chemicals are used to poison 'pests' but these chemicals also impoverish and poison the soil and therefore the food grown in it, and therefore, us. The 'pests' develop a resistance and greater quantities of pesticide are put into the soil every year, which is only healthy for the manufacturers' market.

A few paragraphs previously, we briefly met Hades and Persephone, the latter being the beautiful daughter of Demeter, the goddess of grain and crops. Persephone was abducted by Hades with the approval of Zeus, making Demeter so angry she forbade all crops to grow. Only after Zeus allows Hermes to successfully bargain with Hades for Persephone's return, did Demeter allow the crops to grow again. However, Hades has previously tricked Persephone into eating seeds which are part of Underworld existence and, in consequence, she is compelled to return to the Underworld each autumn. While she is away, the earth is denied crops. This Greek myth obviously parallels the seasons, and perhaps each person's life experience of happiness and fullness followed by loss and suffering. One wonders what other parallels we are now creating with our treatment of Demeter's offspring and what further suffering and loss we may be orchestrating, since we might say that, full of poisonous chemicals, Demeter's produce has already gone to hell.

Love, communication, community are all part of our responsibilities to the unity, since they are the unity.

...on Revelations

We may hope for revelation. Personal revelations can make us lift our eyelids, perceive the unity and our responsibilities to it, and be powerful stimuli for change. We are usually rushing around, amidst many others doing the same, in our hectic world. At the time, all the rushing seems so important but, if we ever get time to examine it, much of it is associated with what other humans have convinced us is necessary to maintain or fulfil our lives. We may remember Apollodorus saying in Plato's Symposium "…I used to go dashing about all over the place, firmly convinced that I was leading a full and interesting life, when I was really as wretched as could be…I feel sorry that my friends should think they're being very busy when they're really doing absolutely nothing."

Revelations can be available to view everyday, if we would only look. They may change our world, but need not necessarily be world changes, indeed, world events as reported by the media may even stun us for a while but, whether or not they do, they are rarely revelatory or leave us any the wiser. When we live more slowly, revelations can be seen or sensed in any event that lifts our perception up and beyond the immediate or merely mechanical; beyond microscopic perspectives; beyond the self. Yet, has this chapter not stressed the importance of finding self, finding out who we are? St. Francis of Assisi gave us the answer in another of nature's paradoxes: 'It is by forgetting self that one finds self.'

Before considering some revelations over the next few pages, we need to recognize that the environment is currently showing us that, far from forgetting self, we are collectively, almost totally absorbed in self and self-indulgence. The overly self-indulgent are usually among the richest third of humanity, enjoying not only comfortable survival but also privileges – health, education, leisure time and disposable income. Too often these privileges have been largely and sometimes almost exclusively used to indulge in games and frivolity, fun and nonsense, drunkenness and debauchery,

Left: with many thanks to the Dahesh Museum of Art, New York U.S.A. for kind permission to reprint this image and also with thanks to Bridgeman Art Library

or many other forms of self-indulgence, none of which make an impressive list and all of which vanish, like froth and bubble, almost immediately they appear. To forget ourselves, in order to find ourselves, we could ask simple questions that have easy answers: What are we doing with our lives? What of substance did we work at? What of substance are we? Am I of any use to man or beast? Has any living thing beyond my own body shell, or immediate family, ever benefited from the fact that I was born? Am I giving, or worthy, dutiful, of service and value to the local community, or wider world, in any capacity whatsoever? Am I correcting my faults? Attempting to face my fears? Solve my problems? In trying to answer these simple questions positively we find our substance; what makes us who we are, and what we would best be working at. In summary:

> Life is mostly froth and bubble,
> Two things stand like stone,
> Kindness in another's trouble,
> Courage in your own.

> *(Adam Lindsay Gordon 1833 – 1870)*

We considered above that revelations may be seen from mountains. They may also be seen or heard in a piece of poetry, or music, or literature, or art (revelatory feelings found manifest in sculpted marble; in oil on canvas…) or in another's artless comment, in accepting or doing a kindness, in receiving the richest smile from the poorest Indian, or a Red Indian in the sun…

An old soldier who fought in the wars waged on Native American Indians was telling a story around a camp fire. 'And the people listened, and their faces were quiet with listening. The storytellers, gathering attention into their tales, spoke in great rhythms, spoke in great words because the tales were great, and the listeners became great through them.' Let us join them quietly and listen to a story: There 'was a brave on a ridge, against the sun. Knowed he stood out. Spread his arms an' stood. Naked as morning, an' against the sun. Maybe he was crazy. I don' know. Stood there, arms spread out; like a cross he looked. Four hundred yards. An' the men – well, they raised their sights an' they felt the wind with their fingers, an' then they jus' lay there an' couldn't shoot. Maybe that Injun knowed somepin. Knowed we couldn' shoot. Jes' laid there with the rifles cocked, an' didn' even put 'em to our shoulders. Lookin' at him. Headband, one feather. Could see it, an' naked as the sun. Long time we laid there an' looked, an' he never moved. An' then the captain got mad. "Shoot, you crazy bastards, shoot!" he yells. An' we jus' laid there. "I'll give you to a five count, an' then mark you down," the captain says. Well, sir – we put up our rifles slow, an' ever' man hoped somebody'd shoot first. I ain't never been so sad in my life…- an' – then. Well, he just plunkered down an' rolled. An' we went up. An' he wasn' big – he'd looked so grand – up there. All tore to pieces an' little. Ever see a cock pheasant, stiff and beautiful, ever' feather drawed an' painted, an' even his eyes drawed in pretty? An' bang! You pick him up – bloody and twisted, an' you spoiled somepin better'n you; an eatin' him don't never make it up to you, 'cause you spoiled somepin in yaself, an' you can't never fix it up."

And the people nodded, and perhaps the fire spurted a little light and showed their eyes looking in on themselves.' (B66 reprinted by kind permission of the Penguin Group)

If we look in on ourselves we will see the need to face what we see and change it, without further delay. Coleridge lamented on '…the difficulty of fixing the attention of men on the world within them'. Perhaps, this is because when we do look, we see that we are mostly Coleridge's Ancient Mariner, with the terrible weight of all the innocent life we have killed hanging heavily about our collective neck.

> For we have done a hellish thing,
> And it will work us woe
> For all we shoot, we kill the root
> That makes all life to grow

(with apologies to Coleridge)

With regard to nature, and collectively speaking, we have surely spoiled something better than ourselves and something in ourselves. If we choose to spend more time with nature, or just love it from afar, we may yet grow closer to it, and each other; grow kinder; grow in our understanding and maturity, and perhaps heal something in us and around us. All this can occur simply and naturally – without 'book learning', research, or any other human construction or intervention – just by spending time with nature and / or by loving from afar, since love dissolves not only differences but also distance, in all but physical senses.

> O happy living things! No tongue
> Their beauty might declare:
> A spring of love gushed from my heart,
> And I blessed them unaware…

(Coleridge)

At this moment, the carcase of the albatross the mariner had pointlessly killed, and which had hung immovably around his neck, drops from him, disappearing into the sea. Now his onward journey began, as a sadder but wiser man.

Personal revelations, by liberating us from self, automatically make us aware, and then consciously part of, the unity of life. Alternatively, appreciating the unity of life, liberates us from self. Which is cause and which effect? Either way, when one frees oneself from self, unity is all that remains. Now we can see our error in taking life wantonly or interfering with it without good cause and due humility. Nature's exquisite masterpiece may be viewed and studied. It can be copied as often as we please but it should only be adjusted in very particular circumstances, and then only in accordance with the patterns already displayed (otherwise, as above, we spoil something in ourselves and something which is better than ourselves). Making nature available, without restriction or regulation, to the military, commerce or science is to make an original Rembrandt available to some very young children wielding felt pens and their first 'carpenter's tool set'.

Nature's response to our inner condition is not a way of 'punishing' us; it can be seen as a

Background image: Gustave Doré engraving for the Rime of the Ancient Mariner

way of showing us who we are and, what is more, allowing us some time in which we may harmonise more closely with her healthy, life-sustaining model, and improve who we are. The reflections are interactive and educational, so nature's reactions are not only a mirror but also a guide – and a sure guide, to health and to truth. We have seen that there is little in this life of which we can be sure. However, when we learn from nature, whether via others' experiences such as those of Corbett, or via our own, we know we can rely on it: can rely on the veracity of that pugmark; or that bent stem; or some feathers on disturbed ground showing a drop of blood; we can be sure that buds promise a flower; or that coloured leaves promise autumn.

Similarly, modern urban and city life leads us to some knowledge and wisdom, by signs along the way, if we would only look and exercise some interest: when we do we can choose between alternative paths, between; helping to poison the soil, or eating organic food; tacitly or otherwise endorsing the abuse of forests and animals, or supporting conservation organisations; orthodox banks or ethical banks and fair trade; ignoring human rights abuses or Amnesty International; environmentally abusive or environmentally-friendly commerce. In each case we must identify and utilise the healthy path, keeping it clear of weeds, while calling to others who cannot find it, and warning of the dangers of taking the other paths.

If we fail to read and act on such signs we must accept walking into danger or disaster. We had best practise both our jungle lore and our 'concrete jungle' lore if we will navigate the future safely. Just as Corbett had a sense of unseen but impending danger, so too our 'concrete jungle lore' tells us of impending danger. We might not always be able to 'prove', provide all relevant facts or fully articulate our impressions of the general abuse of power, of corruption, greed and stupidity, nor the abuse inflicted on nature in particular, but we 'know' it in a deeper sense, since we can see their reflections in nature and people around us. Moreover, our impressions are substantiated by every form of physical evidence we could wish for. Corbett sometimes found the trail of a man-eater led into dense undergrowth, which provided neither tracking surfaces nor space in which he could defend himself. He sometimes commented that to continue would have been to commit suicide and so he worked his way back and picked up another path to approach from a different direction and thereby avoided situations too dangerous to cope with. So far, our collective response to environmental risks is to continue walking, if not running, into the teeth of the danger with a crassness and wilful blindness that beggars belief, but which will richly deserve all that it receives.

Of course, neither all of nature nor the entire world is accessible to our faculties (we never have complete knowledge) but the signs we see tell us surely of the path we are on. If all governments, scientists and businesses tell us one thing while nature tells us another, believe nature. We have already looked at our dangerous agricultural practices; at our inadequate preparations to ensure sufficient future supplies of freshwater; at polluted air and oceans (which maintain the oxygen content of the air – more detail in next chapter). These examples and more can be checked by you, the reader, using libraries, Internet, educational institutions, talking to people who are directly involved with the topic you are investigating, and using your own experience and judgements. The environmental scientist, Jim Lovelock referring to wildlife moving north in response to global warming says that, due to living in the English countryside, he can already see the changes (New Scientist magazine 24/01/09 'We're doomed but it's not all bad' or at www.newscientist.com). In North America the checkerspot butterfly has already died out in the southern section of its geographical range and has become a northern species. We can all 'feel' the seasons and we can all talk to locals (the older ones providing more comprehensive accounts). If near the coast, look at what the waves wash up. If able to sail the oceans, you may see the 'islands' of floating, mainly plastic, man-made rubbish and debris collected together by ocean currents. There is, so far, one in the Indian ocean, two in the Atlantic and two in the Pacific, the largest in the north Pacific of an estimated six million tonnes covering an area approximately twice the size of Texas (in addition to posing various toxic threats to whole ecosystems, the rubbish may be ingested by whales, fish and birds, leaving them debilitated or dead). Talk to an organic farmer or talk to fishermen about the mismanagement of our fleets to the point of risking the future of the industry itself. If you are privileged, go looking for tigers, or rhinos or elephants. Talk to locals and hear their memories. Go to mining areas (there are open-cast coal mines adjacent to some Indian Tiger Reserves. Consider your own thoughts and feelings in view of them (and of the little old ladies carrying sacks of coal on their backs)). In India, more than 95% of the tigers are gone and 85% of the forest. Go to, or watch documentaries on, areas where logging is taking place and feel the voracious appetite and frightening speed of the machinery laying waste the earth.

What you will feel is the truth. If reactions include an internal disturbance and feeling sick, this is healthy. If no disturbance, no nausea is felt, this is sickness. We have surely destroyed much that was better than ourselves. Some of the destruction has been so extensive and ruthless it might, for a moment, have disturbed the deeper and better judgements of even the most money-minded (money-blinded?) of executives and curbed their activities in consequence. Yet, swept along with their particular herd, too timid or comfortable to act or even speak against it, while indulging in more material extravagances, deadens the voice of conscience and the tiger's roar.

You may combine these signs with other signs detected by your 'concrete jungle lore' and draw your conclusions. Do not allow yourself to be confused by humans who make profits from the abuse of nature, who may try to fool you, or themselves, with 'data'; the harsh laws of economics; that someone else would do it if they didn't etc.; or by politicians' or scientists' doubts and disputes over global warming; or by the 'need' to know if GMOs are safe (even though they have already been allowed to spread over the earth, while a few businessmen count their profits). Look to nature for your truth. As you are reading this book you must know that, as one amongst far too many other examples that could be chosen –

The tiger is almost extinct: almost completely wiped off the face of the Earth, forever, along with innumerable other species of animal and plant, by the greed, selfishness and stupidity of man.

There is the truth. We need this to be reported but have no need for further associated Newspeak implying that it is some inevitable consequence of 'progress'; that the tiger 'can't adapt'; is an enemy of rural economies; is necessarily being eclipsed by other priorities; or similar verbiage and smokescreens. Yes, it has been reported correctly that the tiger is a victim of political, socio-economic developments – but *it need not be,* and this gets virtually no coverage or emphasis. The tiger's extinction is not inevitable; it is a matter of human choice. We have scientific evidence for the tiger's significance in ecosystems, and those systems' critical role in maintaining global life-support systems (see chapter V). So our reason can be satisfied. Emotionally speaking, we

recoil instinctively at the prospect of man's detruction of the tiger, without need of 'information' or debate, since our collective consciousness, the insights of childhood, our knowledge of nature alive within us, all demand the tiger's survival. Spiritually speaking, the tiger (and much else besides) is a victim of human (short-term) self-interest, greed, ignorance and incompetence. Hence, we have to save the tiger, if only because in doing so we overcome these vices – and again we see the correspondence between spiritual and physical survival. That the tiger is about to die forever, tells us for sure that something is deeply and dangerously wrong. Any who deny it reveal ignorance or ulterior motives.

(Zoos have a place and could play a more significant role in conservation but in this context they are irrelevant – we do not need tigers preserved in man's artificial environments; we need man and tigers conserved in natural environments, for the health of all).

We need that insight, that immediate perception of truth, as experienced by Akbar just before the hunt commenced, and by Chiefs Seattle and Standing Bear. In the unity of their experience, we begin to sense the Unity of life. A closer inspection of Hindu texts reveals Prana to be associated with all that moves. Energy moving and concentrating through plants into herbivores and then into carnivores was referred to in the opening pages of this chapter. All these concepts are compressed into tigers since they possess 'a strength savage, ferocious, alive in itself, the essence of life in that it is the potency of motion, the elemental stuff out of which the many forms of life have been moulded…' (B47b) Tigers are highly concentrated Prana.

If you are ever privileged enough to spend some undisturbed time very close to a tiger (even one in captivity and, if so, better a young tiger, not one deadened by years of confinement in a cage, and preferably with some new stimulus in its compound), you will know that the shimmering vitality of life it exudes is spellbinding. From an external compound, moving slowly in a low crouch, a three year old Siberian tiger came through the open door of his cage, to examine a chemically inert paper I had placed to catch his scent (Appendix I). He had seen neither me nor the paper before, so he approached cautiously, his enormous yet lithe body a manifestation of controlled ease, one leg and paw extended at a time, slowly, precisely, perfectly balanced and ready for instant action. This striped energy gradually reduced the distance between us while the eyes of his exquisitely marked and heavy head were fixed on me and the paper. The whole animal was a living expression of contained and concentrated power, some escaping through the eyes, and making them glow. I am convinced that the energy transmitted over the intervening space would, for any sentient human being, reach their earth, where some sort of sensory skin pigment equivalent to chlorophyll would capture it and concentrate it into points of tingling, burning sensation.

When standing next to the bars with a tiger's muzzle not six inches in front of one's face, one's eyes trace the bony, muscle-bound head wrapped to apparently teddy-like softness, but actually to firm stiffness, by short fur in a visually stunning set of colours. The large eyes look into yours and the jaw might sag open to reveal wet, black gums and a rough tongue lolling between canine teeth so long, broad and stout one shivers to be so close to power potentials so far in excess of one's own physically feeble frame. After a few minutes in close and attentive proximity, the tiger's fire will ignite fires within you. Once kindled, they turn to raging infernos when we face the fact that it will die forever because a few obese people will become even more obese; because our inner tigers will not challenge corrupted, profoundly ignorant and greedy men (whose own tigers are close to extinction, due to them feeding their inner leeches and parasites so excessively). We are currently allowing them to take the tiger from us forever – in exchange for more manufactured artefacts, which in comparison, are as nothing. We're going to lose everything for nothing. Again Akbar's anger will be our anger, and Akbar's revelation will be our revelation, and we must hope that, like Akbar, it comes in time for us to stop the obscenity. And we had better stop it since, the tiger having a place in everybody's heart, we will all be very, very sick when that part dies. To have reached our current condition, to have removed so much concentrated Prana, is to have already removed much of our life force, and means our sickness is well advanced. Yet the crisis of the illness is now, and the result dependent on your tigers.

Whilst serious dangers result from distancing ourselves from nature, many benefits grow from getting closer to it. This would be especially so (for all of us) if those powerful people whose decisions affect so much of nature, spent some time closer to it. The reader is most probably interested in tigers but please consider how far distant from nature many city and towns folk are (and not just from tigers but even the nearest woods). Many of the world's wealthy third would need to be led step by step and preferably with bare feet, back to a consideration of nature. They would need to lay aside for a while not only lap-tops, mobile 'phones and office procedures, shopping and driving, but also parties and promiscuity, drugs and alcohol. Some are so blinkered by and absorbed in the modern, mechanised scramble for self-indulgence, they need prompting to remember their mother.

So let us imagine some senior executives of multinational corporations which sell so much of what distracts us, and destroy so much of what sustains us. A few days would be needed to leave behind the suffocating air and deadening insulation of financial wealth and privilege. No entourage allowed. No first-class travel. No comforts and special allowances. No-one fawning over and assisting them. They will not experience any great hardship but do a simple job of physical work outdoors, getting their hands, arms and legs wet. There will be no towels to use but they'll soon feel warm, working against the chill of the air. Simple, wholesome food will be available, but not too much. They will explore the natural surroundings, wade through rivers, have plants and trees identified and be shown how green materials are inextricably interwoven with their lives and businesses. They will sit under the stars at night. Next morning, if in an appropriate setting, they will be given a stiff broom and rough flat stone to help wash a working elephant – when you are that close, life so large cannot be ignored.

They will later ride that elephant in the hope of sighting the tiger in its natural habitat, perhaps witness something of its life, and feel something for its life. During the night, while time flows at its slowest rate between a forest path and stars above – uninterrupted by 'walls and all the little works of man' – and when completely alone, a tiger will be close to them. In some captive situations it would be possible to arrange for there to be no bars between them but, even if present, bars will not interfere with the energy transfer, since tigers are also life writ large, but in different notes to those of the elephant. They will now be close to their tigers, their distance from nature's energetic ambassadors minimised, and their prana will be ignited by Prana.

If now, our captive executives are told that their decisions will wipe this creature off the face of the Earth forever, it is difficult to believe that any one of them could be so thin of blood or mean of spirit as to say that it did not matter, or that they did not care, and would not therefore consider the environment as priority in all of their future decisions. The distance between decision-makers and the effects of their decisions is the gap in which so many atrocities, environmental and humanitarian, occur. Separation in space or time means that we cannot touch – or be touched. 'Localisation' brings us closer to nature and each other.

All tigers are highly concentrated starlight; sunlight; Prana; concentrated life force, and LifeForce concentrates on their conservation to conserve life force.

Dawn departure for LifeForce personnel on the Tawa reservoir, Satpura Tiger Reserve

This chapter has followed a path offering a few glimpses of vast regions of intellectual and spiritual territory, pointing out a few landmarks to, hopefully, link each stage of our journey. Much time and many pages could be spent on each landmark, let alone the intervals between, but we would lose the concepts that tigers represent and, while thinking of abstractions, lose tigers around us. If, as and when we have protected the environment we can, as opportunity offers, return to explore these regions more thoroughly.

In the meantime our principles of personal experience, personal responsibility to take action, and that all necessary truth is reflected to us by the world, means that we have no need of text books or human beings with specialised training to demonstrate or 'prove' life's most important lessons.

Just as tiger conservation all too often takes tiger conservationists out of the forest, the above sections have not referred to the tiger directly as often as would have been liked. The reader may have thought they would not read about topics such as multinationals, politics and television in a book about tigers and may have initially wondered what organic food, cleaning products and ethical banking have to do with tiger conservation. Hopefully the reader can now see that the answer is: everything! The principle of unity indicates that all things are connected – and not only socio-economics and tiger conservation but also you, and me, and the actions we take. Apathy and ignorance are as dangerous as greed and criminal behaviour. Ignorantly or wilfully condemning the magnificence of the tiger to extinction measures, in inverse proportion, the depth of our corruption in either capacity. The next chapter deals with practical tiger conservation as directly related to these topics. If, by the end of chapter V, you are still not convinced, this author has failed to identify the connections, failed to show where these branches and boughs lead back to the trunk – but please do not dismiss the concept due to the inadequacies of the sketch. It deserves to be investigated by you – can you afford not to? The connections are there, independently of opinion, and need identifying and addressing for all our healthy futures, including those of tigers.

When, in an environmental context, England might see blossom in January or bumblebees in February; or people paddle in the froth of pollutants at the seaside; or Asian tribal people tell us that it is many years since the tiger's roar was heard in the forest or his pugmarks seen on its paths, we do not require specialised training to understand the implications. We can trace the chain of connections that link tigers to commerce, corporations and politics but changing those connections must begin with internal changes and personal commitments. (The reason so many revolutions are bloody is that the revolutionaries take action externally before they do so internally. Moreover, without personal commitment to personal change, most revolutions must fail, since there will be as many revolutionaries who favour short-term self-interest, as among any previous ruling elite. If we can neither adhere to moral principles nor face our responsibilities, how can we legitimately criticise, take action against, or ever prevail over others who exhibit the same laxity?)

Our journey through life is our personal responsibility and involves inner exploration as much as outer. "We carry within us the wonders we seek without us" (Sir Thomas Browne 1605 – 1682. English author with a broad knowledge of medicine, religion, science and esoterica). However, as referred to above, Coleridge (the poet) lamented "…the difficulty of fixing the attention of men on the world within them." If our journey so far has fixed your attention on the world within by asking you to reflect on the world without, let the tiger within you save the tigers around you – and the tigers around you will help preserve the tigers within you. The world is the way it is because we are the way we are. Each of us must look into the mirror and judge how healthy the reflected image appears. When we sense the symmetry and realise that the worlds without and within are the same, and all part of one grand unity, we will take action to protect our earth, our tigers and our children. Part of that action will be forming our character, re-establishing our inner balances; finding our sense of proportion, being happy with a material optimum, while rejecting minimum and maximum; facing our responsibilities to control those who do pursue maximum at the expense of the majority; selectively using our time and money while making sure we put people and principles before profits, and morals before money (money should only come before morals in the dictionary!)

We have found another clue to our purpose, which lives in the multi-layered purposes of other lives – human and non-human – in a vast network, not only of interconnections but interdependence. All purposes intertwine and all are rooted in nature.

Looking around us, we know that none of us, or all of us put together, could make a tree, or a tiger, or even an insect, much less arrange our creations into an integrated, self-sustaining system. For all our self-proclaimed intelligence, Jack London's assessment of our life as 'a maggot's life' relates to more comparisons than that of physical size.

Even looking around our human, artificial, world, most of us would have to answer negatively when we ask ourselves 'could I make a light bulb?' or any electrical / electronic appliance…or saucepans, cutlery, carpets, clothes? etc. The labour and ingenuity of other people provide us with much that we need and enjoy. In addition to equipment, we might consider our social systems which provide so many benefits e.g. law, libraries, education, medical assistance, emergency services…These systems teach us nature's order and 'The state of man in divers functions, Setting endeavour in continual motion' and inviting our participation so that we may learn what nature teaches; 'The act of order to a peopled kingdom'.

We may also admire the practical skills or the strength, courage and efforts (not necessarily achievements) of others, in various and numerous ways, all of which contribute to our 'kingdom'. Hence, we can see the dangers of the media making icons of mediocrity or the mundane, and those representing it acquiring fabulous wealth and status – gaining everything for nothing (one reason why we will all lose everything for nothing). If we allow such standards to take root and, by familiarity and ultimately fatigue, fail to weed them out, truly bright blooms will be choked and wither, our gardens become unkempt and overrun by weeds, and society mediocre and mundane. That all this falsehood and fabrication is manufactured and promoted by money-making concerns reveals the root and truth of the problem.

Helping to map and organise our societies according to nature's lessons is the most valuable study for science, and far better than attempting to make nature comply with our toy-town and self-indulgent societies. Although much of this chapter has taken us beyond areas available to scientific analysis, the profound concept of unity referred to in this chapter has also been approached by science. Scientific discovery, so long thought to relate to an objective 'reality', 'out there', independent of human observers, has led us, step by step, to recognise the observer as part of that 'reality', and therefore to begin to see ourselves.

In terms of unifying principles and concepts, Newton's and Einstein's work stand out distinctly. One of the great intellects of the 20th century, and one of the very few who immediately understood and championed Einstein's work, was Sir Arthur Eddington (1882 – 1944) the English astronomer, whose masterful account of Einstein's General Theory of Relativity concludes: 'The theory of relativity has passed in review the whole subject matter of physics. It has unified the great laws, which by the precision of their formulation and the exactness of their application have won the proud place in human knowledge which physical science holds today. And yet, in regard to the nature of things, this knowledge is only an empty shell – a form of symbols. It is knowledge of structural form, and not knowledge of content. All through the physical world runs that unknown content, which must surely be the stuff of our consciousness. Here is a hint of aspects deep within the world of physics, and yet unattainable by the methods of physics. And, moreover, we have found that where science has progressed the farthest, the mind has but regained from nature that which the mind has put into nature.' (B24)

The next quote is of Newton followed by another from Eddington.

"I do not know what I may appear to the world; but to myself I seem to have been only like a boy, playing on the seashore, and diverting myself in now and then finding a smoother pebble or a prettier shell than ordinary, while the great ocean of truth lay all undiscovered before me."

"We have found a strange foot-print on the shores of the unknown. We have devised profound theories, one after another, to account for its origin. At last, we have succeeded in reconstructing the creature that made the foot-print. And Lo! it is our own."

(B24 Eddington quotes reprinted by kind permission of Cambridge University Press)

Tracking far enough along any trail, including that of science, will lead us to our own footprints and another mirror.

'Thus it was, after the fashion of the human, that Johnny made of himself a yardstick with which to measure the universe' (Jack London Short Story: 'The Apostate'). In the context of this book, this truth could be approached in one of two ways: one way is to see ourselves deservedly mocked for our arrogance to think the universe could ever be measured by us and our definitions, theories, egos and conceits. Another way approaches with the greatest humility, and is thereby exalted, through the awesome and inspiring truth that the universe reflects our characters and that it is in our power to change both.

Nature reflects us, and in that capacity could be said (if we will only look and listen) to teach us, guide us, reward us and, when necessary, correct us.

I had picked up the pugmarks again and found they led to people; that people led to pugmarks and that for as long as footprints can follow pugmarks they lead to a future for both. We began this chapter by considering animals, including tigers, 'within' humans. Whilst we had to leave the forest for a detour through concrete jungles, commerce and politics, science and some philosophy, we have been led back to vital connections between and within: forests, animals and humans but can, perhaps, now see them in a new light.

As mentioned in Chapter I, it was only 'yesterday' that we thought to study the tiger, to listen to what the tiger could tell us, but by tomorrow it looks likely that we will have killed it. Hence we must take action today. We saw above that science shares some ground with intuitive and emotional perspectives, if only in equating beauty with truth. Therefore the tiger's beauty must be telling us a truth – and probably a more comprehensive truth than science tells us about the tiger. The tiger is telling us that to kill it is to kill ourselves – not today, or tomorrow, but the day after tomorrow. Hence tiger conservation is people conservation. This is the fundamental axiom of LifeForce Charitable Trust, which works toward tiger conservation in central India, of which more details are given in the next chapter.

In this chapter the tiger's truth also tells us that to kill it, is to kill beauty, dignity and nobility, and thereby an important part of our potential for character development; it is to kill the fire which can smelt our moral mettle.

What the hand dare seize the fire?

Your hand must seize the fire. And my hand must seize the fire. Each of us makes our own decision whether to or not. The choice is now. Be it the extinction of the tiger or any abuse of nature, all are consequences of human weakness, lack of power, lack of tigers – choosing self and vice instead of duty and virtue: there's the truth; there's the guide; there's the problem and there's the challenge. If every human heals himself, all nature heals. Complete success will elude us without you, the reader. Yes, it can be a lonely path to take and, of course, the selfish and greedy will continue self-indulgence while you suffer by comparison. Yet choosing the right code of conduct, exercising and walking with tigers, will satisfy you as nothing else can. You will also preserve the path to a healthier future for others to find, when they realise they are heading for the abyss.

To conserve tigers is to conserve nature as a whole, life itself, qualities of character and therefore part of our purpose – from local and cosmic perspectives, from here to distant deeps and skies.

What is left?

Amongst the countries responsible for conserving their sub-species, India has a number of Tiger Reserves (28 at time of writing) set amidst some of the largest blocks of tiger habitat left on Earth. Although rarely enforced, protective legislation and penalties also exist and, despite numerous and enormous problems within India, these factors form some sort of foundation on which to base conservation efforts. Limited time, knowledge and resources in an unpredictable world make all assessments questionable but, all in all, India seems to offer the best chances for long-term tiger conservation.

After searching for pugmarks over great distances in northern and central India, they were finally found in sufficient numbers in the forests of Madhya Pradesh (M.P.) Whilst the actual numbers provided by global censuses may be questionable, they suffer from similar problems, so proportionally they are probably correct and indicate that M. P. holds one fifth (20%) – not of India's – but the whole world's remaining tigers. Moreover, forest 'corridors' still (but only just) connect the State's Tiger Reserves (some crossing into Maharashtra). Additional factors include the density and diversity of M.P.s forests, and the longest poaching routes to borders. Hence, Madhya Pradesh offers some of the best chances for saving the tiger.

Now my efforts would be focussed entirely on conservation and trying to ensure that those pugmarks led into the future.

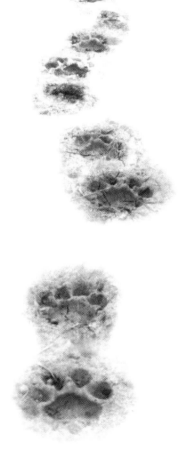

*Satpoura Tiger Reserve,
Madhya Pradesh*

CHAPTER V

LAMBS AND TIGERS

Conservation and Environment: Humans are the Endangered Species

This chapter is concerned with action: action in accord with the principles and practices referred to in the preceding chapter; action whereby physical, mental and spiritual elements are harmonised; and action which is direct, literally on the ground – ground still trodden by tigers.

The 'Tiger State' and the State of the Tiger

The Indian central State of Madhya Pradesh (M.P.) is of critical importance, not only for the tiger but also for India and her people;

'"She is not any common Earth, Water or Wood or Air"

from "Puck's Song" by Rudyard Kipling.

Madhya Pradesh is indeed not common earth, for not only is it the largest State in India, but it also occupies the very heartland of this great country. Its rocks are amongst the oldest in the world, dating back to pre-Cambrian and Palaeozoic days. Geologically the Central Indian plateau is a part of the Gondwana Plate and through it, running from West to East, are the only true rift valleys in India, the valleys of the Tapti and the Narmada Rivers. Indeed these rivers are amongst the oldest in the world, pre-dating the Ganga by at least 150 million years. This is an ancient land, but it is also one which moderates the climate and the water regime of the whole of peninsular India. More even than the great Himalayas, at least in the Indian context, Madhya Pradesh is the watershed which feeds the rivers of the North, the East, the South and the West. From the highlands of the State flow rivers in all directions of the compass. But more than topography it is the forests of the State which sustain these rivers and ensure that the rainfall over this vast area is evenly distributed and shared with the rest of the country. It is the large heartedness of the heart land which in fact permits the rest of India to be a granary…The great river systems of India owe an enormous debt to the highlands of Central India, but more than that, to the forests which clad these hills. Every tree cut in Madhya Pradesh is not so much a loss to the State but a direct blow to the water regime of the States which benefit from the flow of the rivers emanating from here…

Satpura Tiger Reserve, Madhya Pradesh

Madhya Pradesh is basically a hilly State, with ranges generally running from east to west, though the Kaimur and Panna Hills are north south orientated. Much of the State lies on plateaus. Topography naturally makes the State a tableland from which water runs off towards the plains in all directions of the compass. Therefore, Madhya Pradesh constitutes a watershed and because the rivers are major, it becomes a very important watershed. The Amarkantak plateau may well be the most important watershed in India, giving rise as it does to the Son, Mahanadi, major tributaries of the Godavari and the mighty Narmada itself.

The water originating from Madhya Pradesh owes as much to the forests which cover the hills and valleys as it does to the monsoon. The forests are the arresters of the downpour, the moderators of run off and flow, the storehouses which gradually release water during the dry season, the preventers of drought and protectors of the thin topsoil which covers the underlying rock. Minus the forests there would be no water and no soil; and there would be desertification of a large part of the country.

Satpura Tiger Reserve

The Madhya Pradesh forests are the providers of jobs and nutrition to forest dwellers, fodder for cattle, fuel and timber to the villagers and raw material for industry. They also lend a beauty to the landscape which makes the State almost ethereal in its loveliness. These forests are now under stress, threatened by encroachment, endangered by so-called development projects, eyed with jaundice by those who want to extract the minerals lying underneath and facing extinction by the never-ending demand for fuel and timber. The seed gene banks they contain, the marvellous variety of fauna they shelter, are all likely to disappear in the discernible future. If that happens not only would an atrocity be perpetrated on mother earth, but even the sustenance of life in the heartland of India would become a question mark.

Because the Madhya Pradesh forests are so critical a factor in ensuring the health of the nation, they must be studied and written about, both by way of documentation and as a process of educating people about their endangered heritage...

The health of the Narmada and its sister river, the Tapti, is also the health of Madhya Pradesh. If its rivers become sick, M.P. would become very sick indeed. How important the Narmada is to the State, can be gauged from the fact that...All its major tributaries, the Banjar, Tawa, Denwa,

Machna, Sonbhadra, etc., are contained within the State. Almost the entire flow of the Narmada catchment is contributed by M.P. Without the forests the Narmada is dead, without the Narmada Madhya Pradesh is dead...' (B11)

Since this was written, M.P. has been reduced in size – from 2004 the south-eastern section of what was Madhya Pradesh has become the new State of Chhattisgarh. However, more importantly from our perspective, some of the largest remaining tracts of tiger-inhabited forest in India (if not the world) live within Madhya Pradesh, and incorporate a number of important Protected Areas (P.A.), such as Satpura Tiger Reserve.

Satpura Tiger Reserve

Any P.A. of National Park (N.P.) status means that, in law, it should be free from human presence and human activities, except guards to ensure as much. A Wildlife Sanctuary (WLS) allows for the presence and residence of people but prohibits the cutting of trees or killing of animals. As of 2001, Satpura National Park combined with Bori and Pachmarhi Wildlife Sanctuaries became Satpura Tiger Reserve, thereby qualifying for extra financial support from national government budgets. Like many National Parks and Tiger Reserves, Satpura still has human settlements within its core area. Some details of LifeForce support for voluntary re-location programmes are given below.

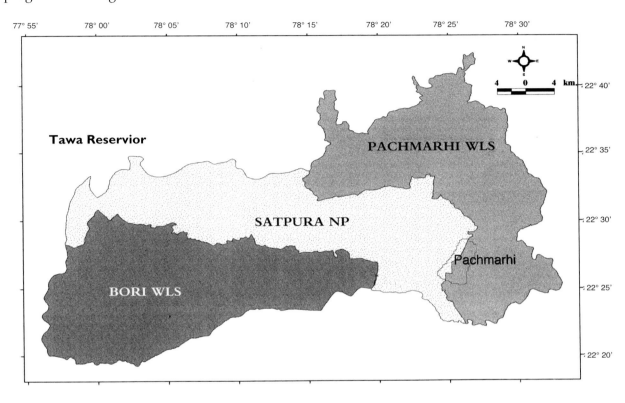

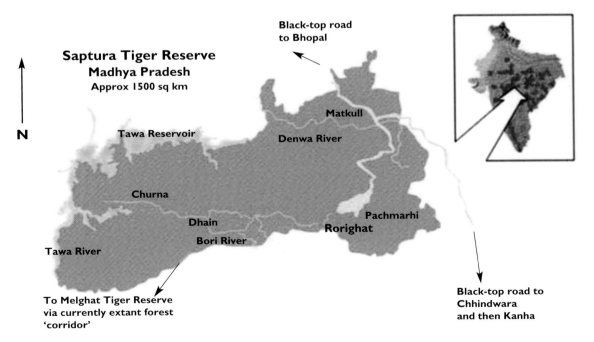

M.P. is traversed by the Mahadeo 'hills' (which would be considered mountains in most other countries). Sitting on a plateau amongst these hills of Madhya Pradesh and within Satpura Tiger Reserve, very close to the geographical centre of India is Pachmarhi, an old British hill station, one of the few, if not the only example of a British hill station still existing largely as it was originally built. Richly forested gorges, ravines and rocky terrain provide much ruggedly beautiful scenery and numerous beauty spots, including waterfalls and breathtaking views, which attract many Indian tourists, while pilgrimages to the local sacred sites and holy shrines ensure a constant stream of devotees.

LifeForce Charitable Trust established a base at Pachmarhi in 1996, from where conservation programmes were organised, particularly with the villagers remaining in Reserve's core area.

The cultivated fields of Rorighat, a village located within the core area of Satpura Tiger Reserve (as indicated on the map above in what was previously National Park)

Formal, recorded history of the area begins in 1857 with Captain James Forsyth, Acting Conservator of Forests, who 'discovered' Pachmarhi. His informative book 'The Highlands of Central India' provides much detail about the culture of the indigenous natives – the Gonds and Korkus – and a wealth of accurate and interesting information about the natural environment. Forsyth built, partly with his own hands, Bison Lodge (1862), the first masonry building in Pachmarhi, now housing the Forest Department's natural history museum.

A later successor to Forsyth as Conservator of Forests for the same area was A. A. Dunbar Brander, author of 'Wild Animals in Central India' published in 1923. Dunbar Brander was one of the few hunter/naturalists who made sincere and serious attempts to observe wild animals' natural behaviour. He and his book are well-respected names in the study of Indian natural history. Dunbar Brander's wife is buried in Pachmarhi's cemetery, under a rather special headstone and surround, amongst many other headstones, holding a few poignant details of long forgotten stories.

Another of the 'old hunters' and later, author, who tried to learn something of their quarry was James Best (whom we met in chapter I, musing on the moon and the tiger that knew best). He was familiar with this area and his books refer to the Bori valley and its villages of Churna, Dhain and Bori. The village of Dhain was, after much effort by LifeForce and the Forest Department to satisfy the 'red tape brigade', the first village to voluntarily re-locate out of Satpura Tiger Reserve and, as of summer 2005, enjoys a much-enhanced life-style just north of the Tawa reservoir.

The British built two churches and both are now well over a hundred years old but still displaying impressive architecture, masonry and marble. The British also established a military cantonment which is still active and houses the Army Educational Corps. 'The Club' at Pachmarhi – still standing but now controlled by the military – was the focus for all social activities and the main meeting place for visitors and guests.

I have it on the authority of a neighbour, Lt. Col. B. Rao (retd.), who knew Pachmarhi as a boy, that one of these visitors was Jim Corbett. This would have been during the 1940's and might relate to the fact that just over 100 km south-east of Pachmarhi is Chhindwara, the district where Orde Wingate's troops were trained for the Burma Campaign of WWII. Corbett, then too old for active service, travelled far from his home in northern India to train many of these men for life in the jungle. A war veteran wrote to the editor of the Daily Telegraph newspaper:

> 'Sir – Many of us who spent our time in India and Burma during the war will remember the help Col. Corbett – that almost legendary figure, Jim Corbett in Peterborough's words – gave to those training for jungle warfare.
>
> His rambles through the jungle with officers and men taught us how to live on jungle produce and overcome our difficulties. No man, he showed us, should ever starve when in the jungle. He told of food sufficiently sustaining to keep one alive for a month without supplies.
>
> When out on expeditions with him I found it was common for him to call animals to him by making the appropriate call. He would place the party in trees, and then make, say, a leopard call, and unless the leopard had moved out of hearing it would walk to the exact spot.
>
> Corbett's powers in the jungle are uncanny. With his quiet and unassuming manner he is indeed a king of the jungle.
> Yours sincerely,
> Michael J. Squibb, Capt.
> Maidenhead.'

(The author has tried to contact Capt. Squibb, both out of interest and to seek formal permission to quote his letter, but without success.)

Another occasional visitor to the Club was Alan Glyn Hughes who had received a serious head wound during WWII. Partly due to this, he and his widowed sister, Mrs. Williams, decided to live in India after Independence and purchased a farm called 'Mandikhera', located at Matkuli, 'next door' to Pachmarhi. There is only one road to Pachmarhi and, after passing through Matkuli (identified on the map above) and crossing the Denwa River it starts the climb to the c.1000 m. plateau on which Pachmarhi sits. Matkuli is so named since, in the days of the British, it was the last place before Pachmarhi that the coolees could stay, 'mat' meaning 'group' and 'kuli' as in 'coolee'. Some of Hughes' adventurous hunting life is recorded in his well-written book 'The Lonely Tiger' (the author using the pen name 'Hugh Allen') which includes references to Pachmarhi in its text.

The remains of Hughes' house at Mandikhera. The upper stepped parapet and the colonnaded arches were added after Hughes' residence. However, the veranda is where the tiger was standing during the terrible storm, as described in the chapter 'Tiger in a Typhoon' of Hughes' book.

Hughes' driver 'Battu' who lived in Matkuli until his death in Sept.'06

This author has good reason to believe this is Alan Glyn Hughes (the author Hugh Allen) but cannot trace any information relating to the photograph or photographer.

In some of the villages where Hugh Allen had adventures with tigers and leopards, LifeForce, a few decades later, was giving Health & Hygiene Workshops and encouraging conservation of tigers and leopards which, like Hugh Allen, now mostly remain only in locals' memories. Satpura Tiger Reserve sits adjacent to what were once Hugh Allen's lands and still, at time of writing, holds some tigers and leopards, although, in terms of numbers, nothing like the days just referred to. Just one generation ago, Pachmarhi residents would not walk after dark along the single main road, bridging the lake, for fear of leopards. Although its stock has been much depleted, the Tiger Reserve retains an importance due to its being located at the north-western tip of one of the largest blocks of forest (and the largest block of tiger habitat) remaining in India, if not the world. The majority of Madhya Pradesh's Tiger Reserves (T.R.s) are still (but only just!) connected by forest 'corridors' between them. The map above indicates the direction of the link between Satpura T.R. and Melghat T.R. From Melghat T.R. the forest stretches east to Pench T.R. (which straddles the border between the States of Madhya Pradesh and Maharashtra). From Pench the forest forks south-east to Tadoba-Andhari T.R. (in Maharashtra) and north-east to Kanha T.R. (Madhya Pradesh) from where it continues north to Bandhavgarh T.R. (Madhya Pradesh).

These corridors are essential for the integrity and health of this remaining forest block although they need not, in themselves, represent optimal habitat, nor be of a size to accommodate tiger territories. Provided they offer sufficient cover and some possibility of prey and water, these corridors fulfil the crucial function of connectivity between other areas of optimal status. In December 2007 Dr. Y.V. Jhala of the Wildlife Institute of India reported a tiger, which was radio-collared in Kahna, found in Pench Tiger Reserve Maharashtra, some 250 km away. There was, until recently, a diagonal north-west to south-east forest link between Satpura and Pench but, sadly, the middle section of forest has now been cut. Whilst LifeForce has, as a short-term measure, repeatedly encouraged the authorities to classify these corridors as protected, it believes that by working regularly with their inhabitants, providing adequate education and employment, the corridors will be protected by the people, for the people, without legislation or its enforcement being necessary.

These ancient forests hold most of the world's remaining tigers, which still tread Madhya Pradesh's primeval rocks. Their ancient dust, as Chief Seattle tells us, still lovingly responds to the touch of tigers' paws, which are conscious of its sympathetic touch. Their pugmark trail leads all the way from hidden mists of time and the world's first forests, rivers and grasslands, right up to today and the few tiny remnants not yet totally destroyed by Man, and where, unless we face our responsibilities, the trail will end.

A little something of the richness of plant, animal and human life that has been impressed on that same soil has been given in the brief sketch above. History's 'pugmark' trail, shows where we have come from and where our trail is heading. Surely Forsyth, Dunbar-Brander, Corbett, Hughes and others would urge us, if not out of respect for our father's fathers and children's children, but for reasons given above by Mr. Buch, to immediately make all efforts to conserve what remains, for tigers, people, India, the Earth and Life.

A precious few are making those efforts and among them are the even fewer we are going to consider now. When all the personnel running Non-Government Organisations (NGOs) and funding agencies, and all sincere government officials are asleep in their beds, the first, last and only line of defence for tigers in the forests of the night is the dedicated Forest Guard. Not all

All the way from hidden mists of time, trails of pugmarks still appear in Satpura Tiger Reserve

guards are dedicated or even fully competent. Those who are (usually unknown and unsung heroes) often labour without full or proper equipment, support or appreciation. For years, LifeForce has talked directly to the Forest Guards and asked them what they needed to do their work to maximum efficiency and effectiveness. Their responses, and LifeForce's, are detailed on the website (www.lifeforceindia.com).

However, before considering conservation efforts, let us consider why tiger conservation is so important. The previous chapter explored some speculative spiritual possibilities but now we will establish the physical, biological and ecological reasons only touched on in previous chapters.

Why Should We Save the Tiger?

The LifeForce Presentation to Forest Guards reproduced here (copies in Hindi are given to the guards) provides some answers. It was written to enhance the Forest Guards' education and boost their morale since their work, sadly and mistakenly, is considered to be of low status. The guards are mainly Hindu or Mohammedan and a few are Christian so, at relevant places, Scripture supports scientific conclusions.

THE LIFEFORCE PRESENTATION TO FOREST GUARDS

The knowledge of the forests and its inhabitants you use day to day is greatly admired. In this booklet we will look at the value of your knowledge, and work, in the bigger picture of India as a nation and, indeed, of the whole world.

'CONSERVATION': Why such a fuss? Why should wildlife be protected? The town or city-dweller seems to get along without it. Villagers' crops are raided, cattle are taken by tigers or leopards and grazing restricted.

Whatever their colour, race or religion, most men are concerned only about their work, family and putting food on the table. Few think beyond this – on what their work and food ultimately depend. By thinking beyond these points we will be able to answer the questions above.

Some of the following principles and facts you will already be familiar with. By reminding ourselves of them we can be sure we are all starting from the same place – see Diagram 1

With sunlight, water, air and soil the plants and forest grow, providing food, cover and shelter to insects, birds and herbivores, which, in turn, provide food for carnivores.

By referring to Diagram 1 you can see that each group of animals forms a level in a hierarchy. Each level does not merely rely on the level beneath it for food. The benefits are mutual. For examples, the insects and birds pollinate or fertilise particular species of flowers or other plants. The herbivores and monkeys eat fruits and later distribute the seeds around the environment in their droppings.

Herbivores do not kill the plants they feed on and many show preferences for particular species of plant as food. This point introduces an interaction, which is more subtle and less well known than the examples above.

The following example is from England but the principle still applies to the Indian ecosystem: A disease purposely introduced by man to the rabbit population of southern England was very effective and the number of rabbits suffered a steep decline. The rabbits fed on Meadow grass (a tall-growing type of grass) and, in their absence, it grew rapidly and abundantly (Indian cheetal deer also favour tall-growing grasses for food). Meadow grass crowded out the flowering plants and many herbs. It also eliminated open-ground ant colonies, on which the caterpillars of the Large Blue butterfly fed. Now, while rabbit numbers have recovered, the Large Blue butterfly is almost extinct. Man's interference with the ecosystem produced changes he did not expect nor previously understand.

In a similar way to the example just given, predators reduce the competition among prey species, so that no individual species crowds out another. For example, in the rock pools of the west coast of the U.S.A. the community is made up of the starfish and 15 other species (including algae, sponges, barnacles, mussels and limpets) 3 of which it feeds on. The starfish is at the top of the food web (like the tiger in the Indian ecosystem). Researchers removed the starfishes from some of the pools. In these pools the mussels crowded out the barnacles, all but one species of algae disappeared for lack of space and other species moved away for lack of food. The number of species dropped from 15 to 8. The other pools where the starfish remained, maintained the original community. So, removing a top predator from a complex food web has an unhealthy cascade effect.

Note: It is well known that predators usually take the old, the young and the sick – leaving the healthiest members of the herd to reproduce and maintain the population (which, of course,

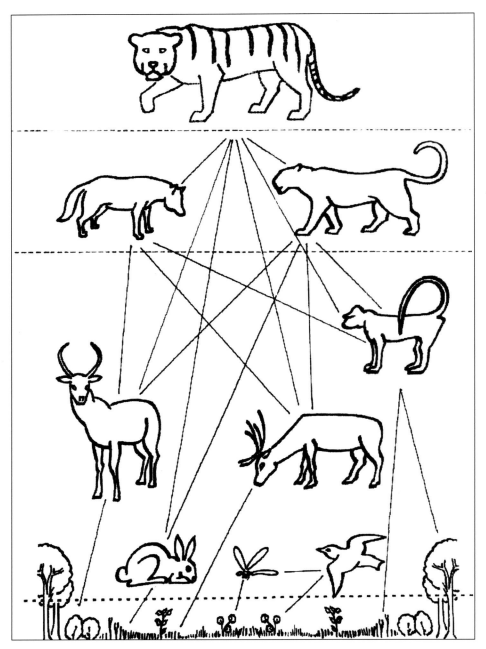

Diagram 1: By following the connections between the top level and the bottom you can see that the tiger has an influence on which plants grow.

Note: Nature favours a diversity/variety of species.

also maintains the predator's food supply). Unfortunately, poachers primarily take the reproductive members, concerned only with today but not tomorrow.

All natural ecosystems are delicately balanced quantitatively, and in time and space, and keep the great cycle moving – see Diagram 2. We do not fully understand the details of these balances, relationships and dynamics – only the principles. Consider the complexity of ecosystems, taking into account the roles of invertebrates (e.g. insects, crabs), amphibians (e.g. frogs, newts), reptiles (e.g. snakes, lizards), fish (e.g. mahseer, herring), birds (e.g. eagles, sparrows) and mammals (e.g. mice, elephants, tigers, bats, dolphins) with varying temperature, rainfall and light.

Diagram 2: example nutrients in the soil: Potassium (K) Nitrogen (N) Calcium (Ca)

So, the ecosystem is complex and, some say, beautiful – so what if it is? Let the tiger die. Why not kill all species, except for rice, wheat or corn – plants that are useful to us? This may be the opinion of a hardened town or city dweller. Let us try to answer this question.

The following information is summarised in Diagram 3. The forest acts as an enormous water pump, taking water from the soil and releasing it from the underside of each leaf into the atmosphere. This moisture contributes to the formation of clouds, which rain on the crop of our city dweller. Water (H_2O) is also held in the soil not only for the land area covered by the forest but also for the surrounding cultivated and industrialised land i.e. the forest maintains the water table – used by village wells and cities alike. This function, and the daily interchange of oxygen (O_2) and carbon dioxide (CO_2) with the atmosphere help maintain climate and temperature. The deep roots bind the soil together, which prevents it being blown away by the wind or washed away by rain. The canopy of the forest also protects soil from erosion by the heavy, direct impact of the monsoon rains. The roots of our city dweller's crop do bind the soil slightly but the roots are shallow and when the crop is harvested the roots wither and the soil becomes prone to erosion. The nutrients of the crop soil are also depleted, whereas those of the forest are held in the soil. We used three examples of nutrients in Diagram 2; Calcium (Ca), Potassium (K) and Nitrogen (N). Researchers in the U.S.A. studied one forest and then cut down half of it. The loss of nutrients from the cleared area was compared with the loss from the forested area (some leaching by water and soil movement can take place even in the forested area). The losses from the cleared area were all significantly higher by factors shown on Diagram 3. (The forested area actually showed a gain in nitrogen whereas the cleared area lost this amount 60 times over).

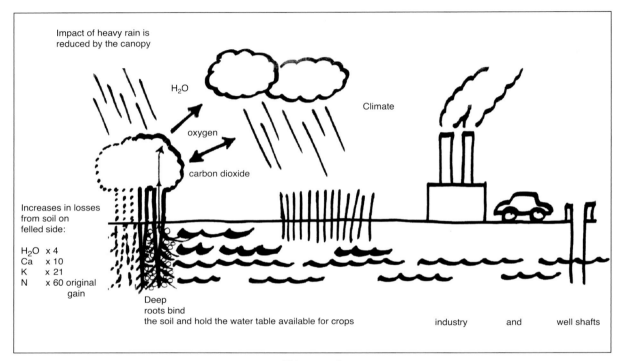

Diagram 3

So we can now see that Diagram 2 is not quite complete; it is the forest that stores the nutrients in the soil – see Diagram 4. Without the forest these nutrients are washed to the sea where, for all practical purposes, they are lost to us forever – they are irrecoverable.

We have noted that Nature always favours diversity/variety. Standing crops of single species like wheat etc. are vulnerable to natural disasters or specific diseases. Variety holds resilience, strength and health. (Man-made pesticides, herbicides and fertilisers ultimately impoverish and / or poison the soil. So they ultimately impoverish and / or poison us, and our children, when we eat food grown in that soil, and the same for herbivores and carnivores. Hence, buying organic food helps humans, herbivores, forests and tigers, because it is grown in accordance with nature's laws and prohibits the use of artificial and poisonous chemicals).

These are all pieces of knowledge that we have but there are probably other, essential pieces that we do not know or understand. Apart from its role in the ecosystem, consider those things

Diagram 4

the forest provides directly: food, sources of energy, clothing, medicine, shelter and shade. Truly, in every sense, man depends on the forest but...see Diagram 5.

Man depends on local and global ecosystems, of which the forests form an essential part. Who has the knowledge to say, "Let us kill off this or that species and this will be the effect"? We depend on the health of the forest but we do not fully understand how the ecosystem works, so how do we know when the forest is healthy...?

The forest is healthy when ALL the animal types represented in Diagram 1 live in it! The tiger can only exist if all the levels beneath it exist. Therefore the tiger is an indicator of health for the whole forest.

You are the guardian of this most precious forest. Its green is more valuable than gold or silver. We all depend upon it: the man in his office, or working on his computer, or driving his car, or riding rockets to the moon – all depend on healthy forests.

India's ecosystems are so special! It is one of the few remaining countries with a worthwhile part of its natural ecosystem and forests left (but only approximately 15% in terms of land area covered (10% is forest suitable for tiger)) and it holds some of the most spectacular species on Earth. Some authorities think that only India can save the tiger, and all that it represents, from extinction.

At the beginning of the 20th century tigers were classified into 8 sub-species across Asia – see Diagram 6. During that century the Balinese, Javan and Caspian tigers became extinct.

Although a crude representation, the few remaining pugs indicate approximately where they

315

This was the situation in your grandfather's day

This was the situation in your father's day

This is the situation today. Your day. Nothing follows this,
unless we reverse the direction of the sequence

Diagram 5

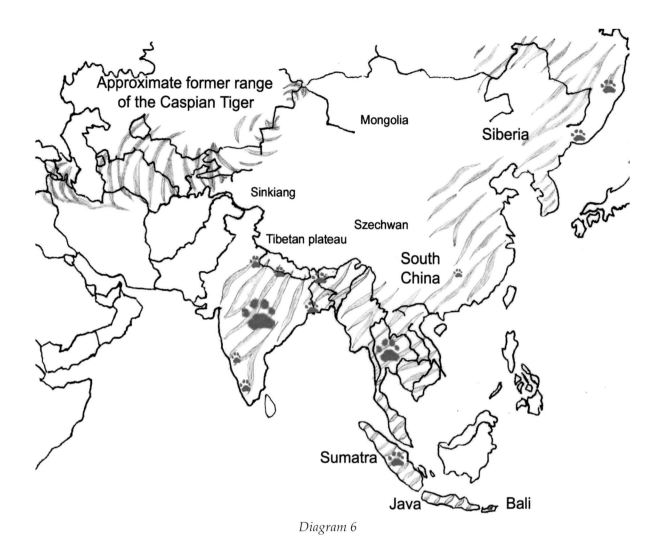

Diagram 6

can still be seen, in contrast to the enormous areas where stripes have faded from view during the last few human generations. (According to Perry (B53), up to the 19th century, stripes could still be seen along a (relatively) narrow band joining the Caspian and South China populations, sandwiched between Mongolia in the north, and the higher altitudes of the Chinese Sinkiang and Szechwan provinces, both contiguous with the Tibetan plateau). Pugs represent a figurative concentration of the populations local to that general area; smaller and larger pugs corresponding to smaller and larger populations. Accurate information for most of Malaysia, Myanmar (Burma), Thailand, Laos, Cambodia, and Vietnam does not appear to exist, so has been summarised by a single pug near the centre of their combined landmass. For India, Nepal, Bhutan and Bangladesh, pugs also represent localised groupings. However, whatever the representation used, it reveals that the tiger is too close to disappearing from the map, and the world.

The remaining populations per nation are all numbered in hundreds, if not fewer, except one: the Indian sub-species, which possibly still, but only just, has a population in four figures – even though these figures are not known exactly (1000 – 1500?) However, this is no reason for complacency. In a country the size of India this is a very low number and the decline this century has been drastic – see Diagram 7. Which way will we continue this graph in the future – how many years will there be a future for humans if the graph plots the tiger's extinction?

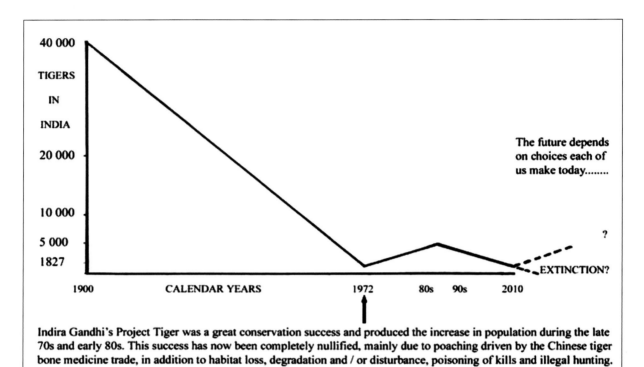

Diagram 7

If we cannot save the tiger, what are we going to save? Maybe not even ourselves, or our children. So many of the tiger's problems (and ours) stem from many people's short-term view that 'only today matters' e.g. poaching, timber felling, 'slash and burn' agriculture or shifting cultivation (many, many years ago when the whole country was predominantly forest and the human population relatively low, this was not an environmentally dangerous practice but now the relatively small areas of natural ecosystem left and the demands of more people leave no time for it to recover. So resources are being consumed but not replaced). What about tomorrow?

In a very real sense, you are doing one of the most important jobs in the world. Thinking and caring people all around the world admire and respect what you do. To them you are heroes.

We have referred in Diagram 7 to Indira Gandhi's Project Tiger, now we quote her: "The interest in conservation is not a sentimental one but a rediscovery of a truth well known to our ancient sages. The Indian tradition teaches us that all forms of life – human, animal and plant – are so closely interlinked that disturbance in one gives rise to imbalance in the other...Nature is beautifully balanced. Each little thing has its own place, its duty and special utility. Any disturbance creates a chain reaction which may not be visible for some time".

Wise words, but do we need politicians or scientists to tell us the value of living things? The value of plants and animals is enshrined in religions. Think of the ficus, banyan, emblic, neem, mango trees and the tulsi plant. Think of Ganeshji, Hanumanji and Durgaji. Surely, their role in the ecosystem – our life support system – is partly, if not wholly, why they are sacred. Not all people of ancient populations could be educated, so making these animals sacred ensured the protection of the life support system without explanation being necessary. Now we understand – and are killing them!

This quote is from the Upanishads:

"This universe is the creation of the Supreme Power meant for the benefit of all His creations. Individual species must, therefore, learn to enjoy its benefits by forming a part of the system in close relation with other species. Let not any one species encroach upon the other's rights"

(Note; we are just re-discovering this truth and call it 'ecology' – see previous examples of how one species can "encroach upon another's rights" and how each, in Nature "form a part of the system in close relation with other species". Man disturbs this relationship.)

The Quran Majeed contains numerous references to the rights of animals and man's responsibilities toward them. All of the following quotes are taken from the book 'Islamic Concern for Animals' by AI-Hafiz B.A. Masri.

The Holy Prophet Muhammad declared:

"There is no man who kills (even) a sparrow or anything smaller, without its deserving it, but God will question him about it. He who takes pity (even) on a sparrow and spares its life, Allah will be merciful on him on the Day of Judgement."

"Whoever is kind to the creatures of God, is kind to himself."

The great Moslem theologian Sayyid Abu A'la Maududi said: "Regarding the beasts of burden and animals used for riding and transport, Islam distinctly forbids men to keep them hungry, to take hard and intolerable work from them and to beat them cruelly. To catch birds and imprison them in cages without any special purpose is considered abominable. What to say of animals: Islam does not approve even of the useless cutting of trees and bushes. Man can use their fruit and other produce but he has no right to destroy them...Islam does not allow the waste of even lifeless things; so much so that it disapproves of the wasteful flow of too much water. Its avowed purpose is to avoid waste in every conceivable form and to make the best use of all resources – living and lifeless". ...observations of the Qur'an Majeed lay down...basic principles. Firstly, that the preservation of species is of paramount importance...

"It is understood that the inanimate elements of nature perform the act of worshipping God without articulate utterances. They do it by submitting themselves (Tasleem) to the Divine Ordinances known as the Laws of Nature.... All the elements of nature and all the animal kingdom function in harmony with God's laws; it is only some humans who infringe and thus bring affliction on themselves. The Qur'an Majeed dwells on this theme repeatedly to emphasize the point that man should bring himself into harmony with nature, according to the laws of God – as all other creation does."

From the Bible

Deuteronomy 20:19 "...do not cut down...trees...you may eat the fruit but do not destroy the trees, for the trees of the field are man's life."

Ecclesiastes 3:19 "The same fate awaits both humans and animals; one dies just like the other. They are both created by God and given breath by Him, so man has no pre-eminence over the animals...all is vanity."

Hosea 4: 1-3 "...Listen to what He (God) says: 'There is no faithfulness or love in the land, and the people do not acknowledge me as God. They make promises and break them; they lie, murder, steal, and commit adultery. Crimes increase and there is one murder after another. And so the land will dry up, and everything that lives on it will die. All the animals and birds, and even the fish will die'."

From an Indonesian proverb:

"Tigers are killed without forest and the tiger-less forest is cut down – so the tiger should guard the forest and the forest should guard the tiger."

Let each of us look to ourselves and where we need to change our habits or behaviour to protect our environment and hence ourselves, and our children. We cannot expect a change in the world if we cannot change ourselves. Mahatma Gandhi said "You must see in yourself the change you want to see in the world". How will we answer to Allah / Brahma / God for how we have treated His creation and gift to us? I do not think you are doing the government's work – I think you are doing God's work. For all that you personally do to protect the tiger, the forest and hence all of us,

THANK YOU

We are not separate from Nature but part of it. Whatever we do to Nature we ultimately do to ourselves.
All things are connected. The only thing that is partial is our understanding.

END OF PRESENTATION TO FOREST GUARDS

Four sides of A4 pages follow with practical suggestions for actions that Indian citizens can take to help the environmental situation. Pachmarhi also happens to be the location for the Forest Guard Training School for all of Madhya Pradesh so, each year that LifeForce personnel are available, the new recruits have been given this presentation, and time for questions and discussion afterwards. It is also important to involve, educate and re-direct the aspirations of local towns' people to include nature as their priority, since the markets and money they represent, via a circuitous network of connections, ultimately impact on the forests and their inhabitants. Hence a slightly modified presentation has also been given to local citizens, many schools and colleges, and to Police and Teacher Training institutions (the presentation to police cadets reminds them that abuse of the environment steals from everyone and everything. It is to steal the health of all, and steal the future from children).

For decades, a growing environmental crisis has also been growing evidence that we cannot rely on governments to safeguard our life support systems (it is also evidence of our laxity in allowing it). As indicated in the previous chapter, governments (in addition to those of tiger range countries) allow the IMF, World Bank and WTO to wield enormous socio-economic power in ways that seriously damage the global environment, while what laws there are to protect the environment are ignored with impunity (trees and tigers disappearing are other ways in which nature reveals where humans are failing). Despite this situation, the suggestions of some conservation organisations, funding agencies and wildlife magazines (particularly with regard to protecting tigers) reduce to law enforcement and 'governments should be doing what governments should be doing'. Well, of course they should – but what do we do if they are not? This is rarely, if ever covered and if the tiger's, and environment's, continuing decline only continues to generate complaints about governments, there can only be one result. The remedial action taken by individuals and NGO's is critical, and more is urgently required, so articles claiming that 'governments should be doing what governments should be doing' should not leave their analysis at that but should also be championing NGOs on the forest floor, and recommending many of the actions contained in this chapter.

Without exaggeration, the work of LifeForce and other sincere NGO's is essential for life itself. This is not a self-congratulatory assessment of our own importance – it is an accurate and undeniable assessment of the importance of the *work* (whoever sincerely does it) and of nature as our one and only life-support system. The supreme importance but hen-tooth scarcity of remedial work lends any sincere and effective NGO a significance out of all proportion to its size. The conservation projects and programmes of such NGO's are often pure and healthy both in principle and practice, but in most cases, currently too small to cope with the scale of degradation. However, LifeForce and the groups it is working with, plus a handful of others in India and around the world, have gradually grown their sphere of influence and perhaps, with your help, might grow further yet.

Obviously, good, if not ideal, governments must be part of long-term solutions but the environmental situation in general and the tiger situation in particular are demonstrating that we do not currently have long-term perspectives, nor good, let alone ideal, governance. One notable exception, in the context of conservation and environment, was Indira Gandhi's government, not only for the Wildlife Act in general but also for Project Tiger in particular, which was a success due to being actively driven by her and her government. However, in general terms, causes of problems known for decades have been ignored for decades. A few governments have recently taken some emergency actions but they are still drastically inadequate and, as a consequence of being emergency actions, always in danger of not succeeding.

Although global economics are driven by multinationals and powerful media interests distant from tiger habitats, their effects reach down, literally, to forest floors, tigers, and tribal people's lives. From wherever natural resources are extracted, Western markets command maximum prices (e.g. hard wood that was tiger habitat ends up, for example, in garden furniture or frames for double-glazing in Europe and the U.S.A. The most lucrative markets for tiger-bone medicines are in the Chinatowns of New York, and the Western-style markets of Hong Kong and Taiwan. Previously London was such a lucrative market but, on a cheering note, at the time of writing and for some years previously, the Wildlife Crime Unit of the Metropolitan Police has made real and significant progress in reducing, if not eliminating, the trade in London). The Western cartel of multinationals employ a proportion of populations to supply Western or Western style markets while creating the socio-economics that leaves vast numbers of people unemployed, some of whom become poachers and timber thieves. We're back to an interconnected whole and nature's mirrors. It is because we in the 'West' have consumerism foisted on us by media-backed corporations, and allow those businesses too much influence over governments, that poachers and timber thieves plunder forests thousands of miles away.

Poor government, voracious corporations and the resulting environmental situation now oblige us, as individuals; to inform and educate ourselves, and then others, about the situation and its wider implications; to face our responsibilities and take action to protect nature; to control corporations and later, only after having secured our life-support system; to improve government. (Henry David Thoreau in his Civil Disobedience calls for improving rather than abolishing government — "I ask for, not at once no government, but at once a better government").

The Guard's Presentation above illustrates why healthy forests are important for all of us. So, what can individuals do to help conserve forests, tigers and, as a consequence, people? The following sub-sections describe some of LifeForce's attempts to answer these questions in theory and practice.

Conserving Forests

Satpura Tiger Reserve

Forests the world over have been plundered for centuries. Obviously, much of value to humans has been acquired and foundations laid for civilisations in terms of materials for buildings, transport and fuel. However, by the late 20th century, forests were being felled merely to clear space for commercial fashions and maximum profits e.g. cash crops such as soya beans and palm oil, and pasture for cattle to become beef burgers. Forests were also felled for timber planks to shore up the foundation pits of Far Eastern skyscrapers. When the concrete was added the timber was withdrawn – and burned. There are easily available alternative methods and, for example, no skyscrapers in the U.S.A. are built using this obscene wastage of natural resources. Commercial fashions and construction techniques change but the forests and their wildlife, which took millennia to grow, are gone forever.

After decades of mismanagement, waste and alarmingly dwindling forest cover, public outcry and / or the actions of a few sensible politicians resulted in some of the drastically reduced but still remaining pristine forests being protected in law. In India, people still dependent on these remnant forests and who had no part in, nor even knowledge of, commercial markets thousands of miles away, found it had become illegal for them to take from those forests what their ancestors had taken for centuries. Few if any alternatives have been offered and, unsurprisingly, reactions include bewilderment, followed by resentment and resistance. Most tribal people have no choice but to continue grazing their domestic animals in the forest, collect firewood, grass for thatching, plants for medicine, and take the odd sambhar or wild pig for the pot. Forest Department officials may detect these activities and detain those involved but this often leads to increased antagonism and the deliberate setting of forest fires and even violence toward officials. LifeForce's first-hand experience has shown that all these problems and a host of other disturbances and environmental damage can be reduced or eliminated by education and practical support such as providing bio-gas generators, seeds for winter crops, sewing machines, tube wells and training for employment.

When working with the tribal people, LifeForce always invited the Forest Department to be present and, as a consequence, relations between the tribal people and the Forest Department were greatly improved. Reports on the website record, for examples; how domestic animals have been retrieved from the forest before the Forest Guard knew they had strayed into it; how fire-watching replaced fire-setting and how co-operation in general flourished.

When working with honest and reliable Forest Department personnel, LifeForce has also contributed to direct protection of the forests by, for example, donating patrol vehicles (the reports on the website record how valuable these have been in arresting poachers and gangs of timber thieves (preventing more trees being cut and confiscating timber already felled)). Protection has also been enhanced by improving the welfare and efficiency of Forest Guards by supplementing their equipment requirements e.g. providing them with torches, water flasks, mosquito nets, fire-beaters etc.. One simple but significant and heartening piece of feedback received by LifeForce was that incidences of malaria had noticeably decreased after the distribution of free mosquito nets to Forest Guards.

Important as protection is, conservation cannot be confined to law enforcement. Such an approach is very 'black and white' – almost as if timber thieves and poachers wear black hats while forest guards and conservationists wear white hats. It reinforces the idea that only large organisations can do anything and is analogous to allopathic medicine treating symptoms rather than causes. Even if law enforcement was rapid, efficient and applied at appropriate scales, in the context of the previous chapter, this approach is predominantly 'yang' or 'male' and also allows us to avoid facing personal responsibilities (it's all 'their fault'). Few have looked longer or deeper to ask why people poach or take timber. Without finding the answers to these questions, poaching and timber theft will continue, no matter how many are arrested. Balancing the yang approach with yin, acquiring knowledge through feeling, identifying causes not symptoms, reveals why many of those on the forest floor (not the chain of criminal middlemen in towns and cities) are poaching and thieving. LifeForce has made its own investigations and concluded that the majority are just trying to feed their family, which has become increasingly difficult since they have been marginalised by local and global economic systems, and new laws born of those systems. Hence, effective conservation requires identification and analysis of those connections which, in turn, brings knowledge and, when we use it to treat causes rather than symptoms, something of wisdom.

Generally speaking, tribal people have (when not corrupted by external manipulation and bribes) learned one of nature's fundamental lessons, which is 'take some, and leave some'. The same principle applies in the ancient Western arts of coppicing and pollarding in forests (or even, at the most local level, growing vegetables in the garden – taking all one's home-grown produce ensures nothing for the future). If you take some and leave some, you can return tomorrow. Take everything now to guarantee you will have nothing tomorrow, and then no tomorrow. The principle applies to gardeners, individuals living off a forest and multinationals living off the world, and all in between. It is equivalent to finding the balance point, exercising self-control to happily accept the optimum. In making nature yield more, we ultimately receive less. The Earth has abundance for all, if its resources are not abused. Although there is much modern debate over what constitutes 'sustainable' it seems that 'take some and leave some' would make a good, common sense foundation on which subsequent studies could be built to help quantify the principle.

Whilst the principle applies to both the man in the forest and the multinational in the world, the two examples are in stark contrast: Nature automatically teaches an individual these principles, and even to form 'friendships' with and within the forest. Taking what they need but not as much as they could, they also take care to respect and protect the whole, recognising that they and their family are part of that whole. Caring for the forest is the same as caring for your family. Multinationals are not interested in principles other than those which make maximum profit in minimum time. They are separate from the forest (or other natural resources) and have no feeling for them, taking only 'What I want' and 'as much as I can' for the immediate, short-term future. Resources are taken excessively and wastefully while creating pollution and, often, environmental devastation. Waste also means that costs, and therefore prices, are higher than need be. As vast profits and capital accumulate, big business gains significant influence over economic, political and legal systems, more firmly securing these damaging and dangerous practices in an increasingly plundered and weakened natural world.

Foremost on LifeForce's conservation management plan is maintaining mature, natural forests – essential for healthy terrestrial habitats, and healthy agricultural, industrial and residential environments. This can be achieved by direct protection and by helping to create markets for products made from sources other than forests. Perhaps the most obvious example is paper, which can also be made from old cloth, bamboo waste and / or re-cycled bamboo pulp. Re-cycled paper can also be beneficial, provided the production process is environmentally-friendly e.g. avoids chlorine bleaching. With regard to timber, we should only purchase that grown in purposely managed plantations, which often utilise quick-growing trees such as pine and eucalyptus. While commercial pressures on the forest must be reduced or removed, so too must those due to tribal people still directly dependent on forests. Training, support and advice can be provided to help them find alternative sources of energy and income (some details of such assistance are available on the website (www.lifeforceindia.com) and below with regard to a collaborative 'Employment Cell' project with the Satpuda Foundation).

All these practices directly contribute to conserving forests. As do finding and practising optimum, balance, concern for others, taking some and leaving some (and, where and when appropriate, giving some of what we have taken to those unable to reach their share) and selectively spending and investing money.

Establishing a set of values, virtues, morals and re-evaluating priorities are now critical issues for individuals, corporations and nations alike, and crucial to our survival. However, corporations and nations are made up of individuals – the only ones who can choose these options.

Conserving Tigers

If we conserve the remaining forests, what of the tigers remaining in them?

All the problems affecting forests as described in the previous sub-section also, of course, adversely affect the tiger. In addition, tigers are directly affected by specific problems stemming, once again, from villages remaining in core areas of Tiger Reserves, including pollution, interruption of animal migration routes or other behavioural routines, and vulnerability to poachers (when a guard challenges a man found in a Tiger Reserve, the guard is told relatives in a village within the Reserve are being visited. The distance is too far for the guard to immediately check this. If the stranger is a poacher, by the time the guard can check his account, it is already too late). As referred to in chapter II, other specific problems include the removal and / or spoiling of food sources for prey species and the displacement of prey species by domestic stock. The latter leads to a much more serious problem in that any domestic animal killed by a tiger or leopard may later be poisoned by the owner. The predator dies soon after returning to feed from the carcass. Government compensation schemes pay the value of the dead animal to its owner and this has had beneficial effects, where Forest Department members do their duties diligently, and where payment is not delayed by bureaucracy.

What can be done about these problems? With regard to tigers in India, various NGOs pursue a variety of projects. These include supporting neglected Forest Guards with reward schemes, education, insurance and equipment; supporting tribal people by providing medical aid, education, employment and alternative sources of income and energy. Other NGO's do great work pressurising the law to tackle timber thieves, poachers and the illegal trade in animal body parts. As nearly all NGO's struggle to survive themselves, these projects can only be conducted as funds allow – sometimes in fits and starts and, all too often, on small and inadequate scales.

Can these projects save the tiger from extinction?

- Supporting Forest Guards with reward schemes, insurance and equipment will *not* save the tiger.
- Medical aid and education for tribal peoples will *not* save the tiger,
- Pressurising the law to tackle the illegal trade in animal body parts, poachers and timber thieves will *not* save the tiger.
- *Nor will* the re-introduction of prey species or bio-diesel projects, bio-gas generators, seeds for winter crops, sewing machines, tube wells or employment schemes.

However, *conducted regularly on adequate scales*;

- Supporting Forest Guards with reward schemes, education, insurance and equipment *and*
- Medical aid and education for tribal peoples *and*
- Pressurising the law to tackle the illegal trade in animal body parts, poachers and timber thieves *and* the
- Re-introduction of prey species, bio-diesel or solar-energy projects, bio-gas generators, seeds for winter crops, sewing machines, tube wells and employment schemes

all together stand a good chance of saving the tiger in the short-term – especially when combined with consumers of all nations, but particularly Western ones, spending and investing their money selectively to reduce or eliminate the abusive and wasteful commercial exploitation of natural resources.

When and where a Tiger Reserve has a 'good' Director and such 'on the ground' actions as just listed gain the full co-operation of the Forest Department much can be achieved. Yet we must remember that if all governments and government departments (and, again, not just those of tiger range nations) were doing what they should, we wouldn't have a tiger crisis. Improving government departments depends on educated and empowered citizens facing their responsibilities and insisting on public servants doing their duties fully and / or properly. This will take longer to happen, if it ever does, than the tiger has remaining so, in the current situation, much 'real' tiger conservation depends on a few dedicated individual officials within the Forest Department. Such dedicated officials do exist (although they are also a rare species) and their collaboration allows the efforts of NGOs to yield their best results. However, the tiger is so valuable from an ecosystems perspective, NGO programmes such as those listed above would, ideally, be applied over all remaining tiger-inhabited tiger habitat even if the results are only partially successful (in the current circumstances, partial success is preferable to none). However, in reality, it is a struggle to fund even one or two projects in one area.

It would not be quite such a struggle if more people wanted to support the projects – not necessarily just with money but also with thought, attitude and actions that stimulate changes of heart and mind in themselves and others. We have considered in chapter IV why this brings 'real' change. In the sub-sections below we will consider how it can be made manifest in our daily lives. So, whilst tiger conservation projects definitely need funding it also needs people, whether they live in tiger range countries or not, to review their priorities, life-styles, investments and consumer spending. In fact, it is people living far from tiger habitat who have a greater ecological impact on the world, due to their vastly greater consumption of energy and resources, and due to them generating greater quantities of pollution and waste. By taking responsibility for their lifestyles people ultimately, of course, conserve themselves.

Conserving People

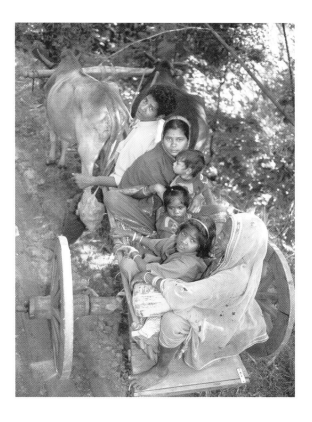

We have seen that forests are essential for holding the water table in the land and nutrients in the soil – which also support cultivation, industry and just about all and any other human activity. Healthy human environments are dependent on healthy natural environments, most critically forests, and healthy Asian forests hold tigers. Hence, as illustrated in the reproduction of the LifeForce Presentation to Forest Guards, tiger conservation is people conservation.

Forest

and

water

and

wheat

make...

the bread of life, healthy people and a healthy planet

At a LifeForce presentation to a group of tribal women in 2004 at the Barli Institute for Rural Women in Indore, the importance of the tiger as representative of a healthy forest was stressed. At the end of the presentation, one girl said 'I don't know what a tiger is, but our village has a water shortage problem.' The importance of tiger conservation in one sentence! Only 10% of India's land mass is still tiger habitat. Even that is decreasing and, at the same time, still subject to poaching, timber theft and commercial exploitation. These last few fragments of natural habitat should, ideally, be free from all human disturbance.

So, for conservation of forests, tigers, and people, for the reasons given in chapter II, and in this and the previous two sub-sections, relocations of villages remaining in Tiger habitat represent a top priority.

In retrospect, the only real flaw in Indira Gandhi's Project Tiger turned out to be the forced re-location of some villages. When handled insensitively, as it was on too many occasions, this policy resulted in physical violence and a negative public reaction (not toward violence but toward conservation!) As a result, tribal relocation became a political 'hot potato', the pendulum swung to the opposite extreme and now tribal rights are paramount, and NGOs have even formed to protect tribal people from anything they might see as 'abuse' or exploitation. However, in LifeForce's first-hand experience, the villagers request, sometimes plead to be relocated, since they have seen the benefits of suburban life and know their own lives are very hard – in the forest there is no electricity, medical care or support; no flood or drought relief (depending on how heavy or light the monsoon has been); and no schooling for their children. Although they might just about survive on their crops, they have to travel many hard miles on foot or bullock cart to the nearest market to sell their crafted wares for a few rupees. They know their lives would be much easier out of the Tiger Reserve, where all these problems are easily solved. So LifeForce supports *voluntary* re-location schemes to help villages move out of Tiger Reserves.

However, the time scales these re-locations require and the sheer number of villages remaining inside Tiger Reserves and other Protected Areas, means completion of this programme (under prevailing circumstances) is also far in excess of the time remaining to the tiger. Hence, realistic short-term conservation programmes must include solutions to problems stemming from people still living in Tiger Reserves. These people, the tribal people, have always lived self-sufficiently in and off the forest but, by the late twentieth century, 85% of India's natural habitat had been cultivated, industrialised or cleared for residential use. When legislation was passed to protect the remainder, many of the tribal people's ancestral practices became illegal overnight but without adequate (in some cases, any) alternatives being provided. Of the few programmes available, some are not environmentally-friendly and are therefore ultimately self-defeating. In consequence, unemployed tribal youth have become the major factor in all the immediate threats to tigers: habitat degradation, collection of forest produce, domestic animals feeding in the forest (and the poisoning of any domestic animals killed by predators), arson, poaching and timber theft. These people poach and thieve for their own survival needs. In addition, there are also cases (especially involving timber) where 'businessmen', in some cases even politicians and other officials (including some from the Forest Department), pay a pittance to unemployed labourers (including tribal people) to poach and illegally fell timber. The 'sponsors' thereby protect themselves (in case the workers are caught in the act) while taking more than 90% of the resulting profits. Hence unemployed people, tribal or otherwise, represent one of the biggest threats to tigers and tiger habitat, directly, indirectly or by complicity. Living literally 'at the crime scene', tribal people are relatively easily subjected to the law by the Forest Department and police, breeding even more antagonism and poisoning their minds against the law in general and conservation in particular.

Enabling people to acquire sustainable income and energy for their daily needs applies not only to resolving the tiger crisis but also to resolving the world's environmental crisis. From both perspectives, forests are essential. Hence, for the immediate future, providing people with education, sources of income and energy not directly dependent on, and away from the forest, appears a better-balanced, co-operative approach with immediate, practically beneficial results than blind calls for law enforcement. It keeps forests healthier (for all), conserves and protects tigers and gains all of us time to work on longer-term solutions. In accordance with previous observations, focussing exclusively on profits, targets, mechanics, rules and regulations ignores what is of most importance about the activities all these categories relate to. Life is about other people and other life forms. Life is about life. In conservation terms, long-term success can only be achieved by constructively involving local people.

So this is what LifeForce Charitable Trust is trying to do by funding a completely new initiative, an 'Employment Cell' project, launched in December 2006 to address these issues across all the Tiger Reserves mentioned above, with plans to, eventually, include the 'corridors' in between. LifeForce is working in collaboration with the Satpuda Foundation which conducts the Employment Cell project 'on the ground'. The Employment Cell provides training and placement in employment, support for 'Self-Help Groups' (SHGs), conservation education, training in organic agriculture and khadi (the latter two where circumstances allow. Khadi – homespun cotton – was constantly promoted by Mahatma Gandhi as a solution to a variety of problems: In addition to providing employment, income and independence to people (however poor they may be) it is suitable work for women, who tend to spend any money they make on their family. It also narrows the ever-widening gulf between cities (where industrialisation and consumerism dominate) and rural communities with their crafts and local economies. It also helps prevent power and profits concentrating into fewer and fewer hands – as Gandhi said "We don't want mass production but production by the masses." Wherever possible, khadi will be developed with organically grown cotton). Other skills taught include crafts such as the making of mats and candles, while training and positions found for trainees include shop, security and hotel work in nearby towns.

In the previous chapter it was mentioned that the reader may have been surprised to read of topics such as employment and economics in a book about tiger conservation. By now, hopefully, the same reader can see how conservation and, for example making candles commercially, all combine to keep lights and flames burning.

Due to relationships made, trust earned and benefits brought, the Employment Cell project (if continued funding can be found) forms a foundation on which additional 'levels' can later be built e.g. further education, health & hygiene etc. Small though it currently is, it can be grown like the seed it represents. By taking people out of the forest, giving them new skills, employment, some dignity, independence and some education, it is possible for an appreciation and understanding of the value of the forests, and the tigers within them, to grow, and people conservation becomes tiger conservation. In the Guards' presentation we have already seen how tiger conservation is people conservation. As in all natural and healthy relationships; they are mutually supportive and cyclical, making cause and effect interchangeable.

Assessing requirements and capabilities

Learning how to make candles

Matting made of legally cut bamboo

Conserving Forests, Tigers and People

With regard to LifeForce work in general and the Employment Cell in particular, strategies are sound insofar as they: address the environment and its sustainable use; conservation of the neighbouring natural habitat; provide employment and education; avoid mass production and altogether represent healthier, localised socio-economics. Any system will always need refinement, adjustment to changing conditions and general improvement but, in principle and much practice, the strategies are holistic and healthy for all, conserving forests, tigers and people.

LifeForce works in one of, if not the, largest block of tiger habitat left in the world (which still actually holds tigers). This is also, as described above, essential for the health of nothing less than India, and therefore, ecologically speaking, the world. LifeForce plans, all other factors being equal, to continue this important work for as long as it can raise the necessary financial resources, and some income and resources for itself (to date the work has been voluntary). However, LifeForce is conscious of its limitations and the enormity of the problems faced. No implication is intended that LifeForce has all the answers, or that it can alone mount effective opposition to the powerful forces against which it, and all environmental NGOs, struggle. The tide can turn only when sufficient people understand, face their responsibilities and take action. If some of that action includes supporting LifeForce, the scales will not be tilted so heavily against it. However, for LifeForce, support does not equate entirely to donations. People taking action by changing their life-styles in accordance with the suggestions in the sub-section below entitled 'You Can Make a Difference' would also be a great advance, as would any help fostering the interconnections between currently isolated groups (please see LifeForce Report 2005 – 2006 Sub-section 'The Larger LifeForce', available on the website). Quoting from LifeLines Issue No.3 'Even if people recognise the gravity of the situation, (an) attitude frequently adopted is "I know there is a problem but thank goodness some people or groups are doing something about it…" We and other people or groups who are doing something about it are tiny in comparison to the forces opposed. We (all conservation groups) are losing the fight. Collectively, we may win a few battles but we (and this "we" now includes you) are in danger of losing the war.' Money is important, but not as important as people facing their responsibilities, and changing their priorities and / or life-styles accordingly. If they do, money will flow in the right directions. Making 'money' the most important priority is the cause of the problems in the first place.

According to the previous chapter, our best bet to change the world is to improve our priorities, our values… ourselves. 'He who knows much about others may be learned, but he who understands himself is more intelligent. He who controls others may be powerful, but he who has mastered himself is mightier still' (Lao-Tzu. 6th century B.C. sage and principal founder of Taoism). This tallies with the Biblical reference to 'he who controls himself is greater than he who controls cities'. As characters grow healthier, societies and cities grow healthier, which then grow healthier characters…which make a healthier world. Personal, self-willed change, enlightened self-development, has potential to change the world and, due to its importance and scarcity, it lends individuals or small groups who practise it, a significance out of all proportion to their physical size.

The 'mind-set' that nature requires of us (in order that we receive what we require of nature) is akin to the personal growth and commitment demonstrated by Mahatma Gandhi's keenest followers, who provide examples of significant change achieved by peaceful, direct action, to the point of voluntary suffering and loss.

Gandhi was asked by an ornithologist about the importance of protecting birds, and replied that we should protect people. He did not mean that protecting birds is unimportant but knew that when people were protected, the level of collective character development this indicated would automatically ensure the protection of birds…and animals…and nature in general (reminding us of the Lakota, referred to in the previous chapter, telling us that a lack of care for nature leads to a lack of care for people. Hence, by caring for people we learn to care for nature). When we care about people, we firstly ensure practicalities; that they have the basics of water, food and shelter. To ensure this in the long-term necessarily involves healthy agriculture and conservative consumption, re-cycling and re-growth of natural resources, and fair distribution of resources. All these activities must, if they are to be on-going, involve us with caring for and respecting the environment. In another of nature's symmetrical arrangements, treating people with care and respect is reflected in the environment, while treating the environment with care and respect is reflected in people. These are ways in which our own lives, as individuals, have the most direct and powerful relevance: for each of us and for the world, and simultaneously so.

Let us explore our own world, find our own treasure within and so change *our* world and thereby *the* world. 'Be a Columbus to whole new continents and worlds within you, opening new channels, not of trade, but of thought…What was the meaning of that South-Sea Exploring Expedition, with all its parade and expense, but an indirect recognition of the fact that there are continents and seas in the moral world to which every man is an isthmus or an inlet, yet unexplored by him, but that it is easier to sail many thousand miles through cold and storm and cannibals, in a government ship, with five hundred men and boys to assist one, than it is to explore the private sea, the Atlantic and Pacific Ocean of one's being alone…It is not worth the while to go round the world to count the cats in Zanzibar. Yet do this till you can do better, and you may perhaps find some "Symmes Hole" by which to get at the inside at last.' (Henry David Thoreau. *John Cleves Symmes was, in 1818, a proponent of a 'Hollow Earth' theory, access to which was gained via holes – 'Symmes Holes' – located at the poles*).

Beneficial changes to the world will only be maintained for as long as we personally maintain our inner changes, our improvement of our characters. Practical support or money offered to movements for change, without personal commitment to permanently change oneself, bring no permanent change to the world. The character of the world is a composite of its inhabitants' characters, the development of which is mainly influenced by the beliefs and values of the people they develop amongst. Even within his own lifetime Gandhi's non-violence was tarnished by those who claimed allegiance to him but had not changed internally and so used violence to oppose others or impose physical change on them. Nowadays, Mahatma Gandhi is, at least in India, revered, almost worshipped; but his message and practices are, en masse, neglected. As we observed in chapter IV, the world cannot change permanently, until individuals change permanently. Gandhi lamented that "everybody wants my picture but nobody wants to follow my teachings". Similarly, religious teachers such as Siddartha Gautama and Jesus of Nazareth did not ask people to follow them, but their example. It is for each of us to model our behaviour on those who are our ideals. 'Mahatma' means great spirit or soul. He and other great souls can act as guides, as lights along the way. Neon lit 'celebrities' are not the stars we need.

Despite Gandhi's defeats it might be said that he and his circle's achievement of Independence represents a permanent change. Sadly, Independence remains in name but it has been compromised not only by internal corruption but also by external influences. After de-regulation began in India during the 1990s, Western commerce and big businesses moved into India. In consequence 'The General Agreement on Trade in Services (GATS) signals the end of national government. When investment is open to all comers, when financial services are run by global banks, when local trade cannot be given preference, when the local language and culture cannot be protected, when governments are forced to sell essential services to multinational corporations, when even the land of a poor country can be appropriated by the rich – what is left? Exit democracy.

Democracy brought an end to famines in India in 1947. The new government gave priority to livelihoods, food security, land distribution and it imposed a ceiling on land ownership. In 2002 famine returned to six states in spite of overflowing grain stores. Why? The World Bank had forced India to dismantle its humanitarian structures in favour of trade and commerce. Without democratic influence over economic content, politicians can now only bid for votes on the basis of prejudice, fear and hate. Communal violence, cross-border aggression and starvation are back.

The IMF (International Monetary Fund) is un-democratic and its proceedings are as opaque as crude oil.

- World population: India: 17%   US: 4%
- Share of votes: India: 2%   US: 18%

Wealth-based voting was rejected by the American Founders and was abolished in Britain in 1832.' (B10 reprinted by kind permission of Alastair Sawday Publishing Co.)

A fuller examination of the activities of the WTO and 'agreements' such as 'GATS' will take us too far from the main point of this section. However, these issues are so important with regard to all of our futures, including that of the tiger, further details are given in Appendix III.

Again, of course, the problems with government, big business, the World Bank, IMF or any other organisation, group or endeavour can be reduced to problems with human nature. Whatever socio-political system might be adopted, now known to humans or new, it will founder as it is manipulated for personal advantage and / or abuse of the community. When the members of any group, be it of individuals, nations or anything in between, put self-interest above group interest, that group will become dysfunctional and ultimately die ('Every kingdom divided against itself comes to desolation, and a house divided against itself falls.' (Luke 11:17)). Environmentally speaking, the individual's long-term interest is group interest. Neglecting the latter will bring disease or death to the former. It is only each person by their own free will that can change themselves and improve their character and contribution to the group, which underlines why each person is not only relevant, but *essential*, if the world will be changed.

Some readers might see the value of personal development but might also see personal dilemmas in extremely difficult circumstances, as for example, for those who faced Hindu / Muslim violence during the birth of Indian Independence or those faced by people who opposed the Nazi regime in occupied territory or, in a different way, deciding whether or not to try one's luck against another man-eater terrorising people many miles away from one's own comfortable existence. However, most readers of this book have not, nor (thankfully) ever will, face such difficult choices. Let us not reject the potential for personal change because we cannot imagine, say, finding the courage to oppose a Hindu / Muslim mob, Nazi bullies or follow up another man-eater. Most of us have the luxury of improving our moral stature and virtue by making sure our life-styles respect the environment; by being a little more kind and generous to others, especially those less privileged than ourselves (human and non-human); by being more scrupulously honest and diligent in our daily lives; by being more patient and tolerant; taking interest in how we invest or spend our money; taking interest in how and where the products we buy are produced; taking co-operative and supportive action in our communities locally (e.g. schools, healthcare), nationally (e.g. government accountability, the law of the land) and globally (e.g. environmentally, human rights, U.N.) etc., as Gandhi said "In a gentle way, you can shake the world."

When we consider our own characters, it is easy to gain false comfort by comparing ourselves with obvious ogres such as Hitler or Stalin. Yet, we have to assess ourselves within the context of our own 'empire' even if that is limited to our own house and backyard. Where we seek to expand our own borders at the expense of our neighbours' lands, ignore (or increase by negligence) the suffering of those less fortunate than ourselves, practise prejudice and discrimination, impose our will only by force, we are as guilty as Stalin and Hitler. That we cannot command uniformed bullies does not diminish the culpability of the mental and spiritual attitudes which are the precursors to such developments. One's life is a record of one's own little 'empire' and is equivalent, for each of us, to history's global empires, especially with regard to how we wield our power within them. In the context of conservation, each poacher or timber thief could claim that the quantities they have stolen are negligible compared to the whole. Even considering those who poach and thieve not for survival but for extra money (and therefore take as much as they can) this is, in one sense, true, yet at the same time and by the same token, it is also true that the tiny fraction of tigers and trees entrusted to their knowledge and wisdom, to their vision and care, were killed off for a few rupees immediately it was possible to do so. The magnificence of natural treasure, impossible to buy with money, was traded for a pittance of man-made currency, which will even fail to achieve any long-term worth since acquiring it killed that which gave it value and meaning. Their behaviour, their characters indicate that, had they access to the whole, they would trade it for money. (Of course, exactly this type of person does currently have access to the whole, and they are trading it for money – although they are not called poachers and timber thieves, nor do they wear dhotis, but the best suits money can buy).

However, if the reader is still not convinced that enlightened self-development is an answer to our most important problems, let us consider the importance of individuals in another way:

There is today neither a government nor a geographical location left unaffected or uninfluenced by global socio-economics and corporate power. Nor can one support or join any large organisation or action group which is independent of global socio-economics or unaffected, directly or indirectly, by corporate commerce. Hence, in the absence of any truly independent and completely healthy group, the individual has even more importance as an agent for significant change since it is only individuals who can start behaving in ways which are healthy for all – from which will grow new, independent and healthy groups (some examples given below). Amazingly, corporate and other global giants are now juxtaposed with the opposite extreme; individuals and tiny groups. The mouse may intimidate the elephant. David will slay Goliath. Incredible as it may seem, the problems are now so large they can only be addressed by individuals! As the largest systems bring about their own demise, enlightened individuals represent new and healthy seeds. As these join relatively new and currently small groups of like-minded people, seeds will shoot and sprout into healthy new growth.

Where these new, small shoots have already appeared we must nurture them and support them, e.g. ethical and environmentally-friendly businesses, non-profit groups, NGO's, charities, civil liberties groups, those monitoring and opposing abuse of political power, and groups or individuals who provide education, training for employment and relief from disease.

As these small and caring groups eventually become successful will there not be a repeat performance and their business elements, at least, turn into another set of heartless giant conglomerates taking us back to the brink of disaster? One solution to this problem, briefly mentioned in the previous chapter, was the strict control of big business by independent government to prevent environmental abuse, avoidance of tax etc. The same result could also be achieved by the senior personnel voluntarily observing agendas additional to profit and / or power, including community responsibilities and making contributions to them beyond Public Relations exercises and tax write-offs. However, a solution with more healthy connections would be if, guided by nature and operating within just laws, these healthy initiatives grow as repeating patterns of small units, which remain integrated with and connected to local communities (preventing profits being drained from people and nations into a few pockets) i.e. more 'localisation'; less globalisation. In healthy human communities, life is about people, not profits. Put profit first and community health declines. 'Localisation' promotes community health.

The effects of globalisation are not confined to commerce. In addition to environmental abuse, an obvious social example would be news media reporting a nigh-on continuous catalogue of international problems and disasters which make most individual listeners feel helpless, and then hopeless. Of course, prior to globalisation, news reports covered international affairs but many modern international problems are actually the results of globalisation and its socio-economic consequences. Local community affairs reported to local individuals who took some responsibility for their community and local governing bodies (especially where big business has been 'localised' as suggested above), would result in fewer world problems since each small and healthier community cannot help but make healthier larger communities. This reminds us of the previous chapter and RNG's vision of the contributions the Indian Express could make to such a process. Our individual contributions are to do what we can to promote connections with, and care for, local communities – of people and the natural world. That requires an inner commitment from each of us, which cannot be commanded or imposed from without. 'Donations' of time and effort are often more important and valuable than donations of money.

We, in the West at least, have been conditioned to think that money provides all things. Multi-million pound advertising and marketing strategies convince society that consumer products provide all needs and wants, and corporations monopolise the supply of both, while multiplying the wants. Some still think they can 'buy' conservation solutions or even buy the necessities for their survival when ecosystems start to fragment and collapse. Real, long-term conservation is a result of a way of life, a mind-set working with a heart set on husbanding and nurturing the life force; living with a real respect and care for life in general; protecting all species and their habitats in numerous and various wild areas 'left sacred to nature' (B1). If we allow ecosystems to collapse, socio-economic systems follow, and in extreme scenarios, money will be worthless, since it can only ultimately represent natural resources and processes.

Some years ago a saying arose in America that 'nice guys finish last'. 'Nice guys' might finish last but 'nasty guys' finish everything. In the previous chapter we considered how failure can actually forge a stronger character than (what is conventionally called) 'success'. Many people aspire to practical accomplishments and are encouraged to be the 'best', 'winners', 'champions' etc. There is much that can be creditworthy in such aspirations, and the determination and discipline required to achieve them – provided balances are maintained, along with the ability to meet defeat with dignity. Without balance, the craving to be the 'best', 'biggest', 'richest' etc. is another manifestation of self indulgence and pursuit of maximum. Being able to lose, to admit defeat gracefully, is easier when one recognises the real value of the endeavour – the effort.

Effort is all that each of us is actually in control of, the self-sacrifice and commitment, including the determination and discipline just referred to. 'Success' and 'failure' are two fickle impostors that associate with that effort, just like Kipling's 'triumph and disaster'. Again we see the inverse relation between spiritual and physical 'successes'. The system that profits by promoting material success often has to promote as 'winners' and 'success stories' people who might exhibit the least desirable spiritual characteristics. At the same time and for the same reason, those who are materially poor, downtrodden or unknown become, in the system driven by material values, life's 'losers', yet may represent the highest spiritual development.

(Before continuing, it should be noted that, in this author's experience, the happiest people met with on this Earth have been, materially, the poorest and often found in Asian communities.

In contrast, the most miserable and / or aggressive people ever met with have been living in Western materially wealthy communities).

However, let us consider those who might be called 'losers' – living in materially wealthy countries but materially poor themselves and unhappy with that situation and their inability to improve it. Perhaps we might also include those who fail to achieve their own objectives. From a spiritual perspective, we can see that it is these so-called 'losers' who have, as a consequence, the best opportunity to grow their characters since, the greater the failure, defeat or disaster, the greater grace, determination and courage needed to continue. From the meek and modest earth of failure and defeat, trodden underfoot by all, straight and tall characters can grow – which is maybe why the meek shall inherit the Earth. 'Nice guys' may finish last but they may also, by doing so, become the 'greatest guys'. Meekness does not mean weakness. In this context, meekness means humility, the absence of arrogance. Meekness, as might be identified in Mahatma Gandhi, Luther Standing Bear, Jim Corbett, or country yokel Joe, has quiet dignity, doing right without self-importance, self-promotion or material success. Although Joe is a fictional character, Joes do live in this world (and their friendship is true wealth). Neither Gandhi, nor Standing Bear, nor Corbett, nor 'Joe' could be called weak or timid, and by their light we can see the falsehood of 'winners' who are nought but neon-lit, showy self-indulgence. Such people all too often seek, not self-improvement, but only 'experiences', thrills, and self-indulgence, mainly associated with extremes in modes of transport (fast cars, speedboats, aeroplanes, skis, etc.) and in this emphasis on 'matter in motion' we see links with contemporary Western culture, science, technology, wealth, leisure... and losing our way.

Although sharing and caring attitudes are recommended in this book, we need to pause briefly to identify falsehoods appearing under this guise in Western society's current 'politically correct' culture. As part of the pendulum's swing to an extreme position, ridiculous, inappropriate and even counter-productive policies have become commonplace. We have already mentioned legislation that favours pupils over teachers, criminals over their victims; etc. (which prompted some wit to revise the story of the Good Samaritan who, on finding a person badly beaten and lying in the gutter, merely moves on commenting 'The person who did this needs help'). The trend has run throughout much of Western society and, in the resulting 'nanny States', everyone is supposed to be protected from everything (except ecological Armageddon) which can, as with all extremes, make a mockery of common sense, healthy standards, justice and truth. Meekness rests at the pendulum's mid-point and while fully compassionate and tolerant, does not shy from speaking the truth, or from traditional values (including protecting one's property and family from criminals), confronting corruption and condemning laws more concerned with state revenue than justice.

When its human inhabitants find their balance, the world will be balanced. Each person has to examine their own life and improve it according to a scale of values in which morality and virtue are paramount, despite any fears or dangers we may have to confront in consequence. By facing our fears, we seize our tiger's fire. There are so few tigers left in the world because there are so few tigers left in people. Nobility, grace and dignity are overshadowed by herd-like behaviour at best, and parasitism at worst, which provides another reflection of the importance of each person's involvement and contribution. Tippu Sultan of Mysore, India (c 1750-99) is said to have declared that 'In this world I would rather live two days like a tiger, than two hundred years like a sheep' apparently modifying the original and ancient Tibetan proverb which contrasted one day as a tiger to a thousand years as a sheep. Either way we understand their meaning. Yet, from our current environmental perspective it is our sheep-like behaviour that is shortening our lives and our tigers which will win us life, if we would understand their significance, face our responsibilities and act accordingly.

Tippu Sultan, however, judging from some aspects of his life, celebrated more of the tiger's fiercer characteristics. To face our tigers and survive we must be able to tame our tigers, learn to control them, which is part of finding our balance, our poise. 'And the chief thing demanded by these intricacies of civilisation was control, restraint – a poise of self that was as delicate as the fluttering of gossamer wings and at the same time as rigid as steel' (B47c). In terms of physical tigers, we see the same principle manifest in strength and hardness woven with soft, teddy-bear cuteness. The author Jack London described a very agile and strong man 'springing to the deck with the weight and softness of a tiger.' In terms of human character we are reminded of Plato's ideal of braveness woven with gentleness as referred to in chapter III on Corbett. The ideal is, of course, yang and yin poised in perfect balance. Mother Nature waits for us to acquire it for ourselves and, while patient with our clumsy attempts, has no patience with no attempts, and is stirred to anger…

It can only be by well-informed personal actions that the balance can be achieved, internally and then externally. However, to be well-informed in today's world requires more emphasis on personal effort since formal education has become evermore selective and specialised. This is partly a reflection of specialisation due to technology, and partly by design, since capitalism tends to train people only to fit the demands of the labour market. From the capitalists' perspective this also prevents the dangers of fully educating the majority (since the educated understand how capitalists are exploiting them). In the U.K. for example, the 1871 Education Act was strongly opposed by mill owners, iron foundry owners, bankers and railway interests. Traditional Conservative Party policy is to restrict the breadth, quality and quantity of State education and this was continued right up to the most recent Conservative, Thatcher government. Her Chancellor of the Exchequer referred in one of his speeches to training people for jobs which were 'not so much low-tech as no-tech' and hence requiring little or no education.

Whilst it is true that millions of people are required for mindless, repetitive work, does not our modern, highly technological world also require highly educated people to maintain and develop it? Yes, but highly educated only in the sense of being highly specialised. For example, the computer engineer (unless by personal effort) learns little or nothing of socio-economics, environment, politics, Disraeli, Marx, Morris or Ruskin etc. This example of the computer also prompts us to consider that technology, if used for the benefit of the majority, could help us all spend less time in mind-numbing jobs and more time educating ourselves and / or developing our natural talents. Yet technology is used to increase or multiply markets to bring more profits for its few owners, rather than provide the majority, the working population, with the best possible working conditions and / or more leisure.

If a person has only a limited grasp of socio-economic issues, their grasp of environmental issues is likely to be similar, and for the same reasons. Moreover, an increasing proportion of the population live life-styles insulated from nature, so in addition to being denied a full formal, 'rational' education they are not even naturally 'absorbing' knowledge, or care and concern. In consequence, ever fewer people are aware of nature's essentially balanced interconnections, either by direct experience, or by commanding a suitable breadth of rational knowledge. These trends affect people of all levels and abilities. Over-specialisation has not only isolated some scientists and philosophers; there are even farmers who fail to understand the importance of wildlife to farming. Those relative few with broad perspectives and a balanced understanding are rarely in positions of power. Politicians or senior businessmen who do have power (including those organising the selective education of the majority) are equally insulated from nature, hold only specialised knowledge (if that) and are compelled by current trends to concentrate on a restricted set of issues, either for some chance of office or to attain and maintain their position on the board.

Few would trust their health to a 'doctor' who had no training or experience, or themselves and their property to tradesmen or professionals lacking the same. Yet the most important offices in the land can be occupied by, as Durant put it, those who 'stumble out' of industry or commerce. Surely statesmanship should only be trusted to those who have had rigorous training in it – and statesmanship of the sort described by Plato, not that identified with seeking status and privilege, while creating the right image with the media. Part of that training would include critically important knowledge of how civilisations develop or decline. There is no more important group within society to be fully familiar with history's record of how, for examples, injustice, affluence, decadence, unsustainable agriculture, pollution and other environmental abuse, ultimately bring about the decline and fall of civilisations. In worrying contrast, it would appear that too many members of today's governments know little of these subjects, but much about how to play games with the media to achieve their own short-term goals.

It is difficult to think of any truly independent and authoritative body with a panoramic overview and long-term perspectives, capable of guiding and coordinating the community at large, for the benefit of the community at large. Of course, the government has an army of specialists, scientific and otherwise, on which it can draw for facts, information and professional opinion but these too, by definition, suffer from the same blinkered over-specialisation and can comment only on their own microscopic perspective (some of the dangers we face because of this are described below). Political manifestos still concentrate primarily on taxes, education and health – and the latter two only in terms of the selective education just referred to, and mainly allopathic, drug-based medicine. Obviously these are all important concerns, but not as important as the environment.

Therefore part of our current personal responsibilities must include broadening our own education and (if natural habitat is available within travelling distance) directly 'absorbing' knowledge from nature. As a result, we should be able to adjust, and then set examples by our own life-styles such that others can see, understand and then mirror their understanding in their own life-styles. Gradually, if nature allows us sufficient time, individuals' knowledge and attitudes permeate organisations and institutions such that society reflects the concerns of its citizens. Changing one's life-style can be relatively painless; many environmentally-friendly and ethical choices are available and they largely fulfil the same function as their harmful counterparts. Changing one's values and priorities may be more of a challenge but, as we will see below, the rewards are worth more than any material gains which might be lost in the process. Encouraging others to behave in an environmentally responsible way (which is best for them also) is another worthwhile activity, but a bigger challenge.

Should we be trying to influence others? Should we not all just get on with the life each of us wants to live? It is partly such freedoms which have contributed to, and are now threatened by, the environmental crisis. All indications are that people will be suffering drastic changes to the 'lives they want to live' or will be simply trying to survive, since current trends indicate that our life-styles will be subject to severe changes imposed by nature – without reference to any of us. Any positive, constructive changes we make now will help lessen the impact of changes that are coming. If any feel uncomfortable influencing others, they had best realise that we are in this mess because too many people have already been influenced by others in the forms of commerce, marketing, media, advertising and the groups referred to above (WTO, IMF etc.) with detrimental results to our collective life-support system. If we're going to re-balance things (and, barring suicide, every aspect of our lives demands that we do), we have no choice but to counter harmful influences with healthy ones. Life imposes change on all, and all social change (beneficial or otherwise) is produced by people influencing others – so it may as well be for health as for harm. Principles of ecology can be interpreted as principles of community, as in the quote from the Upanishads used in the presentation to Forest Guards above.

We can all see the sense of allowing people to make up their own mind with regard to their views on, say, fashion or football, but environmental abuse damages the life support system *for all* and hence carries a unique and supreme importance, which should not be subject to opinion or personal preference. We are all on the same 'bus heading at top speed for the edge of the environmental precipice. Yet most passengers are totally absorbed in their own immediate surroundings; their comfortable seat, perhaps with their work they have brought along, or ipods, computer games, mobile telephones or in conversation with those next to them. They're not sure who the driver is and hardly anyone is looking out of the windscreen. Politicians and the public, some scientists and artists, journalists and reporters can see great and interesting views from the side windows, some can even see far into space. A few are looking through the windscreen and, horrified, trying to alert the other passengers and communicate with the driver. As the edge looms closer their efforts become more animated, prompting some passengers to comment derogatorily on those efforts while still refusing to look out of the windscreen for themselves. No-one can get off the 'bus until the next and final stop – when no-one will be able to get off the 'bus. Even the supposed saviour, science, has become so specialised that it is often focussed on the last atom of the last hair on the last leg of the last fly landing on the rearmost window as we are all, scientists included, about to go over the cliff edge.

Environmental health is one topic, perhaps the only one, on which we can all agree – if we can get people to consider it. Supposed differences of opinion are only that – opinion. The truth is evident enough when not obscured by personal agendas, profits or 'political correctness'. Conservation might seem to be an 'interest' in some peoples' eyes but it is actually a survival technique. If we do not conserve the tiger, which appears to have a place in everybody's heart, what are we going to conserve? While tigers might be exotic creatures for many people, it is as much our distance or insulation from nature immediately around us that allows conservation to be considered an 'option' or an 'interest', a misapprehension fostered by the media referring to 'environmentalists' or 'greens' as if there is a viable alternative position. The only other positions are ignorance (sometimes fearful, sometimes wilful), stupidity or greed, but none of these are viable. If 'environmentalists' or 'greens' represent some sort of club, being born confers obligatory membership. Everyone is an environmentalist but many do not yet know it, so influencing them to realise it is to their own real and lasting benefit. Almost incredibly, as the crisis advances, articles have appeared (even in broadsheet newspapers) referring to 'greens' as the new Bolsheviks, or a new religious order. Such classifications must necessarily imply that the reader, the journalist, and the anonymous, sensible majority, are not in these groups of fanatics or extremists. Articles have included suggestions or implications that features of civilisation such as travel, hot water etc. would no longer be available if these 'greens' achieve their aims. These and other exaggerations are presented in standard journalese, attempting humour and camaraderie with the reader, in order to mock such 'greens'. Having personally met hundreds of people who are concerned about the environment, this author is not sure such fanatics exist, however, at least one article suggested that if such extremists were allowed to gain power, compliance with 'green' behaviour might ultimately be enforced. If necessary, force will certainly be used: not, however, by 'greens' but by nature.

Whether these articles' attempts to misinform are stimulated by hidden agendas to maintain the status quo by influencing readers to be 'anti-green'; tell readers what they want to hear (and sell a paper); by genuine ignorance or fearing to face reality, is difficult to determine but what can be determined is (for those who believe all they read in newspapers) the dilution of even that minimal environmental awareness it has taken so long and so much effort to raise in the general public. Thomas Carlyle's (1795 – 1888. Historian, teacher, writer) reference to journalism as 'ditch-water' may seem harsh when we think of genuinely concerned and talented journalists who have tirelessly pursued justice on many issues, including environmental ones, for many years. However, journalism mocking sincere and sensible environmental advice is in danger of polluting ditch-water to the point of toxicity.

While some try to find their way back to nature's path, others do not realise the direction in which they are heading, so those who can see the path have to make extra efforts, in as many ways as possible, to point it out to those who are lost: perhaps organise and / or support meetings, campaigns, and / or convince others to put ethical and environmental criteria above personal preferences. Whatever is sincerely attempted usually means some sacrifice; of time, energy, peace of mind, comfort, social and / or romantic contacts, health, sleep, money etc. A few have gone further and sacrificed all or most of these for the cause. We met some Battle of Britain pilots in Chapter II and Churchill's words regarding them will, if we survive, be just as applicable to pioneer conservationists such as Marsh, Corbett, Carson and Leopold, since never will so much have been owed by so many to so few.

However, whilst these people helped win some battles, achieving the ultimate victory for conservation requires more sacrifice than the total capacity of all currently concerned people and relevant NGOs can possibly make. If we are to survive the environmental crisis in general and prevent tiger extinction in particular, more individuals will have to help. The more who contribute, the less sacrifice each has to make – emphasising why media articles mocking environmentally helpful life-styles are doubly reprehensible: they are not only discrediting the practical actions taken by a precious few but also discouraging the expansion of a healthier collective consciousness and, consequently, of healthier collective actions.

Chapter IV identified personal character development as the most important single factor for our collective health since it incorporates all necessary components of understanding (personal experience and self-education), harmonising the internal and external environments, commitment to action and willingness to make sacrifices for the collective good. Hence, this chapter will suggest practical actions that enlightened characters can take to help themselves, and every other living thing on the planet, and thereby shoulder their universal responsibilities.

Given the current reality, a revolution of individual character development in sufficient numbers of people is not likely to happen in the time remaining to the tiger. While we wait, hope for, and encourage the necessary changes in hearts and minds, conservationists must concentrate on conservation work; which requires funding. Hence, money must be acquired to fund projects – to save what is most important for all. Although much has been said against an exclusive focus on money, conservationists need money – to help repair the results of an exclusive focus on money!

In another of nature's symmetrical relationships, money spent on conservation not only buys us more time (by preserving life-support systems), but also actively contributes to the growth of enlightenment and awareness, including attitudes toward money. Changing attitudes are more important than money – since sufficient people changing in this way would reduce, if not eliminate, the need for donations to any sort of charity. Money used in ways that promote health and life helps grow changes in other heads and hearts. These, in turn, reduce the exaggerated importance of money and, in turn again, positively influence the character of the developing generation.

This deeper perception is crucial for long-term health but is often forgotten in the hustle and bustle of daily life – increasingly frenetic due to the dominance of the 'money culture', and hence we travel down the wrong path ever faster. The previous chapter referred to financial executives whose greed and stupidity brought about the current financial crisis while their own 'financial packages' (a salary and 'bonus'; possibly in seven figures) remained largely unaffected. If only one of these people were to give just one of their bonuses (to fund well-planned and co-ordinated conservation initiatives), it alone could probably save the tiger from extinction for the foreseeable future.

However, in the context of this sub-section we must remember that, even if there were such an enlightened financier, such 'donations' are not a long-term solution. Such thinking would lead us back into the trap of 'money solves all problems', which is the very cause of these imbalances and, via a chain of connections, a major factor producing the tiger, and many other, crises. It is similar to hearing of extremely rich people who donate generously to charity – the broader perspective reveals they are a significant part of the system which makes charities necessary. The same pattern prevails in the arts: perhaps the most famous historical example being the Florentine bankers, the Medici, who sponsored and donated money to art and artists. Modern-day multi-million dollar donations from corporations to art galleries, artists and a variety of arts programmes seem to confirm their continuing 'generosity'. Yet money supporting the arts hides all the art stifled by the system channelling so much wealth to so few. If the distribution of wealth were more equitable, the corresponding increase in leisure time for all, particularly the staff of corporations, might well reveal many more and diversely talented people who never find sufficient time or energy away from work, either to discover it for themselves, or be discovered. From broader perspectives, are you generous if you orchestrate a system whereby thousands or millions suffer deprivation in one form or another but, from the extreme wealth which results, donate to relieve the suffering of a tiny fraction of those people? When the vast majority of one's activities provide a variety of rich fruits, while laying waste gigantic areas of the Earth and most of its inhabitants, is the donation of a juicy grape or two, sufficient compensation? Whatever one's opinions on the views presented here, few could deny that we live in a materially obsessed world with massive gulfs yawning between the super rich and the barely surviving poor. Aristotle advised, and history records that extremes of wealth and poverty provoke revolutions (and the messy, violent type).

Along with the rest of humanity, conservation organisations can only start from where they are; here and now. Running all the projects mentioned above (and others yet to come) simultaneously in all remaining tiger habitat takes money, and hence conservationists seek it. Since finances remain insufficient to fund all projects, or even one project on a completely adequate scale, conservationists are obliged to select priorities, as described in the sub-section 'Conserving People' above.

This sub-section is entitled 'Conserving Forests, Tigers and People' and its exploration of people's priorities and values, and their abilities to change them, is relevant not only to physical tigers but also to their inner tigers and we see again the interconnections between what is within and what is without, and the crucial importance to forests, tigers and people, of making inner and outer correspond and harmonise healthily.

Whilst the danger to the tiger is from people, its survival is also dependent on people. So much is true physically. The tiger is also dependent on people in spiritual ways; on the strength within people to do what is right. Hence, in the spirit of Kipling, and weaving together physical and spiritual interdependencies, we might say that the strength of the people is the forest. The strength of the forest is the tiger. So the strength of people is the tiger, and the tiger depends on its strength within people.

If people fail their tigers, the forests will fall, followed by people.

Reflections on Extinctions

Conservationists who predicted, and still predict (including this author) that both recent and current trends indicate the imminent extinction of the tiger, have met with criticism because it is still possible to point to a few extant populations (although, during 2009, the probability of extinction has been more widely recognised). Remaining populations are obviously of crucial importance but we should not let them lull us into a false sense of security. Firstly, previous predictions of imminent extinction might well have been correct but prevented their own fulfilment by stimulating reaction to the prediction. Some of the greatest efforts to avert extinction included those of group(s) who made the predictions, and none were happier when they were not fulfilled.

A glance at the graph of the tiger's 20th century in India (see above), or for that matter, the world, will show that no-one who talks of extinction is alarmist. Conservationists have long been aware of that graph, how steeply its gradient plunges toward extinction and how close it is to meeting zero population in the wild. That they have drawn attention to it is right and proper. This author does not believe anybody knows exactly why that graph has not actually touched extinction just yet. All efforts should be made to turn the graph in the other direction, thankful that we can still, perhaps, just about, do that, rather than split hairs and discuss whether conservationists were 'wrong' to have flagged imminent extinction. It would be better to realise by what a hair-breadth's margin we have kept the tiger and then do everything possible to make sure that neither extinction nor near extinction could ever again be a topic for debate; itself an indication that the situation has already gone too far in the wrong direction.

Why should we be concerned about 'near extinction'? Everybody knows that extinction means zero population – not one left alive. Surely if we have some left, any left, we can claim some sort of success? A LifeForce report: referred to "…a misguided complacency that, as long as there are some populations still in existence, the tiger is not 'actually' or 'completely' extinct. To LifeForce this is like looking at what remains of some previously magnificent classical architecture in a war zone, and focusing on a beautiful arch or façade that still precariously remains, while all around is rubble and outlines of what was once the full glory and splendour of the whole creation. Yet, some people consider that, if these few examples remain, we have 'saved the architecture'."

Counting numbers, as if tigers were only money or stock, reveals the poverty of this sort of one-dimensional thinking which only provides more information. Those who only want to count tigers might add biological refinements by suggesting the number of breeding females as the more important statistic, or perhaps the minimum number of individuals representing a viable gene pool (scientific calculations on this – indicating that no genetically viable population remains – have already, thank goodness, proved inaccurate and unreliable), but these refinements still trap us in information, in this case, statistics. "I can prove anything by statistics – except the truth" (George Canning 1770 – 1827. British statesman and politician who served as Foreign Secretary and Prime Minister). Knowledge calls for relevant connections, and wisdom cries out for us to recognise the implications of that knowledge.

More important than statistics and information is to consider what tiger populations mean about the health of nature, the connections they affect, the stability of ecosystems, their contributions to global life-support systems; and to assess what nature originally provided and the consequences of destroying that model. Then we can see the truth.

Statistics *in conjunction* with all this other knowledge have relevance. At time of writing, the next nationwide official Indian tiger census is planned for February 2011 with results published in March 2011. If the figures offer even a glimmer of hope for the future, a full understanding of the problems and their solutions can only be achieved by analysing them in conjunction with both the ecological connections just referred to, and the relevant political, socio-economic connections, such as national and State government policies, employment and commercial developments.

There are those who consider that a species may be 'saved' by storing elements of nature (in this context perhaps genes, gametes, individual specimens, captive breeding populations) and such storage is a solution to our abuse of nature. Where a particular species has, in geological time, 'just' disappeared and all other ecological factors remain much as they were, then wonderful and worthwhile re-introductions of, for examples, Arabian Oryx and Père David's deer may be achieved, using populations which had been maintained in captivity. However, where ecosystems have suffered major long-term degradation, re-introduction of stored specimens to the wild would first need the ecosystem to be returned to a functional state all bar that particular species, and humans are unable to achieve this (other than allowing nature time to recover). Hence full protection of what remains of mature ecosystems is crucial even to conservation via captivity and refrigeration.

Imagining man can make functional ecosystems at global scales is another human arrogance since, compared to nature, our techniques are toy-town. Our experiments trying to establish even relatively tiny ecosystems have failed in their objectives but did succeed in proving our ignorance and inability (those who claim this is temporary and our attempts will improve in future should remember that our collective behaviour is both threatening, if not rapidly reducing, that future). Whatever knowledge we might have, history teaches us that we are probably unaware of other essential factors. Even if we had knowledge of these factors, it is a long way from being able to re-combine them functionally and self-sufficiently in physical reality and in short order. Suggestions that humans can independently re-establish climax ecosystems reveal a sort of symmetrical stupidity equivalent to our allowing them to be destroyed in the first place.

The ancient Greeks believed that hubris is always followed by nemesis – that arrogance always precedes its own downfall, if not disaster. They recognised that this applies to human-to-human relationships and human-to-nature relationships. It is still proverbial (pride followed by a fall) but now seems only to be recognised with regard to human-to-human relationships.

From nature's perspective (the only one which ultimately has any significance) original habitats and wild animal populations have been devastated. Obviously, conservation should be concerned to protect precious remains but it should also, at the same time, aim to restore as much as possible of what Nature originally provided – just one reason why LifeForce promotes the protection of the remaining forest 'corridors' between Tiger Reserves and, if time and resources ever allow, extensive re-planting of indigenous species, while removing non-indigenous species. Merely counting National Parks, Tiger Reserves and their resident populations and leaving the assessment at that, is the same sort of commercial mentality that has produced many environmental problems, treating them as stock or goods, with no understanding of factors more fundamental than money, material or objects. The emphasis is on information, with little knowledge and no wisdom – which are themselves also products of nature, provided we exercise interest and pay attention to our lessons. The Lakota reminded us of the futility of opposing nature and Jack London of our 'finity'. Each are healthy anti-dotes to hubris, offering us opportunities to learn – and thereby avoid nemesis.

Hopefully some parts of the Guards Presentation above have reminded the reader that the forest need not be seen as merely 'supporting' a particular species. The forest and all that lives within it can be seen as an integrated and interdependent whole. In recent times we have heard that some species can cause damage to the ecosystem and need to be 'culled'. This occurs when, due to man's direct or indirect interference, numbers of some animal species have exceeded nature's balance. Perhaps the most obvious example is that of culling elephants, when their numbers result in excessive damage to trees and land. Yet, when nature, not man, controls their population numbers, the same 'destructive' capacities can be seen as constructive capacities since they can be seen as 'jungle engineers', making paths and clearings while exposing water and minerals for the use of other species, with beneficial effects for all. Since elephant populations of balanced proportions do not cover all areas at all times, smaller scale 'engineering work' is also carried out by, as another example, sloth bears, digging up roots and soil and breaking open termite mounds, exposing nutrients, minerals and insects otherwise inaccessible to other species. When we wipe out some species, cut off migration routes or otherwise confine movement of others, or drastically and artificially shrink the habitat around animals, we see how damaging to the habitat too many animals of some species can be!

Sloth bear

Interdependence does not mean that all species die if one species dies but that all are reduced from optimal health – in a sort of ecological equivalent to Donne's lines linking lives together quoted in chapter IV. Donne told us each death diminishes us – and how we have been diminished! Satellites provide a stark image of how serious a situation we face. For example, of the massive sub-continent of India, only 15% remains as nature provided it. 10% is suitable for tiger. Just 1% is fully protected in law. If we add sanctuary areas (which have some protection 'on paper' but are open to human dwellings, disturbance and dangers) the total comes to 4.5%, but even these last few areas, which should be sacred and the nuclei around which re-planting and re-growth begin, are under continuous threat from criminal and commercial activities.

John Donne and Chief Seattle could see the web of life. Our growing knowledge (seeing more connections) is now showing us how one death does not destroy, but does diminish all. The goal of knowledge should be to construct a web of knowledge that is the analogue or counterpart of the web of life, to see how each part interrelates, how all things are connected. Yet we have broken many, many strands of the web before we have even completed the crudest framework. Scientists, supposedly those most informed about, and involved with making our web of knowledge, are often, due to the commercial agendas of their employers, busy with short-term interference with the web, breaking strands and even interfering with the very structure of the web (GMO) without a complete knowledge of all the connections, and therefore, consequences of their interference. Too many stand idle, or actually contribute to the damage and never lift a finger to stop it or even to protest.

Perspectives of Science and Science in Perspective

It is hoped that the information above, previous chapters and the website will have illustrated both the importance of tiger conservation and something of what LifeForce is trying to do to help with that situation in particular and the environmental crisis in general. Most of its work and that of many other environmental NGOs is well-informed common sense.

Even where science is a valid method of investigation to support conservation initiatives, common sense and / or broader perceptions might still be able to add something of value, or set the science in context. As mentioned in Chapter II, scientific research on the tiger (and the environment in general) has only recently begun. Yet some assume that we are finding now, what we might have found had studies begun earlier. In contrast, it is more likely that we are studying nature in a degraded, diseased and probably dying state. One example given in Chapter II was the enormous reduction in tiger population densities over a couple of centuries, which, in the context of geological time, are extremely brief periods. Another example was provided by a mature Indian lady who remarked to this author that animals, including cheetal and sambhar deer, did not seem to have the same sparkle in their eyes, sheen on their coats or general vitality that she had seen in them years before.

All human and animal bodies on the planet since the 1940's contain strontium 90 (due to nuclear explosions), the pesticide DDT and numerous other man-made contaminants. As such elements and chemical compounds increase in our bodies, healthy elements and chemical compounds decrease. Although the following list refers to plants consumed by humans, it obviously implies similar degradation to all plants – which are the basis of all ecosystems and hence affect herbivores, carnivores and omnivores: 'Since 1940 the iron in spinach has dropped

60%, broccoli has lost 75% of its calcium, carrots have lost 75% of their magnesium, watercress has lost 93% of its copper – the list goes on. Selenium, potassium, phosphorus, iodine, molybdenum, sodium, chromium, manganese – over 20 trace minerals have been analysed and the quantity of all of them has been diminishing in a wide variety of fruit and vegetables. It is these minerals that help keep plants healthy and that are essential constituents of our bones, teeth, muscle, soft tissue, blood and nerve cells; minerals that are involved in almost all the body's metabolic processes.' (B10 reprinted by kind permission of Alastair Sawday Publishing Co.) These are some of the nutrients, referred to above in the LifeForce Presentation, which get washed away in eroded topsoil to the oceans where they are irrecoverable to us.

To this depressing list we could add effects of global warming and excess UV reaching the Earth through a depleted ozone layer. More damage and pollution could be cited but the reader can see the point – we are studying a seriously imbalanced, damaged, diseased and impoverished nature. A critic might respond that nature in front of us is all we have to study, regardless of its condition. Whilst this is true, the decline is sufficiently rapid that statistics such as those quoted above could provide diagnostics and an index by which to measure the decline or, hopefully, if we all come to our senses in time, an improvement, in the health of the planet. It is suggested that it would be better, and lead to more effective help and health, if conservationists and scientists adopted a 'bigger picture' or broader perspective geographically, temporally and therefore logistically. Somehow, the same narrow and short-term perspective that has brought about much of the environmental crisis can be seen in studies intended to understand, halt and / or reverse the damage caused by such views. This is partly due to the vast amount of information we have amassed, making narrowly focussed specialisation the only hope of becoming fully conversant with, or even competent in, ever-reducing sub-divided disciplines, and producing specialists who 'know more and more about less and less'. (B23) Meanwhile, all that supports all is being poisoned and degraded.

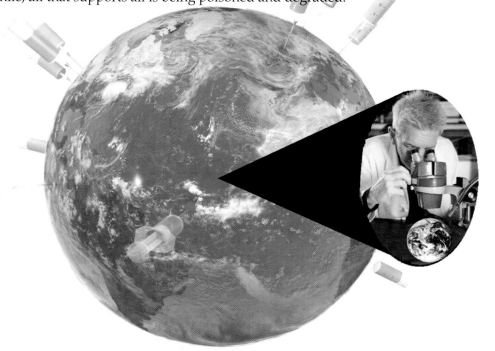

In the glass of nature's microscope, Man is minute yet deadly; miniature yet monstrous.

The Larger LifeForce

For the tigers' survival (if not our own) it is now essential for us to take a broader perspective, to recognise and act in accordance with nature's interconnections, ensuring our conservation strategies incorporate those interconnections – that our strategy corresponds to nature's. To continue with the analogy used above, our 'web of action' should correspond to our 'web of knowledge' and both should correspond to nature's web. This is the pattern that LifeForce's conservation activities (within their severe limitations) attempt to follow. They try to correspond to some of nature's most basic lessons – protecting and conserving the forest, then the tiger, and then the people, each being dependent on the preceding category. If, as in previous examples, these form interdependent cycles, why has this sequence been specified? Our question is answered in time. Both religion and science tell us that forests and animals preceded man, and so time determines the sequence, and priorities. It might be claimed that people are not dependent on the tiger but this is to fail to see connections, the seal of health the tiger gives the forest, and our dependence on healthy forests. As was asked in the Forest Guards' presentation above, who has the knowledge to say, 'Let us kill off this or that species and this will be the effect?' Nor need all essential connections be physical in nature. Claims of our independence from any particular species or aspect of nature are made from severely blinkered perspectives which only understand the simplest, crudest, most immediate connections: the hammer on the nail; not the building of the ark.

As we considered in the previous chapter, we are part of the truth, part of the whole; adding to it as it grows with time, our choices making some connections and not others. The sum total of those choices and the arrangement of connections they make represent universal health or otherwise. However, our knowledge of them is always fragmentary and we may not be able to trace the particular route through the jungle of connections that link the tiger's demise to ours. It may be that some connections have yet to be made, being dependent on choices we have yet to make and actions we have yet to take. Nonetheless, inadequate knowledge does not mean we should ignore fundamental principles, if anything, it means we should follow the principles more closely, and hence, be urgently protecting as much of our original life-support systems as possible. By doing so, we may learn enough to eventually identify some of those as yet unknown connections, and how our choices avoided some and made others. If we lift our heavy lids, exercise some interest in lives beyond our own, and face our responsibilities, we might yet review our choices from a future, healthier and happier world, and find our blood running cold to consider the hair's breadth by which we avoided extinction – the tiger's and our own.

The current environmental situation is irrefutable proof that we cannot rely on governments, commerce or media to safeguard our life-support systems, all of which continue to support groups of humans dabbling with and damaging nature – even though it is more complex and powerful than humans can fully comprehend, and essential to our survival. It is so far beyond our full comprehension, it indicates the very opposite of intelligence to imagine we have any mastery over it at all. Yet such stupidity is most often suggested and / or recommended by those deemed most intelligent. Study should teach us humility, since each part of nature we study reveals more that is unknown, and what is discovered often reveals intricacies far beyond our own abilities to construct. In due humility, we may study and copy nature, but not interfere with, poison or otherwise abuse it. However, by focussing on our discoveries, egos, publications, fame, money and power, we have chosen to learn arrogance, and practise interference instead.

In addition to the problems we know about, what other fearful scenarios are we creating which nature has not yet revealed? An illustration of why harmonising with nature as a whole is essential for our survival, is taken from LifeForce Report 2005 – 2006: '…within the last few decades we have learned that the oxygen content of the air is maintained by photosynthetic algae and bacteria living in the world's oceans. Industry still uses the oceans as a dumping ground for the worst types of toxic man-made industrial waste and filth. It also hides rusting oil-rigs, innumerable wrecks and weapons, as well as thousands of tons of chemical weapons (mostly mustard gas) from WWI (these chemicals have also been discarded among landscapes, waterways and lakes in Europe). The oceans are so vast, some might have hoped there was no limit to the amount of poison and rubbish we could throw into them. However, a recently completed five-year American study of the world's oceans has shown that even in the Pacific mid-ocean, man-made chemical pollutants are present and accumulating in the bodies of whales, at the apex of aquatic ecosystems. In addition to pollution, increasing carbon dioxide in the atmosphere means that more carbon dioxide is dissolving into the oceans, causing them to increasingly acidify.

At what level of toxins, or carbon dioxide, will the oxygen-maintaining organisms start to die? Answer: nobody knows – but dumping at sea and acidification continues.

So when we all start finding difficulty breathing (and that includes tigers), pollution will eclipse global warming as the most dangerous environmental factor – frightening scenarios but, sadly, real possibilities.' If, mercifully, our oxygen supply is not reduced, marine life in general is likely to be adversely affected by acidification of the oceans. Researchers at the Woods Hole Oceanographic Institution in Massachusetts, U.S.A. have, in June 2009, warned of the adverse effects of acidification on many marine organisms. A collapsed, or drastically reduced, fishing industry is a possibility. Millions of job losses globally would follow. This generates further stresses on remaining ecosystems to supply the short-fall in food – and occupations; such that people can afford to buy what food is available. Hence, any attempt to address environmental problems must be all embracing; complete; holistic. To effectively and fully address any particular environmental problem, be it global warming or tiger extinction, we need to be assessing every aspect of the web and the effects of our life-styles on it since all aspects interconnect. Trying to conserve a particular species without addressing socio-economics and other aspects of the environmental crisis is of limited value or a waste of time.

Environmentalists or 'greens' may be described as people who think the environment is the most important issue of our times. Properly educated people know the environment is the most important issue of our times. Those who think otherwise reveal ignorance. Those who claim otherwise reveal vested short-term interests and wilful blindness. If such people hold senior positions of political and / or corporate responsibility their ignorance and / or wilful blindness becomes dangerous to their communities and themselves.

However, in a few specifics and particulars, the environment has begun to feature in public awareness and, in 2005, global warming began to receive some long, long overdue attention by governments, business and media. However, currently weak and limited strategies lead to absurdities such as it being right and healthy for governments to urge citizens to switch off unused electrical appliances, while defeating their own objectives by allowing such projects as, for example, the Geneva hadron collider. The electric bill for this project was reported as £14 million. That's just the electric bill, for one project, and it's also a sizeable contribution to global warming. £14 million could make a decisive contribution to saving the tiger and its habitat. Just two points in the context of this book, and no doubt the reader has other useful suggestions as to what uses this money could be put. Even if the Geneva hadron collider project were 'successful', it brings no immediate benefits to the communities paying for it while we all ride on an increasingly endangered 'spaceship Earth'. Governments' failure to construct a consistent, coherent and holistic strategy means that we still exhibit a collective stupidity, albeit an 'intelligent stupidity'.

On the 23rd March 2009 BBC news in England reported on a few suggestions to combat global warming. The only one which appeared to have had any practical trial was a scientific attempt to increase the population of oceanic algae (which absorb carbon) by artificially boosting the availability of iron (the natural concentration of which limits algal population growth). A reported six tonnes of iron particles were pumped into the ocean. The initial increased population of algae was stopped by a corresponding increase in population of an insect-like predator feeding on the algae. If the experiment had 'worked', to be effective globally, iron would need to be deposited in greater quantities over larger areas. The problem being tackled (global warming) is due to a rapid increase of one substance having multiple and adverse effects. So, trying to learn from the problem we are trying to solve; could artificially introducing another substance in massive quantities also, just possibly, trigger other undesirable effects? We have an unmistakable lesson in this very context: As referred to in the previous chapter, modern cleaning products, particularly detergents, find their way via household sinks and drains to ponds, streams and rivers. Detergents represent abundant supplies of nutrients (mainly phosphates) which, in natural concentrations, are usually limited. The resulting algal blooms in the upper regions of water cut off light to other photosynthetic organisms below them. Compounds produced by some algae, due to the sheer number in the bloom, may also become toxic to the aquatic ecosystem. Either due to toxins or lack of light, the aquatic plants die off, followed by the ecosystem dependent on them, leaving ponds, streams and rivers stagnant. Could this be a warning in microcosm? Could arbitrarily messing around with concentrations of nutrients in the oceans be risking serious imbalances, which would have cascade effects through chains of connections? Surely it should be scientists who are most aware of such possibilities and most cautious about creating similar problems on greater scales? Regardless of context and connections, the same immediate, short-term approach is applied, one-step cause and effect, the hammer on the nail, and is often recommended by the very people most familiar with nature's unified and interacting network.

As the reader will know, there are still disputes over global warming. Let us be clear however: There is no dispute that the 20th century saw a dramatic increase in carbon dioxide concentrations: There is little or no dispute that this is due, in part, to burning carbon based fuels: There is no dispute that carbon dioxide is one of a number of 'greenhouse' gases. So what is in dispute? The dispute is over how much, or the degree to which, human activity has contributed to global warming. That there is any measurable amount means, to this author at least, that there are grounds for reversing our contribution. Why risk doing otherwise? If our activities make crucially dangerous contributions we will have made a wise decision and learned something in the process. If our contributions are negligible and nature will override all our efforts one way or another, then all human activity is irrelevant. The only sensible, fail-safe action is to treat our activities as significant.

We then arrive at all the problems associated with the solutions proposed so far:

- Reducing carbon dioxide emissions involves great problems for both producers and consumers. Even if these were solved, the nations are unable to agree how much of the solution each should be responsible for, either practically or financially.
- Levying a carbon tax involves problems for individuals and industry financially and for governments politically
- The current inadequacies of technology to capture carbon from industrial emissions.
- Carbon credits or permits which may be sold amongst businesses and nations to limit carbon dioxide emissions to permitted levels. There are numerous problems with this new market, not least that it is subject to all the same scams, corruptions and iniquities as any other market.
- Carbon neutrality or carbon-offsetting has been subject to criticisms concerning the validity, security of the off-setting procedures and whether they can produce results in the short-term (which is essential if they are to be of any use).
- The current inadequacies of scale of alternative clean, renewable energies.
- The undesirability of clear-cutting forests to plant bio-fuel crops
- The undesirability of nuclear energy as an alternative

A possible solution which not only renders all these problems irrelevant but also brings other significant benefits is 'biochar', as endorsed by the environmental scientist James Lovelock. Agricultural waste can be burned at very low levels of oxygen to produce non-biodegradable charcoal which can be ploughed into, or buried in, soil. A little carbon is released as carbon dioxide during the combustion but the majority of carbon is trapped in the charcoal. This method would remove significant quantities of carbon dioxide from the atmosphere and do so rapidly. Apparently a similar procedure was used in ancient South America and biochar was also studied soon after the end of WWII but forgotten until recently. Biochar is simple, relatively cheap, brings many benefits to the soil, attracts worms and traps another dangerous greenhouse gas, nitrous oxide. Carbon can be trapped from both agricultural and food waste, biomass and even some plastics. Research in Germany, Australia and the U.S.A. looks promising in terms of its potential for benefits and its widely distributed application.

Whatever alternatives ultimately prevail, the remaining fossil fuels are going to be used, so they may as well be used in conjunction with an effective, carbon neutralising strategy. Meanwhile alternative energy sources can continue to be researched and developed. In this author's view, biochar's very best benefit is that it *restores nature's original arrangement* (putting almost pure carbon underground – where it was either benign or, for all we know, had currently unknown beneficial effects). We therefore avoid the possibilities, if not probabilities, of our own exclusively man-made 'solutions' producing the expected 'unexpected side effects' and our having to chase them as they occur in chain reaction to our purblind interference. This author believes that following human remedies which do not copy nature's original model will generate more problems than they solve.

Currently, carbon capture and storage (CCS), whereby carbon dioxide is chemically removed from power stations' emissions, is being favoured by the EU and USA. Although a CCS station has been working in Germany since 2008, it is too early to know if it answers all problems and, even if it does, there would be a long interval (11–12 years) before it can be implemented on adequate scales. If all these problems can be overcome, a problem of storage remains. Whilst energy companies have successfully been pumping liquefied carbon dioxide into already utilised and depleted gas and oil fields deep underground, it is not sure if this procedure (nor the off-shore aquifers currently being used by Norway) could cope with the enormous amounts of chemical cocktails that would be captured in future, nor whether leakage could be prevented in either short or long-term scenarios.

So, why has CCS currently been chosen by governments? This author does not know but wonders whether biochar, being cheap, easy and available on very short time scales, is not as attractive to decision makers and their contacts as CCS which must represent lucrative contracts for whichever companies win them.

Whilst global recognition of global warming is a positive development it fails to acknowledge the wider global warning. Addressing it in isolation from species extinctions, deforestation, loss of topsoil, pollution, chemical farming and GMO reveals either ignorance and / or continuing influence of commercial interests (the whole list just referred to traces back to improperly regulated big business). Even with regard to global warming, the mass media have taken a selection of scientific evidence by identifying it almost entirely with urban carbon dioxide emissions, yet deforestation (including forests which recently held tigers) makes a massive and significant contribution to global warming (both as 'carbon sinks' removed and because ultimately the wood is burned). Hence, for a full appreciation of our situation, we must educate ourselves and not let media sound bytes of non-nutritional 'food' dull our faculties.

The environmental crisis is the most dangerous situation in recorded history. Before addressing political systems that have allowed such a crisis to develop, we should all, for example, be using environmentally-friendly cleaning materials, eating organic food, composting, re-cycling and buying re-cycled products, saving energy and natural resources, banking and investing ethically and thereby meeting some of our personal responsibilities while setting examples for others, demonstrating our respect and care for nature, including our tigers. This introduces the LifeForce strategy as described on its website (www.lifeforceindia.com):

'The crisis facing the tiger and its ecosystem is but one example of endangered species and numerous other threats to our life-support system…LifeForce holds the view that saving species from extinction is valid if, and only if, action is being taken to address the system that produces all of these problems i.e. there is little point saving a leaf on the top-most branch of a tree whilst the trunk is being sawn through.'

Hence, via newsletters, Internet and public presentations LifeForce recommends practical actions by which individuals can make constructive contributions to the global environmental situation. Solutions to our problems as individuals, communities, nations and a planet, involve a re-evaluation of our personal and collective priorities and the current commercial, socio-economic and political systems.

The world reflects these personal, and hence collective, priorities and is telling us that we need to change them rapidly. The more we learn of nature, the more interconnections are seen and we realise we are studying one enormous and complex unity – this view is in agreement with technical and scientific perspectives and remains valid whatever your reaction might be to the more mystical and mysterious aspects of mirrors reflected on in Chapter IV. Hence, to correct the problems, our strategy should exhibit the same interconnections as those exhibited by nature.

If we had to treat a very sick person with a variety of terminal problems there would be little point in making Herculean efforts to save one organ, or cure one disease, whilst other organs or tissues were fatally poisoned or diseased. The same principle applies to nature and there is no point saving a species or reversing global warming whilst other essential elements of the life-support system are being reduced to conditions that are lethal for all.

The Final Chapter

This final chapter attempts to put together the conservation of forests, tigers and people, as well as the science, mirrors, morals, yin, yang and 'unanswered questions' of the previous chapters. However, its contents remain valid from any single perspective whether that may be scientific as in chapter II or more mystical as in chapter IV or balanced between them, like the chapter between them or, just as all fall between I and V, so all falls between personal experience and taking action to meet one's responsibilities, the perspectives of those chapters respectively.

Socio-economics, corporations, globalisation, political policy etc. and their associated problems are familiar terms of description. Yet, let us not deceive ourselves with jargon and labels. The currently dominant forces behind the window dressing and image-creation of all these categories are self, greed and a selection of other vices. The tiger's imminent disappearance is a directly proportionate index of how powerful these vices are and a serious symptom of our terminal illness. Of course, those wielding power now and for the last forty or more years bear most responsibility but none of us can claim innocence. As for the next forty or more years, those in corporate, commercial and political power will still bear the greatest responsibility for influencing our collective futures but it is now, more than ever before, our urgent responsibility to influence them and we start to do so by adjusting our priorities, our life-styles, our consumer spending and by developing our characters, eliminating vice and self as far as we can. Bigger and better effects grow from these seeds. Conversely, nothing will grow if no seed is planted.

"I didn't do anything to help because I could see that nobody else was doing anything."

"Do you know why they were not doing anything?"

"No."

"They could see that nobody else was doing anything."

Some people claim that they cannot live in an environmentally-friendly way since, for example, they need or want to use a car. On this basis alone, they make no further effort or investigation of their whole life-style and carry on damaging the earth in multiple and diverse ways. If we take their point as sincere and not just an excuse to do nothing, how can it be answered? To get from where we are, to where we should be, will not be an overnight journey. It will be made up of many people taking small steps; making small changes – banking ethically, eating organically etc. If enough individuals adopt the suggestions outlined below, these actions will produce sufficient change (not only practically but in the consciousnesses of other people) such that groups of like-minded consumers form new commercial demographics. In turn, other aspects of society not immediately affected by individual action and purchasing patterns, such as transport and energy production, will be influenced and affected by these environmentally-conscious groups. Groups adopting the new purchasing options and growing in number and size make manufacturers adapt to the emerging markets. In the meantime, our sincerely concerned car owner might buy a hybrid (LPG), or electric car, or use their car less, or organise a car-sharing scheme, or make themselves 'carbon neutral' by financially supporting projects which absorb the amount of carbon their life-style, including their car, emits.

The cynic says that in the face of such enormous problems, the suggestions do not represent much to do. This attitude argues against itself since, if it's not much to do, why not do it? In the absence of other alternatives and the rapidity of environmental and social damage, something is better than nothing. The cynic says any such 'something' or personal changes must be negligible from a global perspective but the concept of 'tipping points' referred to in the previous chapter defeats this objection.

Moreover, individuals' actions can address both causes and effects of the current dangerously imbalanced socio-economic system of the world. For example, the LifeForce programmes providing help to tribal people resident in and around Tiger Reserves represents action addressing some *effects* of the imbalanced socio-economic system of the world. What can be done about the *causes*, the illegal and legalised exploitation of natural resources (not restricted to tiger range countries) by corporations and corrupt politicians manipulating or ignoring protective laws for short-term financial gain? (Politicians may also be openly involved when, for instance, protected areas are 'denotified' – to legally allow their exploitation).

To find causes we must do some tracking, not of the tiger, but of money, from jungle to city street and back again. The forests represent rich pickings in terms of timber and plant products and resources such as coal, metals, uranium, other elements and compounds in their soil, which are manufactured into furniture, fuels, ingredients for cosmetics, components of mobile telephones etc. which sell to consumers, mostly hundreds, if not thousands of miles away. Hence individuals can adjust their consumer spending to retard environmentally harmful commerce while promoting environmentally helpful, sustainable, commerce – and hence beneficially influence socio-economic causes. Via its own spending and investments and via public presentations and publications encouraging others to adopt these practices, LifeForce also helps to address causes as well as effects.

While individual consumers educating themselves and taking active responsibility for their lifestyles can exert an *influence*; consumers acting collectively can *control it completely*: 'No sale' means, directly and immediately: no cutting: no clearing: no poaching: no killing.

In Dickens' 'Christmas Carol', Marley's troubled ghost is chain-bound due to his exclusive pursuit of material profit during his life on Earth. When Scrooge tries to comfort Marley's ghost by saying he had been a good businessman, it heatedly retorts "Mankind was my business! The common welfare was my business…" Due to too few learning Marley's and Scrooge's lessons, not only is mankind our business, but now, all other forms of life. Marley and Scrooge's modern day rich and powerful counterparts (whether corporations or individuals) are unlikely to voluntarily change the status quo – but consumers can do it for them.

Even allowing for creating trends toward ethical and environmentally-friendly commerce, the welfare, and now the repair, of mankind would still seem a formidable task and far beyond any one individual. Yet, in principle and practice, the old saying: 'If every man would mend a man, then all mankind were mended' (anon.) holds a profound truth. In keeping with other principles and analogies referred to above, it has 'inner' and 'outer' meanings. For some, mending the inner man is a pre-requisite to mending another man, but for others, the process works in reverse order. Either way, let's get mending!

You may choose to mend a tribal man by supporting NGOs or, as in chapter IV, by getting an elderly neighbour's groceries or by simply spending time with a lonely soul (elderly people are often in this category. There is a saying that runs something like 'to an elderly person, the smile of a young person is like sunshine on a cloudy day'). In the context of informing, and influencing, others regarding a healthy environment, we might say that 'if every man would make a man aware, then all mankind were made aware'. Awareness of the problems, and their solutions, prompt actions.

"Never doubt that a small group of committed citizens can change the world –
indeed it is the only thing that ever has."
(Margaret Mead 1901 – 1978 American anthropologist)

"We cannot say that the goal is close but we can say that the next step is immediate."
(M. Palmer Hall 1901 – 1990 Author, and Founder of The Philosophical Research Society inc.)

"How wonderful it is that nobody need wait a single moment before starting
to improve the world."
(Anne Frank, a German Jewish girl who kept a diary for two years while hiding with her family in Nazi-occupied Amsterdam during WWII, before they were betrayed and sent to concentration camps, where Anne died, aged 16. Her diary reveals an amazingly perceptive girl with insights far beyond her years)

The sections below suggest a number of ways in which our life-styles can be adjusted. The herein oft-repeated recommendation to spend money selectively features among them as a very powerful way in which we can create healthy change. It is also a way in which one individual can mend *many* men's lives. This is because it reaches all the way from natural resources to boardrooms and all in between; and joins money to morality. The benefits include an immediately healthier natural world and individual people; the control of big business and criminal activities; and rendering corrupt and / or incompetent government departments irrelevant. We automatically practise self-development at the same time. Our part in all these healthy and far-reaching developments is simply to inform ourselves and spend accordingly. In this final chapter, where the emphasis is on action, we must assess our personal, practical contributions.

The poet Wordsworth saw very clearly that we must be in touch with physical nature for our spiritual progression and that we had lost the latter in exchange for physical items of man-made commerce. He expressed this in his sonnet 'The World is Too Much With Us' where he says that 'Getting and spending, we lay waste our powers'. We see the truth of this spiritually but, now that commerce has become so dominant, it is by exercising our 'getting and spending powers' that we may recover our other powers. In the first chapter we were tempted to cast off the cares and worries of civilisation but most of us find we are bound by 'base laws of servitude', chained by circumstance to what Durant called 'the mart and strife of life'. Material, mechanical and mundane aspects of life often frustrate our spirits and, if they are allowed to become dominant, contribute to us living 'lives of quiet desperation' (Thoreau). We need to recharge our spiritual powers as often as possible with music, the arts in general, science, fresh air, sunshine and the beauties of nature in terms of scenery, plants and animals. To maintain all of these, but most importantly nature, we must inform ourselves and then 'get and spend' with forethought and compassion, common sense and responsibility. We must also ensure we get and spend some time in which we do not get and spend. We have to find that middle path, the balance.

Walking in the woods, reading, or listening to music are examples of leisure activities which can regenerate our spiritual powers. However, since society has been saturated with advertising and marketing (vastly increased by radio and television unknown to Wordsworth) 'getting and spending', shopping itself, has become (according to radio and television following corporate agendas) a 'leisure activity'. In days gone by, we went shopping when we needed something. Even for genuine leisure activities such as those just given, advertising attempts to persuade us that we need 'branded' or 'designer' clothes, special shoes and equipment to walk in the woods; the latest 'best seller' to read; or 'ipods' and 'phones and cameras…

Wordsworth lived in England's idyllically quiet and beautiful Lake District, 'far from the madding crowd's ignoble strife' (from Gray's 'Elegy'). His home, Dove Cottage, is now a museum and, some years ago, contained a letter written by Wordsworth complaining about the noise a horse and cart made on the lane outside his window. It passed by once every two weeks. For a moment we cannot help an amused smile. Yet, to what have we become accustomed? What have we forsaken? Think of a life of such tranquillity that a fortnightly horse and cart was a damnable nuisance and needed addressing. Despite the enormous contrast with densely packed human 'settlements' (which could be as noisy in Wordsworth's day as today) we can at least imagine a life of only seeing and hearing nature's sights and sounds; and being at a loss to know why any offensively noisy man-made contraption would ever be made, or allowed to multiply. We are reminded of our visit to Corbett's place and his life in the forests before the motor car and television reached them. However, staying with Wordsworth, we might also sign his letter of protest – and during the next dozen or so days (before the cart passed by again) see further and sooner than most, and find a poem or two within us. In the Lake District today horse and carts have been replaced not only with cars but also ear-splitting jet fighters roaring past on low-level training flights, and much more frequently than once a fortnight. Wordsworth's letter today would probably be more hysterical than lyrical.

With regard to balancing the modern and natural worlds, a personal regret has relevance here not only in the event itself but also in what it represents (and relating it might also provide the author with a little therapy!): sometime during 1996, while looking for somewhere suitable for a LifeForce base in India, I and my colleagues were in an old, battered 4WD exploring some outlying district of, I think, Uttar Pradesh. At that time the emphasis was on getting established; trying to survive physically and financially for long enough to make a serious attempt at the work. Familiarity and confidence with, awareness and command of situations were yet to be acquired. My mentality and senses were on 'receive and scan' and made no allowance for prescience or being proactive.

On the track through the countryside ahead were three young ladies riding their bicycles, each holding, and shaded by a pretty parasol. Neat, spotlessly clean and dressed beautifully in bright colours shining vividly in the sun, their long saris and sashes fluttered gently in the breeze of their motion. As they moved quietly and cleanly through the colours of the countryside, they painted one of the prettiest pictures I have ever seen; made of sunshine; cycling in sunshine; a masterpiece of living motion, in a gallery as beautiful as the exhibits.

Today I would be aware of the dust cloud we were generating and would tell the driver to stop, find an alternative route or wait. To my everlasting disgrace, we drove on and, as we passed, covered them in a cloud of dust, so much so that they had to stop, dismount and shield themselves, squinting and bowing their heads. Compounding our embarrassment was their inoffensive and gentle acceptance of our outrageously crude and gross behaviour. Here was I, some pampered Westerner creating noise and filth amidst nature's beauties, too dim-witted to see a few seconds ahead, not only to prevent this perversity but also to compliment the locals, show some good will and respect. Instead I had allowed this clanking, droning piece of metal to spew carcinogenic fumes and heaven knows what else into the paradise around me and cover three delicate and beautiful butterflies with dust and dirt. I had arrived, and already spoiled something better than myself. Here was I, trying to repair something of all that we have sullied and degraded, off to a great start, damaging more. Ready to challenge the whole imbalanced, industrialised, material world, I couldn't even behave properly myself. The incident, although trivial by global scales, could be seen as a symbol of far greater injustices, some of which may have prompted the following lines. Whether or not penned with events of greater moment in mind, and whether or not the incident just related could be seen as symbolic or not, the following lines capture, in any circumstances (but particularly so in our current environmental situation), the finality of merciless time when we look back to see where we failed to act as we should have done…

> The Moving Finger writes; and, having writ,
> Moves on: nor all your piety nor wit
> Shall lure it back to cancel half a line,
> Nor all your tears wash out a word of it
>
> (Ruba'iyat of Omar Khayyam)

For what little it is worth, I have ever since been aware, when driving, of any dust clouds I am generating and do my best to avoid 'showering' any pedestrians or cyclists. Whenever practical, I offer them lifts. We are all faced with how to balance the modern world's conveniences (which have become necessities for dealing with the modern world) and how to protect the natural world. My only salve is that I was not pursuing or using the 4WD as an end in itself, or as part of scheme to abuse nature. I was using it to see how quickly it could be dispensed with and in order to (eventually!) protect the natural environment, including cyclists. As I write, I recall that some years later LifeForce supported activists cycling through Pachmarhi with their environmental message boards (I was not trying to atone for the incident with the three cyclists and at that time was not even conscious of it, so, hopefully, the ledgers of cosmic accounting were balanced to some degree at least!)

Local Pachmarhi residents voluntarily protest at the abuse of nature locally and globally

To regenerate our powers, and our earth, we must ensure our bodies receive the healthiest and most natural inputs. We have considered some industrialised adulteration of agriculture and hence, our food, the extent of which is so vast whole books have been written about it, listing all the health problems known to be associated with processed food and the various additives it contains. Individuals may not only suffer impaired physical health but also mental health (the most well-known example is, perhaps, hyper-activity in children caused by food additives. Worse still, in regions of the world where people are too poor to mount effective opposition, individuals have died as a result of inhaling concentrated chemicals when passing fields being doused with pesticides and other chemicals). Individuals' health problems are but the beginning of a deeper malaise for society. Whether it is in their roles in the trades or professions, as family members or citizens, people suffering any degree of ill-health are not able to function as well as they might. Ecologically and economically, all things are connected so, as efficiency declines, mistakes occur and all have impacts on other connections, on other people. Their competence may also be impaired, either for the same reasons and / or perhaps due to polluted air and / or water in their areas. All aspects of health and human activity are adversely affected. So, the butcher or the baker etc., may think themselves too busy to be worried about politics, or big business, or the tiger and the environment, but due to nature's interconnections, that means they are also too busy to be worried about their own or their family's health and prosperity – the very reasons they are so busy. In a myriad minor ways that all add up to major trends, nature's connections mean that society starts to suffer the consequences of inappropriate interference with our food (or genetics, or ecosystems, or any aspect of nature) including those making short-term profits from organising the interference. Just as there are multiple, adverse manifestations of one fundamental error (abusing nature) so there are multiple beneficial manifestations of observing only one law (respecting nature) and the sooner we recognise and obey it, the healthier for all.

By modelling itself on nature, economics also becomes 'healthier' since it will begin to reflect real products, real labour and real values, which have consequently beneficial effects throughout society, ecologically and economically. When money relates to real products it reveals the true cost and dangers of 'imaginary money' (please see sub-section below 'The Cost of Money').

If we do not return to organic agriculture, we not only continue to ingest poisons but so also do the forests, which gradually absorb poisons from neighbouring chemically cultivated and industrialised land. These, along with pollutants in the air and water, ultimately find their way into the bodies of cheetal, sambhar and tigers.

In addition to eating organic food, other actions are suggested below. Do not be discouraged by the relative scales of your actions. Initially and globally, the change is small but that is how all change begins and, because all things are connected, you cannot help but influence others, physically, mentally and spiritually. Major trends start with individuals. Insofar as the changes are healthy, the influences will be healthy. Time and patience will do the rest. To convince yourself of the validity of this strategy, consider the situation from the opposite perspective: it is undeniable that long-term healthy global change must mean that nations are changing healthily (nations can change under a Hitler or a Stalin but they are not healthy and are therefore temporary). For nations to change, communities must change. For communities to change, families must change. For families to change, people must change. For people to change, we, as individuals, must change. You can take action for your tigers and your children. You can change your life-style and hence, your world. You are not helpless and need not be a victim. No one individual can cure 100% of the problems but they can work toward curing 100% of their contribution to them.

Banks and financial institutions have invested in ecologically disastrous or unethical, but profit-making schemes. Morally questionable regimes with appalling human rights records have also found funding partners in banks and investment companies. Where do these businesses get the funds from? Us (!), when we bank with unethical banks. We might make a donation to a tiger conservation charity but, as we saw in chapter IV, if we bank unethically, the bulk of our money is helping fund their extinction.

Unless you ensure otherwise, your money, in terms of what you purchase or how you invest it, can be used by big business to fund some of the most damaging and dangerous activities possible. Even when governments do their duty, they work slowly – too slowly compared to the rapidity of damage and destruction. We know that the only criterion by which multinationals operate is profit. Hence, by selective spending, we can ensure that only ethical, environmentally-friendly activities and products produce profits, and this produces change in the world and, better still, change that is rapid, without time-consuming discussion or debate as waters rise around us. It also has another powerful and important effect: it brings change regardless of the character of corporate decision makers. However enlightened or ignorant, however generous or greedy, they

Cheetal or spotted deer

Sambhar

will and must, by the very reason the business exists, respond to decreasing profits on unethical and environmentally-harmful products and activities. Whilst acquisition of vast profits is often equated with power, it actually makes those who seek them vulnerable and weak since, recognising no other dimension or principle, they pursue maximum profits like programmed automata, and can therefore be controlled by controlling those profits. In keeping with the themes of this book, these beneficial changes can only begin when the reader makes suitable choices and takes appropriate personal action. Then nature will ensure, by ways and means as yet undreamed of, that other larger scale effects and changes take place. Moreover, controlling greed and carelessness toward others and the environment in this way automatically improves one's own conduct and character, simultaneously achieving both the major recommendations of this book – healthier internal and external environments.

Using ethical and environmentally-friendly criteria to determine where you shop and what you buy grows those companies and corporations that make ethical and environmentally-friendly products, producing beneficial effects for all (including the businessmen). Situations have become so polarised that each of us has, by virtue of our consumer practices, become either part of the solution or part of the problem. A few brief illustrations of consumer power will suffice, starting with two positive and powerful examples: It was consumers who brought about a rapid change with regard to CFCs in aerosols long before the Montreal Protocol (banning them) became law. The full story behind the public exposure of CFC damage to the ozone layer involves underhand behaviour to gain industrial advantage but is cited here only to illustrate consumer power. Another example is the Brent Spa oil rig which was owned and operated by Shell. When it came to the end of its useful life Shell was going to dump it in the ocean. Greenpeace protested and insisted Shell clean up their mess. Ecologically speaking, it is debatable as to whether transferring it from ocean to land was the best option. However, again, this example is to illustrate consumer power. Shell ignored the Greenpeace objections and forcibly removed its protesters from the rig. News coverage included a response from a representative of government confirming that they would also ignore Greenpeace (regardless that Greenpeace represented the views of thousands of people, in a 'democratic' society). As a last resort, Greenpeace organised a boycott of Shell petrol stations. It is hard to know what percentage of the petrol-buying public responded (5-15 %?) Brent Spa was out of the ocean within a week of the boycott beginning.

Commerce drives species toward extinction not only directly, by damaging habitat, but also by commercial pressure; the species of wheat and rice which sell in the greatest quantities are cultivated by corporations to the exclusion of other species. Hence other species amongst nature's great variety (and therefore ecological stability) are becoming extinct. 'Navdanya' is a society based in Delhi, India which acts as a seed-bank, storing as many of India's disappearing seeds as possible. If a corporation could claim 'ownership' of the best-selling species, they would become all the more valuable to that corporation. So, recent attempts by big business to claim 'ownership' of basmati rice were successfully fought (for now at least) in India by Navdanya. Organic food is also cultivated by Navdanya and some of it sold in its 'slow-food' café in Delhi. LifeForce is a lifetime member of Navdanya and has also (independently) provided training in organic agriculture for Indian farmers in Madhya Pradesh.

Illegally cut timber (including tiger habitat) can still, at time of writing, be bought legally in Europe due to inefficient EU trading laws. Until and unless the law is revised, only selective consumer spending can influence which sells and which does not. On a positive note, the new coalition government in the U.K. has finally outlawed the trade in tropical wood – worth £700 million per year (Sunday Times Newspaper 04/07/10). The article reported that the previous government under Blair had used illegally felled wood for Cabinet Office room refurbishments in 2002 and plywood illegally taken from Indonesia for the new headquarters of the Home Office in 2003. Standard journalese refers to a victory for environmental pressure groups...which it is...as it is also for the reader, the journalist, short-sighted loggers, importers, traders and retailers, governments which failed in their most important duty, tigers, birds and bees, butchers, bakers and candlestick makers, and every other living thing on the planet.

Legislation and the consumer trend toward 'dolphin-friendly' tuna were responsible for dolphins being allowed to escape from drift nets before being hauled in. We may be sure of this since other species, including turtles, swordfish, squid and sharks are still being caught in the nets along with thousands of fish, but left to die in the nets, before being thrown back into the ocean. Even with regard to dolphins, the legislation is only partially effective since thousands of dolphins (and, of course, other species) are still being killed by illegal drift net fishing – because their products still sell. Consumer pressure remains the decisive factor. Illegal fishing (and logging) survives because sufficient people do not use their power as consumers, buying without consideration of anything other than their own immediate wants and needs ('What I want, now').

This author has the greatest respect and admiration for those peaceful volunteers who place themselves between harmless, helpless whales and harpoons. Some individual whales are saved but the industry continues. The advances made and embodied in the IWC's restrictions on trade are gradually and increasingly being eroded by the industry through ludicrous loopholes such as the 'collection' of specimens for 'scientific' study. How can we stop the killing? Kill the trade. Once consumers purchase alternatives, the killing will stop. No debates, no laws, no commissions, no policing needed. Pseudo 'scientific' interest will disappear and whales will live in peace.

If we manage to avoid driving dolphins and whales to extinction and collapsing the fishing industry via any or all of global warming, acidification and pollution, the industry may still collapse due to the fishing methods it employs. In addition to floating drift nets many miles long already referred to with regard to dolphins, weighted nets drag the sea bed ('bottom trawling') collecting everything in their path (including 'fixed' corals, sponges and such like on underwater 'mountains'), wanted or not. Worse still, and despite dwindling fish stocks, millions of tonnes of fish rot and waste on the sea bed after becoming entangled in abandoned nets. Deep sea fishing in the North Atlantic alone is responsible for 780 miles of fishing net lost or discarded each year. These synthetic nets are made such that they will not degrade for a century or more (The Week 04/09/10 quoting Forbes.com). Fish are being killed and wasted or caught in greater numbers than can be sustained by the species' rates of reproduction (not that faster rates of reproduction would make wastage or excess catches acceptable). Scientists advise politicians by setting maximum catches allowable to prevent the extinction of particular species of fish. For example, in 2007 scientists recommended a maximum annual catch of 15 000 tonnes of Mediterranean blue fin tuna. Ministers agreed 29 000 tonnes. In addition, the global fishing industry is subsidised by governments to the extent of $14 billion per year (statistics from The Week 13/06/09). 'Tracking' the money also reveals that the traditional image of trawler captains as old, white-bearded sea salts smoking a pipe, has now been replaced by young businessmen, who arrive at the quay in plush, expensive cars. What can we do? Well, how often do you buy fish? Why not reduce that by half? If sufficient numbers of people did the same or better, the quota caught might approach a sustainable level. Could we be accused of callous indifference to those who work for the fishing industry? What work will be available when the fish are extinct? 'Sustainable' jobs rely on 'sustainable' fish. More importantly, what will be the ecological effects of fish extinctions? When men fish industrially, for maximum profit, ignorance, and then hunger, will grow too large to pass through their nets. When men fish in harmony with nature their work fills their nets with food, and the light of wisdom.

Protection of the environment and conservation of animal and plant species has prompted many earnest appeals, sensible suggestions or recommendations in books and articles, and by speakers and writers on television, radio and the Internet, including scientists and U.N. officials. Who reads/hears these appeals? The majority who do are already 'converted' but most have no official power. Those who do have such power are possibly, if not probably, responsible directly or indirectly for the problems in the first place, and are obliged to continue favouring their party or company's policies, and most likely have neither the time nor inclination to read or listen to such material. At time of writing, governments' responses to all these appeals, and the environmental crisis, are dangerously inadequate. No doubt the authors and readers of these appeals hope against hope that someone in authority will be stimulated to take effective action but, by looking around us we can see that in most cases the wisdom in these appeals passes unadopted and disappears in a sound byte, becoming 'yesterday's news', another minor ingredient in our homogenised, trivialised, highly processed spoon-fed diet, mixed for us by the media.

That same media also pretend to be the public's friend and whether environmentally or, more recently voicing outrage and condemnation over the profits and bonuses still paid to bankers (in banks still majority owned by the tax-payer) whilst we remain in the economic crisis they have caused. Yet nothing happens to rectify the situation; unlike the Indian Express newspaper, the media do not investigate why nothing happens, do not follow up the case until justice is done. While government and media remain ineffective, could the social approval or disapproval mentioned in the previous chapter be an effective influence? This is ineffective due to the 'distance' between those orchestrating the dominance of capitalism and the unity of which they are a part. They ensure they remain apart, living in distant luxury, insulated from their effects on the majority and their responsibilities toward it, and mixing only with similar sorts. Once again, the only way to reach them is via commerce; choosing how, where and why, we spend, bank or invest our money. We can adjust their life-styles for them. Consumer pressure has demonstrated its power on many occasions (and always will, while profits are put before principles) so we need to use it, and use it quickly. While money is made more important than morals we need to use it to literally 'buy us time' to readjust our collective priorities and make morals more important than money. By the same token, increasing profits for environmentally-friendly companies and / or those trading ethically will allow them to prosper and compel others to follow suit in order to survive in the same market place – regardless of any other motives they may have.

Some of the following suggestions are becoming better known than when they were written and the reader can no doubt think of more. However, our situation is too dangerous to risk missing any, so please skip those you have known and practised for years…

Action and the Reasons Why
(Ours *is* to reason why, ours *is* to do and *not* to die)
(with apologies to Tennyson (English poet 1809 – 1892))

Where relevant, website addresses are given in the following sub-section.

YOU CAN MAKE A DIFFERENCE...

We can all reduce consumption, be conservative, clean up our activities, recycle, repair where possible, eat organic food, and prevent others from using our money to abuse other people, other life forms or the environment.

Put your money into an ethical bank or investment scheme
Do not bank or invest with banks, insurance companies and big businesses that invest in ecologically disastrous schemes and / or regimes with records of human-rights abuse.

Use ethical banks and building societies (available, to the author's current knowledge, in Belgium, Germany, Netherlands, Spain, the U.K. and some States of the U.S.A.)

How do we choose our banks? Are you influenced by advertising campaigns focusing on relatively trivial issues? Or do you choose the bank that is the most convenient to you, perhaps just around the corner? As customers, we should be aware of how our money is being used and the ways in which the banks behave. Information on the social and environmental policies of a range of banks can be found on the EIRIS (Ethical Investment Research Service) website. **The Cooperative Bank** has been reported by EIRIS as '"exceptional" in terms of environmental policy and to have "advanced equal opportunities policies" and a "very clear commitment" to community involvement. The Internet bank 'Smile' is a subsidiary of the Co-op bank and also operates according to ethical and environmentally-friendly policies.

Many viable, environmentally-friendly business projects in developing countries never get started because they have no collateral and are therefore unable to get a loan to launch their projects. **Shared Interest** is a building society that, by offering investors 1% less than the base rate of interest, is able to make loans to such enterprises. From one of their newsletters:

> "Opening an account with Shared Interest is about being part of a movement for change;
> a change to the present unjust system of world trade and finance, and a change in the lives
> of those who are not being given a fair chance. Whether you invest the maximum £20 000
> or the minimum £100 you take a stand against injustice and help to change the world."

The '**Ecology Building Society**' and the '**Triodos Bank**' are other ethical banks.

Find out about the ethical policies of the companies you use
Ask questions about the kinds of companies they invest in. Do you know what your money is being used for? If not, please ask. Gradually, changes are occurring to assist ethically-minded investors e.g. from 3rd July 2000, British government legislation obliges trustees of your occupational pension scheme to respond to your enquiries as to their investment policy and their position on these issues.

Is your mortgage with an ethical mortgage lender?
Your current mortgage repayments could be contributing to immoral and / or environmentally dangerous activities.

Give some disposable income to an environmental (or tiger conservation!) charity
If you do, the money is not a donation but an investment – for your and your family's future.

Reduce the amount of chemicals you use around the home
When we close the front door we might think that pollution has been left outside but our homes harbour an enormous combination of chemicals, the effects of which on the environment and our health we are only just beginning to fully realise (see below for sources of information on this topic).

Buy environmentally-friendly washing and cleaning products

Most supermarkets now stock at least one brand – for example, Ecover products which are, to LifeForce's knowledge, as eco-friendly as it's possible to get. If your supermarket does not stock 'green' brands, ask them to. If there is a demand, they will supply it.

Go back to using traditional products for cleaning

Lemon juice, bicarbonate of soda, distilled white vinegar, and soda crystals are wonderfully effective, and do no harm to yourselves or the environment (and they're economical!).

Use organic fertiliser and environmentally-friendly products and solutions in the garden

The National Centre for Organic Gardening (Ryton Organic Gardens, Ryton-on-Dunsmore, Coventry CV8 3LG) will give you information on all aspects on chemical free gardening and you can make your own compost using waste from your kitchen.

Recycle!

Millions of tonnes of solid waste are dumped each year, most of which could be recycled. This 'waste' is being buried, burned or dumped in the oceans (none of which are desirable) whilst the Earth's resources continue to be plundered, to produce more disposable goods.

Buy recycled or recyclable products

Most supermarkets now sell kitchen towels, tissues and toilet paper made from recycled paper, and many office suppliers also stock items made from recycled materials – even letter-quality paper (please check that the re-cycling process is not using harmful bleaching agents or is otherwise environmentally counter-productive). As before, if they don't supply what you need, ask them to! Increased demand will encourage manufacturers and retailers to produce or stock more.

Separate your waste into recyclable and non-recyclable items

Find out about recycling facilities in your area, such as bottle banks. Councils should now provide all households with boxes for recycling card, newspapers, papers, plastics and tins.

Do you receive too much junk mail?

Why not just return it? Put it back in the prepaid envelope they supply and post off with a note (written on it!) objecting to the waste of paper.

Don't throw things away that someone else can use

Charities such as Oxfam take clothes and furniture, while many councils will take second-hand furniture to use for people in council accommodation. Repair shops may take old appliances which they will mend and sell on.

Visit www.freecycle.org to find your local group advertising all the items that other people want to give away, from pianos and furniture to toys and technology, the only condition being that no money changes hands for those items.

Save energy in the home

Work towards running a more energy-efficient home environment. Three quarters of the energy used in the home is for water heating and much of this is wasted. Not only does this waste your money but (due to heat being produced by burning coal, oil and gas) you are contributing to global warming and using up precious reserves of natural resources.

Insulate where possible

Lofts, walls, windows, pipes, floors and hot water tanks. Only heat rooms and water when necessary.

Fit long-life fluorescent light bulbs

They are expensive to buy but more cost effective in the long-term.

Switch off electrical appliances when they are not in use

Leaving them on 'stand-by' also consumes electricity.

Take a shower instead of a bath

It's quicker and cheaper and saves on energy. It also makes having a bath into more of a treat. Alternatively, share your bath with somebody else – being energy efficient can be fun!

Change your energy supplier

It's simple to switch to an electricity supplier offering a 'Green Tariff' that uses or produces renewable energy from sources such as wind-power, and it won't cost the Earth!

Use your power as a consumer

Companies and businesses respond to what you buy, and just as importantly, what you *don't* buy. Supermarkets are displaying fair trade, GM-free and organic foods on their shelves only in response to increased demand.

It was as a result of consumer pressure, that the majority of aerosols became CFC free long before the Montreal Protocol (designed to phase out dangerous propellants) became law in 1989. However, the replacement (HCFCs), were also found to deplete ozone, but more slowly. Subsequent use of HFC (without chlorine) and volatile hydrocarbons seems to have stopped the ozone depletion effect but these gases are many times worse than carbon dioxide in terms of global warming effects. Aerosol cans are also difficult to recycle. It is sometimes said that holes in the ozone layer have 'repaired themselves' since the amount of CFCs released into the atmosphere has decreased. However, an illegal trade in HCFCs (at least) persists and, hence, ozone depletion must surely continue? Nor could any reliable information on China's position with regard to any of these gases be found. The solution to all these problems? Don't buy aerosols at all, and only buy environmentally-friendly fridges and air-conditioning systems.

Re-use or re-cycle plastic bags

Or, better still; take your own re-useable bag.

Avoid products that use too much packaging

Try to buy products that use recycled or recyclable packaging. Write to the companies and /or speak to the staff of the shops that use too much packaging and bring their attention to so many resources being used (creating even more waste). Bigger boxes than necessary are a psychological ploy hiding how little we get for our money.

Buy long-life products that can be used over and over again

Disposable items such as nappies or razors may be convenient but the industrial production and then disposal of items such as these only adds to the greenhouse effect, and our pollution and waste problems.

Buy organically grown or reared food whenever you can afford it

(In the U.K. the logo of the Soil Association is a good guide to the product's genuinely organic status)

Your body can only make new cells and tissues from the material you give it. As well as improving your own health, organic farming helps to reduce the amount of pesticides, herbicides and fungicides entering not only our bodies through food but also the environment via our atmosphere, water and land. It also helps sustain our natural wildlife and the variety of living creatures by the rich microbial soil it maintains. By protecting and nurturing this soil, we protect and nurture agriculture, the most important of human activities.

Local organic farming removes the need for chemical preservation, and for energy-wasting and polluting transport over hundreds, if not thousands, of miles.

Local organic farms form a basis for a viable economic unit, which can be independent of national, continental or global political and commercial fluctuations.

How can you, as one person, help to protect trees, hedges and field margins to provide habitats for wildlife such as beetles, birds and mammals? Buy some organic breakfast cereal!

From a box of Whole Earth cereal:

> "A review published by the Soil Association of organic farms and biodiversity showed that on organic farms there were:
> • Five times as many wild plants in arable fields and 57% more species. Some endangered species are found only on organic farms.
> • More than twice as many breeding skylarks – numbers of skylarks have plummeted by 60% since 1972.
> • 1.6 times as many insects – providing vital food for many birds and their young."

It is also better to eat foods that are in season. Foods bought outside their season are likely to contain all kinds of preservatives.

Some farms produce without ploughing (a highly injurious practice for any soil).

Local smallholdings and allotments are producing good healthy food without poisons. Nature and the future require us to utilise gardens and 'wastelands', to 're-localise' and detoxify our food production.

Want to do more? Tell the shop manager why you will not buy some products and why you will buy others. Tell your friends the same thing, and neighbours, local communities…

Try to buy ethically produced and environmentally-friendly items

Buying Fair Trade and environmentally-friendly products supports progressive companies that are working to improve the environment through use of clean technology, and working to improve pay and conditions for workers in the Developing Countries. It also takes business away from manufacturers not doing so and hence may persuade them to change their ways. 'The Good Shopping Guide' is available from 'The Ecologist'. The Real Green Retail Group (rgrg) is a group of retailers committed to ethical and environmentally-friendly commerce and offers much valuable information on its website.

Buy a green gift for someone

When you can't think of a suitable present for someone why not choose something that will contribute to healing the planet? You could make them a member of, or donate on their behalf to, an environmental charity. There are also several ways to sponsor tree planting, for example the charity 'Trees for Cities' allows you to choose from a selection of sites nationally and internationally.

Use your car less

The car is one of the greatest threats to our environment. Currently, in many cases, there is no alternative, however, much can be done to reduce the pollution they cause.

If it is only a short journey, why not walk or cycle?

You will be reducing car emissions and keeping fit. If the roads are too dangerous in your local area or it lacks cycle-ways, then petition your local council.

Use public transport

Buses become less efficient when there are too many cars on the road to slow them down. 50 people sitting on a bus could mean up to 50 fewer cars on the road – and you don't have to find a place to park!

Maintain your car environmentally

Simply maintaining the correct tyre pressures can save you over one hundred pounds a year in fuel consumption and reduce climate change and pollution.

Send old tyres, batteries and waste oil to recycling centres or a local garage. Don't dump them or pour oils down drains, or into the ground.

Join or organise a car-share scheme

Share journeys for work, shopping or taking the children to school. You can save time and money.

Talk about your concerns

Speak to business owners, shop managers and bank managers about the products you want and why you will not purchase certain products. Share your knowledge with employers, colleagues, friends and family, listen to their concerns. There may be ways in which you can work together to put into practice some of the suggestions listed here or more of your own. For example, there are now Internet websites and 'pages' on which those accessing the site can agree to act in accordance with the particular recommendations presented there, and then monitor the progress and effects of their own and others' actions. Contact politicians and write to them – apparently MPs credit every letter they receive with representing the opinions of 1,000 people.

Educate your children to value their world

Not only to appreciate the beauty of it but also to take care of and respect it. To realise that the world's resources are finite and will run out if we don't take care. Encourage them to enjoy those resources and nature in general in a non-consuming way i.e. playing in the (relatively) fresh air of the countryside and getting their knees dirty etc. as mentioned in a previous chapter. Continued extinction of species can lead to collapse of ecosystems on which we all ultimately depend. Our children might delight at stories about tigers, gorillas, lions, crocodiles, bears – but how many of these animals will still be with us by the time our children are reading stories to their children (if the disappearance of these animals allows them to get that far)? We have the world in trust to pass on to – even to ensure the existence of – future generations, how will they judge us in this role?

Does your child's school have environmental lessons and environmental policies? If not, why not? Do they serve organic food? Do they practice conservation of their resources (e.g. paper) and minimal wastage policies and purchase re-cycled goods? If not, why not?

Useful websites

www.co-operativebank.co.uk
The Cooperative Bank plc. Exclusively ethical and environmentally-friendly

www.eiris.org
The Ethical Investment Research Service

www.foe.co.uk
Friends of the Earth website

www.theecologist.org
Comprehensive environmental magazine including a 'good shopping guide'

www.ecology.co.uk
The Ecological Building Society

www.ecover.com
Ecological cleaning products for the home, made in an environmentally-friendly factory and stored in biodegradable bottles

www.ethical-marketing.co.uk
The real green retail group (rgrg)

www.freecycle.org
All items are free

www.gardenorganic.org.uk
The National Centre for Organic Gardening

www.getethical.com
A directory of ecologically focused retailers

www.greenpeace.org/india
peaceful but very active opposition to all that threatens environmental health

www.guardian.co.uk/chemicalworld
For information on the effects of chemicals in the home and on our health

www.satpuda.org
Defending the highlands of Central India

www.shared-interest.com
Shared Interest Building Society. With projects mainly in the developing nations

www.soilassociation.org
The Soil Association. Pioneer of and regulatory body for organic food

www.smile.co.uk
An ethical Internet bank

www.treesforcities.org.uk
To sponsor tree planting

www.triodos.co.uk or www.triodos.com
Only finances projects with social and environmental benefits

www.wastewatch.org.uk
For guidelines on separating waste

www.woodlandtrust.org.uk
Protecting and conserving Britain's woodlands

Persuading sufficient consumers to spend their money in the right way will bring rapid and beneficial change for all. The sooner this can be done the better, and one way of accelerating the change would be to promote other ways of 'spending healthily' to those who already do so in some ways. From public presentations, LifeForce personnel know that, for example, some who eat organically do not bank ethically and vice versa. Hence, it would be healthier for all if organic produce recommended the ethical bank and the ethical bank recommended organic food. In the example just given, some people do not realise their actions are saying 'Let's eat healthily but indirectly fund unhealthy agribusiness by banking unethically' or 'let's fund healthy ethical developments but eat, and therefore promote, food containing poison.' Similarly with cleaning products, fair-trade and environmentally-friendly products etc. a 'pick 'n' mix' practice often prevails whereas it is best to adopt all healthy and ethical options as rapidly as possible. Multiple interconnected actions produce multiple interconnected benefits, including healthy soil (literally and metaphorically) from which further healthy growth (agricultural, economic and social) may appear.

A major advance would be for ethical and environmentally-friendly organisations to firstly become each others' members / customers and then encourage their own members and customers to so the same, interconnecting these individual initiatives, groups and businesses. (Achieving this 'cross-fertilisation' is not as easy as might be thought, despite it being beneficial to all participants, environmentally and commercially. Please see LifeForce report 2006–7 (www.lifeforceindia.com/news) for details).

The suggestions made above represent a number of powerful astringents that will loosen the jaws of any leech or parasite since, through them:

- The problem of essential, critical knowledge and wisdom being ignored by the authorities (purposely or inadvertently) is rendered irrelevant
- All are within the power of each and every individual
- All can be implemented today

Critics may contend that consumerism cannot have significant effects considering, for example, the oft quoted example of China building one new power station per week. Worryingly, at time of writing, this has increased to two power stations per week. (In accordance with the themes of this book, can it only be coincidence that the Chinese tiger is all but extinct?)

Before considering consumer power, it should also be pointed out that nature will be limiting China's rapid industrial expansion: air pollution is rapidly increasing while water scarcity and desertification have become serious threats to growth and life. China is already 25% desert and acid rain is affecting approx. 33% of agricultural land. Desert is advancing at a rate of hundreds of square miles per year. The Yellow River tributaries, once plentiful in shrimp and fish, are virtually denuded of these species by pollution. The World Bank estimates that environmental degradation and pollution cost the Chinese economy 8% – 12% of GDP annually due to losses in crops and fisheries, closures of factories and medical expenses. Chinese media support this analysis, reporting that in 2003 acid rain caused US$ 13-billion in economic damage, while dust storms inflicted US$ 6-billion in costs and lack of water cost US$ 14-billion in lost industrial output.

However, we are considering how consumer power can affect China. Consulting various estimates, and erring on the side of caution, it appears that at least one third of China's power consumption is for the manufacture and supply of goods to consumers in Western nations. Your pocket wields power over the Chinese government.

If people will start to spend selectively, consumer-led developments create awareness and, as such communities grow, they become increasingly significant in terms of their consumer power, and more easily influence not only cosmetic aspects of life-styles but also large-scale operations such as international trade. With co-operation and contributions from each, we can achieve air without contaminants; water without pollutants; food without poison and areas left sacred to nature. As communities work together and begin to de-centralise economics, government can be freed from the imbalanced, unhealthy influence of big business. Having secured our life-support system, a full, well-balanced education for future generations can be achieved – founded on personal responsibilities, consideration of virtues and morals, development of character, lessons on history and lessons from history, academic knowledge supplemented with guidance toward respect and caring for other lives, and appreciation for what nature and our parents have provided.

Where does this return to health and harmony begin? With the individual – with you! You are responsible for the world insofar as you are responsible for your world. If you are not doing your duties diligently (environmentally and otherwise) and making nature, morality and virtue the guides to your decisions and behaviour, how can the world ever be completely healthy? If your life does not live up to such a description, how can you expect it of others? How are your lapses leading, via connections and amplifying chain reactions, from errors to disasters? Tigers, humans and life in general need you! Will you choose to take action? This cause is not for some media-manufactured film, pop or sport trivia nor even to gain some advantage over other communities or nations; it is to the benefit of all living things. A cause you can wholeheartedly believe in, where everyone wins. You can start today, in the supermarket, the bank, your home. You do not need special equipment, training or support, just the will and backbone to turn what you know 'inside' into action, and thereby change what you see 'outside'. Who knows? You might make a world of difference.

Polishing the Mirror

If we manage to achieve some success in the short-term, the change in consciousness and behaviour is the beginning, if nurtured, of long-term conservation, and the gradual rediscovery of ourselves as part of nature, part of that conservation. The resulting well-balanced integration and unification means health for the community. We will not 'save' animals for as long as they are 'an added extra to our busy lives and aren't we wonderful to find some extra cash and time to help them'. They, in more senses than one, are our lives. It is separation, distance from nature that allows us to see them as something 'other'. Conservation should be part of the community because the community is a result of conservation. If, as a species, we survive long-enough to have our times read as history by future generations, people like Marsh, Corbett, Carson and Leopold, who pioneered conservation and took action to preserve some of nature's elemental treasure, will be seen as having made critical contributions to the future of not just tigers – by then hopefully not confined to history – but nothing less than life, as we know it and need it, on this planet.

If we fail to revise our values and priorities and therefore fail to achieve a healthy environment, more extinctions must surely occur. How many before we face our own? Nature, even while abused, remains all-powerful, and will ultimately win any 'contest' we are foolish enough to enter into with her. Mankind cannot overcome nature nor ignore her lessons in the long-term – all of which reduce to one: to 'husband and nurture the life force'. No matter how clever and sophisticated we think ourselves, nature will prevail over us and we will ultimately comply with her laws. The only choice is whether we learn rapidly or slowly – and conservation helps us learn rapidly. Nature will enforce lessons we are currently so slow to learn voluntarily and the longer we defy her laws, the harsher the lesson, until we find ourselves as the most endangered species. Another and 'ultimate' fearful symmetry reflected to us by the world.

Looking at the world in Chapter I, we found the need for conservation through common sense, personal experience, knowledge absorbed, and feelings fostered by spending time in healthy natural environments. Chapter II focussed on science, and it too confirms conservation as a necessity. In Chapter III Corbett's well-balanced knowledge and insights called for conservation measures and, while spreading the word, he took action himself. Chapter IV explored some of the more mysterious facets of our experience, adding spiritual benefits to the practical benefits of respecting the environment and conservation. In this chapter we have explored some ways in which we may personally take action to contribute to conservation, health and life. On the journey, other sampled viewpoints included mysticism, myth, philosophy and poetry. All these perspectives led to the same conclusion: we are part of nature and nature is part of us. We, and everything else, are part of one grand unity and, as all things are connected, our behaviour affects that unity and hence the health and life of the world.

However, to really emphasise the most important point, to nail it down without any possibility of any person claiming ignorance or misunderstanding, let us dismiss all previous chapters and all the views just considered except one: The one we are compelled to see everyday; the need to buy food from money earned by our labour and / or selling its products. We are obliged to be part of an economic reality, part of our current commercial systems including, these days, global markets. If we look at this 'real' commercial world we see the sale of, say, timber (legal or illegal) and other forest and animal products (many of them directly related to tigers and / or their habitat) and marginalised tribal people just about surviving on minimal food and energy. We cannot help but see markets for food, and hence vast acreages (literally in some cases from horizon to horizon) of single crops. If we look longer, we also see artificially constructed economic situations (some built on stock market gambling with basic commodities such as food and oil) which directly deny people necessities, including food and energy. Although technically 'legal' according to man-made laws, such practices are unjust morally and we see their reflection in poachers, timber thieves and other forms of crime and corruption. We can also see law-abiding tribal, town and city people, locally and remotely, who represent commercial markets with negative impacts on forests and, in this case, tigers. Tiger conservation makes us see socio-economics and when we look at socio-economics we cannot avoid seeing that it is dominated by global multinational corporations wielding enormous power through a variety of channels, but most importantly through governments and via commercially orientated, powerful bodies such as the WTO, World Bank and IMF. These connections cannot be realistically denied. Similarly, we have no alternative but to see ourselves as part of that system, and / or having allowed that system to grow; due to our personal involvement commercially, politically, economically, sometimes professionally, or apathetically and / or ignorantly. To a greater or lesser degree, we are all responsible for socio-economics, and hence, the fate of tigers and – due to the 'grand unity' and that 'all things are connected' – our own.

Some constructive suggestions have been made above that will, if you adopt them, immediately and beneficially affect socio-economics and hence tigers, yourself and every other living thing on the planet. No doubt, you can think of more suggestions.

Whichever viewpoint we choose and whatever method of investigation we use, the mirror reflects the same answer – we are the problem and the solution. Here is a fixed reference point, a reality independent of our particular viewpoint. As Steinbeck wrote 'We've got a bad thing made by men, and by God that's something we can change.' Of critical importance now are the choices we make in view of our fixed reference point. These choices are ultimately concerned with morals, values, virtues and priorities, although they are expressed in economic, commercial, professional and physical ways. And we do choose everyday – but few are conscious of the results and / or implications of their choices. Even if aware, still fewer choose to let the wider results influence their future choices. We like to think we're innocent, trying to spend our hard-earned money and not really responsible for the chaos of the world. It is true that those with political and corporate power bear the greatest responsibility, both for the problems and the lack of adequate solutions. However, every action, especially those concerned with earning and spending money, contributes to health or harm, and we bear responsibility for our own actions.

Our personal significance seems questionable in the context of so many global problems reported to us. Conflict, crime and heart-breaking tragedies are compressed into a few brief reports and, under such compression, all seem to merge together. Few or no solutions are suggested by the report and, since we cannot personally solve all these problems, they are consequently ignored together. One crucial problem that gets merged and ignored with the others is the environmental crisis. Yet, this problem or its solution will either kill or cure all the others and we can each make personal contributions to solving it. Whether it is food, water and air, other natural resources, or natural processes, the human capacity to cure and solve, to heal and repair, depends on nature's capacity to heal and repair. To put the environment at risk is to put all healing and all repair at risk. Moreover, it is through our neglect of nature that we have wandered so far from the path and now find ourselves lost, with an increasing number and severity of problems.

Our top priorities are to protect and conserve what remains of the natural environment and establish healthy agriculture. The two are intimately connected and those few people who remained in close proximity to both, are essential for healing and repairing all else. The closer we are to healthy, wholesome earth, the healthier the earth we are made from, and the healthier our understanding and actions while standing upon it. In 'The Grapes of Wrath' Steinbeck wrote of farmers who had to sell their hard-earned equipment and livestock for a pittance prior to their forced departure from the environmental disaster known as the Oklahoma 'dustbowl': the farmers told those who forced them to sell 'We could have saved you, but you cut us down, and soon you will be cut down and there'll be none of us to save you.' With so much of our global economy dependent on people who buy something, pick up a telephone and sell it at a higher price, regardless of environmental consequences (which requires, we are told, fantastically rare skills, demanding the highest salary packages), we can see that on much, much larger scales, the people who can save everybody are being 'cut down' i.e. disadvantaged, degraded if not actually destroyed, by those who cannot save anybody, including themselves.

 Each of us has the responsibility to educate ourselves and choose what we contribute to: not necessarily by simply giving money but perhaps by pressurising politicians or corporations, or by giving time or raising funds, or simply giving a kind word, a smile and showing some interest in the work of anyone busting their gut to help at the 'coalface' – a tiny drop of human kindness, or just interest, is a potent tonic; physically, mentally and spiritually. Each of us has the responsibility to make some effort, suffer some inconvenience and face our fears, in order to both save ourselves and something so much greater than ourselves.

By choosing to contribute in various but consistent ways (living by principles in harmony with those which your efforts and donations are supporting, and opposing those that are not) you have the satisfaction and independent power born of exercising your free will such that body, mind and spirit act in accordance with each other. You choose not to be duped by a socio-economic system built on greed and do not sit on your backside while the forests fall, the animals die and humans flock toward ecological Armageddon. No matter what the powerful and / or greedy may do, let us control ourselves and be greater than they who control cities, nations, political parties or corporations. The trail of choices we make leads us to another fixed point: those choices, from today onward, all put together, make the biggest choice of all – the solution – choosing life, or not. We meet the results the day after tomorrow.

Affecting that result will be the actions of NGOs. The programmes run by NGO's could be dramatically expanded in scope and effect by adequate money. The money required to fund essential work does not even compare to the amounts of money spent in any number of superficial, unimportant ways. Consider the amounts of money spent (or wasted) in one Western city's 24-hour day; within months of the 'credit crunch' and the beginning of the current financial crisis, the London auctioneer Sotheby's took c. £95 million during a two and a half hour sale of artwork (including more than £9 million for one piece); or consider thousands of pounds, if not more, lost over gambling tables; or ordinary 'accessories' such as handbags that can cost thousands of pounds each; or the cost of 'security' or 'catering' for one entertainment event; or the money paid for one stand with one car at one motor show; or millions spent on technology to shave one tenth of a second off the lap time of a formula 1 racing car; or, ironically, the budget for one wildlife documentary (which would fund conservation projects for years) to name but a few examples. We considered above what one senior city financier's bonus could do for tiger conservation and almost wherever one looks, particularly around the world's tax havens, there seem to be plenty of millionaires and billionaires; hardly any of whom, it would seem, understand what their wealth is really based on.

Capping all these excesses, consider that in 2007 the Exxon Mobil Corporation made the largest annual profit by any company – $40.6 billion. Its sales, generating income of over $404 billion, exceeded the gross domestic product of 120 countries (New York Times 01/02/08). Consider $40 600 000 000 – *profit*. (Incredibly, in the U.S.A. at least, oil production is heavily subsidised, enjoying numerous tax concessions). Exxon's European subsidiary 'Esso' has famously used the tiger for decades as their symbol for energy. Although some consider it only a PR exercise, the oil company has put something into the barrel by donating a few million dollars over a decade or more toward tiger conservation. In the experience of LifeForce, this could save the tiger in the wild, if directed to the right wild tiger habitat at the right time in the right way. Yet, examples of where this Exxon money has gone include conservation education for American school children and a $4.5 million Exxon Endangered Tiger Habitat exhibit opened at the Dallas Zoo, Texas, U.S.A. These, as far as the author can establish, are facts, but the truth is that the tiger is closer to extinction now than a decade before. The money for the Endangered Tiger Habitat alone, if spent judiciously in tiger habitat, would have removed the need to build it since the tiger would no longer be endangered.

Effective projects funded by LifeForce to date, with potential for expansion and integration with other projects, have ranged from approximately £500 to £20,000 per year (approx. US$ 750 / 1000 – US$ 30 000 / 40 000 depending on exchange rates). At these levels we don't even need to consider the likes of Exxon Mobil, or even its tea and coffee bills, one British M.P.'s fraudulent expenses claim could more than cover most of the budgets required. Whilst this money has been difficult for LifeForce to get, and other charities struggle with similar or less, on the scale of global finance, these amounts do not even register. They are, financially speaking, insignificant, yet what such money could achieve is anything but insignificant. This 'loose change' is so small as to make the tiger's disappearance for want of it, an abomination and a disgrace. When one considers the collective values involved it may make one weep, or angry, or despair, or conclude that we are collectively going to get exactly what we deserve. Yet at the same time it must not make us give up our own standards, stop us polishing our part of the mirror. Cleaning up the reflection begins with each of us. As the light becomes brighter, if only for one's immediate neighbours, more are able to see properly to polish their part of the mirror.

People whose views of the mirror are obscured by the worlds of commerce, politics, entertainment or fashion might believe that making a donation means they have 'done their bit' – while living life-styles (or in the case of oil companies, creating life styles) that more than negate their donation, and may actually cause many of the problems their donations are meant to alleviate.

Due to the relative amounts usually involved, money spent on donations is not nearly as important as how all one's other money is spent – not trading with those who make charities necessary is often more effective than donating to one. Some people may believe that their particular life-style, occupation or business is part of the way commerce has to 'work'; how customers' expectations are to be met (including being over-charged); the need to spend money to make money; cope with competition; attract the best 'players' etc. and how it all has to be this way.

Yet none of it *has* to be this way. Even if not threatened with environmental catastrophe, we do not have to approve of, endorse by patronage, or finance through purchase or investment, all the life-style attributes of Western consumerism. Nor do we have to approve, endorse and finance the extremes to which commercially based operations 'glamorise', 'hype' and ultimately manufacture excitement over very little or nothing – such as manufactured pop groups and 'reality TV stars'. However, partly as a direct consequence of collectively adopting these values and rejecting others, we are threatened by environmental catastrophe, which threatens the worlds of commerce, politics, entertainment, fashion and everything else. There is absolutely no need, excuse or reason why the tiger, or many other species, have to die out forever. They do not have to – we choose, now. Having chosen, we need to prepare for paying the price. One way is much more expensive than the other.

Part of the problem of surviving the environmental crisis and saving various species, including ourselves, is actually facing the truth. The world is reflecting to us that we are, collectively speaking, selfish and greedy to the point of suicide and / or apathetic and ignorant enough to allow our communities to be dominated by those who are. Self and greed breed all the commercial excesses, poor quality products and service, image over substance, media 'spin' and all the other sorts of fabrication and falsehood that makes up much of the modern human world. Chapter IV recommended nature as our guide to the way, the truth, and to life, and the state of the planet is undeniable proof that we are going rapidly in the opposite direction.

The most obvious manifestation of self and greed is the Western obsession (now contaminating the East) with acquisition, 'getting and spending'. We must always be 'doing' and 'achieving', rarely, if ever, simply 'being'. This characteristic is so all-pervading it affects even mundane aspects of life, including those far removed from 'getting and spending'. It took time for India to wear away my own Western blinkers, and one instance comes to mind which might illustrate the point. On arrival at the nearest railway station to the LifeForce base, I found a serious problem with the ticket, boding a long and frustrating delay. I needed to take some time to ponder my predicament and, walking across the dry and dusty road to the little bungalow that served tea, I bumped into S, a young, calm, quiet fellow who ran a business back in Pachmarhi. He asked me what I was about and, it being rude in India not to share one's affairs, I explained it to him. He seemed to understand and said he would fetch someone. I am no longer surprised at who knows who in India, after discovering more and more family connections woven across quite diverse places and occupations.

In due course, an older man appeared with S and asked about my problem. Ah, thank goodness, now I would make some progress getting this situation resolved. I explained the problem in some detail to arm him with all relevant facts. On completion of this discourse he replies with a silent head-wobble. After a suitable period of silence, I tentatively ask what could be done to resolve the problem. He does not know. Without boring the reader with the next awkward exchanges and my trying to understand what was going on, I turn to S and say that his contact at the railways did not seem able to do anything useful at all.

"He does not work for the railways" says S.

"But he has an influential contact at the railways?"

"No."

Dumb incomprehension on my part eventually gives way to a question.

"Who is he then?" I ask, my Western mind insisting that some meaningful link must now be revealed.

"He is my friend" says S.

"Very well, but…who…why…???" I splutter, before words and comprehension fail. No expressions or answers from either man.

I then realised that this was the sum total of the situation, I had just repeated at length my problem to a complete stranger who had no meaningful connection to the situation, to no purpose or value whatsoever, other than wasting my time and breath. This not only seemed pointless in and of itself but also caused me a little embarrassment due to my rather old-fashioned British reserve that one sorts out one's own problems, does not waste other people's time with them, and certainly not that of strangers (I only told S about my situation in the first place to comply with Indian etiquette). What had this stranger been doing previously before being taken to listen to some foreigner's dreary account of a problem which, to him, was totally inconsequential nothingness? The heat of the day and my frustrations had raised temperatures but I curbed my tongue while thinking "These two idiots have had me standing here, blathering on, repeating tiresome details to no purpose or value…just what is the point?" Dumbfounded incomprehension was now added to frustration, and concern for yet more wasted time. Nothing seemed to make sense…

As with so many things in India, for me at least, understanding dawned gradually.

… from S's perception, being 'sensible', efficient, achieving a result, didn't enter into the situation. Without having to spout any reasons, justifications, details or logic, S had simply got his friend. Maybe the friend knew something or someone relevant, maybe not. Another person was now aware of the situation and, if there was some unexpected development, it could be communicated to me through another fundamental feature of India – the word of mouth that can find anybody, anywhere, and in short order. These potential practical benefits are enough in themselves, yet there is more, and of greater value; how many Westerners would go to get their friend on behalf of a delayed foreigner? Whether or not the friend could solve the problem, there was the artless idea that here was another to share the problem, the opportunity for simple solidarity in company, and the therapy of being able to explain and express oneself (and to an older, wiser man). When one really sees through to the simplicity and sincerity of 'getting my friend' it is heart-wrenching and humbling in its selfless concern. S would even wonder at all these words to describe what, in India, is obvious.

My Western mind would have initially chosen a mechanical, functional solution rather than simple, sincere support and friendship. While the latter may not solve a problem, it solves all problems. Initially, I was unable to see through the material glass of the show-case to the spiritual diamond behind it, and would have chosen only the glass, the physical screen of the functional, mechanical world, the case and not the treasure but, by continuing to look, I was eventually lucky enough to see through it and perceive the spiritual diamond lying within the material show-case of events. I had wanted to 'save time' (in India!) a country where plenty of time is always available, and where some had just been found for me in which to make new friends, which I had foolishly squandered. Now I could clearly see the idiots involved…actually not two but one…yes, looking away from the diamond and re-focussing on the very dim reflection in the glass show-case, I could recognise him, and that I had known him all my life. If offered friendship, take it and be thankful for the problem that prompted the offer, since its solution or otherwise, no longer matters. 'They ever must believe a lie who see with, not through, the eye' (William Blake)

This example is also consistent with the principle of unity in that problems for any one of us are, ultimately, problems for all of us, just as pleasure for any one of us is, ultimately, pleasure for all of us. Separation is only an illusion. All things are connected. These two men had put profound principle into simple practice, replacing my profound ignorance with a simple, single, universal truth.

In seeking to correct my faults I traced some of their roots to my Western cultural values of focussing on the functional; doing; 'getting and spending', and watching the clock. The Western emphasis on the mechanical and physical, on destinations and functions, result in people either being used or abused (in many modern companies, 'personnel' departments have become 'human resources' departments – at least there's some honesty!) When functions are all fulfilled and destinations reached, we realise that what was really worthwhile, what gave our efforts purpose, is represented by the people ignored, used or abused and left behind along the way. This is too often a description of aspects of Western culture but, while that culture is part of me, I am a part of that culture. As we have seen, culture can influence but not compel me to behave in a particular way. I can choose how to behave and thereby influence culture. I can now choose to put people before other considerations, and society is changed a little.

Real change always means changing ourselves. All political, commercial and socio-economic patterns will, in time, follow our new set of values, our new choices. Our choices made to date have produced the environmental crisis, which includes the tiger crisis. We saw above that, in our roles as consumers, each of us is now either part of the problem or part of the solution. Points just considered reveal that our choices in other contexts also place us in one or the other of these categories. All depends upon each of us.

In contrast, the following viewpoint is common: 'Humanity has always faced, and overcome, nature's obstacles. Now we face some environmental problems but we shall overcome these too.' Anyone who thinks differently and sees unprecedented catastrophes, may be simply classed as pessimists and 'jollied along' with comments such as 'cheer up, that's no way to think about problems. We'll be fine.'

Never before in recorded history has humankind been able to dismantle the life-support system of the planet. Now we can, and are doing so. Moreover, examination of our 'overcoming nature's obstacles' in the past, reveals 'successes' only when we co-operate with nature, when we work in harmony with her laws. When we persistently defy nature, we are corrected – these events are usually called disasters. Despite witnessing many relatively small 'disaster lessons', as referred to in the previous chapter, we have not learned from them, but compounded them into the current global environmental crisis, which is the collective result of innumerable smaller scale abuses. 2010 saw devastating floods in Pakistan and China. Some may think of 'nasty nature' harming humans but, in Pakistan, extensive deforestation and extreme weather conditions, amplified by global warming, were the major contributory factors, along with other human factors including the misuse of millions of pounds meant to protect against such effects. In China, it was soil erosion due to deforestation and hydroelectric schemes, along with the heaviest rainfall in a decade, which caused floods and mudslides killing many hundreds of people and making thousands homeless. Amongst numerous economic repercussions, rising food prices were the most obvious and immediate effect, and again we see that ecology and economies cannot be separated. Environmentally, we have only 'recovered' from previous disasters because there was still some uncontaminated or non-abused earth left to move to or purchase food from – giving the false impression to our jolly but misguided optimist above that we 'overcame' nature's obstacles. Increasing population and technological capabilities leads to increasingly large-scale effects. Now the damage and degradation are on global scales, and there is nowhere else to go.

Whatever space travel lacks as a substitute for purpose (as explored in chapter IV), some have speculated as to whether it could be a practical solution to escape from a dying planet planet (not that the planet need be dying if we paid it more attention - we know more about the surface of the moon than the sea bed). If any such suggestions are serious, they vastly underestimate the rapidity with which Earth's life-support systems are being degraded and / or the inadequacy of our technology and / or the scales of interstellar distance and time, and the little detail that no alternative inhabitable planet has ever been definitely identified. Our planet is the only one we will be living, or dying on, for the duration of the environmental crisis. It is 'make or break'; right here, right now – which should bring any sensible person back down to earth.

Independently of manned space exploration, a programme called SETI (the Search for Extra-Terrestrial Intelligence) involves scanning regions of the sky for radio signals transmitted by alien life. Space is a fascinating realm full of intriguing possibilities. Most intriguing of all is the possibility of locating life in the interstellar fastness. Yet (even if, as previously noted, alien life is not as violent and dangerous as we are), does it really make sense to be listening for life beyond the solar system while life around us is facing mass extinctions? Life is life. Life is One. How can we be interested in alien or 'new' life, when life all around, including our own, is threatened? It is surely only possible when so many connections have been lost, between people and people, people and nature, people and life. Trying to make connections with 'new' life, searching for extra-terrestrial intelligence, when we can't maintain the connections we have, does not exhibit a *balanced* intelligence, only a technical intelligence; divorced from feeling and so many other aspects of real life. We could even say it is divorced from 'life' – while supposedly seeking it. In this sense it will never be found since the seekers can't see it when it's under their noses. Once again to clarify; aspects of SETI are fascinating but to realise them we have to separate from so much else that is all around us – and on which we and our studies depend – and which is under serious threat. To re-connect with those other aspects and then prioritise them starts the healing process, which will eventually find superb SETI scientists amongst those currently begging for bread. That some consider agricultural societies 'primitive' was referred to in the previous chapter, yet it could be argued that more intelligence is demonstrated by the careful nurturing of agricultural practices than building hi-tech toys, some of which actually damage the natural environment. Perhaps we might be better served by a STI.

It is not suggested that space exploration should be cancelled or 'space scientists' made redundant, only that some of the extreme expense involved could be channelled to more urgent needs until we have secured essentials for all. The 'space scientist' may object that space exploration and other specialisms, are allowed for by the division of labour that is the foundation of civilisation while, at the same time and by the same token, other sub-divisions ensure maintenance of our life-support systems. In theory, this is agreed. In practice however, our life-support systems are *not* being maintained, and that requires a re-assessment of priorities, with possibilities that specialisms could be shelved, until their foundations are re-secured.

The 'we'll be fine', jolly optimist may still counter that for all the problems, overall, we're not so badly off. It might be those who are not so badly off that include most optimists: Looked at from a global perspective, the majority of humans are in poverty without adequate or clean water, food, shelter, education or healthcare. The majority of large wild mammals at the apex of 'ecological pyramids' are endangered, as are monkeys, apes and lemurs, along with a variety of herbivores/omnivores such as elephant, rhinoceros, some species of bear, birds and honey bees, along with (as at 2009) over 17 000 other species listed as endangered by the International Union for Conservation of Nature (I.U.C.N.) The vast majority are victims of deforestation and other types of habitat degradation, illegal trading in wildlife and commercial hunting. The most important parts of global life-support systems e.g. climate, air quality, fresh water, forests, oceans, are all being polluted, damaged, degraded or otherwise under threat. Even the bases of all terrestrial ecosystems, plants, are threatened. A 2010 study by the I.U.C.N., the Royal Botanic Gardens at Kew, U.K. and the Natural History Museum in London has found that a fifth of all plant species globally (approx. 76 000 species out of an estimated 380 000 species) are threatened with extinction due to human-induced habitat loss. The implications of all this are obvious, critical and urgent. Yet most people still seem more concerned with profits than prophets. We have to take extensive and urgent action now, and then we can be optimistic about our remedial actions – not use optimism as an excuse for denial, apathy, laziness and doing nothing.

We have produced the most dangerous situation in recorded history – without precedent. The environmental crisis is the most important problem faced by humankind because it is the basis of all other activities and represents air, water and food. Given that the environment is as fundamental as it is possible to get, that we have an environmental crisis is the strongest indicator that, collectively speaking, we have completely and fundamentally lost our way and our priorities. Of course, there are other significant problems – nuclear energy, poverty, disease, etc. but what is the point of curing any or all of these problems, when everybody faces horrific scenarios or disasters produced by collapsing life-support systems? We are all on the same ship and there is poverty on B deck, disease on C deck etc., but the ship is sinking, so should we not secure the ship first before addressing problems on the various decks? What if tomorrow we 'make poverty history' (a wonderful vision) while, as in the example given above, the oxygen content of the air reduces for all? Moreover, as also indicated above, it is the very same factors, the same imbalances in our societies that cause both poverty and the environmental crisis, along with many other symptoms of malaise (e.g. it can be argued with persuasive evidence that the policies of the World Bank and IMF are not only environmentally harmful but will also make poverty for the majority permanent). We shall not make poverty history until we make natural history priority. After the environment, nuclear energy / weapons (and their rapid proliferation) must be the next biggest threat but, right now, the environmental crisis is proceeding apace while the nuclear problem has, thank goodness, not yet caught up with it in terms of scale.

'…the first-graders have never been in the forest because the trees are so contaminated. When children want to see what nature used to be like, they go into a little courtyard inside the building, and the teacher says, "This is a bird and this is a tree," and they are plastic.' Are these lines from a futuristic science fiction film or novel? No, they are the words of Olga Korbut, the former Ukrainian gymnast, after visiting schools in Byelorussia after the Chernobyl disaster. Even if nuclear reactors could be made 100% safe (and no human construction or process ever is) each one represents a target for terrorists and a potential nuclear disaster with subsequent long-term radioactive contamination. However, let us imagine that we could produce a nuclear reactor that is 100% safe and that terrorism passes into history due to enlightened international governance. Few, if any reactors (even if free from all human error in construction and operation) could withstand earthquake, lightning, floods and forest fires (the latter two increasing due to global warming). Despite all these serious risks, proliferation of nuclear energy is once again on government agendas. There is an unsettling parallel between the environmental situation and nuclear energy / weapons insofar as we can all see how and why they develop and where they will lead, reminding us of Einstein's comment on nuclear weapons: "A weird aspect of this development lies in its apparently inexorable character. Each step appears as the inevitable consequence of the one that went before." If our energy source carries the risk of contaminating the land, and hence trees and all other life over vast areas for hundreds of years, we need to find another energy source. Whatever the benefits, the risk is too great since, in the event of accident, natural catastrophe or attack, we lose not only our energy source but also, at the same time, many other aspects of our lives (if not our lives), including those elements that would provide our only path to recovery.

There is a mistaken assumption that progress is equivalent to the passage of time. We need to question what constitutes 'progress' (and whether it must involve evermore sophisticated technology) and what constitutes regress. Society, like its citizens, has the freedom to regress as much as progress, otherwise it's not freedom. Just as we can regress personally and spiritually, so we can regress collectively; politically, environmentally and technologically, even when the latest gadget is more sophisticated than the last. The continued pursuit of scientific specialism and / or technology, despite the horrors and moral dilemmas produced, is never questioned. Why? Science is not questioned by many for fear of being thought a fool so, in silence, we passively watch the dismantling of our life-support systems – and we are all proved to be fools. Like any human activity, science is subject to all our human failings and so should be subject to all the collective controls society develops to manage such failings (transparency, the law, evaluation by those who pay for it or will be subject to its consequences; assessment of its value by (relatively) independent parties).

Despite its fundamental importance, the environment has only recently edged onto governments' agendas, whereas it, and our relationship with the land, should have been the foundation stone of all and any government policies since governments began. Somehow it just does not seem to register on many people's minds; attention has to be drawn to what is most obvious and indisputable. We are, literally and metaphorically, 'standing on' the earth, the soil, the environment, nature – it gave rise to all our other developments.

How do we know what is right with regard to nature, what is best?

Nature is not only our cause but also our guide. Here is a solid foundation. We have many problems but, as mentioned above, the environment is not merely one of them. The healthy environment pre-dates man and all man-made problems. Whereas other problems are the results of human programmes either flawed at the outset or corrupted along the way, environmental problems have arisen from how we chose to abuse an already present, healthy, self-sustaining and self-regulating system. So here we have an absolute, on which we can depend. The environment is not a fashion, religion, political ideology, a cult, a school of thought, the latest fad or any other artificial construction of man's. The environment was functioning healthily before the arrival of man. Once we see the significance of, and our total dependence on nature and nature's laws, all else follows. Having safeguarded nature, we can model our constructions on nature's – our environmental, agricultural and economic policies and practices. Our dependence on nature brings independence from human opinion. If any would tell you that the environment is just one of a number of problems and must take its place equally amongst them, then they are misinformed, misguided or trying to fool you, or themselves. Moreover, this type of foolishness contributes to many other problems, since our mismanagement of our relationship with the land leads to numerous other problems, all with economic and social repercussions.

A once healthy environment also produced us, but there is now a common misconception that Earth is just a ball of dirt, while we are the great scientists, architects and engineers who understand how it all works, fashion it into whatever we want while heroically defying any limits nature dare try to impose on our activities. In truth, all we can lay claim to is great arrogance, ignorance and wilful blindness. All our creations are by the grace and co-operation, not the defeat, of nature. In the face of looming mass extinctions, there are now government officials (in the U.K. at least) who are trying to decide 'how many species we need'. This approach is not only offensive from any but the most selfish and meanest of perspectives but also reveals how ignorance can be dressed as knowledge. We have seen how nature's interconnections can produce unexpected results as one species nears extinction (see the presentation to Forest Guards above), yet still we do not learn, and even government policies ignore what nature tries to teach for the benefit of all. We must save as many species as we can since we have seen that all things are connected. However, when wilful blindness is chosen, as in the cases of Samson or King Lear, events combine to reflect this in physical reality by removing the faculty of sight – in order that we may see. What is now in sight, for those of us who 'lift their heavy lids and look', is the end of nature's patience and the imminent removal of our toys and technologies.

To really place our situation in perspective let us reduce the global situation to a personal one: my exclusive pursuit of profit, my study of science (not immediately beneficial to the environment) and my enjoyment of socialising, entertainment or sport, my self-indulgent pleasures etc. may be fascinating, interesting and / or exciting but none are suitable activities while my mother is dying for want of respectful and compassionate treatment, brothers and sisters starving, tigers disappearing, nor while I am contaminating my own sources of clean air, water and food and threatening their future supply. I need to adjust my mentality, my priorities and face my responsibilities by taking appropriate action to address them.

If you adopt the environment as your cause, your cause is everyone's cause (although, sadly, while you are for everyone, everyone is not for you! In particular, those receiving short-term benefits will oppose you, while those 'dumbed down' by, and now satisfied with, image and emptiness, may not be actively against you, but neither will they be for you.) A speaker on a recent television environmental debate show said: 'We have to ensure the welfare of humans before the welfare of the environment.' In reality, the two cannot be separated. What must be separated is the combination of ignorance and arrogance that produces such views.

There are connections of course between these symptoms and many others of sickness in society but there is not time to examine them all since the environmental issues are most urgent. If we remedy these rapidly, we will gain time to address the others. Good training courses for managers advise distinguishing between urgent and important. The environment is simultaneously most important and most urgent – the only thing lacking is good management. If we can muster ourselves to better manage our life-support system we will find that, in mastering the problems we have created, we automatically gain ground in combating our other problems, since solving environmental problems automatically educates, encourages respect for life and other living things, broadens perspectives and involves us in healthy practices and procedures.

The perspectives of many people are now influenced by media coverage (or absence of coverage). With regard to the recent awakening to environmental dangers, few if any people seen or heard on the media seem fearful of the looming problems or even apprehensive about them, and it is mostly mentioned as just another problem. This, of course, is intentional. However, nature will not be accommodating itself to media bias or its underlying agendas. The new crop of 'eco' television programmes, with their homogenised, light–weight material is presented with the same sing-song, comforting, cajoling, non-controversial delivery as trivia. The content has far too much sugar. As we go into the teeth of the crisis and elements of our life-support system face breakdown, 'television's topical tit-bits' is not adequate or appropriate treatment. We and our earth need better nutrition and stronger medicine than this.

If we cannot rely on media, can we find it elsewhere? Colleagues at work seem unconcerned and may even ridicule attempts to improve the situation. They are too busy with 'real' work and their own family or social situations. Socially, it does not crop up as a regular topic, if at all, since nobody wants to be the party-pooper. Family life is too scarce, too hectic and too precious to be burdened with global problems. In the West. at least, most politicians have responsibilities that do not require any depth of awareness of environmental issues and nature's interconnections; even the minister for the environment will have other responsibilities and where the minister does have an appropriate grasp of essential issues, the position lacks sufficient power to pass legislation without involving many other ill-informed parties and vested interests. Can we rely on P.M.s and presidents then? They are beset by numerous other issues and concerns, including the continual 'fire-fight' against the results of decades of previous mismanagement, currently dominated by the financial crisis, irrefutable proof of the forces controlling the world. We have already seen that the few, lamentably late, government programmes, such as bio-diesel projects, can be worse than useless. So who, or what body, is responsible for, understands and holds relevant powers for the preservation and maintenance of our life-support systems? None! Is this a preposterous exaggeration? If so, why are we in an environmental crisis? No government in the world can be cited as having adequate and fully effective policies and programmes safeguarding our life-support systems.

In 'The Adventure of the Bruce-Partington Plans' Sherlock Holmes refers to the government position held by his brother Mycroft: '…his position is unique…there has never been anything like it before, nor will be again…The conclusions of every department are passed to him, and he is the central exchange, the clearing house, which makes out the balance. All other men are specialists, but his specialism is omniscience. We will suppose that a Minister needs information as to a point which involves the Navy, India, Canada, and the bimetallic question, he could get his separate advices from various departments upon each, but only Mycroft can focus them all, and say offhand how each factor would affect the other…he has made himself essential.' Mycroft, of course, is fictional but in reality the role is now, environmentally speaking, essential and of the utmost importance since it involves the Navy (and all other occupations) India, Canada, (and all other nations) and the biotic question. Of the specialists and scientists available to advise government the marine specialist need not necessarily be familiar with, say, Indian terrestrial ecosystems. We are currently living through evidence that economists are particularly ignorant of history and hence may also be unaware of the environmental factors contributing to the human disasters of, say, Easter Island, or Ephesus, or the Oklahoma 'dust bowl', and so on and so forth.

Yet, surely the crisis cannot be 'real' since our needs are more than met – as evidenced by our comfortable existence. Comfortable existence is restricted to a minority of the world's population and is only a temporary arrangement since the way we have arranged it is unsustainable. We are currently enjoying a feast before a famine – without having made plans or provisions for the latter. We have seen that our neglect and abuse of agriculture threatens to turn the last metaphor into reality and bring us, once again, back down to earth.

Perhaps, some may say, there has been short-sighted mismanagement of farming but nature itself remains as it ever was for us to utilise in new management. Yet, nature is not as it ever was, particularly after we have interfered with its genetic basis, and seriously imbalanced it via global warming; loss of topsoil; deforestation; pollution; and species extinctions.

Consider the disasters we are potentially orchestrating. Can anyone refute the threat to our oxygen supply as cited above? Can anyone refute the threats to seafood and our economies by acidification of the oceans? These are just a few examples of disasters that can be envisioned. There are many more of those and, probably, others we cannot, as yet, foresee. If the environmental crisis is not 'real' for some it is only because its full effects have not yet burst upon our comfortable sunlit stroll and our inadequate preparations for imminent environmental changes.

If you question friends, family and colleagues on these topics, the responses might include 'I am an office worker / a reporter / driver / banker / housewife etc. and have no responsibilities in this area'. In the preceding chapter we considered people hiding behind their occupation to avoid their responsibilities toward their own personal spiritual development, with consequent practical effects. Now we consider the consequences of hiding from one's practical responsibilities, with consequent spiritual effects (another example of cause and effect being interchangeable). Classifying oneself by occupation creates an illusion of distance or separateness from anything other than one's occupational duties. If you suggest that occupations do not fully define people or their responsibilities, and persist with your questions, responses might include opinions that governments and scientists will 'save us' – although it is governments which have already taken us into this mess and scientists are publicly declaring that science cannot deal with the situation.

For those willing to face their responsibilities, we have seen above some recommendations for actions by individuals. Where individuals also wish to pressurise government, the text above suggests some immediate practical recommendations (in addition to the principles of long-term 'panoramic' policies recommended in chapter IV): For examples: 'biochar' could be thoroughly and rapidly researched and, if the results are favourable, implemented immediately; agriculture could be returned to smaller, local, organic farms and this farming to be protected and supported by government policies; aerosols could be completely banned; every naturally occurring (non-nuclear) source of non-carbon fuel could be investigated with a view to immediate implementation; existing environmental legislation could be properly and thoroughly enforced, passing new where necessary; the products and processes of big business could be rigorously monitored, wastage minimised or eliminated and re-cycling implemented wherever possible. There is no need to make advertising agencies richer with public money to convey environmental messages – plain speaking government announcements on and in all forms of media should alert everyone to the seriousness of the situation, and be accompanied by advice on appropriate remedial actions. The predictable response to this will be: where is the money coming from to fund it all?

Biochar is cheap to implement; subsidies to agribusiness (and fishing...and oil...) need long overdue reviews and we saw above how we might save £14 million on one electric bill for one project (which is fascinating research, but which no stretch of the imagination could call necessary – along with its significant contribution to global warming). Consider also the money, resources and expertise of other research projects that could be redirected toward environmental health. Talking of health, we can save millions spent on healthcare when we stop breathing, drinking and eating industrial chemicals, toxins and pollutants which have been allowed to contaminate air, water and food. We can also improve the health of our bodies and bank balances by freeing medicine from the grip of pharmaceutical companies. Re-regulation of stock markets and all aspects of corporate finance will relate financial transactions to real products and services. Financial gambling on commodities essential for people's existence could also be banned. All those with six-figure bonuses or pensions (some of whom are directly responsible for causing so much environmental damage) could also be compelled to make contributions. A complete review of the laws relating to gambling (on stock markets as well as in casinos), entertainments, promotions, celebrities, etc. could save the millions spent on such non essentials, to help us all (including gamblers and celebrities) with essentials. Law should prevent manufacturers' excess packaging of their products – particularly when its purpose is psychological deception. As we start to respect the environment and life, we will disrespect all wastage and falsehood. We will also reject unnecessary consumption and prefer repair and replacement to disposal, automatically saving money and resources.

These are just a few suggestions for funding reforms. However, let us not be led back into the current conventional 'wisdom' that the welfare of humans, and all else, is exclusively dependent on money. Whilst money could be of use as described, we are in this situation due to money being made first priority – especially by those engineering economic systems by which they gain most of it. The 'money mentality' is so dominant that to proclaim in a social setting that money is of most importance will provoke set lips and heads nodding without fear of contradiction. This is the impoverished mentality purchased by money. In truth, nature is most important, since all and anything money represents is ultimately derived from nature and / or put together from natural resources. Hence, one of the most dangerous developments of recent times is money 'made' from products or services that are not 'real', that do not relate directly to natural resources (whilst remaining dependent on products and services that do).

The Cost of Money

'You start with $90,000 and call yourself a bank. You lend it to Peter who wants to buy a house. Peter buys the house from Jane, and Jane puts the $90,000 into your bank for safekeeping. You now hold $180,000 ($90K in cash plus $90K secured on a house).

You can now do the same with Michael and you hold $270,000 (the original $90k plus $180k in collateral). Soon you hold a million, most of it in collateral on houses on which you charge interest. You can now attract deposits at low interest to lend to others at high interest. Or you can invest your notional wealth and make money that way. With enough gall you could have started without even the original sum because they are only computer transactions anyway. The more money you create by putting others into debt the more interest you can charge: The banks have always created money but this system only really took off with deregulation twenty years ago.

Governments make the notes and coins we use but these total less than 5% of the actual money in circulation. Banks and building societies have created the rest in the way described above as computer entries, not notes and coins. The money we use daily was created by private institutions, is owned by them and we pay them for using it, not once but year after year. Banks must maintain 10% 'capital adequacy' so they put aside that amount from net interest; it does not inhibit their ability to create yet more capital, it just puts up the cost of borrowing money and keeps them a nice little reserve…

…Lord Josiah Stamp, former director of the Bank of England (said) in 1937 "The modern banking system manufactures money out of nothing…The process is perhaps the most astounding piece of sleight of hand that was ever invented."…

…Thomas Jefferson was alarmed at the development of the banking system. "If the American people ever allow the banks to control the issuance of their currency," he said, "they will deprive the people of all property. I sincerely believe that the banking institutions having the power of money are more dangerous to liberty than standing armies."

Abraham Lincoln forged America into one nation. Two main causes of Civil War had been slavery and the financial stranglehold exerted by northern banks over plantations in southern states. Reconciliation was a truly great achievement. Had Lincoln lived longer he might have left an even greater legacy. He wrote a paper called "Monetary Policy" which might have led to the end of conventional banking and money power in the US, and the world might have followed suit. A major *casus belli* would have been removed and the bloody history of our age would have been very different. He was assassinated shortly after publishing this document and it was quietly buried.

Lincoln's Monetary Policy is a masterpiece of clarity; this is a key passage: "the government should not borrow capital at interest as a means of financing government work and public enterprise. The government should create, issue and circulate all the currency and credit needed to satisfy the spending power of the government and the buying power of consumers." Lincoln's suggestion that money should relate to things that need to be bought and sold seems fairly obvious but the banks are playing a very profitable game and such suggestions would spoil the fun.

Jefferson and Lincoln's warnings have come true. The loss of liberty, when poor countries are forced to make structural adjustments that harm their social services, has been dictated and enforced by economic, not military, force. The World Bank and the IMF ensure that the requirements of banking institutions are sacrosanct. Within the US the power of money has made it impossible for communities to resist corporate dominance in all their affairs. And the need for government to borrow money at interest from private institutions has made the US dependent on investment from abroad – investment that could be withdrawn should alternative assets be identified, leading to a crash of the US and probably also of the global economy.

The money supply is now three times greater than the value of goods and services available to be bought or sold and the main commerce in the world is currency speculation, untaxed, as $1,500 billion flows around the world every day. All the money that exists attracts compound interest, which is nice for the banks but plunges individuals and governments into debt. Many of the highest paid people in the world are the perpetrators of this destructive and unstable game. It is a game that can destroy nations, destroy even banks that get it wrong, and makes pawns of us all.' (B10 reprinted by kind permission of Alastair Sawday Publishing Co.)

When important elements of our economy and society depend on money that does not represent real products or labour, a man-made game is begun which is based on falsehood. Money only has any real value insofar as it represents a real item, or quantity of labour. Interest, particularly compound interest, or 'virtual' money, allows wealth or debt to increase, unlike the items originally exchanged for the money (the majority of which deteriorate with time). Since we cannot create energy or matter (either physically or economically), but only (sometimes) transform it, all we can do is distribute, in one form or another, the energy provided by the sun (and the material elements produced by previous 'suns' or stars). Interest or 'imaginary' money, if allowed to accrue indefinitely over time, eventually exceeds the human capacity to harness its equivalent from nature, no matter how hard or long work is continued (it is, in effect, an extreme usury), ultimately leading to economic problems and social disturbances (could this be a reason for the Biblical ban on extending debts beyond seven years? Whether or not it is, time offers one important way (and quantity would be another way) in which we can set our own limits, as suggested in the previous chapter, to prevent exponential growth leading to ruin). The man-made game of trying to get something for nothing only leads to deprivation: sometimes for those who play but most unjustly for all those not invited to play and those who don't even know how to play. Nonetheless, because it is played at the 'highest' levels of society, all are drawn, willingly or unwillingly, into this game. The rules are made by those few who already have most (to ensure they continue to get most).

In contrast, nature teaches us that what we use of her resources and / or the products made from them, all depend on the labour of our minds and / or bodies. Those resources, products and labour are symbolized by money, the exchange of which provides us with greater economic flexibility and freedom than the system of bartering goods that preceded it. Aristotle had advised that money was only an instrument of exchange, and should not give 'birth' to money. The Mediaeval objection to charging interest on that money (Appendix IV) was that it is 'contrary to nature, for it is to live without labour' (B68). Money is, and should remain, a token of the matter and energy it ultimately represents, and intimately connected with the natural environment. This 'real' money (and the environment which provides the resources it represents) is the foundation supporting all the 'false money' and any developments financed by it.

In the U.K. between 1987 and 2007 the contribution from the financial services sector to the nation's GDP more than tripled from £31 bn to £95 bn. By 2007, banking was the U.K.'s biggest 'export'. Please note however that a significant proportion of that £95 bn must have included the bad debts and 'toxic assets' revealed by the 2007 crash. During this period the U.K. economy became increasingly dependent on financial services (and other unsustainable stimuli, such as consumer spending and property prices – considered in more detail below) whilst, at the same time, its manufacturing base was allowed to shrink dramatically. The Industrial Revolution had begun in England but was now being stifled in England. Of course, financial services can be useful and important but not to the extent that an economy can rest upon them since they are secondary e.g. banking and insurance are only useful once there is something to insure and money has been earned from the sale of physical products and labour. Moreover, the financial services 'industry' invests overwhelming in that which offers maximum profit in minimum time. There is no interest in long-term growth, community, or national welfare. During the period in question the number of people working in financial services increased, and the majority worked in offices, dealing with all the administrative paperwork associated with buying and selling.

As the number of people who actually make something decrease, spiritual risks are added to economic ones, since doing one's best at making something, and taking pride in that work, provides a sense of satisfaction and achievement. Work which requires some skill or experience relates to part of that person's identity, while defining that person's contribution to society. This lends meaning to their work, becomes part of their purpose and importance and, as a secondary consequence, earns them a living. In contrast, when work is mundane and repetitive, and could be done by virtually anyone (such as much office work), all the satisfaction and importance of one's contribution disappears, money becomes the primary purpose of the work and benefits to (even awareness of) society are superseded by benefits to self. Mundane and repetitive work can also, of course, characterise much industrial work (in the way it is currently organised) and we see the wisdom in Gandhi's recommendation that 'We don't need mass production but production by the masses'. Production that requires skill and / or experience, or even just interest, care and attention, is a manifestation of putting people first (in which both clients and artisans acquire economic, and then personal, importance). 'Financial services' and 'production line' manufacturing put money and profit first, which can lead to views of people, and life, as unimportant or 'empty'. Individual people and / or businesses may aspire to providing first class customer service and this can give meaning to work but we are examining the general trends and principles associated with each type of work and the resulting effects for the health of society.

A primary emphasis on money can also create an expensive 'emptiness'. A good example of this was the rapid and massive increase in house prices in the U.K. over the two decades leading up to the crash. No other factor involved in the cost of house building was advancing at the same rate; neither materials nor labour. The inflation was entirely artificial, made by people whose sole purpose was to make money. It was fuelled by the banks, loans from which are, in the vast majority of cases, for private and commercial properties (in contrast to the very low percentages of loans made to manufacturing enterprise). The trend was also fuelled by private and corporate investors and the trend grew like a bull market on a stock exchange with people joining the rush to make money by buying, and then selling at an inflated price. Those who just wanted a home had to enter the boom market as soon as they could, lest they be left outside all together, which, of course, contributed to the trend still further. All available resources from other supplies (e.g. savings; sale of possessions; parental help) went into the property pot. Hence, housing was distorting, unbalancing the economy, since there was no real extra value in the bricks and mortar. The money paid for them was drained from other areas (just as, on a larger scale, the globalisation practises of the multinationals drain money and resources from the developing nations). Once prices have left real value behind, the property is only 'worth' what someone will pay for it. Just prior to the crash, some properties on the books of Lehman Bros. were listed as being worth $100 000 000 (on the artificially inflated housing market). In reality they were worth 25 – 50% of that figure and so, once the over-inflated balloon burst (when the 'real' or 'prime' market was saturated banks sold loans to the 'sub-prime' market, until debts went unpaid), the emptiness was revealed and prices slid back to approach real property values, leaving the banks with massive losses (from defaulters on mortgage payments) and massive debts (from what they had borrowed on the strength of their artificially inflated assets).

Amazingly, in the U.K. at least, any sign of increasing house prices, no matter how brief or localised, is touted as signs of 'recovery'. Why should prices rise rapidly? Beyond compensation for inflationary effects, house price rises represent an 'empty' or 'imaginary' increase in value, through which a few will gain, while the vast majority will significantly lose, by having larger mortgage millstones around their neck for longer. From the community perspective, the 'increased wealth' is imaginary, since there is no overall increase or decrease, just redistribution generated by the illusion of increasing value of one part of that economy. Again we see that selfishness of individuals and individual corporations detracts from the welfare, health and happiness of the whole community.

Amongst the increasing number of people who cannot actually 'do anything' from a practical perspective are the people on whom the nation's economic security has been allowed to depend – the financiers, whose skills, we are told, are so rare but which have been proved illusory. Of the few manufacturing bases remaining, which can actually 'do something', many go out of business due to the economic repercussions of those who fail in banking. Out of many possible examples, we will consider the most important – relatively few can farm or make the equipment to do so, or make the containers to hold the produce, or the means to transport it, or ovens to bake bread. We all need that bread and can only really buy it from money that relates directly to real resources and associated products and services, which the majority can no longer provide. Just as we do ecologically, we do economically – put ourselves out on a limb while increasing the weight dependent on it, and decreasing support for the main branches that sustain it.

The land, the soil, agriculture, is fundamental to all economies (sources include: common sense, Plato (B32), 'Religion and the Rise of Capitalism' (B68), 'India through the Ages' (B65), 'Small is Beautiful' (B59), 'Topsoil and Civilization' (B20), 'Biology' (B19)). Whether in terms of agriculture, economics, stocks and shares, politics or even space travel, we need to arrange all our activities with our feet standing firmly on the good earth.

The Good Earth

A widely recognised concept amongst economists is that agriculture is the only organised human activity that, in real terms, 'pays' more than it 'costs' and that all other human activities are based upon this surplus. That one man can grow food to feed many allows for the division of labour and the beginnings of civilisation. The farmer not only feeds all but simultaneously provides for the appearance of the carpenter, the cotton spinner, the weaver, the candle maker…the computer scientist and the space traveller – yes, space exploration depends on farming. Cowhands and computer scientists are consequences of that excess food, that stored energy of sunlight in staple crops such as wheat and rice, which ultimately sustains all else (including domestic animals we may slaughter in order to eat their more concentrated energy).

'Among material resources, the greatest, unquestionably, is the land. Study how a society uses its land, and you can come to pretty reliable conclusions as to what its future will be. The land carries the topsoil, and the topsoil carries an immense variety of living beings including man' (B59). The book 'Topsoil and Civilisation' by Dale and Carter (B20), first published in 1955, shows how communities in every civilisation from Mesopotamia to Rome have destroyed themselves by destroying their agricultural base. It also reveals the serious threats to the sustainability of many nations' current agricultural practices, including Europe and the Americas.

When the majority of people consider money more important than land, and a few people make much 'false' money out of nothing, while the majority try to survive on nothing, nature will improve their understanding with an environmental crisis, which reveals as illusory all that does not directly relate to resources, products and labour. This is nature's law and no matter how clever we think ourselves, or how far we run away in space or time, we will ultimately comply with it.

The Law of the Land

Compliance with laws usually makes us think of constraint or restriction. Yet nature's laws are such that obedience to them actually *allows* freedom for exciting and interesting activities while ensuring the maintenance of our life-support system. We have the freedom to break nature's laws but pay the price of doing so, which always costs us more than was gained – if not our life. Goethe and Carlyle, amongst others, knew that excessive or complete freedom (no rules or laws) leads to slavery. Coleridge said as much when he referred to those who

> '…wear the name of Freedom, graven on a heavier chain!'

We saw one aspect of this in the previous chapter when examining the slavery involved in pursuing money or power, which are limitless. It is by setting our own limits that we set ourselves free. We also saw it in relation to the banks which, subjected to no constraints, were given the freedom to ruin themselves (unfortunately, due to their importance in the socio-economic system, they also came close, and may even yet, ruin many other peoples' lives, which is why their survival without reform, their power over government and the latter's failure to properly control them is so dangerous). Many Westerners (at least) growing up during the latter half of the 20th century (already referred to in the preceding chapter as those who rejected traditional values) imagined they were finding freedom but actually found (and founded) a society with significant proportions of broken families, unplanned for and unwanted children, disease and other health problems, and misguided or lost individuals with no standards by which to live. They found the freedom to ruin their lives in a variety of vacuous, self-indulgent ways including drug and alcohol abuse, relationships founded primarily on lust, and gang violence. Our other example was the freedom of the credit culture fostered by Thatcher and Reagan in which there was freedom to spend what one didn't have, and therefore the freedom to ruin one's financial security. Too many freedoms, applied too frequently, leads to slavery (since they upset all balances, and slavery itself is an example of imbalance).

Unrestricted, unregulated and unguided freedom for science and technology also leads to problems. Television documentaries concerning future possibilities tell us we are at the dawn of the age in which the future of life on this planet is in our hands – in terms of genetic engineering, designer babies, 'ownership' of life forms and nano-technology. Few other scenarios could be more frightening. Even the commentator scientists see the possible, if not probable, misuse and dangers of these developments and appear bewildered by the seemingly inexorable drift toward such situations. If it is not to immediate military or commercial advantage, science is left much to itself and proceeds according to what can be done, and personal agendas and interests, regardless of whether or not society wants that research and development. Whatever medical benefits may result from reading the human genome, will they outweigh all the dangers of dabbling with lives yet to be created (naturally and artificially) and the immense, tangled jungle of responsibilities and practical effects that result? We have done it, simply because we could, without reference to guiding principles and purposes previously agreed in consultation with society in general. It would now seem that the mechanical processes studied by science also define some scientists – mechanically following their tangents, in some cases far enough from Earth orbit as to actually appoint themselves as gods, self-appointed designers of future life on Earth.

Nature is our guide and model and leads to health. We need to work in harmony with her and obey her laws in simple, straightforward ways before practising such extreme specialisation that we can navigate robots in capillaries too fine to see (as referred to in the previous chapter), while bellies swollen in hunger for all to see, provoke so little reaction we may as well be the robots. Even to enter into debate as to whether genetic engineering (or any other highly technical speciality) is not also 'part of nature' is to have already missed the point since in pursuing these extreme specialities we are neglecting fundamentals, and we can only debate them because those fundamentals are still, but only just, functioning. When those systems start collapsing, our extreme specialities will collapse, forcing us back to fundamentals in consequence, when we will re-learn their importance and value, but by harsh and painful, rather than easy, lessons.

The previous chapter referred to fundamental laws being ignored and resulting in the multiplication of petty laws. The multiplication of petty laws is akin to over specialisation since both represent too many small disciplines, details and specialities, each ensconced in their own little world with no knowledge or even memory of how they all connect to one shared support system. This pattern of ignoring fundamentals in order to concentrate on specialities can be seen in legislation, politics, economics and science. Too many leaves believe they live independently of branches, boughs and trunk.

So, should all specialism or subdivisions be brought under the control of one centralised authority? Let us use some examples from industry. One chief executive's biography will describe how his giant company was ailing from central, all-encompassing authority dictating from afar without knowledge of local conditions. The CEO sees the stifling effect of this 'blanket ruling' and introduces smaller sub-divisions while maintaining connections between them. This strategy revives the company's fortunes. In contrast, another mogul's biography will describe how all the satellite offices and / or distribution centres were operating virtually independently, sharing little more than the company name, and that giant company was ailing due to the absence of a co-ordinated strategy. This time a re-unification, a revival of some centralised power solved the company's problems. Which is right? From which can we gain worthwhile advice? Does one system apply to one type of product or business? The reader will know the answer; the optimum strategy is the balance between the two extremes, and it applies to all types of human endeavour.

For all those endeavours, time and resources are limited so, individually and collectively, we also have to divide our activities proportionately. In this context we see another value to rituals, festivals and holi-days; timetables which help us divide our time proportionately, harmonising us with nature's rhythms, as referred to in the previous chapter.

Appropriately, the dangerous contrast between extreme specialism and fundamental elements can be illustrated by considering, literally, fundamental elements. Today, in the atomic age, elements describe the ninety-two naturally occurring types of matter making up the material world (there are some additional man-made elements but these usually exist for only brief time periods. They were obviously preceded by the other ninety-two and, being man-made, could in one sense at least, be said to be made from the natural ninety-two). As elements, they cannot be reduced to any other sort of material and are defined by their atomic weight and number and arranged, according to their chemical properties, in the Periodic Table. Our knowledge of the atomic or chemical elements is, of course, of great value and interest, and won for us by exceptional people. However, the environmental catastrophes we are now risking means we need to re-learn the importance of nature's four elements as recognised by the ancients: earth, water, air and fire.

(Strictly speaking, the ancients also referred to a fifth element 'aether' which, according to Aristotle, did not give rise to the other four elements. However, Paracelsus (1493 – 1541 physician, astrologer and alchemist) believed the four elements of the ancients were derivative forms of one undiscovered element common to all, and called this prime element 'alkahest' – a concept equivalent in some ways to the Prana of Hinduism).

Earth, water, air and fire are elemental to our directly perceived experience, and therefore of unique and critical importance since, through these, all other knowledge arrives, including that which finds atomic elements. The elements of the ancients are one way in which nature can 'talk' to us, they make up nature's mirror (that we should be looking into) and teach us nature's laws. We know for ourselves when we are dealing with them. We can, directly by our senses, perceive the effects of salt on our earth, taste it in our food and on our skin, but we cannot directly perceive that it is composed of sodium and chlorine. Earth, water, air and fire are the elements of our lives, and make immediate and significant differences to those lives. We can benefit much from the fascinating and painstaking discoveries of the atomic elements but we impoverish ourselves to subsequently proclaim the ancients 'wrong'. They were working at other levels of perception, which remain valid, and are supplementary and complementary to modern investigations at other levels (the four elements of antiquity have found some parallel in modern science as four states of matter: solid, liquid, gas and – possibly corresponding to fire – plasma). The elements of the ancients will convince us personally of the truth of Bacon's observation referred to in the previous chapter that nature 'cannot be conquered except by obeying her', and the following few selections offer some considerations in that context.

In Appendix II and above, we have looked briefly at soil, at our need to 'obey' the Earth. When we disobey its laws we threaten, in the long-term, our food supply both in quality and quantity. Earth is fundamental. We have also seen how we must obey our 'earth', our material body, in the sense that when we do not, illness forces us to readjust ourselves to nature's laws (the Vedas – the ancient scriptures referred to in the previous chapter – consider illness as 'divinely sent chains' to bind those who break eternal laws).

What of our other fundamental 'elements'? Our need to 'obey' water is obvious and above we looked at warnings about approaching fresh water problems. Our obedience is not only required with regard to water we need to drink. When we abide by the rules of the sea as revealed by varying weathers, currents and tides, we may ride in our ships while marvelling at its beauty and power. Ignore its lessons or oppose it in any way, and our destruction barely makes a ripple on its surface.

With regard to the air: we obviously have no choice about obeying hurricanes and tornadoes, and we have already referred to the threat to our oxygen supply posed by pollution and acidification of the oceans. We may also remember that, due to totally unnecessary depletions of atmospheric ozone, we now need to be aware of the dangers of eye cataracts and skin cancers from 'excessive' sunshine.

Concentrated sunlight turns us to fire which, like the other elements, exists independently of us but, unlike the other elements, is one in which nothing lives. Also unlike the other elements, humans can usually choose what of fire we will create or extinguish..

When we use our free will to learn; harmonise with; apply nature's laws and, above all, obey them, we can achieve the nigh-on miraculous and sit with seven tigers or measure the curvature of starlight. Break them, and the same tigers or sunlight soon return us to our elements.

Opposing the elements, breaking the laws of 'raw' nature usually has immediate effects. Breaking moral laws or living without virtue, usually has delayed effects, giving us more time (within limits) to learn the lessons they offer. Mahatma Gandhi drew up a list of his own seven deadly sins, laws that should not be broken, and they incorporate much of what has been referred to in this book. They are:

Wealth without Work
Commerce without Morality
Pleasure without Conscience
Knowledge without Character
Politics without Principle
Worship without Sacrifice
Science without Humanity

In different ways we have touched on all of these categories through this and preceding chapters. All can be produced by, or associated with, an emphasis on 'self'. Incredible as it may initially seem, and despite the complexity of the world and life upon it, all ignoble, ugly, unhealthy and harmful events orchestrated by humans, from national to personal levels, can be traced to a selfish motive. In contrast, all that is noble, beautiful, healthy and wholesome can be traced to unselfish motives. What is corruption, except favouring self over duty? The irony and tragedy is that self is best served in the long-term by doing one's duty to others.

It might be appropriate at this point to clarify a misunderstanding often used to justify selfish behaviour. It is sometimes claimed that doing something 'good', such as helping someone or something else, gives the doer a pleasant feeling or 'warm glow' and is therefore selfish, since a personal reward is gained. Therefore, so the reasoning goes, since all acts are selfish in one way or another, we can be selfish with a clear conscience. If, for a moment, we accept this premise and classify acts intended to help others as 'good selfish' and acts intended to help ourselves as 'bad selfish', we will easily see the flaw in this argument. 'Good selfish' action benefits *both* parties; the benefactor *and* the beneficiary: the benefactor gets their pleasant feeling and the beneficiary receives the help given. 'Bad selfish' action benefits only the perpetrator and usually at the expense of the other party or parties. Moreover, the two types are mutually exclusive; doing one destroys the other. The 'all acts are selfish' defence of selfishness highlights the epitome of selfishness: assessment of a situation solely by considering one's own internal perception of it and, when challenged about it, projection of the same insularity and microscopic vision to others. An extreme example emphasises the point: two people stand next to a starving person. One shares his bread while the other eats all of his and claims to be equivalent to the sharer, since both acted according to their respective sorts of self-interest. The starving person's view would be most relevant but is not even considered in this sort of analysis, the selfish (by definition!) considering only their own internal feelings. The selfish person only sees the starving person visually, whereas the sharer sees more than an image, connecting at levels beyond the physical senses, experiencing sympathy and empathy, identifying with the sufferer. The selfish person, in similar ways to capitalism and science, only monitors the material, physical aspects;

identifies with no suffering – unless it's their own – they are 'all head' and 'no heart'. (An argument might even be put for capitalism and science to operate in this way – provided other elements in society balance their effects to maintain the overall health of that society). Individuals acting in this way exhibit serious personal, spiritual imbalances and spiritual immaturity. It is superficial humbug to claim all acts are selfish and therefore equivalent.

It is also naïve and simplistic to imagine that 'doing the right thing' necessarily generates a 'warm glow'. With regard to the environment for example, consistently and repeatedly trying to do the 'right thing' can turn life into a waking nightmare – opposing the wealthiest and most powerful with the poorest and weakest facilities and resources, endless anxiety and insecurity, and regularly watching the defeat of one's finest efforts, to mention but a few associated realities. The only warm glow experienced, despite every effort to avoid it, is the heat generated by the fevers of all the tropical diseases acquired along the way.

Whether economic, social, cultural, romantic or any other aspect of life governed by choice, and whether national, communal or individual, all negative, harmful and unhealthy effects trace to selfishness, while all positive, helpful and healthy effects trace to unselfishness. Consider it from your personal perspective: every hurtful action of lovers, friends, family or neighbours stem from them putting themselves before you; whilst every pleasant experience arises from them putting you before themselves. So too do we choose by our own behaviour to harm or heal, hurt or please. So too for the world, since it is comprised of numerous individuals choosing self or others. The unity of life confers importance on each of us. Learning to discipline self is of crucial importance for the whole – and hence, simultaneously, for each of us as individuals.

It was just mentioned that capitalism and science could operate totally 'mechanically', provided other groups in society (particularly an independent government) control them by law and balance their operation and effects (with meaning, purpose, compassion etc.) to maintain the overall health of society. We currently have the former but not the latter. The elements in society trying to balance the operation and effects of improperly controlled capitalism (and improperly managed science and technology) are relatively few and weak. Hence we all suffer the effects of imbalance, and its offspring, such as 'military-industrial-political complexes'.

Uncontrolled capitalism is the socio-economic expression of obesity (acquiring and retaining far in excess of what one needs), which is an expression of selfishness. These excesses also prevent others from acquiring sufficient for their most basic needs. From a spiritual perspective, capitalism must ultimately bring itself (and many innocent people) to ruin because of its exclusive focus on self, and from practical perspectives as well, because of the extreme imbalances it generates.

Would it not be beneficial for all (including, ultimately, the powerful and the greedy) if government reviewed and addressed its loss of power to non-elected bodies, to the media and other big businesses; its loss of common sense and justice in the application of the law? Would it not be to the benefit of all if science looked to broaden and balance its current exclusively mechanical approach by complementing its studies with subjects now dismissed by scientists as invalid? One model for a new science is not so new; it was suggested by Johann von Goethe (1750 – 1832). Best known as a literary genius, he considered his scientific work of greater importance. He recommended that science attempt to understand natural phenomena holistically and include not just quantities but qualities in describing them, emphasising the value of subjective personal experience. However, science proceeded down the path of rigidly impersonal quantification and measurement, leaving Goethe's science misunderstood for centuries. It can now be seen as complementary to and not in conflict with modern orthodox science.

Amongst many other accomplishments, Francis Bacon established scientific principles sufficiently rigorous to inspire the founders of Britain's Royal Society. However, once again, the modern scientific view of his proposals is highly selective and much of his work has been ignored for centuries. Francis Bacon proposed a study of nature vastly broader than one confined to impersonal measurement, and paired a 'selfless scientific inquiry' with religion and postulated a 'scientific charity' (B9).

Emerson proposed a concept of an 'intuitive intelligence', which must surely be another way of combining yin with yang, and provides another viewpoint from which scientists may study nature, and from which science itself may be studied. (Ralph Waldo Emerson. 1803 – 1882. American essayist, poet and philosopher).

Science, as currently practised, can study some aspects of subjects such as religion, meditation, alternative medicine, spiritual, psychic and supernatural phenomena, psychokinesis, faith-healing and telepathy. However, where it cannot cope with studying these subjects, why not define and develop a new science?

Including personal experience and qualitative approaches with orthodox science could contribute to solving the environmental crisis. Their current separation is starkly apparent in magazine or television interviews with scientists or other 'experts', giving their views on the environmental situation. In most cases there is a mismatch between what is being said and the demeanour of the scientist or 'expert' – and bearing in mind that the content, by virtue of being broadcast, has already been diluted. There is a fine line between the necessarily detached objectivity of a scientific or journalistic observation and the fact that the scientist / presenter is also a human being with a set of faculties and responsibilities extending beyond science or journalism. The detached delivery is suitable for the science or journalism – but humanity and common sense demand more, or even some, information about remedial action and advice relating to the predicted serious difficulties, if not disasters, which rarely, if ever, accompany the science or report. As with so many human problems talk, and nothing but talk, is insufficient to solve them but is, nonetheless, the most frequent response of individuals, nations and the global community. To solve, or reduce the adverse effects of the environmental crisis requires us to combine impersonal, objective data with personal, purposeful actions, to rapidly re-establish conservative and compassionate use of natural resources and processes.

A generally prevailing attitude seems to be that we humans and our products are the impressive parts of this world. Air, water and food provided by nature have always been, and always will be there, while we manipulate natural resources into whatever our genius decides. This attitude persists even in the face of the environmental crisis. Television documentaries regularly present scientists and other professionals working on high-tech equipment, telling us of their work and plans for the future. For them and the viewer, eating our meals, drinking water and breathing air are not even mentioned because, of course, such things are ordinary, well established and secure. In reality, none of these things are ordinary, well established or secure! Moreover, the high-tech equipment in question might even pose a threat to the quality and / or availability of these necessities.

What are we to make of the cool reasoning and articulation of scientists, presenters or journalists in such documentaries? Most probably, only that their relaxed demeanours indicate they still have a nice salary, nice house, and / or are being paid to pontificate for, say, the camera and / or 'plume their egos' and / or enhance their C.V.s and, most significantly, that they do not *really* understand. Their minds understand the facts and figures but their hearts don't understand. They are 'seeing with and not through the eye' and don't feel it in their guts – or they would be organising every possible remedial action and telling the cameraman to dump the damn thing and join those groups trying to preserve life and civilisation as we know it. But, of course, if they did, they wouldn't be seen on television. (Although they are rare, all credit to those television crews who have taken action according to what they have witnessed and founded charities and / or other methods to alleviate the suffering they have just filmed. Such people represent ideals in the terms of this book). Usually, the cameraman continues to do his work because he also has a nice salary and house etc. and so does the science presenter or editor, the politician, the butcher, baker and candlestick maker, who all have appointments to keep, bills to pay, family to be with, careers to advance and everywhere one looks there are people with reasons to maintain their own microscopic world and so very few who realise that their little world is totally dependent on the world at large. Thomson told us the reality in chapter I: we are 'naught but weakness and dependence'. Serious threats to our air, water and food supplies are referred to in the appendices but most are being ignored by the relevant authorities or actively exacerbated by them. The tribal candle makers, and others with skills and education gained as part of the Employment Cell Project described above, probably have a better understanding of economic and ecological connections, as well as environmental issues in general and tiger conservation in particular, although supposedly not as sophisticated as Western professionals.

In the event of life-threatening ill health, everybody knows that time must be taken from their normal schedule to ensure recovery. Yet nobody can spare any time from their schedules when the threat is to everyone's health and life. The former is forced upon us but the latter relies on us to consciously make the effort to understand and take action.

Again, verification is available to you directly; talk to people about the imminent catastrophes we are openly inviting and encouraging by our behaviour. Most will give no worthwhile response at all, including 'well-educated', highly intelligent people (much information, some knowledge, no wisdom). Such ignorance or indifference is itself an indication of serious problems with our societies, education system and collective priorities. Of the few who have some grasp, even most of these will be physically doing very little to avert what they themselves know to be coming. Standing on a railway platform in England, I tried to understand the reality that I would be unable to approach any of the people who were also waiting on the platform in order to discuss the most important topic conceivable. Had I done so, I might well have been considered 'weird' or 'mad'. So, in individual isolation we waited and, when the train arrived, shuffled in silent sanity onto carriages heading for the precipice.

We might agree with Hamlet's famous and fundamental question from a philosophical perspective but, from a practical point of view, 'to be or not to be' is not the question. Given that we find ourselves 'being' and that the option 'not to be' is fraught with all the uncertainty he so eloquently describes, 'to do or not to do' forces itself upon us as the next question. Hamlet does briefly consider it before losing it among his thoughts on suicide, since suicide initially seems the easier option. Jacob Bronowski pointed out that the play explores Hamlet's growing maturity. Having learned the truth of his father's death, much of the rest of the play is about his maturing enough to meet his responsibilities and his struggle with his free will choices in regard to them. (So perhaps the murdered father's return as a ghost is to initiate the process that will both smelt his son's mettle and remove the malignant presence on Denmark's throne. Revenge is the briefest and simplest reason the ghost can use to achieve the dual purpose). When the emphasis moves from thinking to doing, answers to Hamlet's questions are provided for him – and the rest of us. Having found ourselves in the physical world we must take physical action, firstly in order to survive and secondly such that our communities may grow and prosper. Experience and common sense teach us that the most beneficial procedures and practices, by which progress is achieved, are co-operative – firstly with nature and then with each other. By such co-operation we overcome the problems the world presents us with. Even where there are individual difficulties, or even failures, much is learned for future reference and characters grow and mature. Action is unavoidably imposed upon us by virtue of 'being' in the material world, teaching us to take arms against a sea of troubles (physically and spiritually) and by opposing end them. If not, environmentally speaking, it must be our 'end', rough hewn or otherwise, which is currently being shaped by our destinies. Incredibly, and unlike Hamlet, we have not, collectively speaking, matured sufficiently to meet our responsibilities, and are not only contemplating suicide as the easier option, but actively working toward it.

The Few

Amongst the few who do realise the gravity of the environmental situation are the even fewer who are prepared to do something about what they know. If you have read this far, you are probably among that precious 'Few' and you have probably already been taking action.

However, just as the original 'Few' halted the advance of darkness over the nation's doorsteps, they could not, on their own, win the war. Others were needed. In the same way, you may live as ethically as you can, have reduced your impact on the environment and halted the advance of darkness over your own doorstep but, lest all your efforts to live healthily within your own home go to waste, we must now educate and encourage others to do the same. 'Human history becomes more and more a race between education and catastrophe' ('The Outline of History' by H.G. Wells. Pub. 1920). In our current environmental crisis too many people are inactive or semi-active, not because they can't or wouldn't help but because they do not *really* understand the gravity of the situation and / or do not know of remedial actions and / or the situation is too fearful to face and / or partly because the scientist or television presenter did not seem too concerned. Even if people are concerned about environmental reports they can, immediately afterward, lose themselves in the majority of media's trivia, puff and nothingness. Therefore, part of the activities of the Few must be, as Wells' observed, to educate, to make aware, but also and most importantly, to motivate and stimulate appropriate *action* in others.

Without our attributing priorities and purpose to it, science cannot help us, since it merely provides information. Its objectivity is like the impartial camera informing us of scenes that can horrify both the cameraman and the audience. The camera, and science, are rich in information but poor (bankrupt!) in knowledge and wisdom and hence, solutions. It is for the audience, the scientist and the cameraman (by putting the camera down), to find solutions. Currently, the most common behaviour is to continue research, or move on and film more of the same, much of which results from our not having solved problems filmed previously. Both camera and science are needed but they are not all that is needed. Their continued use instead of appropriate remedial action renders them as offensive as the 'wise' who see approaching disaster but do nothing to prevent it.

Without exaggeration or melodrama, the future health and security of the atmosphere, water and food are all under serious threat (at least insofar as they can sustain human life). There is no longer time for pretence that society may have a few problems but basically all is well and 'progress' will continue. The world is currently controlled by big business and facing dire and frightening changes as a consequence. Corporate pursuit of profit, and only profit, has unbalanced both itself and the system it is part of. Self, greed and power have assumed monstrous proportions and are as a malignant growth or leeches on our society, now literally threatening the continued life of their host. However, tumours and leeches are manifestations of the same or similar aspirations within the community, insofar as individuals admire or aspire to the same wealth, power and status (without further qualification or examination). An increasing emphasis on money, material and mechanism, combined with cut-throat competition, results in the ever accelerating pace of life and, all go to make up the organised chaos about us.

'The chaos about thee is but the confusion within thee' was a saying of Amos Bronson Alcott (father of Louisa May Alcott, author of 'Little Women'). It applies personally and collectively. (Amos Alcott's close friends were Emerson and Henry David Thoreau and all were very familiar with Eastern philosophy in general and the Bhagavad Gita in particular. Thoreau once owned what was thought to be the largest Oriental library in America (given him by an English friend, Thomas Cholmondely) and loaned books to Emerson (whose disciplines of personal exercise closely paralleled yoga)). Alcott, Emerson and Thoreau are are some of the precious few who have tried to make us aware.

As each character exercises an interest in life, follows nature's guidance, and faces their responsibilities, obeying morality and practising virtue, the apparent 'glamour' and the desirability of extreme material wealth diminishes, while dismay at conspicuous excess and waste increases. Waste of resources only affecting oneself is reprehensible, but waste of materials, energy and, worst of all, food and water, when others are in desperate need of the same is offensive in the extreme. As the trappings of toys and over-priced man-made products become less fashionable or attractive, and the methods (both economic and practical) of producing them become public knowledge, fewer people will aspire to them and we may gradually balance and stabilise our citizens and societies, feed the hungry, educate all, save our tigers and, perhaps, acquire some nobility or, at least, a little dignity.

We have touched on a number and variety of possible actions to help alleviate the environmental situation. Could these actions solve environmental problems and save species – if not society and civilisation itself?

Banking and investing ethically will *not*.
Eating organic food will *not*.
Buying environmentally-friendly and fair-trade goods will *not*.
Pressurising politicians and corporations will *not*.
Getting involved in local communities and monitoring/influencing social trends will *not*.
Nor will practising personal self-development.

However, *conducted regularly on adequate scales*;

Banking and investing ethically *and*
Eating organic food *and*
Buying environmentally-friendly and fair-trade goods *and*
Pressurising politicians and corporations *and*
Getting involved in local communities and monitoring/influencing social trends *and*
Practising personal self-development

all together stand a good chance of solving environmental problems and saving species, if not society and civilisation itself – and definitely would where they influence and then gain the co-operation of corporate boards and government departments. Each individual who manages to practise the majority of these actions (and who else can but individuals?) creates effects that spread within society, and hence change society, especially where they actively educate, motivate and stimulate others to do the same. So much of 'real' progress and mass movements depend on a few dedicated *individuals*. 'Do not wait for leaders; do it alone, person to person.' (Mother Teresa of Calcutta. 1910 – 1997). These actions will be decisive if the few can become the many. Both categories are measured by the number of individuals within each. If you, your family and friends become some of the few, the few will no longer be the few.

Individual self-development and its associated behaviour is not only a way to change the world, it is *the only way* to change the world – in any worthwhile and meaningful way. Due to the actions of the original Greenpeace founders, Friends of the Earth and similar groups around the world; due to field workers and authors, teachers raising awareness in their pupils and due to discussions amongst friends and family, the consciousness of individuals has already been raised to some degree such that, when these people find themselves in decision-making positions, the environment and social responsibility are already part of their heart and mind-sets. Since corporate decisions are made by individuals, and more enlightened individuals will, eventually, be found in boardrooms and amongst shareholders, corporations will also begin to reflect this growing consciousness. The critical factor of course, is time. Hence the urgency with which we need to adopt the above recommendations and spread the word.

Adopting the suggestions above are all valuable contributions toward our survival and development. Out of those actions, acting responsibly as a consumer, to promote the sale of ethical and environmentally-friendly products and services is, in our current circumstances, the most powerful action it is possible to take. It produces immediate, beneficial effects for the earth and life, it forces manufacturers to comply with the purchasing pattern promoted, it brings changes rapidly and independently of the character of corporate decision makers, and independently of governments, and does so without debates or discussions. Moreover, in accordance with life's essential symmetries, by controlling greed, self and carelessness in these ways, we also simultaneously begin to improve our own conduct and character – we will be framing our fearful symmetries. We achieve personal growth *and* a healthier world, each reinforcing the other.

What is left?

For us to make our choices – and put them into action.

The Light that Remains

There is another sense in which we may pose the question 'What is left?' The reader may consider all recommendations made herein, from purchasing patterns to self-development, inadequate. The author believes he could make a good argument in agreement! Yet what is left? What else can be done? We and our tigers have a choice of complete darkness, or darkness with a thin bean of light before us.

Recommendations to spend money with a social and environmental conscience while practising personal character development are not only all that's left to us but also, happily, all that's important, since, if an ideal society could be created by magic wand, its description must include both these features as extant, defining characteristics as well as part of the process of achieving that ideal society. Hence, by adopting them, we cannot but help the situation, and broaden that beam of light. Fittingly, it is in 'Paradise Lost' that Milton (John Milton 1608 – 1674 poet, author and civil servant) tells us 'Long is the way and hard, that out of Hell leads into the light'. Although the way out is long and hard, it is better than staying where we are. If we deny this, and only wait for some future benign or philanthropic corporation and / or government to solve all our problems, we not only choose what has already patently failed, but also choose to deny our tigers. Physical and spiritual tigers disappear as people opt to be a member of a herd or, worse still, a leech or parasite. Let each of us live as if we were already part of the ideal society.

With regard to such a society or 'city', Plato tells us that 'perhaps in heaven there is laid up a pattern of such a city, and he who desires may behold it, and beholding, govern himself accordingly. But whether there really is or ever will be such a city on earth...he will act according to the laws of that city, and no other.' The ideal man will live by ideal laws, even in less than ideal societies.

'The great hope of society is individual character' said the American minister William Ellery Channing (1780 – 1842. He graduated from Harvard where he subsequently became a 'commencement speaker', and amongst those he taught, was Henry David Thoreau). We have used Corbett as our example of character and one of his habits was making long hard walks – which build strength and character, and strength of character. Corbett lived in the Himalayan foothills which provide a perfect physical setting for Hesiod's spiritual metaphor, which will bear repeating '"the path to vice is smooth" and being short, can be travelled without sweat, whereas "before virtue the immortal gods have set sweat, and the road thither is long and uphill and rough at the outset, though when the summit is reached, the going is easy, for all its hardness."' (B32). The view from the summit must be extensively panoramic and it is fitting that the lands of the highest mountains gave rise to some of the world's deepest scriptures, including the Upanishads, which refer to finding and developing oneself, finding truth, and our relation to the Absolute, the Self, the Universal. The Upanishads have been called, appropriately, the 'Himalayas of the soul' (this author is unsure of the origin of this particular expression but believes it should be credited to J. Mascaro whose translation of the Upanishads was published under that title in 1938). If we choose to scale the Himalayas of our souls we "will look back upon our lives as in the hills we saw our days' marches laid out behind us." (B42c) The lands of the highest mountains and deepest scriptures are also those of the tiger, and karma, and cultures rich in spiritual symbolism, all together making the perfect setting, physically and spiritually, by which to assess our choices of path and our consequent, personal, physical and spiritual journeys.

On that journey we learn spiritual and physical laws. Although a deeply religious person, only Isaac Newton's physical and mathematical laws were used to form a foundation for Western science. Much of his work, like Goethe's and Bacon's, has been largely ignored. However, Newton's mechanics taught us that to every action there is an equal and opposite reaction. We know that life is immensely more complex than mechanics but one wonders if there is some sort of equivalent ecological law such that the imminent extinction of the tiger carries with it a sort of negative, ugly and catastrophic reaction, in some sense equivalent to the positive, handsome, healthy energy the living tiger represents. There may also be an equivalent spiritual law, by which we automatically replace the health and beauty we destroy by equal measures of disease and corruption. Two options, and which prevails is directly dependent on each of our choices. We can choose between danger and beauty, between black and orange.

This is not to say that the disappearance of the tiger might be felt immediately (by human time-scales) but that the disappearance of the tiger's 'guardianship' of the forest (as recognised by tribal people living with tigers, and touched on in chapter II) will ultimately affect the world and hence us all. Do we have any evidence for this? The following could be called coincidence but perhaps coincidence is a label for connections we neither see nor understand: The tiger's decline during the 20th century has already been accompanied by unprecedented damage to the Earth and life. The decline of the tiger could already, without speculation or qualification, be used as an index of the decline of the world. If the tiger disappears we will find out the effects in the relatively near future, and similarly with regard to all the other life energies, the other guiding-lights we are extinguishing.

Those who point to progress during the same period are usually thinking of technology and all that has been built with fossil fuels. Yes, we have more machines, gadgets and toys but these in themselves, and the processes by which they are made, have also caused devastation to the environment. Neither the resources used, nor the wealth and knowledge they generated, have been used to prepare for a healthier or even a sustainable future – in fact the future has been put in peril by them, because such progress was not accompanied by spiritual progress; by character development.

Full health for most Asian ecosystems corresponds to tigers in forests, similarly; lions in African ecosystems; jaguars in South America; polar bears in the Arctic etc. Animals are not merely decoration or entertainment for humans. It is common for human adults to enjoy their children's amusement or fascination with animals. Such children show more sense than those parents who, through ignorance or apathy, are active parts of the system destroying the animals, despite the child's future depending on their continued existence.

The few who still try to find their way by the light of nature's guidance, those who can see the dangers of the current over-emphasis on money and materials, are usually better balanced individuals – the few who have most closely balanced yin and yang, internally and externally.

Yin and Yang

Since the 'whole wide world is only he and she', the whole wide world's ideal is to harmoniously balance these two elements. It is absurd (but often the case) to argue for one or the other exclusively. We know the irresolvable arguments and debates that follow from taking one or the other of their manifestations as 'right' and the other 'wrong', or one as 'better' and the other 'worse', when both are necessary. So, none of the comments herein reminding us of science's limitations should be taken as denigrating orthodox science. A rejection of science is not being recommended. Insofar as science is yang, we have to combine and complement it with yin aspects of life such as 'knowledge with feeling', intuition, religion and other examples given above and in previous chapters.

What is recommended is a change to the prevailing modern Western view that science is the only path to truth. Some experience of life, and a woman's intuition, brings us in line with Kipling's view that "A woman's guess is more accurate than a man's certainty". Any male reader who has had a serious relationship with a female will recognise this reference to female intuition – and female readers already knew it would be referred to! Kipling's observation reveals a truth. However, the whole truth can only be reached by combining and balancing yin and yang which, in this context, are the two different types of knowledge – not arguing which one of them is truth alone. In this sense, we could say that any dispute between science and religion is a marital one! When both join together, balanced and harmonised, we find unity and truth. 'Science or religion?', or any other suggested choice between yin and yang, are invalid premises. The debate, and challenge, is how to combine them harmoniously.

Even if we ignore Eastern philosophy and religion, there is still no direct conflict between science and religion, since the goals and practices of each are not comparable. Neither science's methodology (looking without) nor the majority of its subject matter (which is just that; matter) need clash with religion's methodology (looking within), or the majority of its subject matter (which is spirit). Moreover, science itself, shorn of opinions or suggestions, is not in conflict with religion (more comments in appendix IV). The supposed conflicts are details that, when carefully examined, cannot be considered decisive either way and, through over-specialised and irresolvable disputes, we miss the more obvious treasure trove of complementary investigation each discipline could represent for the other. Scientists' *opinions* are often given great credibility because of their other, but in this context, irrelevant accomplishments, and we are reminded of our intrepid explorers being inappropriately treated as gods because they produce fire from matches. Yet 'science or religion' is now a commonly mentioned and supposed dichotomy and debates are organised around it. Our conjuring master is playing more tricks on the public (and again, some scientists). There is no conflict. Yet, given the false premise 'science or religion', intelligent people can be led off on a false trail and wonder why no destination can be reached or valid conclusions drawn. Science provides some answers to the question 'how?' while religion provides some answers to the question 'why?' Answers to 'why?' provide meaning and purpose. Answers to 'how?' provide knowledge (and more questions!) and help us achieve our purposes, but no matter what we discover about matter in motion, 'meaning' will not be amongst it – we find that within. 'For a fact is nothing except in relation to desire; it is not complete except in relation to a purpose and a whole.' (B23. Previously quoted more fully in chapter II. Reprinted wuith the permission of Pocket Books, a division of Simon & Schuster, Inc., from THE STORY OF PHILOSOPHY by Will Durant. Copyright © 1926, 1927, 1933, 1954, 1955, 1961 by Will Durant. All rights reserved)

Science can no more replace religion than a computer can replace compassion. Adopting a more holistic view with humility and compassion will be an important part of saving the tiger and surviving the environmental crisis. There is a well-known saying that our best hope is a 'thinking heart and feeling brain', which summarises the requirement to allow both sides of our nature expression and involvement. Let us treat each other, and all sincere searches for truth, with equal regard. Let us sit again in Akbar's House of Discussion and improve our understanding by 'listening while doctors of the law, Brahmins, Jews, Jesuits, Sufis – God only knows what sects and creeds' and scientists, philosophers, poets and any other seekers of Truth, discuss views from their various standpoints and examine each other's interpretations of what they can see.

As mentioned in chapter IV and appendix IV, science conducted without morality is as dangerous as commerce conducted without morality. Hence, it is imperative that we learn how to combine religion, or at least its moral elements, with science and commerce.

Neither full understanding, nor full health and security will come without combining hearts and heads – within people and between people. In the previous chapter we heard some of Jung's conversation with Ochwiay Biano, a 'noble savage' with a broader vision of a world he had never seen, than many of those who have travelled all around it. Jung spoke of the poverty of knowledge gathered by reason alone, the Western way to 'plume ourselves on our cleverness' to avoid facing that poverty. He found that: 'In talk with a European, one is constantly running up on the sand bars of things long known but never understood; with this Indian, the vessel floated freely on deep, alien seas.' Let us listen in again:

'I asked him why he thought the whites were all mad.

"They say that they think with their heads," he replied.

"Why of course. What do you think with?" I asked him in surprise.

"We think here," he said, indicating his heart.

"See…how cruel the whites look. Their lips are thin, their noses sharp, their faces furrowed and distorted by folds. Their eyes have a staring expression; they are always seeking something. What are they seeking? The whites always want something; they are always uneasy and restless. We do not know what they want. We do not understand them. We think they are mad."'

Jung 'fell into a long meditation. For the first time in my life, so it seemed to me, someone had drawn for me a picture of the real white man. It was as though until now I had seen nothing but sentimental, prettified colour prints. This Indian had struck our vulnerable spot, unveiled a truth to which we are blind. I felt rising within me like a shapeless mist something unknown and yet deeply familiar. And out of this mist, image upon image detached itself: first Roman legions smashing into the cities of Gaul, and the keenly incised features of Julius Caesar, Scipio Africanus, and Pompey. I saw the Roman eagle on the North Sea and on the banks of the White Nile. Then I saw St. Augustine transmitting the Christian creed to the Britons on the tips of Roman lances, and Charlemagne's most glorious forced conversions of the heathen; then the pillaging and murdering bands of the Crusading armies. With a secret stab I realised the hollowness of that old romanticism about the Crusades. Then followed Columbus, Cortes, and the other conquistadors who with fire, sword, torture, and Christianity came down upon even these remote Pueblos dreaming peacefully in the Sun, their Father. I saw, too, the peoples of the Pacific islands decimated by firewater, syphilis, and scarlet fever carried in the clothes the missionaries forced on them.

It was enough. What we from our point of view call colonisation, missions to the heathen, spread of civilisation, etc., has another face – the face of a bird of prey seeking with cruel intentness for distant quarry – a face worthy of a race of pirates and highwaymen. All the eagles and other predatory creatures that adorn our coats of arms seem to me apt psychological representatives of our true nature.' (B40 pp.233 – 234 reprinted by kind permission of Taylor and Francis)

Of course, the tiger and other big cats are amongst the predatory creatures used as emblems. For some, the emblem symbolises only the power of domination, intimidation or, as in Zen, manipulation of others. This mentality fails to frame the fearful symmetry – it prefers to project power over others rather than reflect the power of the emblem onto ourselves and then, humbled by the comparison, emulate its qualities. To emulate the tiger is not only to exercise power but also to practise restraint and avoid the senseless indulgence of power. Immaturely, we think we acquire the emblem's qualities merely by association. We feel it a fine thing to be powerful, dominant or hold associated characteristics (popularity, fame, glamour, respect or even to be feared) as a consequence of that association. Temporarily in charge, in control, we can pose and strut in our microscopic playground choosing not to see our immaturity in the classroom mirror of the macroscopic world. Such behaviour reminds us of the risk of attaching ourselves to sources of power far in excess of our own, as referred to in the previous chapter, when we considered walking with a tiger on a hand-held leash or behaving like the sorcerer's apprentice. Such attitudes are not restricted to those who strive for extreme power but may potentially be seen, at different scales, in all of us, and in everyday events. The challenge is to sacrifice our personal, worldly status, face the mirror and ourselves. Facing our fears, our tigers, takes courage and it helps to remember again Mark Twain's advice that courage is not absence of fear but mastery of fear. It can be painful to see ourselves, our faults and our immaturity, yet we must identify them and then try to master them, and hence ourselves, both for our own, and the greater good. Seeking not to dominate and take; but co-operate and give; thinking not only of ourselves but of others. Then our expanded spiritual vision will be reflected in physical, environmental mirrors.

Hi-tech cultures' physical vision has expanded billions of light-years to the current boundary of the visible universe but their spiritual vision has shrunk in inverse proportion. Cultures without hi-tech and whose inhabitants have never left home, are conscious of the Earth as a whole and try to heal it. Chief Luther Standing Bear referred to the Lakota literally loving all of earth and life. The reference to Ochwiay Biano in the previous chapter included his people believing their prayers were beneficial to the whole world. Other 'primitive' cultures share this global vision and, for example, little prayer flags left by pilgrims to flutter on lines at holy shrines amid the Himalayas

of Tibet, are hung such that the wind will blow the prayers they hold across the whole world. Hi-tech societies are too often characterised by people who love themselves only, have no prayers, and harm the earth and life.

After Red Indian Chief Sitting Bull defeated Custer's army at the battle of the Little Big Horn he took his people across the border to Canada. However, he eventually brought his people back, surrendered to the U.S. army and soon afterwards joined Buffalo Bill's Wild West Show for a season. He earned about $50 a week and sold his autographed photographs, but gave away most of the money to the homeless and beggars. He could not understand how a nation as rich as the U.S. could not feed its own children and decided that "The White man was good at production but bad at distribution." Our brief review of capitalist policies showed that this summary remains true today. However, it is not, of course, that the wealthy try but fail at equitable distribution, but actively and consciously prevent it.

'A criminal is a person with predatory instincts who has not sufficient capital to form a corporation.' (Howard Scott (economist) quoted in Forbes.com April 2010) However, capitalism is predatory to the point of killing all the 'prey' without being able to utilise a fraction of the carcasses. In the Presentation to Forest Guards above, we saw that predators influence which plants grow on the forest floor. Corporate predators are taking far more than they need or could ever use and thereby, through chains of connections, denuding the 'forest floor' and hence signing their own death warrants. This type of commercialism, that has replaced colonialism could, like Jung's description of Western colonisation, also be described as 'predatory'. Similarly, this pattern of forcible acquisition, division, allocation, sale, or other control of all collected parts, could also describe Western science's practices of collecting, separating, analysing and dissecting since science,

although equally capable of synthesis and holism, is largely governed by the culture within which it develops.

Sweet is the lore which Nature brings;
Our meddling intellect
Mis-shapes the beauteous forms of things:
We murder to dissect.

(From 'The Tables Turned' by Wordsworth)

Furthermore, the way science is currently practised and promoted encourages the belief that through our science and technology we discover the 'reality' of nature, perhaps in a way similar to those invaders above who believed they had discovered the 'real' Indians or Africans. They were no more unified with those natives than the scientist is unified or integrated with the object observed. We do not integrate our knowledge with our feelings, do not balance head with heart, or with other methods of investigation or knowing. Ochwiay Biano might have said that the Whites must always 'do' rather than simply 'be'.

We Whites might finally face our obsession with 'getting and spending', collecting, colonising and 'doing'. We might decide to shut-up and sit down. When we rise again, we can seek to harmonise with the patterns revealed to us while we were still and silent – and realise the folly of our frantic efforts to turn nature's academy into a playground of dangerous toys with which we can abuse and bully the majority of other students and species. Western 'doing' is synonymous with expending energy, money and resources – commercially, militarily, scientifically – rather than conserving them. Even Western health and fitness programmes involve maximum energy expenditure, maximum weights or maximum repetitions of an exercise – 'no pain, no gain'. It provides a good example of contrasts with Eastern disciplines such as Yoga, which exercises the body and mind by renewing, conserving, energy. Yoga stops before the pain threshold and, by using conscious awareness and visualisation, relaxes the body even in its flexed position, in this way 'experiencing' the exercise as it is practised. Yoga also focuses on breathing exercises since the Prana referred to in the preceding chapter is brought in with the air as well as with sunshine. Yoga exercises body, mind and soul; which are the only apparatus required and available for free. In yoga, positions are held in stillness and silence and meditation may follow naturally from yoga exercises. Just as spending time with nature teaches us to be physically still and silent (in order that we may receive) meditation teaches the mind to be still and silent: meditation is literally to 'be' and not 'do' (even thinking is 'doing', so this too rests in the meditative state). For those who want them, answers can still come, but without questions being asked. To simply be at one with nature, one has to simply 'be'. One of the slow movements of another Eastern discipline, T'ai Chi, is to carry the tiger (energy) back to the mountain (stillness). Yet, the East now follows the West in terms of industrialisation, consumerism and commerce and is now failing to conserve its energy and its tigers.

Spend or conserve? Which is right or which is wrong? Neither or both. We know that each must be combined with the other in due proportion, in balance. Take some and leave some. Let us follow Polonius' advice and give no 'unproportioned thought' its act. (Hamlet Act 1 Sc. 3)

Western callisthenics do exactly what they claim to do: train the physical body with physical exercises. Many people living in modern cities and suburbs realise the range of physical exertion usually included in their daily lives does not provide sufficient exercise for a healthy body, and make efforts to compensate for this, to redress the imbalance, by attending a gym, or jogging, playing sport etc. It is usually the same people who also recognise that being selective about the food they eat also brings many benefits. All this is well and good and this physical side of life is, obviously, always apparent. If we let it, it can obscure other aspects of life of which it is merely a manifestation ('…that little-understood beast, our body, who, being but a delusion, insists on posing as the soul, to the darkening of the Way, and the immense multiplication of unnecessary devils.' (B42c)) Consequently, it would appear that few of the same people who exercise physically and observe health diets, consider the manifold benefits of being selective about the exercise and diet they give their mind and spirit. In addition to benefits lost are dangers created since they also seem unaware of the mental and spiritual diets they are 'force-fed' daily by advertising and media all around them, nearly all of which is poor quality and carrying hidden agendas. As Aldous Huxley noted, unlike any author's work in history, advertising copy is read by virtually everyone everyday. By design it appeals to our most common psychological drives and, although each piece of copy may be brief, it carries power as a consequence of its constant repetition. This power is used exclusively to stimulate desire, all of which, Buddhists tell us, is dangerous. As advertising appeals by design to our immediate and basic desires, it is even more dangerous to our spiritual development and maturation.

Our scientific studies also, for obvious reasons, focus on the physical and ignore the spiritual. They do not, of course, ignore the mental, yet the way orthodox science is conducted can produce a mind-set that separates us from what is studied, whereas we are actually a part of the nature we study. Even the profound revelations of 20th century physics, most notably Relativity and quantum physics (which reveal, amongst much else, the unity of nature and that our conscious involvement influences physical reality) has not yet adjusted this mind set for many, including some scientists. Moreover, in contrast to its methodology and necessary emphasis on the material world, modern physics' conclusions now emphasise the illusory nature of physical reality (in agreement with Hinduism) and refer to more fundamental realities beyond the reach of our senses (aided or otherwise) in multi-dimensional realms impossible even to imagine. Scientific mysteries have been shown to have much in common with those of ancient religious scriptures. Those religious scriptures, however, in addition to intellectual mysteries and revelations, also emphasise other and more important elements of our lives, those we all experience; love and death, fear and doubt, our personal responsibilities, morality, virtue and the denial of self in order to achieve development. If reason is allowed to work without these elements we become separated from them. As these other elements are essential, not only for our personal progress but also to unite communities healthily, an over-emphasis on reason and the material world is unhealthy for us all. (Communities can also, of course, be united by a variety of propaganda, lies and manipulation but these are not healthy and do not endure). The same imbalance in other human activities, such as an over-emphasis on the material in commerce and socio-economics, is reflected in social unrest, environmental damage, species extinctions…

Our rational abilities are limited in themselves and subject to further limitations such as practical constraints, others imposed by time and space and – as Henry Beston reminded us – those of the 'glass of our knowledge'. We can only study what we can conceive of and, whilst this is a blindingly obvious statement, our successes in pursuing those studies have blinded us to these obvious limitations. Hence overblown, unsubstantiated claims about life and the universe as a whole are made from tiny physical and conceptual perspectives. One scientist with his nose not 'stuck to the canvas' was J.B.S. Haldane (British 1892 – 1964) who thought the universe not only queerer than we imagine but queerer than we can imagine.

Unanswered Questions

Let us beware of the rule of reason alone, and not only because of its limitations. When we think we have reasoned something for certain, that we know for sure, minds close, and we become intolerant of any differing views. These attitudes actually breed more ignorance, along with arrogance and dogmatism. So science, an important investigative technique, which should remain open-minded and eager for new interpretations, can become dogmatic and biased because of the dogmatism and bias of so many who practise it.

'…man, proud man,
Dressed in a little brief authority;
Most ignorant of what he's most assured,
His glassy essence, like an angry ape,
Plays such fantastic tricks before high heaven
As makes the angels weep…'

(Measure for Measure Act II Sc. II)

Those most conscious of limitations, their own and those of their craft, are often amongst the greatest in their field. Is it more than coincidence that the greatest scientists showed the greatest humility? Which is cause and which effect? In contrast, too many see our practical successes with technology and science as justification for inflating our collective self-esteem and as providing certain knowledge – despite the fact that modern science, even within its own boundaries and at its most fundamental levels, offers more probabilities and uncertainties than ever before. Yet this increasing vagueness has had no braking effect on some 'scientists' who claim so much on science's behalf and, while their own house is disordered, dismiss other disciplines. True scientists do not dismiss what has not been studied. Science has studied much, but it is dwarfed by what has not yet been studied, due to our limitations – which are truly profound.

To live a full and healthy life, as an individual or a community, feeling is also needed – both 'knowledge through feeling' ('absorbed' knowledge) and the feelings that grow with it.

Enough of science and of art
Close up those barren leaves,
Come forth, and bring with you a heart
That watches and receives.

(From 'The Tables Turned' by Wordsworth)

Furthermore, whatever knowledge we do have, *all* of it put together is partial, limited, and at best, only probable. Vast ignorance is the only thing of which we can be sure! (Paradoxically, one of the prime purposes of our learning ability might be to learn how ignorant we are). Unanswered questions reveal our continuing ignorance – making us ready to learn, to listen as well as we hear, to be tolerant and open-minded. Unlike arrogance and dogmatism, these attitudes are companions to compassion, to concern and care which, in turn, help us to know ourselves and each other. Perhaps one consequence of there being so many things in nature that we cannot know should be to turn our attention to the only thing we really can know – ourselves. Much of importance can be learned from unanswered questions! Further valuable lessons may be learned from unanswerable questions – not only 'what we do not know' but also 'what we cannot know'. Unanswerable questions teach us patience, tolerance, acceptance.

Chapter IV suggested that our separation, our distance, from nature was so great as to make our reflections difficult to see, and also that modern life obscured any remaining reflections with artificial scenery. Some of this artificial scenery is our 'brick cages', or glass and steel towers, or electric / electronic gadgets, while some of this 'scenery' is a collection of 'dead' facts or simply too much information. Yet familiarity with this scenery and the way information and facts seem to answer our questions gives a feeling of security or comfort.

Similarly, appearances of control and connectivity are conveyed by televised news programmes – someone or some organisation is 'out there' dealing with the situations or, at least, reporting on it – leaving the viewer free to forget their own responsibilities. All that has been built, made and organised seems so safe and secure. Surely it can't be lost now that we have achieved it – can it? Consider the apparent security of modern comfortable homes supplied with electricity, drinking water and access to 'emergency services'. These all vanished overnight for many poor souls in the floods of recent years which, by nature's standards, were not even large scale. The preceding chapter referred to the magazine New Scientist, carrying two major sober and sobering articles considering the collapse of civilisation (and this is a science, not science fiction, magazine). Suddenly denied access to electricity, most people would find life very difficult. Without adequate food or water supplied to their homes or local shops, most people would be helpless. If, due to our own collectively stupid behaviour, nature imposes drastic changes which remove most modern comforts and amenities, including communications and motorised transport, the majority of people (including this author) would find survival difficult, to say the least. Some suggest that we may have to return to a time before electricity was available. This is far too optimistic since we have, apart from a handful of enthusiasts, lost or forgotten the knowledge and skills which preceded electricity, and would be as helpless trying to construct the amazing engineering feats that our forebears achieved with, say, iron and steam, as we would be trying to reconstruct a power station or telephone exchange.

It is not being suggested that the wonders of modern technology should be rejected, only that the foundations of all our activities be respected and protected. Each development can be utilised and / or enjoyed, provided its impact on the environment and other existing developments are carefully assessed and allowed for, adjusting laws and practical processes to accommodate the new developments without abusing their foundations. We should have long since been projecting ahead to the end of a technology's life span and planning years in advance to accommodate it and / or the exhaustion of particular resources.

If, in the absence of such forethought, nature does impose severe changes, survivors may well talk of times when there was television, computers, DVD players and mobile telephones. However, this knowledge would be gradually lost amidst the necessities of survival and eventually become a distant memory, until future generations knew too little about such stories, which would then become legends, if remembered at all. All that humans make is fragile and flawed in its construction, organisation and use. The closer it emulates nature, the more reliable and efficient it is. The more removed from nature, the more fragile, fragmented and fallible it is. Familiarity does not guarantee future security. This pattern also applies economically; since all wealth ultimately comes from nature, the closer to nature, in terms of labour and products, the simpler and healthier our economies. The more removed from nature the more complex and artificial our economies become. They become unnatural and therefore unhealthy.

Critics may claim that some or all of the environmental assessments in this book are alarmist, or exaggerated, or biased in some respect. To such a critic (if genuine and not influenced by hidden agendas) it may not seem possible that sober, intelligent, articulate men and women in senior positions of government, commerce and the media could be so ill-informed, or bullied by vested interests, or tied by regulation or circumstance, or incompetent, or negligent of their duties (even to their own and their family's welfare) as to let the nation, if not the world, descend into ecological chaos. If you are such a reader, please consider that *exactly the same* could have been said in response to warnings of the financial crash just prior to 2007 – which will be as child's play compared to a global ecological crash.

However, for the sake of the more important point, let us agree that the information is alarmist and exaggerated. Since the actions recommended herein can only bring benefits, no harm is done. On the other hand, if the information is neither alarmist nor exaggerated, and we take no action, all harm is done. Each and every recommendation or suggestion made in this book makes the world a better place, regardless of any other consideration – so we may as well do them anyway. When we really examine our situation, we realise we have no guarantees for anything, so we may as well improve as much as we can, as often as we can, while we can.

Even in the realm of pure thought we can find few, if any, definite answers. Perhaps the first significant questions asked without finding definite answers were those of Socrates which still, today, remain unanswered. Sometimes those who offered answers felt foolish when Socrates' further questions revealed those answers to be superficial or incorrectly reasoned. Yet Socrates was the first to admit his ignorance (when told that the Delphic Oracle had declared him the wisest of men, Socrates said that he must therefore be the only man who realised he knew nothing). Shakespeare solved our confusion by coupling both concepts in a paradox: 'the fool doth think he is wise, but the wise man knows himself to be a fool.' (As You Like It Act V Sc. 1)

Viewing the situation from a slightly different angle with Voltaire we can see that while 'Doubt is uncomfortable, certainty is ridiculous.' Is there anything we can know? One of the few things of which we can be sure is our consciousness – the only thing in the universe that we know to 'be'. We use it to make our choices and also to know how these affect the world, other people, other forms of life and the universe around us – even if all these are illusions, we affect those illusions, and they are all we have to work with. We hold what we know as the world, the universe, in our heads, hearts and hands; hence we must be careful how we use them. As Atlas showed us, the universe is dependent on us. Each of us must

"Think as if man never thought before!
Act as if all creation hung attent
On the acting of such faculty as his."

(Browning)

Our world, 'the stage', is cluttered with fragments of what Man's mind, his mortal hand and eye has chosen (with motives, more often than not, concerned with profit and / or power) to take, dissect, probe, analyse, collect, cage, sterilise or separate from nature rather than let his mind and heart 'watch and receive' the whole play. Mostly 'doing' but rarely 'being'. Unable to see anything but what we have selected or collected, we obsess over the physical minutiae of our collection. Doing so in isolation cannot provide wisdom, just fragments of knowledge and lots of information and so we 'lose the plot', forget the original scenery, our place (sometimes in the auditorium, sometimes on stage), our direction and our purpose.

Whether on stage on in the auditorium, the collection of man-made, artificial scenery around us encourages us to believe in image rather than substance – reflected to us in many modern scenarios such as, for just a few examples:

- Computers providing us with virtual worlds within which there are no responsibilities, or even consequences. Once again, it is youngsters who are most susceptible to these trends

- Societies talking most loudly of their citizens' liberty are those whose citizens are most demographically defined, electronically monitored and under constant surveillance by satellites and cameras

- The image of science portrayed to the public is of a pure and noble pursuit after truth (and for a precious few scientists it still is). However, during the 20th and 21st centuries, the majority of science has been dominated by military and commercial agendas, while many of the brightest science graduates have been persuaded to work for financial institutions, with the sole purpose of maximising profits

- Much on media 'menus' is all image and no substance whatsoever but, due to the influence and power of the media, the content is 'believed in' by many readers and / or viewers

- Traditionally, a company *earned* a good (or bad) reputation, and this was generated by their customers. Today, it is marketing and advertising agencies which establish a company's reputation of supposed excellence, but the image rarely matches actual performance.

Falsehood is too often favoured over nature's substance, and hence so much of what today is called 'progress' could, from another perspective, be revealed as regress. Human image creation and falsehoods also allow us to ignore unanswered questions. Surrounded by an artificial world we forget the immensity around us. We view man-made 'stars' and no longer see real stars. Even space exploration is conducted, for most people, from laboratories or offices and viewed, via camera lenses, on a glass screen. We see the world, the universe, through, as Henry Beston reminded us, the 'glass of our knowledge' and much of our knowledge through glass – television and computer screens, windows of vehicles and buildings, lenses and spectacles. A few (such as Henry David Thoreau, Henry Beston, Luther Standing Bear, Chief Seattle, Ochwiay Biano and (despite their windows and visors!) astronauts) who have seen or felt something of the immensity for themselves are profoundly affected and thereafter view life from more panoramic perspectives and are more at peace with unanswered questions.

Important as broad horizons are, we also need to remember a vision more important than any physical view, no matter how large, and Blake's insight to it will bear repeating: 'They ever must believe a lie who see with, not through, the eye'.

The View from Here

Our journey together is almost over.

It might be worthwhile to briefly review where we have been and what we have seen, and assess if we can use it to guide our steps to a healthier future.

The Introduction suggested some perspectives from which you might view the tiger and we have seen some of those perspectives from Chapter I, where we saw two types of complementary knowledge, and considered personal responsibilities and personal experience.

From chapter II we saw that the rational knowledge, scientific or otherwise, could teach us much of interest but could not answer all our questions. Vitally important elements are missing from all scientific, or any purely rational, analysis.

In chapter III we rested at Jim Corbett's place and, while not dismissing knowledge born of reason, found much vital knowledge born of 'absorption'/ intuition / yin. We also saw the importance of character and its development.

From chapter IV we found that the distant deeps and skies within tigers reached far further than we could physically travel. However, we understood a little more by travelling on in hearts and minds, blending feeling with reason, yin with yang, and discovering that achieving their balance was an important part of developing our character. We found that the world without is the world within, a mirror by which we can recognise ourselves and understand the wisdom of the Oracle – Delphic, not scientific.

We also found hints of mysteries that defy both types of knowledge and hence could still not claim complete understanding of any facet of nature, let alone the magnificent creation we call a tiger. It seems that any and all of our attempts to define a tiger are inadequate; that it is beyond man-made definitions. We may capture a tiger physically but we cannot capture its essence completely or conceptually in cages, or art, words, photographs or science. The tiger's majestic indifference to us and our attempts might give us pause. It is beyond us.

If one animal is beyond us, how much is all between and beyond brightest stars and least dust beyond us? Yet by watching and receiving, using both head and heart, we see a mysterious mix of magnificent symmetries – sometimes fearful but all educational – which are as constellations of light amidst the darkness of the unknown. The unknown surrounds us and reflects the same within us. Chapter IV told us one reason we cannot capture the tiger is because we do not know who we are. We have not faced and 'tamed' our own tiger, not brought its elements into harmony

with the rest of our being, or ourselves into harmony with nature. Whilst much remains unknown, the symmetries we are able to see provide the guidance we need, and much to be getting along with, here and now. The loss of our tigers is one immediate and important guide awaiting our attention, and one which brightly illuminates the broader environmental situation.

In Chapter I the still and silent forests of Chitwan illustrated nature's ever turning cycles, which embrace us all. If these magnificent, awesomely complex, beautiful, balanced cycles of nature are to continue to include us, we must now embrace those cycles. This will bring all round health because health is…all round i.e. cycles and circles, which turn best when balanced. This is one of the principles we can learn from nature. Balancing our knowledge with feeling, reason with intuition, mind with heart, allows us to embrace, care for and respect, that which embraces us.

Nature's cycles, both within the forest and those of which forests form parts, are either being broken or made to rotate out of balance and hence, may not be able to embrace us all for much longer. Under these circumstances, stillness and silence are the least appropriate responses. "Our lives begin to end the day we become silent about the things that matter." (Martin Luther King). All sensible, responsible people should be controlling corporate irresponsibility by selectively spending and investing money, while monitoring and demanding answers from those institutions we pay to protect our lives and livelihoods. We, in our new technological world are not brave but cowardly – but we can change that, by facing our responsibilities. We can also look back in order to find a healthier way forward. This relates to our sayings about learning lessons from history, but an old

Russian proverb makes us see that: 'If you keep one eye on the past, you are blind in one eye, but if you forget the past you are blind in both eyes.' We may even need to go backwards a little way to find a better way forward.

This chapter has described something of how we might keep one eye on the past (conservation of what nature provided, history, 'lifting heavy lids' and learning) while finding our way forward, facing our reflections and using them to develop our character, keeping the better parts constant and thereby facing the unknown future with some certainty. The unknown can be fearful, but knowledge helps us conquer fear, as can faith – not necessarily or only in a superhuman deity, but also in the reliability of nature's laws, and the lessons of the life-support system, and faith in other people to co-operate and care. Love can also conquer fear. Now we can see one reason why, perhaps, fear 'lies twisted about life's deepest roots' – because it prompts us to develop knowledge, faith and love. As we travel our life's journey we need to copy nature's designs and cycles in all we construct; treat all sincere methods of enquiry with equal respect, attentively receive what they teach and take action to meet our responsibilities. Application of all these principles allows a better understanding – of our world, and ourselves.

By living with respect for nature we discover more about who we are and thereby identify what needs improving in ourselves. By navigating inwardly more effectively, outward navigation improves automatically, in another of nature's symmetrical cycles. Successful inward navigation reduces or eliminates our exclusive obsession with the material. A life path with fewer material obstacles allows time to run more slowly and we can see more clearly, in retrospect and review, where we have been and why, learning *from* history, both personal and collective. (Goethe said that "he who cannot draw on three thousand years is living from hand to mouth.") We can thereby assess both who and where we are now and find the path to a healthier future. In a close parallel to the Lincoln quote of the previous chapter, but now incorporating our spiritual responsibilities, is this line from Ruysbroeck (John of Ruysbroeck (Jan van Ruusbroec Dutch) 1293 – 1381 Flemish Catholic mystic): "Knowledge of ourselves teaches us whence we come, where we are and whither we are going." The world awaits our choices and will, in due course, show us the scenery from the paths we choose.

The Way Ahead

As we travel our paths, directly experiencing life by walking on our own feet, watching and receiving, looking for reflections, learning to listen, we begin to understand that forests and their inhabitants, all of nature's patterns and features, are myriad multi-coloured messengers. Whatever is studied or created, each and every aspect of our lives indicates our dependence on nature and the need to co-operate, firstly with nature and then with each other (nature first, morals next). Mutual co-operation itself forms a cycle, the circularity within Kipling's 'The strength of the pack is the wolf, and the strength of the wolf is the pack.' Whether we study the natural environment, or what nature produces through us (such as agriculture and civilisation) literally everything from the dust beneath our feet to the stars above, carry the same message, coded in different ways, but all saying the same thing: 'I am *you and your life*. Protect me and I will protect you.' The natural world is not merely pretty scenery and somewhere 'for the kids to play'. In truth, it is our topmost priority and is now having to shout its message to our wilfully deaf ears. Penguins, polar bears, songbirds, insects, monkeys, apes, lemurs, elephants, whales, tigers and many other species are all calling out as they, and trees and topsoil disappear, as climate changes and waters rise.

If, and with urgency, we learn a little more about who we are; our part in nature; our current position and direction of travel; we can then take action to ensure our future path protects the path to the future. Each of us plays a part in the grandest play of all, the play of life, in nature's interactive theatre and concert hall and, for those who have their senses still, our only real duty, that to which all other duties should ultimately contribute, is to cherish, promote and protect healthy life – to 'husband and nurture the life force'. In the context of this book, and because our current situation is so dangerous, we have necessarily considered husbanding and nurturing the life force from an environmental perspective. Once our physical life-support system has been safeguarded, the life force may also be nurtured in multiple mental and spiritual ways. Whilst this is not the place to explore them, cultural disciplines such as music, medicine, literature, art, crafts, community groups or projects, and various charitable works also husband and nurture the life force.

In contrast to my initial impressions of the enormity of the jungle when standing next to it, it is their tiny fragmented remnants globally that now make impressions on us; cathedrals are no longer growing (or being built) and pilgrim feet find little hallowed ground, being mainly lost on concrete. Standing on that path next to the forest in Chitwan thirty years ago, the only thing from my perspective that was larger than the forest was my ignorance. Looking into the forest I could just see far enough to see my responsibilities toward it. From those perspectives, the forest planted seeds in me. However, they required many turns of the earth and incubation by the sun, before they grew sufficiently to mark the path by which I could meet those responsibilities. Eventually, I found a way to return to the forests and make direct efforts to help protect them, some as described in this chapter. The journey between chapters I and V, the walk between the jungles of Chitwan and the forests of Madhya Pradesh, has been all uphill. While walking, Earth's revolutions brought revolutions to my heart and mind and I learned that the life I had felt in, and of, the forest is my life, your life; is Life; that all life is One. One interconnected whole. However, as I write, it seems that all conservation efforts of all sincere individuals, NGOs and officials, will not succeed in stemming the haemorrhage of species, including the tiger, from the collective flow of Life. It currently appears that we will lose our tigers. (The author is among those who sincerely and profoundly hope this will be proved wrong).

Yet, being uphill, the journey has gradually revealed viewpoints from which one can overlook the conventional views of 'success' and 'failure', 'winners' and 'losers'. From this more panoramic view it can be seen that trying one's best to husband and nurture the life force, but failing, is far better than 'succeeding' in ways that harm it. Failure for the right cause is preferable to success in the wrong. Hence, however you see the future, do not let it discourage you from making your contribution to husband and nurture the life force since you are only responsible for your own efforts. We have previously referred to Holy shrines and it is fitting that they are often (especially in the East and definitely in Pachmarhi) high in the mountains (those natural pyramids, atop which tigers live), requiring pilgrims to climb many steps to reach them.

The top is reached at the end of a journey of personal commitment and active interest, regardless of what the rest of the world may be doing, and is ideally made on one's own feet. The pilgrimage is an index of the effort one is prepared to make for what one believes in (the amount of suffering one will voluntarily undertake for love). What is a pilgrimage worth if it is easy and pleasurable (what is Atlas', or our, achievement worth if we carry a beach-ball instead of the universe)? After the advent of roads and railways, Mahatma Gandhi wrote 'The holy places of India are no longer holy. Formerly, people went to these places with very great difficulty. Generally therefore, only the real devotees visited such places. Nowadays rogues visit them to practise their roguery.' Roads and railways removed much of the effort, and therefore much of the value to the pilgrim. Some pilgrims, recognising this, emphasise their devotion and humility by literally crawling, belly to ground, while a helper holds up a flag to prevent traffic prematurely terminating the pilgrimage.

As we all know, much is learned on the journey. Nepal, Thailand, India and their forests showed much that, to me, was new. It sometimes answered questions before I had the knowledge to ask them. Directly experiencing nature first-hand, spending time with wild animals, both in the wild and in captivity, learning some expressions of a tiger's face and eyes, sensing danger before

I could see it, assimilating knowledge by 'feeling' it, almost 'learning how to learn' is, I believe (although I am nowhere near their level) what Corbett refers to when he talks of 'absorbing' knowledge, and Wordsworth when he recommends a heart that watches and receives. It is reason balanced with a sort of 'feeling'; and it is a 'feeling' about the patience and perfection of nature; about the health of a forest; or where to take the next step, either on the forest floor under my feet or to further tiger conservation, which has guided me in this work. It is also by developing conservation strategies with 'feeling' in the conventional sense (e.g. for the local and tribal people and helping them toward healthy, sustainable security) that provides the best hope for long-term conservation of animals. These and other senses of awareness complemented the microscopic academic knowledge it had also been my privilege to gain. Both types of knowledge are available to all who exercise interest with sincerity and humility in any discipline, but knowledge acquired directly from nature, in natural surroundings, brings both yin and yang together, and in balance. Human specialism(s), by virtue of being a specialism, are often imbalanced and become unhealthy as a result, unless we consciously compensate for that imbalance.

Knowledge – however it might be classified – is only worthwhile if it leads to action that conserves and promotes healthily balanced life. Nature's global environmental mirror is showing us that we must change the path we are on in order to save our tigers and ourselves, and that each of us has a responsibility in effecting that change – by each of us changing ourselves, however small each of us may seem from a global perspective. Taking just one mundane but nonetheless important example from our suggestions, we do not pour poisonous or polluting chemicals down the sink at home due to its effects on nature, which is a globally interconnected whole (reminding us again of that succinct, insightful phrase: 'Think globally, act locally': think of the effects on the world but act individually, in your local sphere of influence). Individual action is all we are capable of, and no person is responsible for more than their own conduct and making sure it is as healthy as possible for the whole. Although it seems hopelessly slow as a remedy for our ills, it's the only one that will work thoroughly, purely and permanently, since each individual has to, by definition, be consciously involved in, and personally commit to the process.

This is where an ideal has its value since, if you are like me, you will fail more often than you succeed. However, Swami Vivekananda put this problem in perspective for us in chapter III. Perhaps some of those people mentioned in chapter IV, who triumphed over the most depressing but repeating patterns of human life and history, might be ideal ideals.

'Noble savages' were not included in that section since they needed no change to establish healthy, peaceful, self-sufficient communities. Their societies were already in harmony with nature and each other – until other societies 'explored'. So, in different but related ways, 'savages' or indigenous peoples may also represent ideals. 'Over the years and on several continents I've seen indigenous people enter their landscapes…Human conversation usually trails off, people become more alert to what is around them, less intent on any goal – where to camp that night, say. People become more curious about animal life, looking at the evidence of what animals have been up to. People begin to look all around, especially behind them, instead of staring straight ahead with only an occasional look to the side. People halt to examine closely things that at first glance seemed innocuous. People hold up simply to put things together – the sky with a certain type of forest, a kind of rock outcropping, the sound of a creek, and, last, the droppings of a blue grouse under a thimbleberry bush. People heft rocks and put them back. They push their hands into river mud and perhaps leave patches of it on their skin. It's an ongoing intercourse with the place…A central task facing modern Western cultures is to redefine human community in the wake of industrialization, colonialism and, more recently, the forcing power of capitalism. In trying to solve some of the constellation of attendant problems here – keeping corporations out of secondary education, restoring the physical and spiritual shelter of the family group, preserving non-Western ways of knowing – it seems clear that by cutting ourselves off from Nature, by turning Nature into scenery and commodities, we may cut ourselves off from something vital. To repair this damage we can't any longer take what we call "Nature" for an object. We must merge it again with our own nature. We must reintegrate ourselves in specific geographic places, and to do that we need to learn those places at greater depth than any science, Eastern or Western, can take us. We have to incorporate them again in the moral universe we inhabit. We have to develop good relations with them, ones that will replace the exploitative relations that have become a defining characteristic of twentieth-century Western life, with its gargantuan oil spills and chemical accidents, its megalithic hydro-electric developments, its hideous weapons of war, and its conception of wealth that would lead a corporation to cut down a forest to pay the interest on a loan.' (J18)

Those who only 'get and spend', those featured in Jung's review of Western conquests, and even my initial attitude on being delayed at the railway station in India, are all equivalent examples to Lopez's people who stare straight ahead when walking through landscapes, and their lives. They all characterise a dangerous aspect of current Western culture and its over-emphasis on yang, on doing, destinations and deadlines – rather than simply being, in the here and now, on the journey.

Indigenous peoples, 'savages' are better balanced, stand on their own feet, on their home ground and know about *their* universe (being perfectly balanced must mean, in one sense at least, that we are at the centre of our universe). Many Westerners are dependent on scientists to know about *the* universe 'for them', and are lost in space. Some scientists might consider they know more about the universe than savages do. Maybe, maybe not, but 'savages' do not destroy their viewing platform and for 'savages', the stars above, the dust underfoot, all in between, and their own life, are one integrated, interrelated whole.

No recommendation is being made that we all return to living as savages in forests. The recommendation is to appreciate the balanced, healthy relationships, the patterns they represent, and to reproduce them in our own societies, in harmony with technological developments. By integrating and harmonising with those patterns, our cultures and creations automatically become healthy and truly civilised, including technologies developed in accordance with care for healthy nature. Humans are an integral part of nature, with which they can co-exist harmoniously, whether as a 'savage' or an astronaut, provided that, at each stage of development and expanding influence, nature's laws are observed. This is the concept of Tasleem (referred to in the presentation to Forest Guards above); of submission to the Laws of Nature and that only humans infringe these laws and 'thus bring affliction on themselves'.

Many modern comforts and much technology can be maintained if we learn how to produce them cleanly, in a sustainable way and eliminate wastage. Enormous islands of litter in the oceans were referred to in the previous chapter and hundreds of miles of discarded fishing nets above, but the discrepancy between technological and spiritual development is highlighted by the sophistication of space exploration contrasted with waste and debris left behind in previously pristine environments. There are an estimated 371,500 pieces of debris currently in Earth orbit, collision with which now pose a threat to satellites (The Week 05/06/10). Even the moon landings left a variety of litter and rubbish on the moon's surface. This is one of those situations that require a flash of insight to penetrate the glare of glamour, and see the light. The enormity of the achievement makes even mentioning something as mundane and trivial as litter seem churlish or carping yet in such extreme contrasts the yawning gap between our values can be appreciated. Like children only concerned with thrills and excitement, we are not mature enough to meet our simplest responsibilities, either in class or playground. Again we see that we have not learned the lessons of Earth before boldly polluting new frontiers.

The same yawning abyss between technological and spiritual development can be seen in other modern situations such as some modern scientists and philosophers who may consider they know where the universe came from, but don't know where their bread and butter come from. Is this another preposterous exaggeration? Surely everyone knows our food comes from staple crops such as wheat or rice grown in soil, photosynthesising sugar from sunlight, carbon dioxide and water. Such basic knowledge is only occasionally called to mind – perhaps by the questions of a child – and this simple process provides us with food, which allows us to get on with building the highly sophisticated machines, buildings and processes which make the modern world; so far removed from the simplicities of the soil, or wheat, or rice. In truth, the process by which our food is produced is so complex as to confound the collective power of humanity to understand it. Whilst research into photosynthesis, genetics and ecology has revealed fascinating insights it has also found more puzzles. The complete details of processes by which plants join together the inorganic and organic worlds remain unknown. The description of food production just given has similarities to us saying 'a baby is born': we know what it means and have a mass of practical, technical and scientific information associated with it but, beyond some physiological mechanisms we think we understand, we are still confounded and dumbfounded by all that it represents. The naked truth is that we are as babies to Mother Nature's mysteries.

By comparison with nature, all man-made technology is crude and inefficient. Yet, our toy-town knowledge has been used to 'improve' the process of food production. Papers have been published, profits and reputations made while soil, animals and people have been poisoned, both directly, and indirectly in terms of surrounding natural habitat eventually being contaminated with chemicals used on cultivated ground. Those remaining natural habitats should be sacrosanct but we could now be taken further down the wrong path by some scientists who suggest a *rejection* of traditional conservation strategies (such as trying to preserve natural ecosystems as they are and / or returning ecosystems to what they were before man-made interference or damage). Other scientists have suggested that 'we should not be afraid to "reassemble" damaged ecosystems to improve them' (New Scientist magazine 07/07/08 'Redefining Conservation' or at www.newscientist.com). Perhaps we should be more afraid of such people and their suggestions which, to this author at least, represent ignorance exceeded only by arrogance. Amongst the suggested possibilities for 'improvement', is the introduction of non-native species and GMOs. This is diametrically opposed to suggestions above that non-native species should be removed as part of a conservation strategy, and references above to the completely unknown long-term effects of GMOs.

A scientist who truly appreciates the unity of life as this book has attempted to describe it, could not condone GMO since it not only interferes with and alters that unity but also represents the enormous arrogance and (despite the technical intelligence involved) stupidity of doing so. Of course, as often referred to, we have already interfered with and destroyed much of nature's unity and integrity, but we have never been able to interfere with the pattern, the code, the very structure of nature. We have already embarked on this additional sacrilege, for the sake of personal egos and / or corporate profits (the ways to increase profit are numerous and varied; 'the path to vice is smooth and wide…'). Familiarity with GMO is bred by sober science journals and magazines reporting 'progress', and / or chirpy news media reporting newly created abominations. All this gradually eases public acceptance and apathy. Of even greater concern are developments we are not told about.

Attempts by GMO companies to sell their products in India are a case in point. The market India represents is big by any standards and, since India's de-regulation in the 1990's, corporations have been jostling each other and testing the law to corner large portions of it. Amongst these corporations are GMO companies and public resistance to them has been vigorous. While NGO's and private individuals have successfully fought battles, the war could still be lost by their own government committees. Greenpeace India has revealed that the committees are not staffed by completely unbiased personnel and are subject to ridiculously short time constraints in which to produce decisions (effective opposition always takes time to mount). Recent reports from Greenpeace India in 2010 indicate that decisions to favour GMO may soon be made by ignoring democratic procedures altogether. None of this receives wide media coverage and while people might debate what is 'in the news', it is what does not appear in the news (or only receives inadequate coverage) as in the case of GMOs' introduction to India, which represent critical decisions affecting the lives of millions or, potentially, everyone and everything on the planet.

In the context of chapter IV we can see that GMO incorporates man-made arrogance and stupidity into nature's unity. Critics will point out that humanity, as a product of nature, can only be as arrogant and / or stupid as allowed for in nature's original potentials but this is merely another excuse for ignoring choice and personal responsibility (like a child challenging an adult with words, trying to be clever but completely unaware of greater issues in larger contexts). As noted, nature's amazing flexibility allows us options within fixed parameters. Those fixed parameters are as strong as steel, but allow a delicate flexibility of choice to operate within them. The chief thing demanded of us is to echo the same by using steely self control and the flexibility of choice to choose health and security for all.

Using Jack London's reference to gossamer delicacy combined with steely strength may seem just a poetic play with words but, once again, nature provides an exact physical counterpart, the most well known surely being the spider's gossamer web which, proportionally, is stronger than steel. With GMOs we are now capable of altering not only the spider's web but nature's web, weaving into it the steely strength of arrogance and greed, due to our completely gossamer self-control. These are just a few examples of the yawning abyss between our technological and spiritual development, into which we are in danger of falling. The way ahead will be safer the more we can draw these two types of development together.

That each component, each strand, each connection within life's intricate web has significance is made more likely by nature's precision, a few examples of which follow.

- In Chapter II we read of rodents' abilities to detect the difference of *one gene* in samples of urine from other rodents. In genetics at least, precision cannot be further enhanced and, that a small mammal can operate at this level of refinement, causes even greater concern over humans' purblind dabbling with GMO

- Recent research at Würzburg University, in Germany, has revealed that some honey bees – 'heater bees' – occupy wax cells next to pupae and help to incubate them by generating heat (by flexing muscles normally used to beat their wings). Fascinatingly, a difference of only one degree Celsius determines the future role of the particular pupa – those pupae incubated at 35°C will develop into intelligent forager bees while those incubated at 34°C will develop into 'housekeeper' bees, which never leave the nest

- This book has laboured the concept of learning from nature, especially by closer contact with it, and recent research has found evidence that nature even helps animals learn their lessons – via a bacterium *Mycobacterium vaccae*, which lives in the soil of natural habitats and is blown on the breeze. When ingested or inhaled, it enhances brainpower and also has antidepressant properties (Research by American Society for Microbiology (Internet reporting))

- Moving up in scale, we noted the precision and detail involved in hormonal and chemical communication; in the architecture of the tiger's skull and teeth; and that with which a stalking tiger slides its hind paws into the positions vacated by its fore paws

Moving much further up in scale to our nearest neighbour we may explore a little more by the light of the moon – which, by stabilising the Earth's spin and orbit is essential for limiting the range of temperature and weather extremes to which living organisms are subjected. Its phases are constant for all peoples of the Earth (and tigers too, as noted by James Best in chapter I). Many human communities marked time by the lunar cycles and organised their activities according to them. Julius Caesar is mainly responsible for the disappearance of the moon as a mark of the season and for the timing of rituals, replacing many societies' measurement of time with calendar months. The word 'month' was retained however, leaving the false impression that these new periods were related to the moon. Our knowledge of the moon's influence on planting crops, human fertility and madness ('lunacy') has also largely been forgotten. The moon itself has a 19 year cycle after which the phases of the moon recur on the same dates and, for dates after 1687 (when Newton's Principia was first published), the moon was generally known to be the major factor causing ocean tides.

It is tidal effects with which the life-cycles of various species of birds, mammals, reptiles, amphibians and fish are synchronised e.g. the collective nesting and egg-laying of turtles occurs only during the first or last quarter of the moon's cycle (when weaker tides make wading through the surf easier for turtles and may reduce the risk of stronger tides exposing or destroying nests and the eggs within). The spawning of corals and the breeding cycles of fish are also correlated with the moon and Szamosi (B67) refers to a small species of fish living in California's coastal waters – the grunion – during their time of reproduction. At full moon or new moon, corresponding to highest or 'spring' tides, these fish reach the highest water line on the beach and then fertilise and bury their eggs. During the two weeks the eggs need for incubation they are safely out of reach of

Satpura Tiger Reserve

the waves of all the intervening, but lower, tides. Two weeks is (almost) the exact interval between high tides, so the eggs hatch ready for the next high water and are drawn into the sea. Their spawning pattern has been synchronised not only with daily tides but also with the period of the highest tides which is *fourteen and seven-tenth days*!

On a beach in California we have glimpsed another slender strand of life's world-wide web, glinting by the light of the moon and connecting the night sky with the genetics of sea life. It is extremely unlikely that connections such as these are ever considered in any municipal or public, government or corporate meetings in any way, anywhere, at any time. If such detail was pointed out, the most likely response would be that it should be taught to children. Yet what good is any knowledge unless it informs our decisions? Such strands connect with those that support all man-made webs and are hence more important (and interesting) than our webs, or 'networks'. (Nowadays, 'networks' most often refer to connections between people whose sole purpose is using them to seek self promotion or career advantage. Such networks are anything but healthy and by solely and soullessly seeking status and wealth for self, while ignoring other lives, we impoverish ourselves dreadfully and dangerously).

So, from a perspective of nature's precision and interconnections we realise that all elements have significance, which reminds us of chapter III, in which we noted that changing the inertia of any physical object affects the entire universe; that stirring a flower troubles a star. We are now genetically changing what it means to be a flower, and troubled stars water heaven with their tears. Genes underlie other connections, which trace to bacteria that help us learn, to trees and tigers, and a multitude of other life forms, including you and the people you love. So, by changing bacteria, plants and animals genetically, we are changing those connections, potentially changing how we learn, and love. We are using knowledge without wisdom. We have become clever, more clever and then stupid, because the cleverness is just reason applied and re-applied, mechanically to mechanics and material values, driven mainly by the greedy and powerful few, without reference to larger contexts or other concerns. The greedy and powerful few do not understand that their interference will make the money they gain worthless in the long-term. If they survive the environmental consequences of their actions, other survivors will be able to recognise them since they will be among those trying to get control of more than their fair share of the food, or the fire, or the shelter.

Human abuse of nature may be motivated by profit and power, or by thinking man knows better than nature. To assume man knows better than the system he is part of, is to let the space shuttle be maintained by those early chimpanzee 'astronauts' holding hammers. Whatever those chimps' emotions might be, it will still be us who most often qualify as Shakespeare's angry ape (as referred to in the quote from 'Measure for Measure' above), and it would be comic if it were not tragic. The potential for comedy and tragedy in nature's theatre also arises insofar as scientists have as short a memory as other humans, since history has a record of disasters following human interference with nature, as opposed to harmonious co-operation with nature. It might be said that a scientist not living from three thousand, or even three hundred, years of science history is living from hand to mouth. Moreover, if we continue to allow them unregulated interference with genetics and ecosystems, we will all be living from hand to mouth.

Although we like to think of ourselves as being superior to nature and our environment, so far removed from the soil, each of us is only removed, at a maximum, by the height at which we stand – since, of course, it is the soil we are standing on (even if concreted over). If we are six feet tall and take a lift to the top floor of the tallest building in the world, we are still only a maximum of six feet away from the Earth – because those six feet of body are still dependent on that soil (and, as a consequence, so is the building). Astronauts in space are six feet away from Earth. We may distance ourselves in our minds but our stomachs bring us back down to earth. Yet still we act as if we are superior to the soil and, via concrete, glass and steel, convince ourselves that we are independent of the earth.

Those concrete, glass and steel constructions are surely skilful but whatever skills people have, we usually assume that, when they leave their drawing board, workshop or laboratory, they would be able to dress and feed themselves or tie their own shoelaces. Collectively speaking, we no longer can; we know the atomic structure of wheat, water, sugar and salt, can see yeast bacteria through a microscope but most cannot make a loaf of bread. Most of us could not make clothes or shoes. Most can use a computer or mobile 'phone but do not know when to plant crops according to the phases of the moon. Food itself has become a commodity; commercially identical to computers or CDs such that we no longer know the bread of life. We have made ourselves intelligently ignorant and sophisticatedly stupid.

Modern scientists have been compared to wise men, shamans and wizards of old since they have all acquired some specialised knowledge of nature, unknown to the majority. Yet ancient wise men were still closely connected with nature, lived in harmony with it and with their communities and did not practise what would be harmful to either. They knew the constellations, the positions of the planets in relation to them and when to pick healing herbs according to the phase of the moon and depth of morning dew. The critic says that the modern limitations of specialists are due to them knowing so much more than previous generations…yet much of that extra knowledge is academic, in all senses of the word. Perhaps it is only information. Moreover, previous knowledge and wisdom is not only mostly forgotten but, where fragments remain, they are often dismissed or derided by the modern specialist – without the least study of what is dismissed or derided. If it does not fit the current dogma, it must be 'old wives tales'.

We can learn much without specialising: by viewing nature from the paths followed by 'savages' – some of whom we have met in this book. Many people will walk a path for exercise but the experience will be richer if they also exercised their interest, like Lopez's indigenous peoples. We may always wonder at what we see, since in nature nothing is known completely. Ochwiay Biano told us that the sun represented our father. Westerners might not agree but most Westerners are dependent on a vast industrial complex for the simplest of life's requirements as well as their information about the sun and other stars. 'Savages', who acquire all they need for themselves and know the stars with their own senses, have cosmic connections without spacecraft and a global vision gained without leaving home. The same 'savages' exhibit true nobility, concern for and protection of life, on both grand and personal scales and, if necessary, self-sacrifice to preserve it – in stark contrast to recent media-manufactured Western-style 'nobility', concerned mainly with self and status.

From the humblest to the noblest; the poorest to the richest; the dullest to the brightest; we are dependent on dirt, the dust of the good earth, the soil that supports all. There is no peasant or savage, nor any crown or president, not dependent on nature's bounty.

> Kingly crown and warrior's crest
> Are not worth the blade of grass
> God fashions for the swallow's nest.
>
> (Thompson)

Nowadays, not having learned our lessons, the blade of grass and the swallow's nest are actually under serious threat from kingly crowns and warriors' crests.

With even a little direct experience of life and the natural world we know for ourselves, profoundly and indubitably, without need of debate, discussion, texts, television or scientific 'proof', that destroying nature is practically stupid, morally wrong and spiritually empty – it is to bankrupt one's account with Life, with nature, the best of all banks; which always repays real interest; offers the best and safest returns on your investments; never disappears with those investments; does not fail you or sell you worthless investments, but does include free education and growth – of that which never deteriorates or devalues: reminding us of Corbett's comment referred to in Chapter I regarding his opening a credit account with the Bank of Nature and his interest earning him his jungle lore, which was a never-ending source of pleasure to him. For each of us, spending some time with nature, preferably in stillness and silence, simultaneously informs the mind and gladdens the heart.

For those of us living in towns and cities, developing our knowledge of nature as well as our 'concrete jungle' lore, will guide us to the right path. For some time now on our current path, trees have become scarcer and sparser, with a few remaining in isolated groups. Wildlife in general and tiger pugs in particular are even fewer and much further between. The soil itself is poor quality and powdery; by nature's standards it is dead, but can still turn a profit if continually injected with chemicals – a description which might apply to many people subjected to the same socio-economic system responsible for the condition of the soil. Looking around us, others seem to be running blindly along different paths or not on paths at all. The majority, unlike good pilgrims, have opted for the easiest, smoothest paths and few are looking around with interest or trying to understand their surroundings. The views from the path of healthy, balanced life are the best yet, even if and when we find it, we must make the effort to actually look and consider what we see.

Those on the right path with open eyes and minds are walking into the 21st century and can still (but only just) see the tiger in the forests. If we learn to see the forests in the tiger we might save our natural environment. Even if completely insulated from the natural environment, exotic or otherwise, we can still see a tiger in a zoo and, by exercising our interest, can see in that tiger awesome energy behind black bars. Looking longer and deeper we see that we have some of that energy; a power we can use to transform ourselves, to realise the part of nature's potentials that are our potentials, and thereby free ourselves from our cages. That energy flickers and changes, transforms into various symmetries – some that Plato and Hugo saw, Blake and Montaigne questioned, Wordsworth felt and Corbett lived.

Learning from their insights and our own; from academic disciplines; from time spent with nature and from personal experience, nature teaches us to know for certain that we don't know for certain. Yet, even in the face of that uncertainty, we see that our own survival and health depends on co-operation, duty to and compassion for other lives. Every individual can examine the path they are on and assess their contribution to the health or harm of the community – and hence themselves. Our application of virtue and morality in interactions with other lives, human and non-human, results in our character development and provides a purpose for every individual at the same time as it is inseparable from society. It is the same for the scientist (since humanity incorporates science) unless scientists pretend (to themselves) that science incorporates humanity. Of course we need to seek knowledge – most of all of ourselves. That we are, as Shakespeare said, all fools, is only partly due to ignorance. It is also due to fear and immaturity. When we put emphasis only on information we remain fools – well-informed fools and / or foolishly intelligent, but still fools! Gaining knowledge, faith and love, helps conquer fear. Wisdom arrives with maturity and is marked by realising that we are as children.

Realising our immaturity is something of a relief since, if we considered ourselves the 'finished product', disappointment and despair follow. When we realise we are as children, understanding dawns, hope arises and we continue the climb, improving our view all the time. Although the view improves, we are never able to see all. Even those who lifted lighter eyelids and saw most, such as Socrates, Newton, Corbett and Einstein, knew they knew least. Any individual, or all individuals put together, are dwarfed by nature, not only in terms of physical size but also in terms of complexities, subtleties and mysteries. 'The reasonings about the wonderful and intricate operations of Nature are so full of uncertainty, that, as the Wise-man truly observes, hardly do we guess aright at the things that are upon earth, and with labour do we find the things that are before us.' (Stephen Hales, Vegetable Staticks (1727), p.318)

What can we cope with in the face of the unknown, of all that is uncertain? What is left to us? Ourselves.

We are the only part of the universe we are required to work on. All materials are available, and immediately to hand, on time scales that each individual can cope with. Our guides are nature, morality and virtue and by following them we shall find the way ahead to a healthy future for all life on Earth. Developing ourselves also provides us, and those around us, with some constancy and therefore a measure of certainty, while simultaneously defining our character.

Tracking Inner Tigers

'It is an old saying, and one of fearful and fathomless import, that we are forming characters for eternity. Forming characters? Whose? Our own or others? Both – and in that momentous fact lies the peril and responsibility of our existence. Who is sufficient for the thought?' (Elihu Burritt. 1810 – 1879 American philanthropist and social activist)

'A good character is, in all cases, the fruit of personal exertion. It is not inherited from parents, it is not created by external advantages, it is no necessary appendage to birth, wealth, talents, or station; but it is the result of one's own endeavours.' (William Hawes. English physician 1736 – 1808)

Characters can only develop in response to challenges. Now we can see why we must live with uncertainty since, if we found certainty, we would lose challenge – and hence our character's full potential. We seek certainty due to the apprehension or fears that uncertainty brings, but facing our fears is another character-building process. The absence of certainty also allows for the growth of humility, tolerance, patience, acceptance and co-operation. Uncertainty is an essential ingredient of 'experience'.

> I stepped from plank to plank
> A slow and cautious way
> The stars about my head I felt
> About my feet the sea.
>
> I knew not but the next
> Would be my final inch –
> This gave me that precarious gait
> Some call Experience.
>
> (Emily Dickinson 1830 – 1886)

Curiously, by relaxing our search for certainty, and opening our minds to questions that cannot be answered, we can approach closer to truth, all bound up at the heart of nature, a unity in which all others beat (not in unison but in variations on themes and movements within a symphony). We can sense it; feel it, by trying to match the rhythm of our movements to nature's lead, letting our pulse beat in time with the universal beat (e.g. recycling materials, eating seasonal, organic food (but only sufficient to fuel our activities during the day), planting, nurturing and harvesting in all our activities and sharing the results. If practical, getting up with the sun and going to bed not long after it sets. Admittedly, due to variations between summer and winter, and the demands of the socio-economic systems we have built, this would be a difficult regime to follow too strictly. However, the closer we get to it, the better we feel). By harmonising with nature we can, without certainty or all questions answered, accumulate some probable knowledge, meet challenges, find purpose and begin to know the part we play in the unity.

The part we play is an important one since human behaviour determines the fate of so many other lives. Therefore should we not play that part, despite our uncertainties, as we would be pleased to view it? That is, choosing and doing what is morally right and virtuous, regardless of doubt, discomfort or even danger. Is this not what we like to watch our heroes do, on the stages we make? Do not our heroes struggle against nature's elements with limited resources and time, sometimes wasted on false leads or unreliable accomplices, and need patience and persistence; determination and courage, to master skills and gain knowledge? What our heroes do physically we have to do spiritually, struggling with internal obstacles and enemies of self and vice as much as the external ones they produce. Imagine yourself as the hero of the book/play/film of your own life on nature's stage. The idea can help us in both personal and environmental challenges.

Knowing we are struggling with life's challenges as best we can, while aspiring to be the powerful, self-disciplined hero we would like to watch in the film of our own life, brings some peace and contentment to our hearts and minds. Whether waters rise around you or corporations fall, your choice of action to improve yourself and your world will, despite the fears and privations it brings, achieve that which is of most significance – both for you personally, and for the world, whether or not you can see the results.

Alongside the acquired abilities and knowledge, uncertainty and unanswered questions always remain, as does the necessity to press on in spite of them. Showing courage, persistence and a commitment to complete our tasks, play our roles, without guarantees or certainty, undaunted by personal sacrifice. Trusting that, as experience teaches, a greater purpose is revealed gradually as our maturity grows to understand it – embryos and seeds reveal their identity as they grow. And it is this very process of doing what is right and virtuous, in the face of uncertainty and sacrifice, that matures our character.

Our ability as a species to affect all other species is a unique capacity and therefore carries unique responsibilities. Our rapid destruction of nature needs even more rapid revision, firstly for survival and then for continued opportunities to grow and mature. Our maturation must include the development of compassion and pity for lives currently dependent on us. Decisions by directors in boardrooms can wreck the lives of people and animals many miles away, unless the distance is bridged by compassion or pity – for the man in Bangladesh who needed to take that tree and for the tiger habitat consequently damaged.

Animals are even more helpless than many humans since they cannot even voice their protest, seek aid or appeal to authorities. The helplessness of animals, especially young ones, is juxtaposed in the modern world with the seeming omnipotence of mighty Man bestriding the world. If Man had half the intelligence he claims for himself he would realise that it is *he who is dependent on the animal* for his own welfare, and that nature is currently accommodating the extent of his arrogance, greed and cruelty. As we speculated above on Olympus, justice is at work, the symmetry is active and karma's wheel is turning, swerving not a hair, while we seal our fate with our own hand. The arrogant upstart Man is cutting down the forests, and the fawns and cubs within, with his mighty machines, another manifestation of the bully behaviour we have seen in societies in general and socio-economics in particular. However, on meeting the consequences of his actions he will soon reveal the cowardice of all bullies and be cringing and pleading with heaven, hoping for forgiveness from dumb mouths. Call it common sense or karma's wheel, it is coming around, even as you read, and will crush us, lest we change direction.

Will those dumb mouths forgive us? Or perhaps ask us if we even know the meaning of pity? Perhaps the only reason we may deserve pity is for being pitiless, although it's a gossamer defence, especially in the absence of the steely strength of self control we should have developed while we had the chance. Taoist sage Lao-Tzu named pity as the first of his 'three treasures' to take through life (the themes of this book are also in keeping with a fundamental premise of Taoism which is that by solitary contemplation of nature one can ultimately harness the powers of the universe). Let us learn from Lao-Tzu and the legend of Akbar seeing the chinkara fawn as the hunt was about to commence, seized with such a rage 'as none had ever seen the like in him before' ensuring that 'active men made every endeavour that no one should even touch the feather of a finch'.

Have we not also heard the 'tongue-less tongue' that spoke to Akbar? He listened to it and took action accordingly yet, collectively, we have tried to ignore it, and harmed far more than the feather of a finch. It spoke of unity and therefore mutual interdependence. Interdependence depends on balance, and pity is a part of balance since it prevents excess or extremes. Hard as Mother Nature can be, if we watch and listen long enough, she will even teach us pity: Corbett watched a tigress stalking a month-old kid. The kid sees her, starts bleating and the tigress abandons the stalk (as carnivores will often do, once detected, as the chance of getting close enough for contact has usually gone). Amazingly, she walks toward the kid and, even more amazingly, the kid goes forward to meet her. Their noses touch briefly before the tigress walks away.

To be referred to as a beast is usually derogatory. In a denial that cleverly affirms worse than what is denied, Shakespeare, as usual, has already said it:

> 'No beast so fierce but knows some touch of pity.
> But I know none, and therefore am no beast.'
>
> (Richard III, Act 1 scene 2)

…and is, sadly, not alone. If we mature sufficiently to cultivate our compassion and our pity; to meet the responsibilities revealed by them; to achieve our most important current purpose – now so close to earthy, earthly, Earth failure – perhaps greater, more 'cosmic' purposes will be seen and understood.

In Shakespeare's 'Tempest' Caliban, a half-human creature 'not honour'd with a human shape' inhabits an island. He is 'gross and earthy, without the rudiment of a moral sense. This constitutes his hopeless inferiority, for he is not devoid of intellect. His mistake((s) *are*) rather the effect of ignorance than stupidity…With all his sensitiveness to physical impressions, Caliban is a moral idiot. He is not, as has been fancifully maintained, the "missing link" between man and brute; but he does indicate what man would be if his progress had been solely upon intellectual lines.' (Richard Garnett 1835 – 1906 scholar, biographer and poet). There is much of the Bible in Shakespeare and in this context we see the deeper meaning of the Biblical injunction to 'subdue the earth' – to develop our better moral selves, rise above our elements of earth. 'Subdue the earth' does not mean abuse the planet and destroy your life-support systems (perhaps originally thought unnecessary to specify). One measure of our success in subduing the earth is *not* how we exploit it but how we learn nature's lessons and apply them to control, care for and appreciate it. In the process we develop our higher faculties, subduing more earthly influences such that they do not control us. Moreover, our choices and activities have life and death influences over other lives, which should prompt a reassessment of any view in which the earth is seen only as a commodity and / or playground for our exclusive amusement and enjoyment.

The physical world is reflecting that it is *our* immaturity, *our* immorality, *our* imbalances, *our* emphasis on yang and *our* emphasis on self, which now threatens Earth and all life on it, including our own. We have to restore our personal 'inner' balances; putting morals before money, others before ourselves; duty before fun; professional before personal; serious before superficial; formal before casual; substance before image. We have to restore lost ideals such as decency instead of vulgarity, self-effacement instead of self-promotion, privacy instead of publicity.

We also have to learn to strive for, and be happy with, a material optimum instead of maximum. When initially assessing what our optimal choice has brought us we might be as children pouting that we could have had more, yet with maturity of character we realise the power to choose is worth more than what is materially lost. Goethe tells us that 'the master reveals himself in his restraint' and we can each be our own masters. Too many seek not only maximum but also the power it brings; power over others – whether it is one nation which, or one individual who, manipulates another – as mentioned briefly when we looked at Zen's types of tiger – and history is dominated by those who have achieved such power as leaders of nations or empires. Even modern historical documentaries may refer to such achievements in tones of awe and reverence. Such power can, initially, seem appealing, yet barely has there been a 'great' nation or empire established without brutality. Violence has been the common currency of most, if not all. The titles of 'Tsar' and 'Kaiser' were derived from Caesar and 'greatness', fame and glory are too often associated with force of arms and men of violence. However, power over others is always temporary, eternally shifting and difficult to maintain – because it is not healthy for the whole. From spiritual perspectives this type of history does have greatness – but of tedium, since, although it includes interesting interludes, events and characters, it is fundamentally an account of imbalanced and tyrannical egos seeking to force obedience and servility on others, on whose backs they attempt to climb out of their own internal spiritual abyss. The following account refers to Napoleon, but many names could be substituted for his, and the general meaning is clear.

'A little while ago I stood by the grave of Napoleon, a magnificent tomb of gilt and gold, fit almost for a dead deity, and gazed upon the sarcophagus of black Egyptian marble where rests at last the ashes of the restless man. I leaned over the balustrade and thought about the career of the greatest soldier of the modern world.

I saw him walking upon the banks of the Seine contemplating suicide; I saw him at Toulon; I saw him putting down the mob in the streets of Paris; I saw him at the head of the army of Italy; I saw him crossing the bridge at Lodi with the tricolor in his hand; I saw him in Egypt in the shadows of the pyramids; I saw him conquer the Alps and mingle the eagle of France with the eagles of the crags. I saw him at Marengo, at Ulm and Austerlitz. I saw him in Russia, where the infantry of the snow and the cavalry of the wild blast scattered his legions like winter's withered leaves. I saw him at Leipsic in defeat and disaster, driven by a million bayonets back upon Paris, clutched like

With thanks to photographer Siren who has placed this image in the public domain, free of copyright.
Bas-relief on marble by Pierre Puget: Alexander the Great meets the philosopher Diogenes.
(Tyrants all too often block the light).

a wild beast, banished to Elba. I saw him escape and retake an Empire by the force of his genius. I saw him upon the frightful field of Waterloo, when chance and fate combined to wreck the fortunes of their former king. And I saw him at St. Helena, with his hands crossed behind him, gazing out upon the sad and solemn sea.

I thought of the orphans and widows he had made; of the tears that had been shed for his glory and of the only woman who had ever loved him pushed from his heart by the cold hand of ambition.

And I said I would rather have been a French peasant and worn wooden shoes. I would rather have lived in a hut with a vine growing over the door and the grapes growing purple in the kisses of the autumn sun. I would rather have been that poor peasant with my loving wife by my side, knitting as the day died out of the sky, with my children upon my knee and their arms about me. I would rather have been that man and gone down to the tongueless silence of the dreamless dust than to have been that imperial impersonation of force and murder known as Napoleon the Great.'
(Robert G. Ingersoll 1833 – 1899 American. A friend of the poet Walt Whitman, who said: "It should not be surprising that I am drawn to Ingersoll, for he is Leaves of Grass... He lives, embodies, the individuality I preach. I see in Bob [Ingersoll] the noblest specimen... pure out of the soil, spreading, giving, demanding light.") Personal ambitions need not extend to the conquest of nations before they cause others deprivation or distress.

(The way of the warrior can be one of spiritual progress, of climbing the spiritual mountain, but examples of these are rare, and they usually start from level ground at least, rather than within their own abyss. Too often humans see strength in what is actually weakness. Real strength can be seen in the meekness of Mahatma Gandhi, Red Indians, ascetics or gurus, and many aspects and qualities of yin).

Eclipsing all the catalogue of 'great' leaders or warriors is a greater power, greater than all of them put together – the power to control oneself, which can be as permanent and total as one chooses. Such complete control is achieved by facing the greatest challenge – to conquer self. Nothing else in the entire universe has this power over you. The only thing in the universe that can, in these ways, change you, is you. Vices can only be turned to virtue by one's own free will. For example, the only thing that can completely control greed is free will. The law and social pressure can only ever guard against it or confine it; never end it. The power of free will is an important part of what the tiger's power symbolises for us.

For many in this world, power over others (to elevate self) seems a damn fine thing, whereas in truth (unless it is to justly serve the majority) it is a damnable thing. Those who seek it can spare little time for self-improvement while those who seek self-improvement spend no time seeking power over others. Virtue and morality are their own reward and also bring health and prosperity for all – people and other life forms. As these add to our self-chosen constancy of character, further fruits are grown in healthy relationships.

Whether or not we bear kingly crown or warrior's crest, each of us can say, in accordance with both science and religion: I am not only part of the universe but I also affect the universe. The Chinese say 'it is impossible to know the consequences of our actions' but our actions surely do have consequences. Hence, each and everything I do is best done with appreciation and care, especially my work and duties since they most directly or indirectly affect other life forms. I am part of a network of connections extending throughout the cosmos and each action, even if seemingly trivial, has an effect – might even be amplified – as it passes through those connections.

However, by using nature as my model and practising morality and virtue, the full effect and consequences, while remaining unknown, will be consistently healthy, through all connections, locally or in distant deeps or skies and will, eventually, return to me. All the enormous and complex global problems – including corrupt and / or incompetent governments, the greed of financial institutions, multinational companies and all the rest – ultimately reduce to individuals making decisions. We bear responsibility in proportion to the power we wield.

The power that is currently manifest, particularly in Western society, of the military, corporations, politics, and even muscle-bound Hollywood heroes, are all exactly the opposite of true power and symptomatic of how far we have wandered. A recent media trend is to refer to the American president as the 'most powerful man in the world'. The media, and to the degree they accurately assess their audience, seem so impressed, and obsessed, with power – but crude, immature power: power that can be wielded over others. This juvenile attempt to impress could also constitute an unhealthy distortion of democracy but, to whatever degree it holds any truth, the 'man who bears most responsibility' would be a more mature and pertinent description. As we have seen on our journey, the most powerful man in the world is the man who has most control over himself, who can balance and carry his responsibilities. He is the man who has not destroyed his tiger but tamed it such that the qualities can be utilised and admired, without allowing its dangerous elements to imperil himself or others.

That statesmen and corporate executives so often fail to meet their community responsibilities, fail to frame or tame their tigers while indulging their lower life-forms by favouring vested interests, corrupt regimes etc. is too well known to require elaboration here. Yet how can we criticise them if we cannot meet our own responsibilities, which correspond to our own powers? If these are relatively small, what can we say for ourselves if we fail to meet even these? When we are confident in our own conduct we can then call others, especially elected representatives, to account for theirs.

In Britain's democracy the chief minister is the 'Prime Minister' which means 'first servant' – he/she is leader of the government and servant of the people. The recent trend to call politicians 'political leaders' is another indicator of the shift of emphasis away from democracy and citizens' responsibilities to govern politicians. We have let servants become 'leaders' since it seems, at first glance, to make our lives easier, allows us to complain, blame others and be concerned only with 'me, my family and my home': the very things threatened by ignoring community responsibilities – via banking crashes, crime, unemployment, ill-health and now the multiple threats of an environmental crisis. Democracy suffers since 'leading' lies close to 'commanding'. Politicians would not gain so much responsibility if more of the electorate faced their own – and we can all see where and what our 'leaders' have led us into.

If we had faced our community (local, national and global) responsibilities earlier we could have demanded of governments that the environment be treated and respected as the basis of political, commercial and any other human activity (since it is!). The issues are now more complex since they involve many interconnected and mutually reinforcing factors that have grown around the imbalanced foundations, such as, to name but a few; the erosion of civil liberties, the 'dumbing down' of the population and the rise of a 'money mentality' that is virtually ubiquitous. Ultimately, as described above, the vacuum left by an increasingly secular society and an electorate ever more disinterested or uninterested in voting, has been filled by corporations, most notably the media. Hence corporations have gained more control over politics than the electorate.

Recognising politicians as public servants does not equate to disrespecting them. Those trying to do their duties honourably and sincerely; focussing on the welfare of the community and prioritising it above their own, deserve the highest respect. There will always be those grubbing around, falsifying expense claims, benefiting family members at public expense, avoiding tax and seeking personally lucrative and influential contacts etc. They need to be identified and removed from public office but let us focus on the genuinely sincere, the right and the honourable. Putting community welfare as one's top priority is usually a weary weight for anyone to bear since, no matter how laudable or beneficial one's best efforts are, there will always be those who find fault, make problems, are parasitic or never satisfied. To press on for, say, a decade or more, in the face of ignorance and ingratitude while battling the enormous forces of a corporate controlled world, takes a firm backbone and great personal characteristics.

Whether we are politicians or not, we craft our character and our karma simultaneously (karma may be translated in summary as 'action' or 'sum of actions'). Such self assessment means we must ask ourselves: Am I doing my duties to the best of my ability? Am I husbanding and nurturing the life force? Am I helping someone or something less privileged than myself or my family? What am I taking? What am I giving? What have I – *excluding money* – done for the healthy future of my children and grand children? Including money, have I invested in programmes doing more harm today than any good that money might bring in future? If you find your answers are less than inspiring then, for your sake, for your family's sake, for tigers' sakes, for God's sake, change them.

So much of life, from personal to global situations, complex or sophisticated, reduce to fundamental principles: Keep your own house in order; do your duty; earn your share of Earth's resources while conserving them; clean up your mess; look after each other, in particular the needy; respect nature, natural resources and other things that are not yours and look after those that are; appreciate and be grateful for what you have while making children aware of what they receive. Then we can play with our toys. The same applies to individuals, communities, nations and the world.

Unfortunately, most of us prefer to play; the rich play with big shiny toys, scientists with hi-tech toys; and the media and politicians play games with each other. Meanwhile children starve, waters rise, trees and tigers disappear and we all approach 'game over' due to the neglect of our foundations and duties. Immaturity always prefers playtime to school. When we have done our duty; faced our responsibilities, we may turn, for a time, to our space exploration, science and art, fashion and football etc. Human interests and hobbies are not being disparaged; this author hopes to spend some time on amateur astronomy – provided he is satisfied with his contributions to conservation and environmental protection beforehand.

Too frequent public parades of immaturity and self-indulgence, let alone greed and stupidity, help convince us they are 'normal', even acceptable. Everyone else seems to be 'out for themselves' and so few make efforts for the greater good, it seems much easier to join the herd. Yet, at the same time, essential environmental threads are unravelling – those which provide that herd with its wants and needs, and those that hold our communities together as viable ecological and economic units (the two are inseparable). There is no time left to ignore the unpalatable or 'spin' the information. Only the truth can help us and if that's not 'politically correct' then politics is not correct.

Some will question what we know of truth, and global warming is an example of doubt being raised over the extent of human contributions to it (for the sake of a more important point, we will ignore reports which emerged after Kyoto that car manufacturers had purposely hired scientists to dispute evidence of global warming in order to delay or demolish any resulting carbon dioxide emission legislation that might reduce profits or competitive advantage). We will agree that humans cannot know for certain the whole truth about global warming. This leaves us with two options; continue to live as we wish (or, more accurately, as corporations wish) or adjust our life-styles to take into account a weight of evidence that suggests we are orchestrating our own destruction. Mmmm, which should we choose? Even in the absence of certain proof the only intelligent course of action is to err on the side of caution for all and everything we hold dear. The practical, political and commercial problems of what action to take were dealt with above by reference to 'biochar'. If global warming was the only environmental problem perhaps there would be more ground for debate but when we think of definitely man-made damage such as deforestation, species extinctions, loss of topsoil, pollution…then global warming seems to fit the catalogue very well and gains credence as another symptom of our malaise.

Purely rational approaches; picking over the evidence, examining conflicting data (that reveals how much we don't know)…whilst ordering another cup of coffee…all too often speak of complacency and misplaced confidence. Climate debate reveals again the 'poverty of reason' employed alone and too many 'pluming themselves on their cleverness'. Such approaches are themselves as indicative of wrong relations with nature as the problems being considered. They smack of arrogance; that man's toy-town mechanical analysis of sophistication so far beyond him has ultimate validity. We considered above those who might pontificate for the camera, and Huxley refers to the self-satisfied complacency of intelligence. Experts tend to talk with comfortable self-assurance, and the next television programme is entertainment; lavish jet-set life-styles, or sport, or drama…all encouraging the idea that humans are in control and have everything arranged securely to serve their needs and wants. Nothing could be further from the truth. Realisation of our limitations and our current situation would breed some humility and appreciation in the face of nature, and these attitudes automatically lead to behaviour that respects and conserves nature. It would help if we spent more time admiring nature, and less time admiring ourselves. Some are too clever, detached and comfortable to know if climate change is real. Climate is changing because we are not. It's changing because we're firmly fixated on self, greed and / or apathy. By these criteria we can be sure climate change (and much else that is taking shape in nature's mirror) is a real reflection of our condition.

If unconvinced of global warming as seen from spiritual perspectives, let us employ some common sense from practical perspectives – if billions of tonnes of carbon (previously 'locked away' for millions of years underground) are released into the atmosphere over a couple of hundred years, would it not be more surprising for it to have no effect? Thompson and Einstein told us stirring a flower would trouble a star. Will the release of billions of tonnes of carbon dioxide trouble flowers and stars?

Above we considered nature's precision in recording alterations of single, tiny elements, such as the alteration of a single gene, which has the potential to manifest as changes in the world at large. Will tampering with genes, beyond the laboratory, alter nature's original designs? How can it not? What new global gene pool are we in the process of making with our hotchpotch of genetic 'engineering' (if purblind dabbling can be called such)? We have not the slightest idea.

Not only environmental conditions, but also nuclear energy, poverty, epidemics, genocides, rising crime rates, murder and mayhem around the world are also symptomatic that human civilisation cannot continue on its current course. In our blindness (wilful or otherwise), fear or ignorance we want to continue in our same old ways, letting law enforcement, civil servants or scientists solve our problems, while, overall, we 'progress'. However, unlike the other problems just listed, environmental ones (such as the tiger's demise) are fundamental to all else and indicate unmistakeably, from all the perspectives viewed herein, that we must change ourselves to survive. On a positive note, surely it is us, as individuals, who can act as the single, tiny elements that nature can use as the catalysts for healthy growth to produce worthwhile effects in the world at large.

Once again, whether viewed from spiritual or practical perspectives, common sense tells us that we should be cleaning up, controlling and restricting many of our activities, whether or not each and every activity can be 'scientifically proved' as critical to mankind's limited understanding. Will we ever grow wisdom from knowledge? Will we ever have the courage to face nature's mirror and see that our cowardly New World is dominated by ego, greed and selfishness, to the point of suicide?

James Lovelock's work on chlorofluorocarbons (CFCs) helped ensure a ban on these chemicals (used in aerosols, refrigerants and air-conditioning units) which damage the ozone layer when released into the atmosphere. He also propounded the Gaia hypothesis in which the Earth can be viewed as self-regulating. Isaac Newton had suggested very similar ideas, as had the ancient Greeks before him and the Earth as an organism is a concept in agreement with the Bhumi Sukta (Hymn to the Earth) of Hinduism's Atharva Veda. However, Lovelock was the first to support the idea with modern scientific data; naming gases, specifying quantities and explaining processes.

(That ecosystems exhibit self-regulating equilibrium had been an accepted view for years and gained scientific support in the 1960s and 70s until, soon after, other scientific studies claimed that apparently balanced ecosystems were illusory and that an ecosystem would, for example, fail to re-establish its equilibrium in the event of a significant disturbance, such as an extensive forest fire or flood. New species could colonise the area and a different ecosystem emerge. To this author at least, these views are not really in conflict but reconciled by considering which level of organisation is being studied. Until a significant disturbance occurs, ecosystems do exhibit stability due to interactions between the environment and organisms comprising the ecosystem, some via 'feedback loops' and / or other natural laws. When a major disturbance disrupts this ecosystem, the newly emerging ecosystem might well comprise 'new' species, but the developing ecosystem will still be subject to the same natural laws and patterns of development (succession and zonation for examples). It is these laws and patterns – from soil formation to micro-organisms, to plant succession and growth of an ecological hierarchy up to and including predators – that constitute the self-regulating equilibrium and the model of nature so often referred to in this book. This model produces stable ecosystems, of whatever particular type they may be, balancing over time and exhibiting interactions which can justifiably be called interactive systems, and tending to equilibrium, until a disturbance of sufficient magnitude repeats the whole process.)

Lovelock is better qualified and experienced than most to draw conclusions about the status of Earth's life-support systems and his views are bleak and blunt (New Scientist magazine 24/01/09 'We're doomed but it's not all bad' or at www.newscientist.com). He expects the human population of the planet to decrease by 90% or more during this century due to the effects of global warming. He dismisses most of the current attempts to reduce carbon emissions as ineffective either in principle (they use more energy than they save) or practice (inadequacy of scale). James Lovelock sees 'biochar' (briefly looked at above) as one solution but considers that 'they' will not do it. If research confirms biochar's potential, and we take a more active part in our democracy, with sufficient citizens insisting on this action, 'they' will have no choice about implementing it.

In the article Lovelock, ninety years of age in 2009, seems unperturbed about his own prediction since he has been through 'this kind of emotional thing before' and refers to his experience of anticipating, and then living through, WWII. This author has great respect and admiration for James Lovelock's scientific work. However, his personal *sang froid* does not sit comfortably with the principles explored in this book. As we know from everyday life, reason and emotion are continuously present as fundamental, elemental parts of being human. We may as well say we have 'been through rational things' before. While we draw breath, reason and emotion are not only unavoidable, valid and valuable, but each is necessary for the other to function healthily. It is understood that the onset of WWII was for many an emotional and frightening time, as was living through, and for many, dying in it. Horrific though it was for millions abused, burned, maimed or killed; 90% of the population did not die and in consequence some infrastructure remained to supply, and then help re-build, community facilities; nor did WWII rearrange nature's fundamental processes.

It is healthy, natural and normal to be apprehensive, if not afraid, and also angry, at the unprecedented dangers and disasters now facing millions of people due to mismanagement, greed and ignorance at the most senior levels of government and commerce. These emotions also act as spurs to action, remedial measures and for those 'who know' to tell and motivate those who don't. When sitting in comfort we can be tempted to philosophise and speculate but, whatever our views may be, we try to avoid physical, mental and / or emotional pain – especially on behalf of loved ones. We tend to philosophise from a position of comfort but when disaster, danger or even discomfort disturbs us, we do not 'review' our conclusions – we do not even think of them. We are reminded of Shakespeare's philosopher with the toothache. The reader may have heard people who say that extinction is natural and that maybe Man too is destined for extinction. The reader may also have wondered what these complacent prophets may say and, more importantly, how they will behave, when there's a delay to dinner being served, let alone ecological Armageddon. Philosophy is a product of spare time and a full stomach. Opinions and abstractions are forgotten when pain arrives, hunger gnaws, bullies rule, or loved ones suffer. Moreover, 'when death looms up suddenly at the foot of the hill we try to see beyond it into another hope.' (B23. Previously quoted more fully in chapter II. Reprinted wuith the permission of Pocket Books, a division of Simon & Schuster, Inc., from THE STORY OF PHILOSOPHY by Will Durant. Copyright © 1926, 1927, 1933, 1954, 1955, 1961 by Will Durant. All rights reserved)

James Lovelock's age may be a factor influencing his complacency and / or resignation, and this is respected. However, if people around middle age or younger, share his views in this regard, this book is suggesting that to wait, in quiet acceptance, while the results of others' greed and ignorance seriously harm our loved ones, is not only to deny the elements of the tiger within but to exalt the leech, or the worm, or even the bacteria within us. We have a choice. Even if victory seems impossible, it is better to take action for the right side than the wrong side – and forget about which side might 'win' since, without remedial action, every side is the losing side.

Is there any hope on the horizon?

Framing Fearful Symmetries

Lovelock's Gaia theory, the Earth as a self-regulating system has, in this author's view, much validity. Perhaps as a reaction of Gaia, or at least, an example of the principle, growth of some organisms which absorb carbon dioxide and / or other greenhouse gases, might appear naturally.

Another (and for all we know related) possibility comes from the scriptures of the Baha'I faith "I swear by God! But for the divine Decree, and the inscrutable dispensations of Providence, the earth itself would have utterly destroyed all these people!" (Bahá'u'lláh, Kitáb-i-Iqan, p 172 'Book of Certitude').

For years Scandinavia has exhibited more advanced and civilised behaviour than many other Western nations. As of 2009, Norway has signed an agreement with Guyana in South America, by which its rainforest (covering 75% of its land area) will be conserved in return for c. £150 million provided by Norway, as some contribution toward preventing further global warming.

Other hopes are provided by environmental NGOs; those businesses providing ethical and environmentally-friendly products and services; and those who are their customers. Authors who spread environmental awareness serve some purpose but only insofar as they stimulate appropriate action. This author hopes that, however few or many readers this book may reach, they may (if they have not already) adjust their own life-styles according to its suggestions. If not, writing it has been a waste of time and resources, since action alone is of critical value.

Action and hope form a powerful combination as illustrated in the following summary of three postings on the LifeForce website 'updates' page. Tadoba Andhari Tiger Reserve (TATR) is one of the Reserves in and around which LifeForce funded training for tribal youth and subsequent placement in employment, in conjunction with education regarding the importance of conservation. The forest outside the imaginary boundary line of the Reserve, but adjacent to it, is called Lohara and forms an important part of the 'corridors' connecting Reserves, as mentioned above. Central government allocated a corporation a 'coal block' at Lohara; 1, 750 hectares of core jungle area on which it could start mining – beginning with felling 1, 200 000 mature trees. This would have disastrous consequences for wildlife and the environment in general. On July 20th 2009, a brave local conservationist named Bandu Dhotre began a fast unto death in opposition to the mining operation. As his hunger strike entered its ninth day, the nearby town of Chandrapur saw conservationists, social organizations and political parties (Congress, BJP and Shiv Sena) unite and collectively call for a general strike in his support and for the mining permissions to be revoked. Traders in Chandrapur kept their shops closed in the main market in the morning. Students were turned away from schools and colleges. Even petrol pumps and cinemas closed (emergency services such as hospitals and medical shops remained open. No support for the cause came from government offices or banks, where attendance was normal). By 1st August 2009 LifeForce received news that the permission for the mine had been officially revoked. Conservation work in the wild is, all too often, about fighting losing battles and retreating to ever reducing defensive positions. It is hard to describe the elation born of this success, not only because of its rarity but also because it was achieved by peaceful solidarity between people of all walks of life, and because another threat from big business, another giant ogre, was faced by a very brave man not, in this instance, called David, but Dhotre.

However, none of the reasons for hope just cited, nor any other possibility of reprieve, release us from our personal responsibilities and, as these are all we are in absolute control of, we have our work immediately to hand. When we remember 'the great hope of society is individual character' (William Ellery Channing, as above) we realise that we ourselves are our best hope. Incredible as it may seem, and enormous as the problems are, we, each of us, are the solution. Individuals exercising free will are the only variable that is ultimately significant as a cause, and ultimate effects can only be changed by affecting ultimate causes. Hence, it can only be individual change that brings permanent, healthy changes to the world. Each person has some power in the world: in how they spend their time and energy; how they earn and spend their money; how they behave toward other people and life-forms, how they value virtue and morality. When each is using these powers properly, they automatically have a beneficial influence on the world. Most would say only very little and that they would make greater changes to the world if they had greater power. Yet most characters live their lives misusing even the tiny fraction of power they do hold – why would their character and use of power suddenly improve if given a nation or city to control? Such power would more likely corrupt completely. Only having a little power to manage is something to be grateful for. When it is mastered then greater responsibilities can be accommodated and we see the wisdom of Lao-Tsu's and the Biblical advice that having power over oneself is greater than having power over cities.

Celebrity, fame for nothing of note, extreme self indulgence and any other public display of I, me and myself, are all opposite to; duty to others, dignity, self-control, self-effacement, discretion, and all pose a threat to self-development and the opportunity to know ourselves.

Those who insist that the world can change only if millions of people change virtually overnight, only reveal the crudeness of their analysis – they only recognise shovels; not scalpels. In a system as exquisitely refined as nature, all change is relevant and recorded. We considered above that changing single genes, and individual people, can manifest in the world at large. Those readers who have typed a large word-processing file will know that the computer will register the alteration of a single character and ask if you want to 'save the changes'. Similarly, nature records the alteration of a single character and, if the changes improve what we are authoring, we want to save the changes. If we do, nature notices by recording the effects, until our next edit. The document and the world change, whether we can personally see far enough to recognise it or not.

We already create change by our everyday actions, yet not necessarily for our own or others' best benefit, so we had best examine and adjust our behaviour to ensure we do. Incredibly, you can change the world for the better, today, by deciding to act on any of the options suggested herein and / or others with similar effects known to you but, perhaps, not referred to here. Your scalpel's touch may only clear a capillary or two but that contributes to health at the heart of your community, your world, your universe. The power that created the universe beats in that heart, and yours, and the tiger's, but it is your shoulder and your art, that can twist their sinews. Even though our changes are made in a relative microcosm, we know from our studies of hearts that each element, however small, is important, since each and every heart cell needs to beat in synchronous rhythm to maintain the health of the whole heart. Firstly when differentiating into heart cells, and then with respect to each chamber they form.

"Our problems are man-made. Therefore they can be solved by Man. For, in the final analysis, our most basic common link is that we all inhabit this small planet, we all breathe the same air, we all cherish our children's future and we are all mortal." As spoken by President John F. Kennedy, at that time, the most responsible man in the world. With a few precious exceptions we have, since then, increased the stress on this small planet, polluted the same air, threatened our children's futures and made our mortality as a species a possibility, if not a probability.

We noted in the previous chapter that the City of London and Wall Street were the two capitals of international finance throughout the period leading directly to the current financial crash, which was the ultimate result of at least two decades of economic deregulation and liberalisation, beginning with the Reagan and Thatcher governments. Environmental degradation went hand in hand with the financial boom preceding the bust. Blair's 'Labour' government in the U.K. favoured big business in the same way as had the Conservative government of Thatcher/Major. In the latter case government held a stronger position but, by the time of Blair's government, big business – particularly the media – was using its accumulated power to influence political results in order to maintain or increase its own power.

However, it is not suggested that all was sweetness and light before the Reagan and Thatcher governments. We have already noted the growing power of multinationals since the 1950s and it is also accepted that national economies were being crippled by the industrial action of unions, some with political agendas. However, if economic deregulation and liberalisation was a magical solution, governments could not get that genie back into the bottle and, proceeding unchecked; it has grown to monstrous proportions. Whatever power the unions held has been multiplied by orders of magnitude and presented by governments to banking and financial institutions. Bankers were foolishly allowed to multiply it still further and assume economically dominant positions such that governments became bankers' servants instead of public servants.

In the previous chapter we looked briefly at some of the economic and environmental consequences of World Bank and IMF policies, all part of the globalisation orchestrated by them and multinational corporations. Their policies are designed to blatantly serve self interest, despite the worst possible consequences for nations, people, natural resources and the environment. In 1980 the poorest of the world's human population (more than four hundred million people) lived on less that U.S. $1 per day. Reagan and Thatcher claimed that their policies of deregulation and liberalisation would create wealth that would 'trickle down' through all strata of society. Twenty years later, just after the turn of the century, the same proportion of the world's population are still living on less than U.S. $1 per day and, since the 2007 crash (the direct result of those de-regulation policies) unemployment and bankruptcies will be 'trickling down' through all strata of all societies, except the strata holding those responsible for the crash. People in general and politicians in particular have been manipulated by the rich and powerful, who thereby maintain their wealth, even in the face of the disasters they orchestrate. Millions of people are again adversely affected in terms of income, unemployment and consequent difficulties, if not tragedies. This, as well as all the other imbalances and declining standards previously mentioned damages homes and families, which can psychologically damage children, who then enter society and damage it further by manifesting their problems on innocent citizens.

Amongst those on less than U.S. $1 per day, some poach tigers and fell trees (such as the poor man in Balpakram National Park who invited the guard to shoot him). Hence, politicians and corporate decision-makers thousands of miles away from tiger habitat are as much (if not more) responsible for tiger deaths and forests falling as those who set the traps, fire the guns, or wield axes and chainsaws. Corporate and political power operate through interconnections between natural resources, commodities, prices and employment. Hence the people we considered in chapter IV who believe 'real life' equates to business and know nothing of the environment, need to understand environmental connections – if only to really understand their business. Any business transaction, whether of multinational industries or the local corner shop, can be traced within a few steps, from consumer choices to natural resources. Yet still in 2010 this author has heard the same short-sighted observation that these environmental measures are all very well but they will not survive unless they can 'turn a profit'. It is we who will not survive, unless we can turn our priorities around.

Above we were heartened by the collective action of people living around a Tiger Reserve. Some readers may have thought it harsh to call the mining company another giant ogre since, currently, the world's energy requirements are met to a significant degree by coal and the company is merely trying to do its job. Well, just as for the oil companies and governments in power during the latter decades of the 20th century, the present environmental situation is no surprise; we have known that we have been heading toward it for all those decades. Instead of having invested in timely research into alternatives, and despite the recent attempts to start looking for them, most corporations have continued to mine, or log, or deplete other natural resources while there is anything left to exploit. Such a policy represents, if nothing else, an extreme. It also represents, as in so many environmental scenarios, professional suicide, since it is to 'kill the goose laying the golden egg'. The stock answer will be that 'somebody else will if we don't' and again we see the value of an independent and sensible government, which would rigorously protect resources from excessive commercial exploitation. Although the coal industry was defeated in a battle over one Tiger Reserve, they have not changed their agenda and have been lobbying the Indian government for permission to mine much of the last few precious percent of India's land mass still currently protected as National Parks and Tiger Reserves. That the tiny 4.5% fragment of habitat protected in law cannot be left 'sacred to nature' proves that some giant industries look on laws protecting the environment as empty labels, to be removed when all other resources have been plundered. This is of major concern in itself. When we remember the natural habitat's invaluable contributions to all our life-support systems, destroying the last few percent may defeat the very purpose for which it is destroyed since any viable industrial and/or commercial future depends on environmental health. Even from purely commercial perspectives, alternative sources of energy will have to be found after the relatively brief period of coal extraction and habitat destruction. So, with regard to tiny remaining fragments of tiger populations and natural habitat, at this eleventh environmental hour – and the necessity of finding alternatives immediately after they are destroyed – common sense *and commercial sense* surely demand their inviolate protection?

We know of the devastation wrought by humans on tropical and temperate forests but now, instead of learning the lesson, the last remaining and previously undamaged major forest on Earth, the boreal, or northern, forest covering much of northern Canada, Alaska, Russia and Scandinavia, is being degraded by logging, mining, urban development and associated human activities. We have noted the numerous and essential functions of forests, but in the context of the current concern over global warming (itself increasing the risk of forest fires), the boreal forest represents a third of the Earth's remaining forests and hence a third of the carbon stored by them. Russia's share is most degraded and again we see the link between economic volatility and environmental degradation. (J5)

Yet, despite the behaviour of corporate executives and governments, we shall not abandon our principle of personal responsibilities. Let us not fail to frame our symmetries. If the tiger becomes extinct, the final forests fall and rain and rising oceans flood critical areas of what remains, then each of us has failed. No matter who or where we are, we can respect the earth in the way we lead our life. If we only live for self-indulgence, convenience and comfort, we will have failed ourselves, our families, our forbears and our tigers. All things are connected…

'If you are a poet, you will see clearly that there is a cloud floating in this sheet of paper. Without a cloud, there will be no rain; without rain, the trees cannot grow; and without trees, we cannot make paper. The cloud is essential for the paper to exist. If the cloud is not here, the sheet of paper cannot be here either…If we look into this sheet of paper even more deeply, we can see the sunshine in it. If the sunshine is not there, the forest cannot grow. In fact, nothing can grow. Even we cannot grow without sunshine. And so, we know that the sunshine is also in this sheet of paper…And if we continue to look, we can see the logger who cut the tree and brought it to the mill to be transformed into paper. And we see the wheat. We know that the logger cannot exist without his daily bread, and therefore the wheat that became his bread is also in this sheet of paper. And the logger's father and mother are in it too…Looking even more deeply, we can see we are in it too. This is not difficult to see, because when we look at a sheet of paper, the sheet of paper is part of our perception. Your mind is in here and mine is also. So we can say that everything is in here with this sheet of paper. You cannot point out one thing that is not here – time, space, the earth, the rain, the minerals in the soil, the sunshine, the cloud, the river, the heat. Everything co-exists with this sheet of paper. That is why I think the word 'inter-be' should be in the dictionary. To be is to inter-be. You cannot just be by yourself alone. You have to inter-be with every other thing. This sheet of paper is because everything else is. As thin as this sheet of paper is, it contains everything in the universe in it.' (Reprinted from *Heart of Understanding: Commentaries on the Prajnaparamita Heart Sutra* (1988) by Thich Nhat Hanh, by kind permission of Parallax Press, Berkeley, California, www.parallax.org).

How many of us throw the universe into the waste paper basket because of one mark or crease on otherwise pristine paper? Valuing what we have, realising how precious it is and being conscious of these connections lets us review this passage from the practical perspectives of today and may provide a paper-trail leading us out of our current critical danger, so (with apologies to Thich Nhat Hanh):

If you are human, you can clearly see a forest in this sheet of paper; without a forest this paper would not be. If we look into this sheet of paper even more deeply, we can see the forest's life, including animals as pollinators, planters and cultivators, and the water table, nutrients and other elements, also essential for human life. We also see legal and illegal loggers, and forests disappearing even while we look. As forests disappear, terrestrial ecosystems necessary to humans also degrade and disappear. Forests, animals, man-made products, employment, politics, socio-economics and multinational corporations, are all in this piece of paper, but they are currently arranged such that they cannot continue to inter-be.

Thich Nhat Hanh's passage is complete in itself and conveys his message beautifully. However, considerations in our current context would point to one thing that is not in the piece of paper, not yet in the entire universe – your future choices; what you will do, what actions you will take, about inter-being with every other thing. The whole world and parts of the universe (since, by its very name, all parts have relevance for all other parts) can be seen as one interconnected whole. This concept reveals how special, how valuable, how precious our free will is – since this enormous and beautiful, self-sustaining system of life is influenced by, responds to and reflects human free will. Like so many of nature's lessons, much may be missed unless we pause to reflect upon it.

We are here to look into the mirror, to find out who we are, not scientifically work out every last detail of the mirror's mechanism, while ignoring our reflection. 'Know thyself, presume not science to scan / The proper study of mankind is man' (with apologies to the poet Alexander Pope (1688 – 1744) who wrote 'God' not 'science' in his verse. However, sacred or secular, the recommended study remains the same). When we find the courage to look into the mirror, most of us will then need to find even more courage to improve the reflection. Some may have to work on images as ugly as Dorian Gray's portrait, while all of us can find ways to clean up a little more; comb our hair, pull up our socks and make ourselves as smart as can be. Our spiritual condition is often revealed by our physical appearance: '…the outward habit and garments, in man or woman, give us a taste of the spirit, and point to the internal quality of the soul; and there cannot be a more evident and gross manifestation of poor, degenerate, dung-hilly blood and breeding, than a rude, unpolished, disordered, and slovenly outside.' (Philip Massinger 1583 – 1640. English dramatist and poet). As we would expect, Massinger's near contemporary Shakespeare guided us similarly 'For the apparel oft proclaims the man.' (Hamlet Act 1 Sc.3)

Can it only be coincidence that during the 20th century, as the Western world lost its way spiritually and hence environmentally, scientifically, politically and commercially, it also adopted a virtually ubiquitous uniform of denim? In April 2009 the Wall Street Journal asked why Americans insist on wearing jeans wherever and whenever, lamenting the 'trend toward undifferentiated dressing, in which we all strive to look equally shabby no matter what the occasion'. America is not alone and denim, along with track suits and training shoes, are now all too common for many Europeans as well, whose clothes rarely reveal any quality or cut, smartness or style. For men, suits, collars and ties are becoming scarcer, as are dresses, hats and heels for ladies. Drab, dull and baggy seem to summarise the majority of Western clothes and, all too often, the people who wear them. So many relatively wealthy 'bundles of rags' walking around in the West, are in stark contrast to so many relatively poor people in the East, who are clean, colourful and neat. The cultures are dressed in different values and it is not apparent whether the West is richer for having lost the values and priorities of the East. The East is spiritually richer and, due to its clothes and dress sense is, in that sense at least, materially richer! Regardless of an increasing presence of Western rag-bags in Asia, traditional Eastern styles are still very much in evidence. Despite the dirt and decay in India, Indian people are personally as clean as can be. Ladies in particular always appear immaculately dressed, complementing their saris with a grace and elegance of movement. Even in traffic-choked, fume-filled cities (with maladjusted or worn diesel engines belching black clouds of toxic filth), whether riding side-saddle pillion on a scooter weaving in and out of traffic, or on foot negotiating some filthy slum area next to, say, a railway station, these serenely composed ladies are spotlessly clean, have not a hair out of place, and are a tonic to see. How they maintain such cleanliness amidst so much dirt remains a mystery to me and many others who have noted it.

Of course, some occupations require functional clothes (although even here, effort or no effort is clearly visible). Similarly, there is no need to be buttoned from head to toe all the time since casual can also be stylish and smart. In the privacy of our own homes we may like to relax in our well-worn slippers, baggy trousers or cardigans – and this is the point; when we are out in the world, we need to be doing our duty, and not only to earn our wages but also for other people in terms of courtesy and consideration, conducting ourselves with manners and discretion. In how we present ourselves to the world, conduct and appearance should not be in conflict. If we are relaxed in one, we are likely to be the same in the other, and we show disrespect to our fellows, whereas a smarter appearance demonstrates the opposite. During WWII, King George VI and Elizabeth (the mother of the present Queen Elizabeth of England) would visit people who had survived air raids amidst the rubble of what had been their homes. On one occasion a courtier asked the Queen if it were entirely appropriate for her to wear her best clothes amidst the dust and debris of the bomb sites. The Queen replied that the people would wear their best clothes to visit her, and she would wear her best to visit them.

Neither taste nor clothes need be uniform and others need not like what we wear, but all can see when an effort has been made and this speaks not only of respect for others and attention to duty but also of an inner discipline. As referred to so often in this book, self discipline or self control is our greatest power and, appropriately exercised, brings long-term beneficial change to the world. A slovenly appearance says that the wearer is concerned only with themselves and their own comfort, which therefore speaks of a lack of self-discipline and / or selfishness; the root of most of mankind's problems. Scruffiness says 'I do what I want, I know what is best (*and we see in the individual the same arrogance that currently characterises many societies*), I go my own way (*which is the quickest way to lose oneself*), I don't care what you think.' A smart person says 'I do care what you think, I try to do what is best for myself and the community in the long-term, and that requires effort and self discipline, small sacrifices of comfort to maintain standards, some evidence for which you can see in how I present myself to you.' When out in the world, remember your inner animal spirits and show off your striped tie, leaving your woolly cardigan at home! At least Tibetans and Tippu Sultan would approve!

These are just a few interconnections, and Buddhists, physicists and poets tell us of many more. Such interconnections are not static, they are not dead. Everything we do eventually affects everything else – and we choose much of what we do and how we do it. So every individual and their choices, their priorities and decisions, have effects, and therefore significance. Nature is our guide and it is also 'real' in the sense that the results of following that guide can be agreed and appreciated by all e.g. health, abundance of good food, clean water and air, forests, and other habitats, well-stocked with healthy animals.

For most people, the majority of their activities are (understandably and necessarily) concerned with where their salary comes from. Most occupations are directly or indirectly involved with commerce, by which we are automatically drawn into the world of products, sales, media, marketing and advertising, inevitably connected with wealth, and consequently leisure, and then entertainment which generates still further connections to our everyday lives; soap operas, 'chat shows', fame and 'celebrity' etc. From a solid reality we pass almost imperceptibly into realms of falsehood and fabrication, but these fickle and empty constructions are perceived as, or actually become (for as long as the bubble lasts), daily 'reality' for thousands of people. Entertainment and media have also, via their presentation of commerce, politics and science, become our guides, although they arise from extremely biased and almost exclusively commercial sources. At the extreme, a celebrity's new hair style, or such like, is presented as of national concern while ecosystems teetering on collapse are effectively ignored. Moreover, 'celebrity culture', which truly is meaningless, is part of that Western culture which sees life as meaningless! We are reminded of pendulums, opposites and extremes.

Due in no small part to these influences, many modern Western individuals' choices, priorities and decisions are currently dominated by material – commercially and intellectually – and have produced people who consider the material world is there merely to serve them, as if that which gave rise to us is there to serve us. This 'pendulum at the opposite extreme' is revealed in the reversal of the traditional order in various aspects of Western culture: we previously considered JFK paraphrasing Gibran to remind citizen's not to ask what their country could do for them but to ask what they could do for their country. Too few took heed and the reverse trend continued, manifesting now at family levels wherein modern Western parents serve their children, whereas in the East, in the traditional way, children still serve their parents. It would be healthier for all if we now, with urgency, consider how we might serve the Earth (since, as Socrates, Plato and Chief Seattle told us, she is our mother), our nations, our communities, our parents and then, and only then, ourselves.

This is accomplished by the choices we make and actions we take. 'People and their choices' were referred to above but 'people and their power' would, without changing its meaning, re-focus our attention. Control and management of our personal power is our sole and exclusive responsibility and is made manifest by our choices and actions, while building our characters and lives. The consequences of those choices and actions and the concept of karma tell us that we are living what we have earned and earning what we will live. Whether or not karma is rejected as a religious philosophy extending beyond each earthly life, the speed of our effects on Earth is now sufficient for us to see its truth within an earthly life. More worryingly, as we saw in Professor Orr's article, damaging change occurs rapidly while beneficial change occurs at glacial pace. Our actions have effects on other lives. If we lack empathy or sympathy, we sentence ourselves to experience that which we make others experience for, if we refuse to feel for others, it is only by experience that we will understand; that we will know. Improving our character improves our karma. Karma is the ultimate law of cause and effect and fundamental to religions that grew from soils responding to the touch of tigers' paws, and karma's tigers are more fearful than physical tigers. We can 'count the cats in Zanzibar' or we can count on karma's cat, Zen's most frightening tiger, the one holding most power and most potential – the one revealed by facing ourselves. Here is an adventure more meaningful, exciting and dangerous than any other, and it's available to each and every one. We have the opportunity to shrink from the tiger or to seize the fire and smelt our moral mettle, letting the inner tiger burn brightly through our dross. Human footprints led into the tiger's cave but did not come out. The old character meets death so that a new character lives, so that all life continues – Shiva, Brahma and Vishnu. The eternal struggle between the spiritual life and death of an individual, such that healthy life for all may continue, is concentrated with all other potential energies at one point in space and time – *you and now!*

We should be thankful if, as mentioned above, we have the luxury of improving our morals and virtue by doing our everyday duties, practising honesty, selflessness and caring for other lives. If so, our transition between old and new, between death and new life can be a quiet and peaceful one, not a violent one, which is unpleasant and disturbing to witness. Due to our imbalances, the modern world's environmental imbalance is tilted too far toward Shiva (the destroyer of life), maximising her while weakening and minimising Brahma and Vishnu, and is therefore fatal for tigers, the environment…and us. Brahma, Vishnu, Shiva, the environmental crisis, and the tiger, are all telling us to change ourselves today; spiritually, and hence physically: since the struggle between physical life and death, such that healthy life for all may continue, is concentrated with all other potential energies at this global point of space and time – *us, here and now!*

This harmonises with another and truly universal sense of 'here and now': Set against the scales of cosmic space and time, our lives, individually, and even collectively, are but an instant. If we can 'lift our heavy lids' and look, we can decide whether to make our lives a contribution to the cosmos and the ascent of man, and of Life – or detract from it. Below we shall consider the critical importance of hindsight and foresight. This will fit with our previous references to long-term perspectives being healthier than short-term perspectives, and help us to live wisely and healthily in the present – 'in the now' and right here.

Wherever 'here' happens to be, we are at the centre of our universe, and can see that the environmental crisis is not just another among many other worthy causes – it underpins all others, underpins everything. It is not another test for the ingenuity of man to 'conquer'. We, all of us, and our self-important institutions, are merely a part of nature and we must measure our, and their, development by reference to it. We don't need more research on some abstruse specialism; we need more compliance with nature's laws; laws that can be learned by all. We need more simplicity and localisation. We need more people to favour ethical and environmentally-friendly trading; to face their responsibilities to the community; to force governments to pass and enforce relevant laws protecting our common, natural heritage. The world is the largest and best 'joint-stock company' and we all have a share in it.

History and personal experience records that life is a continual struggle between right and wrong but now, due to our failure to learn from history and experience, our repeated failures to face responsibilities, and lost opportunities to improve our character, this struggle is for Life itself. The most important choice is now, for all of us, since the scales of our influence are global, critical, and we have nowhere else to go.

While there is always room for personal improvement it would appear that, healthily and happily, the majority of people are not obsessed with self and greed. Those who are so obsessed must, by definition, be amongst those who are the most acquisitive and manipulative, forming and / or becoming part of the richest organisations, and continually seeking to be richer. Since resources are finite, it is only possible for them to become richer, if the majority become poorer. The ultimate physical manifestation of this trend is what we currently call globalisation. Hence, the most acquisitive and manipulative characters become the architects of global socio-economics, affecting all other lives and the world itself. The state of the world reveals the results – and even the minority currently wallowing in wealth will soon be re-assessing their situation in the face of the environmental response. Wealth, power, and / or secrecy also help overcome or avoid any resistance from the common sense and decency of the majority. The acquisitive and manipulative have a further advantage in that common sense and decency usually mind their own business. However, while the decent mind their own business the less than decent are also minding it – manipulating laws and political policies to favour themselves while quietly robbing common sense and decency of their rights, and the voice and wherewithal to change things when they realise what has been happening. The community is everybody's business ('because the Truth involves us all') and our attention to community affairs (the eternal vigilance advised by Jefferson) must not be forgotten lest Burke's advice that evil prospers while good men do nothing will yet again prove true, but this time for our lives and on global scales. The struggle is as old as the world but is now as big as the world.

Be it Blake's, Corbett's, Kipling's, Zen's, the environment's or your own personal potential killers, it is only by seizing our tigers' fires, facing our fears in life's furnaces, that smelts our moral mettle. When we have achieved these inner balances, society will begin to reflect them in the restoration of outer balances. Hence, each of us can become a physician of the life principle itself. The environmental / spiritual crises are identical. Outer reflects inner. The extinction of tigers accompanies the extinction of beauty and nobility. As forests fall, self and greed rise. As money is loved, morality is hated. The darker forces of the world are the darker forces within us. Pollution in the world reflects pollution within us. What's wrong with the world is what's wrong with us. As the tiger's fire diminishes, darkness expands.

> But black sin hath betrayed
> To endless night
> My world, both parts, and
> Both parts must die.
>
> J. Donne. Holy Sonnets, V.

Truth is what we all want but fear to face. We seek it, yet flee it, because it brings responsibilities, self-reliance, suffering and self-sacrifice. Yet it also brings life, beauty, strength, and sets us free. In our personal physical, mental or spiritual prisons we can pretend, blame others, avoid responsibilities, be dependent, lock the window grilles and hide from ourselves in darkness. Physical crises (personal or planetary) are often spiritual crises – a fearful symmetry. The current fearful environmental symmetry is one that we can still, just about, frame, since we are both the problem and the solution. Yet we must face our reflection and the responsibilities it reveals immediately, for the light has almost gone.

The light and heat needed to smelt our moral mettle, and which are almost gone, are those of the tiger's fire and the previous chapter referred to our unique free will ability to choose what of fire we extinguish or conserve.

Perhaps these are clues to some sort of spiritual / physical correspondence between our free will and fire? In our struggles with free will we surely feel its heat when we have to make important decisions in life, our minds overheat from friction between right and wrong, self or others, in a furnace of fears and choices. This furnace either forges the chains that hold us to the material world or kindles the spiritual flame that illuminates, and then animates the truth that sets us free – according to our choices. The tiger's flickering, changing energies, either burn us or free us from earth. Each individual person has to choose. This idea might be a variation on, or interpretation of, the concept of hell-fire and the torment of perpetual burning – we do not go to such a place but carry it with us, consigning ourselves to its flames by continually misusing our free will to favour self, never freeing ourselves from self due to fear of losing out, and thereby losing all.

> I sent my Soul through the Invisible,
> Some letter of that After-life to spell,
> And by and by my soul return'd to me
> And answer'd: 'I myself am Heaven and Hell.'
>
> (Ruba'iyat of Omar Khayyam)

> 'The Kingdom of Heaven is within you.'
>
> (Luke 17: 20-21)

Various scriptures provide various descriptions of 'hell'. Distilling the common essence of Hindu, Egyptian, Buddhist, Islamic, Judeo-Christian, and Dante's or Milton's Biblical interpretations, we find that all refer to an experience of severely restricted freedom, even close confinement and / or extreme pain, as part of an exacting spiritual rehabilitation. Despite the variations between the scriptures, our consideration of free will as the critical factor before, during and after such experiences is consistent with all of them. That at least four of the above sources also refer to fire being involved offers other correspondences.'Nothing burns in hell but the self.' (Theologia Germanica).

However, when we look inside ourselves we may find more than one self within. A feature film called 'Harry Black and the Tiger' is set in India and features a prolonged hunt for a man-eating tiger. It is based on David Walker's novel 'Harry Black' in which there is an incident of a doctor being called to attend an emotionally distraught Mrs. Tanner. She manages to reassert her self-control in the doctor's presence but without his aid, after which she leaves the room: '"Shock," said Dr. Roy Chowdhury, M.D. "What do we know of this? We know the chemistry, the physics of humanity, oh yes indeed, whole global poppycock and atom bombs we know. But the mystery of Mrs. Tanner snapping out of it by free will, now do we understand such things, tell me, Mr. Black, I ask you? The strong are strong and the weak are weak, we say. The good are good and the bad are bad, we say, all such sort of fiddlesticks. And when I, personally, look into beastliness of self with intentions nice and wicked totally mixed up and actions unforeseen, I know we are merest Doctor Babies in the Wood."' (B70)

When, in Robert Louis Stevenson's novel, the predominantly good Dr. Jekyll first releases his predominantly evil alter-ego Mr. Hyde, Mr. Hyde is small and weak. By repeatedly choosing to exercise him, he grows in strength and is soon more powerful than Jekyll. This subtle but crucial feature is missed in most film adaptations and even critical reviews. Some have asked whether Stevenson wrote a dark novel warning us that evil ultimately triumphs. The crux of the novel is moral choice, and that the frequency, and way in which it is exercised, will determine our fates. Whilst we may speculate as to why Jekyll chose wrongly too often (perhaps he became obsessed with what Huxley refers to below as '…ambition…or lust for power or fame…' or '…the nobler, but still all too human …scholarship and science, regarded as ends in themselves…'), such speculation is of real value insofar as it makes us assess the health and vigour of our own Hydes – remembering Hyde is the epitome of self, unrestrained by morality, compassion or pity. Jekyll made one wrong choice too many. This is the 'spiritual tipping point', the 'straw that broke the camel's back choice', the 'one too many self-indulgences choice', the 'one too many forests cut or tigers taken choice' and beyond it, all Jekylls become too weak in comparison with too frequently exercised Hydes. Obviously, our alternative, prior to that spiritual tipping point, is to exercise and develop our Jekylls, our morality and virtues – the choice is ours.

Jekyll and Hyde might initially suggest a correspondence with the lamb and the tiger respectively. Yet other musings, including the saying of Tippu Sultan referred to above, remind us that there can be more dangers in sheep-like behaviour than in strength of character and dignified behaviour.

So, by viewing these reflections, framing these symmetries, we begin to understand the Vedas' and Delphic oracle's advice to 'Know thyself' and see some of the answer to the Vedic question 'Who am I?' It is not that there is a fully formed character already existing: we find such knowledge, 'grow' the answer, during the process of life (reminding us of our observations in the previous chapter on 'truth' – which involves us all, and all that is in us, and grows as we do). Some may say that it is character which determines our choices. Yet this is to miss the point that our characters are not static, not fixed, until we choose to make them so (and again we see alternating cause and effect). How do we monitor our progress or regress? Nature reveals the effects of our choices and actions – if we look. Improving effects nearly always equate to denying self and improving our efforts to 'husband and nurture the life force', but only become evident in the long-term. Hence, we need to be persistent with and committed to our choices. If we choose superficiality and are weak willed, our character can be washed away in the first shower of adversity, or rising sea levels. Our character is developed, continues to be created, through the choices we make in the situations life presents us with. Socrates said '…for great is the struggle, a far greater contest than we think it, that determines whether a (person) prove good or bad…the soul's attributes turned in the wrong direction become as useless and harmful as the opposite's would be useful and beneficial.'

Out of all the choices, those of morality and virtue are most important – those in which we favour the greater life force instead of self (and thereby secure our personal life force at the same time). When we are confident of choosing morality and virtue, we are ready to keep our characters constant. When we do, nature will reflect it to us and we will enjoy full health in harmony with her cycles. Turning in time with nature's cycles brings repetition without tedium. Agriculture again provides an apt example: when we remember how to grow food in accordance with nature's lessons, we may enjoy variety in healthy, wholesome foods, spices, sauces, herbs and fragrances in innumerable varieties of combinations, feeling the benefits physically and socially, mentally and spiritually, both in their own right and also because we will no longer be ingesting chemicals and greed, or other products of egos, profit motives and 'meddling intellects'.

Who we are, and who we become, is also influenced by nature and society. Above we had reason to consider the character of Caliban in Shakespeare's Tempest. We may also consider the close parallels between Richard Garnett's perspective and Einstein's view that: 'The individual, if left alone from birth, would remain primitive and beastlike in his thoughts and feelings… The individual is what he is…by virtue [of being] a member of a great human community that directs his material and spiritual existence from cradle to grave.' To live apart from these influences is what Aristotle meant when he wrote that 'To live alone, one must be either an animal or a god.'

Of course, most humans would not survive if left alone before maturity and we see another value of our slow maturation, extending the period of influence from one's surroundings and contacts, emphasising the importance of one's family and friends, the benefits of good company and the dangers of bad. As we mature we, in turn, are influencing others.

These patterns of influencing, and being influenced, form a network of alternating and multi-layered sequences of cause and effect. Mortal hand or eye cannot identify all the sequences or even one sequence completely, nor the distant deeps or skies to which they ultimately trace back. Yet, whatever the combination of connections with which we find ourselves living, they cannot prevail over the universe's ultimate power – our free will choice. Free will, guided by nature, morality and virtue, ensures the 'husbanding and nurturing of the life force' and prevents the twisting and entangling of perspectives, attitudes and values. In the chapter on Corbett we considered how some perspectives and values had become twisted in the brief interval between his time and ours. In the same chapter we also considered his illustrating, in conjunction with Hesiod's metaphor, the practical and spiritual benefits of long, uphill walks, which provide invigorating views, and healthy perspectives for body, mind and soul.

To those who, in our terms, have struggled up the long, steep road to the highest spiritual development and enjoy the best views, this passage of Aldous Huxley's applies '…their actions are uniformly selfless and they are constantly recollected, so that at every moment they know who they are and what is their true relation to the universe and its spiritual Ground.' (*Huxley points out elsewhere in the same work that, in addition to these attributes, 'recollectedness' also brings knowledge of how to behave toward other lives*). Of the vast majority of us, Huxley writes 'it may be said that their name is Legion – much more so of exceptionally complex personalities, who identify themselves with a wide diversity of moods, cravings and opinions. Saints, on the contrary, are neither double-minded nor half-hearted, but single and, however great their intellectual gifts, profoundly simple. The multiplicity of Legion has given place to one-pointedness – not to any of those evil one-pointednesses of ambition or covetousness, or lust for power or fame, not even to any of the nobler, but still all too human one-pointednesses of art, scholarship and science, regarded as ends in themselves, but to the supreme, more than human one-pointedness that is the very being of these souls who consciously and consistently pursue man's final end, the knowledge of eternal reality.' (*'The Perennial Philosophy' by Aldous Huxley. Copyright © 1945 by Aldous Huxley, renewed 1973 by Laura Huxley. Reprinted by kind permission of Georges Borchardt, Inc., for the Aldous and Laura Huxley Literary Trust, Mark Trevenen Huxley, and Teresa Huxley*)

The knowledge is within each of us but to see it, we also have to struggle up that mountain. Until we do, most of us continue to know Dr. Choudhary's quandary with multiple personalities, since his middle name is the same as most of ours; Legion. Without constancy of character there can be no one name, since we cannot identify who we really are.

In chapter III we read of a member of Corbett's audience considering him as close to a saint as they would meet. From the brief biographical details given in chapter III, and from the Huxley quote just given, we might cite in this context, his selflessness, his 'recollectedness' (i.e. knowing his relation to nature, his self-possession). Yet, perhaps his most significant characteristic is his simplicity – his profound simplicity, perhaps all the more profound since he was not conscious of it. In the author's view, it is this which is reflected in his writing style and is the quality which reviewers struggle to identify. 'In the world, when people call anyone simple, they generally mean a foolish, ignorant, credulous person. But real simplicity, so far from being foolish, is almost sublime. All good men like and admire it, are conscious of sinning against it, observe it in others and know what it involves; and yet they could not precisely define it. I should say that simplicity is an uprightness of soul which prevents self-consciousness.' (François Fénelon (1651–1715) French Roman Catholic theologian, poet and writer). Part of the charm of animals, some young children, noble savages and many Indian people in rural communities, is that their behaviour is not self-conscious. As a result, they exhibit the same sort of sublime simplicity that is free of the masks, posturing and posing that so many of us use for life's stages, to hide the fears we collect along our journey. If we fail to climb our mountain of self, we maintain our name of Legion; our multiple and inconsistent characters; our masks. When we are overly concerned with self, duty is difficult to maintain since ensuring short-term self interest often requires us to fail others. Again, Shakespeare has summarised it for us: 'For never anything can be amiss when simpleness and duty tender it.' (A Midsummer Night's Dream Act V Sc. 1)

In chapter IV it was seen that the vanity of self could be extinguished by considering (from the right viewpoint) our collective development (Jacob Bronowski's 'Ascent of Man' television series was used as an example). We also saw that mountain ranges, or Jack London's 'White Silence' are antidotes to self, since they are regions where we may forget ourselves or, we might say, forget our names. To lose our name of Legion we must continue the uphill climb.

> Does the road wind uphill all the way?
> Yes, to the very end.
> Will the day's journey take the whole long day?
> From morn to night, my friend.
>
> (Christina Rossetti. 1830-94)

As we considered above with regard to our personal 'empires' (however little or large they may be), our challenge is to leave the world a better place than we found it – better for other people and other forms of life, and do so without seeking the 'bubble reputation' for ourselves. 'Do good by stealth, and blush to find it fame.' Corbett's last words were to try to make this world a happier place for others to live in.

In general the world is rapidly becoming a less and less happy place due to the globally dominant effects of the socio-economic trends identified in this and previous chapters, and the accompanying decline in standards and characters (in effect, a global, social and economic expression of an exclusive focus on self, and the resulting influence on the generations growing up within it). It has also affected disciplines supposedly independent of the 'mart of economic strife and gain' such as art and science.

A definition that could apply to both great art and great science is 'identifying the universal in the particular'. The spirit of true art and true science is both immanent to and transcendent of the work and connects with the same that is both immanent to and transcendent in us (since we are also spirit in matter, from both religious and scientific perspectives). In an increasingly secular, materialistic world, cut off from nature, it is true art, and some aspects of science that can provide, for some people, the only remaining means by which their souls may briefly free themselves from matter, and revive spirits so weakened by the current dominance of money and material values. Part of Einstein's pleasure in science was that it freed him from the merely personal. The spirit of true art and science appeals to both heart and mind, and when our personal spirit recognises it, they are unified. We recognise that what is within us is also outside of us, and our spirituality is thereby, in one sense at least, liberated.

Our physical body, even all physical matter, might be seen as both crude carriers of and, at the same time, prisons to that spirit. In an increasingly physical, material and secular world the value attributed to emotive and spiritually liberating works of art and science, sometimes amounting to worship, becomes more than they can bear since, as ends in themselves, they are meaningless and worthless. In his autobiography, Rudyard Kipling referred to 'material things passionately worked up into Gods' by his wealthy neighbours and concluded that it was due to their 'immense and unacknowledged boredom'. It can also be a sign of our being lost. A piece of art or science is ultimately a piece of life. The very essence of art or science, their spirit, which communicates with and connects us, is of life itself. Real people (including some potentially great artists), let alone whole animal species, suffer and die while immense material wealth is spent on one piece of artwork – to display the owner's appreciation of art and life! It must surely be an abomination against life, arts and sciences (let alone ethics) to wallow in wealth that cannot be spent in a lifetime, while other lifetimes are terminated prematurely for want of pennies. The portrait of such an 'art lover' must be as Dorian Gray's. 'Decadence' can be defined as a decline in art and morals. The two are not coupled by coincidence, and go some way to explaining why much modern art is rarely worthy of the word.

Views in which we see relationships between art, life and morality are akin to those views of forests we considered in chapter I – the sensing of something shared, something of life and spirit. Can these threads be woven together? Art, animal life and morality are linked for us in the views of Ludwig Wittgenstein (1889 – 1951. Austrian philosopher and mathematician). Wittgenstein particularly studied the works of the philosopher Schopenhauer, who was greatly interested in and influenced by Eastern thought in general and Hinduism in particular. Wittgenstein highlights our uncertainties regarding animal consciousness and '…reveals that our perceptions are also projections. How much consciousness we ascribe, for example, to other persons, animals, or extra-terrestrials will depend on how much their behavior reflects our own. This is epistemically ironic because it keeps us from having any clear criteria for judging if a being with a completely strange physical appearance and incoherent behavior is in fact conscious. Indeed for Wittgenstein, we would have no way of attributing consciousness (or significance) to the behavior of any being whose natural history differed sufficiently from ours. Ultimately, as he reminds us at several occasions, our ability to ascribe mental states to other minds varies by their degree of affinity with us:

Wittgenstein: "Only remember that the spirit of the snake, of the lion, is your spirit. For it is only from yourself that you are acquainted with spirit at all…The same with the elephant, with the fly, with the wasp."

Our ordinary experiences of living objects are not inferred through intellectual calculation. They are pre-theoretical (*reminding us of Rousseau's and Wordsworth's views as seen in the previous chapter – author*). In addition, the distinctive character of each form of life continually develops through its…existence, and is therefore never ultimately defined. Hence, each form of life is an indefectible source of knowledge and meaning.

One therefore "listens" to living phenomena in an especially singular way. When we admire a sunrise, a soaring eagle, a song, a dialogue, a poem, or a story we are in a sense "listening" to life as it emerges through its perpetual transformative processes of action and interaction. Wittgenstein hence reminds us that all art is founded on this very concept.

We can now begin to see the full ontological significance the concept of "form of life" holds in Wittgenstein's general conception of ethical value: "What must be accepted, the given, is – so one could say – forms of life." Forms of life are the principle objects of ethical value, for the extinction of a form of life constitutes an irrevocable loss of future knowledge and meaning. One could naïvely imagine for example that the world would be much more pleasant without certain rather unappealing biological forms of life such as mosquitoes, cockroaches, rats, fleas, viruses, or even humans – depending on one's point of view. However, their extinction would ipso-facto compromise the essences of the forms of life that we value so much by opposition. Life is completely inter-twined, both empirically and conceptually. The extinction of one pest can just as easily spell extinction for some fantastic predator, as the extinction of a fantastic predator can lead to the arrival of new pests. Similarly, a loss or overabundance of prey or flora can reduce a noble and beautiful animal into something useless and / or repulsive.'

Now Wordsworth's and Ruskin's perceptions of morality in nature, as referred to in the chapters III and IV respectively, gain philosophical substantiation, as do our considerations of truth involving all forms of life (referred to in the previous chapter).

'…Forms of life…both determine and constitute what we consider most valuable. Each of our ordinary and extraordinary experiences of ethical value functions according to a particular natural history through which we have gained a common sensibility to any phenomenon that is also a result of that same historical fabric. We are hence the products of a temporal continuum populated by innumerable forms of life in which we have a natural disposition to find aesthetic, ethical, and epistemic import…The massive extinction of biological diversity that humanity is currently bringing about is therefore also the extinction of a part of its own world, that is to say, the extinction of a part of itself. And this conclusion is certainly in line with Wittgenstein, for as he himself so succinctly put it: "I am my world".

Wittgenstein's account of the interdependence of aesthetics, meaning, and value hence provides a strong theoretical basis for environmental ethics. It demonstrates that the ecological and biological wealth of this planet is not only a reservoir of scientific information, but also a perpetual source of inspiration from which language, art, culture, and human experience in general become enriched. Imagine all the various forms of life that must have sparked myriad new ways of perceiving and describing the world. How would human experience and communication have evolved without an environment rich enough to amaze, astound, shock, and bedazzle us time and time again? Take but for example the transformation of the caterpillar into butterfly, the soaring eagle, the swim of the penguin, the two thousand year old sequoia, the salmon run, the blossom opening out. Imagine that half of the species known today had never existed, and how much human experience, culture, and language would have in turn become impoverished. Now imagine that some fifty percent of the world's flora and fauna disappear over the next century, as Stuart Pimm and many other conservation biologists now predict.' (This assessment of Wittgenstein's work is reprinted by kind permission of its author, Julian Friedland Ph.D. Assistant Professor of Business Ethics, Eastern Connecticut State University U.S.A.)

So, on our journey we have considered animal and human characteristics, the unity of life and some of its spiritual aspects, our moral responsibilities and our cultural activities. This piece on Wittgenstein has linked all these concepts. However, as usual, the poet said it first, and Andrew Marvell (English 1621 – 1678) saw that the mind finds it own likeness, and that all its creations ultimately have their root in nature.

The mind, that ocean where each kind
Does straight its own resemblance find;
Yet it creates, transcending these,
Far other worlds, and other seas;
Annihilating all that's made
To a green thought in a green shade

(From 'The Garden')

(Painting by John Singer Sargent. American Artist. 1856 – 1925)

With regard to both Art's relationship to nature, and 'listening' to animals, Walter Pater (1839 – 1894 English Essayist, art and literature critic) said that all art aspired to the condition of music and considered some paintings an expression of when 'life itself is conceived as a kind of listening', reminding us of Karen Blixen listening to the rhythm of Africa in chapter III, and of nature, or meditation, teaching us to be silent, so that we may listen and learn.

Perhaps the ultimate link between art and life is recognition that we are, in one sense or another, 'creating art' by living each day. We communicate our impressions and interpretations of life to others, and create effects with them, everyday. Not necessarily by brush or chisel but by gesture or smile, letter or telephone. The more conscious we are of this, the more we try to make them beautiful or useful or both. As Einstein asked 'Is there not a certain satisfaction in the fact that natural limits are set to the life of the individual, so that at its conclusion it may appear as a work of art?'

What art have we created with our lives? What we produce culturally is indicative of our inner condition. Some have finally been able to recognise much of modern art as a sham and falsehood and say in public that the emperor has no clothes, similarly with architecture, and all other aspects of culture, since they stem from the same root (the spiritual condition of individuals and society). So far science has escaped healthy critical review, yet in science we also find too much influenced by self-promotion or profit, and too little by justice and beauty.

Achievements in the arts, the sciences, in life, only have value if they lead us to care and compassion for other lives; to wholesomely integrate with the unity. How do we measure the creation of the world's greatest masterpiece of music, art or science while children starve to death? How do we assess our contribution to life, or find beauty in our brush strokes, if we never spare a minute or penny to help? What value is any of our creations if they cannot bring us joy, and what sort of joy can there be while extreme suffering dominates the very globe itself? What are they worth to us in these circumstances? To others? To the children whose bellies brought them such pain? If we had all knowledge, knew all secrets, what would it be good for – unless we help, protect and nurture other life? What if we find the 'theory of everything' (although this is a misnomer and is better labelled a 'theory unifying all current physical theories')? Such a theory is a truly fascinating intellectual quest but consider its completion on the same day as the freezing of northern Europe (due to the potential for melting Arctic ice to shut off the Gulf Stream), the tiger's extinction, or the imminent collapse of global ecosystems, is announced. We seek to know everything in a theory, while its exclusive pursuit proves we know nothing. We considered above potential SETI scientists currently begging for bread. Amongst those beggars are also potential Michelangelos and Mozarts, Newtons and Einsteins. Leaving them to beg is not only a crime against morality but also against art and science, especially when, in preference to helping, we considered our own scribbling to be of more value (yes, this scribbling follows many years of effort on the ground for the causes described and is now only offered in the hope it will benefit, in one way or another, those causes).

What can be done? Give donations to provide food? As an emergency response this is, of course, critical but simply and only giving food to starving people is the sort of 'one-dimensional' thinking referred to above, and only a short-term solution, not a long-term one, which requires a multi-dimensional approach to radically readjust the socio-economic system that produces hungry people (please see Appendix II). Hungry people, due to nature's connections, are associated with environmental damage and disappearing species, including tigers.

Hunger is one consequence of population size exceeding the number of people able to purchase food via the prevailing socio-economic system, but population size itself is intimately related to socio-economics. In India, for example, there is no welfare state and only government jobs provide pensions. Hence future security for the vast majority of people can only be achieved by having children. Studies in Scandinavia have shown that with some affluence and security for old age, birth rates decrease to balance death rates. Admittedly. the situation in India is complicated by religious and social factors (such as the importance of producing sons, and ignorance of family planning techniques).

Hence, 'husbanding and nurturing the life force' does not equate to a one-dimensional focus on increasing population numbers. It includes caring for and working toward healthy, fulfilling lives, taking into account conditions and circumstances at all levels of community, from nations, cities, towns and villages (if we can get these balances right, international collaboration to ensure a stable global population would be easier to achieve). In this regard, good governance should be similar to prudent would-be parents, who assess their circumstances to ensure they can provide adequate welfare, security, education etc. for their children before taking on the responsibilities of creating new life.

Our roles in achieving such communities still includes spending and investing ethically, buying environmentally-ftiendly and fair trade produts etc. but can also include our own family planning, and helping with the provision of employment, education and health programmes. In all these ways we help to control population, feed the hungry, educate the illiterate, employ the unemployed and, amongst a range of other healthy effects, keep trees and tigers alive, due to the network of connections that is Life.

All these concepts are part of, and lead us toward, the great Unity of Life. Our principles of unity, and our dependence on nature, show us that humanity is totally integrated with planet Earth; its size and mass, geology, climate, crops, other plant and animal species, its particular moon, its position relative to the sun and other factors, many of which are probably, as yet, unknown to us. This integrated, interrelated whole both produces us and responds to us and, as we grow and groan in the process, it is also growing and, no doubt, groaning. As we struggle along the winding uphill mountain paths of the 'Himalayas of our Souls', en route to the 'Universal', the 'Self', the 'Absolute', the view, while becoming more comprehensive, is always changing. However, we can create some constancy and certainty by discovering who we are on the climb, choosing to improve ourselves according to morality and virtue, and make those improvements permanent. We thereby play our part in healthily maintaining Life's network of connections.

We are all on different paths or at different positions on the same path, on one enormous mountain called life. As there is one mountain so there is one summit (and, spiritually speaking, we may see there another sort of unity). Manifestations of this unity included the Prana of Hinduism, Paracelsus' Alkahest or Jack London's 'elemental stuff out of which the many forms of life have been moulded'. In addition to one destination and one process, the previous chapter has referred to there being only one lesson, one law that subsumes all others. Again, a poet has expressed as much and more in fewer words:

One God. One Law. One Element
And one far-off divine Event
To which the whole creation moves.

(Tennyson. 1809 – 1892)

462

A similar universal vision was expressed by the Stoic philosopher and Roman Emperor Marcus Aurelius (121 – 180), who noted '…For things have been co-ordinated, and they combine to make up the same universe. For there is one universe made up of all things, and one God who pervades all things, and one substance, and one law, and one reason.'

We may combine these insights with the principal points of this and the previous chapter (namely nature's mirror and the critical importance of each individual's character improvement) to see that, amazingly, there is only one ultimate and simple answer to the multiple, enormous, complex and diverse questions troubling the world, whether they are environmental, social, economic, commercial, political, cultural…or the all embracing 'What can be done to improve the world?' Ultimately, the single answer to all is 'Improve yourself; your character'. Hence, complementing the views of Tennyson and Marcus Aurelius, we can see that there is only one lesson, one purpose, one question, one answer and one thing to work on, which is immediately to hand – oneself. By surmounting the overly egocentric identity (the one that goes into the tiger's cave but does not come out) oneself disappears into One Self.

Facing personal responsibilities is almost synonymous with developing one's (non-egocentric) character. For as long as we spiritually ignore or avoid personal responsibility, the practical consequences, such as multiplying laws and / or military-industrial-political complexes, and / or environmental problems, only 'complicate and augment (*our*) maladies' as Socrates told us in the previous chapter. As characters degenerate and decadence grows, society deteriorates, even as laws multiply in response.

In contrast to science (or, more accurately, misguided scientists) telling us life is meaningless, experience of life teaches us that science is meaningless without being endowed by us with purpose, a purpose that is both born of life and is life. Scientists currently seek a single, unified law accounting for all physical phenomena, but look for it without yin, without morality and virtue, without responsibility, which are all part of the unity. The purpose of science, or art, or any other human endeavour, is to husband and nurture the life force, physically, culturally, mentally, spiritually. Without this truly unified (and unifying) purpose we arrive at the current situation identified by Einstein in a radio intervioew when he said that our age was characterised by perfection of means and confusion of goals.

No human endeavour should be primarily about fame, fortune or being 'first', nor is any human endeavour an end in itself. We are back to our choice between a larger life force and oneself (between the Self or the self), and can see how extremely imbalanced our current priorities are, at least insofar as media coverage of fame, fortune and ego currently represent them. As a sort of inverse to science, and cynics, telling us life is meaningless or futile, recognition of one's unity with the Unity endows every life with every possible meaning. We separate from the unity the more we are conscious of self – and the more emphasis on self, the more likely we are to take. By always taking, we harm the unity on which we depend, and so we see that selfishness leads to suicide. The more emphasis on the unity, the more likely we are to give. In giving, we ensure our ability to continue taking.

Our needs and wants can only be supplied by investing time, energy and money in the larger entity that provides for our needs and wants. Such efforts do not always produce results and / or rewards immediately and personally and this, in itself, allows the projection of intent and purpose beyond the personal and immediate - all part and parcel of the growth and maturity we need to achieve. One symptom of our currently going in the wrong direction is the popularity and ever-increasing availability of immediate gratification – fast food, computer games, TV, Internet etc. All encourage and fulfil the immature attitude of 'I want it now' and, when wants are not met immediately, the potential for tantrum type behaviour, which may include a vigorous denouncement of reasoning such as this, denying that we can know anything in such metaphysical realms.

It is true, of course, that in the face of nature, we do 'know nothing' and this is recognised by the humble and sincere seeker after truth as well as by those who would use it as an excuse to avoid personal responsibility. Yet, at the same time and within our tiny perspectives on Earth, nature does teach us some things for sure, or we wouldn't be here to discuss it. These lessons are, admittedly, fundamental and relate to how we treat soil, water, air and fire. Even though basic, it is these lessons we are ignoring and those resources we are abusing, for the sake of technological toys and a few people becoming rich.

Voluntarily reducing the time we spend with our toys to help the larger life force is a difficult choice but we can understand the right choice if we imagine ourselves to be among those suffering due to our abuse of it. If we cannot imagine it (and act accordingly), current conditions indicate that nature will be arranging for many more of us to experience suffering for real, in order that we may understand what we would not imagine for ourselves.

We have used art to see something of spirit, and considered our spirit as imprisoned in matter. Perhaps the following analogy makes the point a little more forcefully – we have studied every aspect of our prison; from the dust on the floor to the stars, seen through bars of space and time. We know every detail of our prison's dimensions but not considered for a second why we are in prison. Hence we condemn ourselves to remaining in prison – knowing many facts and figures about it, but never looking for the truth (which would set us free). Collectively we make ourselves busy to find the reason how, to avoid finding the reason why. Prison is a metaphor with negative overtones. A more positive metaphor would be school. Perhaps both aspects can be combined by considering that we are as young children in detention but without supervision, we are not paying attention to why we are in detention and / or what has been presented to us for our correction. Instead we have begun to explore, looking far beyond the classroom, even trying to look into the headmaster's study, where we have seen references to matters beyond our full understanding. We continue to examine them in evermore detail – never once examining ourselves, a deeper understanding of which, followed by appropriate action, would free us from detention.

This pattern is not confined to collective perspectives. It can be seen in individuals' lives, in people who purposely make themselves busy enough to avoid facing themselves. So, as referred to in the previous chapter, those noted by Apollodorus in Plato's Symposium as "…dashing about all over the place, firmly convinced (*they are*) leading a full and interesting life…" may include those hiding from themselves; those who are rich enough to keep sampling all that's on offer without need of alternative views; and those simply happy to be caught up in the excitement of being busy and popular. Whichever of these it may be, they are all, as Apollodorus said 'really doing absolutely nothing'.

Let us choose to be doing something of significance. Above we looked at why we should save the tiger from various practical perspectives. As we would expect from the concepts explored herein, spiritual perspectives are in agreement, and also demand that we save the tiger, because it is being killed by ignorance, incompetence, greed and stupidity – and it is essential for us to overcome these failings and vices. The tiger's imminent extinction is showing us our failings and, if we allow those failings to triumph, the virtues the tiger represents will be disappearing with it, just as they are disappearing from us.

We have arrived at the same conclusion as any and all who have ever considered mankind's problems, throughout recorded history, and the same perplexity shared, for all we know, by God Almighty Himself, as to why humans, who have such potential for dignity, if not nobility, persistently and repeatedly choose to be so small, mean and selfish; materially, mentally and spiritually.

Although humans appreciate dignity, nobility and magnanimity when they see them we find it difficult to choose them since they all involve a denial of self. Similarly, we all say we want to know the truth, but run away as it approaches since it involves a revelation of self, a forced look into the mirror, or at our life's portrait.

Our portrait, our reflection, whatever we may call it is, ultimately, our own personal responsibility. Whilst other people's actions matter in the physical plane for all of us, in this context, the actions of others are irrelevant since they are powerless in the face of our own free will, our ability to choose our own actions. 'The robber of your free will does not exist.' (Epictetus III.22.105 Greek Stoic philosopher 55 – 135 AD) We are responsible for ourselves and, insofar as we have any influence in life, however small, we are responsible for Life. Life is One, all things are connected. Harm a part and you harm it all, and hence yourself. Change yourself and you change a part and hence you change it all. We must think for ourselves, find our truth and commit to it, come global warming and high water. Since, in the end, your character is the only thing you have that is truly yours, that is uniquely 'you', it is the only thing that has any real value or significance. In this context you can forget every other form of man-made, toy-town trinkets and all 'such sort of fiddlesticks' that pass for value; forget every form of publicity, publication, prize or poppycock that passes for status; forget the emptiness of media, marketing, man-made 'stars', modern celebrity 'culture', corporations, commerce, badges, braid, kingly crown or warrior's crest. You must do what you know to be right for life on Earth, for the blade of grass and the swallow's nest, not only for survival, for health, for life itself, but also to avoid total disgust and shame. 'Disgust and shame' as shown by other people's reactions to us? No, far worse – as shown by our reactions to ourselves when we fully face nature's mirror. Only you have the power to escape self-loathing. You can do it by using the greatest gift in the universe: the free will to choose. Only when we control our use of free will do we define, and then discover, who we are.

Whoever we have chosen for our ideal can help us make our choices. All too often, morality and virtue are absent in ideals offered to modern youngsters – if their absence is not actually celebrated. Modern ideals include being the 'greatest' sports-person, artist, scientist, film star (although what 'greatest' means is unclear since any ranking within or between these categories has only limited validity. Each person and their achievement are best measured and understood in their own context). One measure of our character is our control over the various urges and drives we all experience (hunger, sex, status, will to power etc.) in favour of morality and virtue. Yet ideals offered to modern youngsters are often those who actually indulge all these urges and drives, to the point of excess and vice.

A common and popular aspiration, although vacuous, is simply to be famous or rich or both, regardless of any other consideration. Others who acquire extreme wealth without work, including inherited wealth, have not really achieved anything since their wealth is dependent on a series of chance events, socio-economic imbalances, fashions and 'flavours' of the moment, whims of fickle people and fate etc. and could as easily apply to the next person as to them. Such 'external wealth' is not an expression of 'internal wealth'. This type of rich person can buy anything but has achieved nothing. Those with great internal wealth are rarely associated with great material wealth and it is these people who make better, healthier and more wholesome ideals for youngsters.

'Life's not important, only what you do with it.' While this author cannot find who this quote should be attributed to, its truth is plain. The same could be said of money. The same could also be said of energy or matter (we now know the two are interchangeable). Consider a large lump of matter, say, marble. To announce 'I have a large block of marble' is of little or no interest. To announce 'I have sculpted La Pieta' is of interest. By simply owning a large amount of money, people are often viewed with awe, admiration, respect etc. Why? So what if they have much money? What will they 'sculpt' with it? Spectacular self-indulgence? Acquire many over-priced, material products for themselves? How empty headed (and empty hearted).

Some may say that it is the acquisition of wealth which generates admiration, yet this too is falsely founded since, if not inherited, newly acquired wealth results from effort *and* a hotchpotch of chance events, coincidence, contacts and fashions of the time. Effort, hard work and personal talent is common to millions of people, most of whom are poor, and therefore these factors cannot be all that is necessary to acquire wealth. Social Darwinism is inadequate as an explanation for the 'survival of the wealthiest' since '…the race is not to the swift, nor the battle to the strong, neither yet bread to the wise, nor yet riches to men of understanding, nor yet favour to men of skill; but time and chance happeneth to them all.' (Ecclesiastes 9:11) These unpredictable, illogical, non-mechanical aspects of life provide us with the time and chance to find our morality and compassion, find ourselves and our tigers. They provide us with the time and chance to be a character, not a product of mechanical laws. They provide us with the opportunity to 'sculpt' our life, to produce the work of art, as suggested by Einstein, to be framed by the limitations imposed on our life.

We have twice referred to Einstein's observation of limits defining a life as a work of art. We also read in the previous chapter (sub-section 'on Optimum') that, due to the limitless nature of power, setting limits sets us free. Setting limits for ourselves, in what we do with what we've got, also helps us find proportion and balance (reminding us of the value of laws that prevent ruin through excess freedom). Proportion and balance may also act as ideals, within and between the physical and spiritual, the rational and intuitive, yang and yin elements of our lives. Limits define proportion and balance, and these in turn define beauty, power and grace, which bring dignity of demeanour – all that we see and admire in the tiger. Yet the challenge is to acquire these characteristics for ourselves, not via the tiger's skin and bone but by our own skin and bone, taking proportionate action according to strength and decisive action but also according to compassion, morality and virtue and, by doing so, lend an atom of dignity to our demeanour. Let us use the tiger's fire and our own alchemy to transform the principal elements of our life into little gems. Hopefully, you will not fail in the attempt as often as this author.

Some or all of the above observations and recommendations may be called obvious or common sense. Yet it is the obvious and common sense that is so often being ignored, passing under foot without gaining our attention, just as much of nature and the environment. It is so easy to adapt to our immediate, but increasingly dangerous circumstances, continuing with our routines while passively watching global developments that must mean disaster for us all. Even locally, the most astounding abuses of common sense, let alone justice, are approved of and enforced by official bodies while we grumble, shake our heads, carry on, but *do nothing* about the abuses or dangerous developments. Numerous and various individuals and organisations refer to the value of saving life but the vast majority, including creditable and laudable NGOs, usually mean 'human life' and pay scant regard to any other sort of life – which ultimately defeats their own purposes, since that other life sustains human life. Hence, this chapter's focus has been on making an effort, *taking action to do something* for our common life-support system.

Making the effort is all that it is ours to do since, as the Chinese told us, we cannot know the consequences of our actions and hence we cannot know what success and failure really are. Even if we did, they result from circumstances in addition to our effort and beyond our control. Our control is confined to our choices, and the actions we turn them into. In Ken Kesey's novel 'One Flew Over the Cuckoo's Nest' the principal character, McMurphy, is confined to a mental hospital with his fellow inmates (many of whom are there voluntarily) and bets them that he can lift a steel and cement 'control panel' about half the size of a table and, using its weight, break through the window screens to freedom. His fellow inmates bet against him. He takes a little time to find his best grip on the unit, position his body, and concentrate briefly, before exerting his best effort. Despite straining with all his might, his strenuous effort fails to move it. He, and everybody else, knew beforehand he couldn't lift it but, on leaving the room, he comments that he tried, that at least he did that much.

Attempting to lift what one knows cannot be lifted might be called pointless (if nothing else!) and, like so much else viewed simply from a physical, mechanical perspective, yes, it is pointless. That is so. Yet, pondering a little more, we remember that there is much more to life than mechanics. That is so too. When someone is making a physical effort toward a clear and worthwhile objective, an observer is provided with an opportunity, right here, right now, to lend a hand. No one came to McMurphy's aid, thinking only of their bet and money to come, and thereby losing all the more important potentials on display before their very eyes, among them, their own chance of freedom. They remained trapped in their own prisons, behind screens of their own making, reminding us of the metaphor used above about us avidly learning all details of our prison, except the reason why we are imprisoned. Finding this reason would set us free but requires painful self-realisations, and so, mixing metaphors, we don't try to lift our weight of personal responsibilities, although with them we could break the window screens and gain our freedom.

Even if, after receiving help, lifting the weight remains impossible, making the effort to do what is right is consistent with various principles explored above:

- taking committed action oneself, regardless of what the rest of the world may be doing
- effort is all that is ours to make (applicable to nations as much as individuals)
- forming our character by seizing the spiritual fire
- morals triumphing over all other considerations
- using our free will for the highest purposes
- facing our personal responsibilities
- carrying Atlas' burden and not letting the universe, or ourselves, down

and all of this remains valid regardless of the presence or absence of physical results.

On embarking to try to make some contribution to conserving the tiger LifeForce personnel knew the chances of success, both from the world's perspective, and even their own tiny perspective, were virtually zero. We knew we couldn't 'lift it', but that was no reason not to try. Some precious few saw us trying to 'lift' the dead weight of imminent extinction from off the tiger and came to our aid, but sadly, too few, which is mainly due to this author's failure to make LifeForce's efforts known to sufficient people of the right type, in the right places, at the right time. However, regardless of LifeForce, soon the window of opportunity to help any and all sincere, struggling NGOs to lift that weight of extinction will close; and close with screens, grilles and bars beyond any human ability to ever open again. We will not be confined in our cage of questions (finding the answers to which promise keys to freedom) – we will be confined in our own cages of self, greed and stupidity. Having destroyed essential elements of our life support system we will have destroyed our hopes of escape, thrown away the keys to freedom, after actually holding them in our hands, heads and hearts.

In the very act of choosing to try, we already find some freedom (which is why we refer to freedom of choice) if not success. Trying to husband and nurture the life force is the most important cause conceivable, ultimately the only cause, and so we must choose to make the effort, even if not meeting with immediate, material success, as understood from the majority of contemporary human viewpoints. What is the alternative? To stand idle while the magnificence of the tiger, and all it represents, is wiped from the face of the Earth by greed and stupidity; and continue to stand idle while our families suffer the same fate? Where else, other than in trying to respect and protect healthy nature, will we find our self-respect? Fears, of multiple and varied types, including those of failing and losing out, have brought us to this point. If we can't face those fears, mature a little, help other lives, we will lose all.

Attempting to lift seemingly immovable weights gives a start point – in terms of the previous analogy, maybe McMurphy's efforts had some unseen effect, made some miniature fractures, which later allowed the big and strong inmate, Chief Bromden, to lift the 'control panel' and use it to break the window screens and escape. (Bromden could break free physically because he had been freed spiritually by McMurphy's comradeship. Just prior to breaking out, Bromden had freed McMurphy, by suffocating his post-operative and vegetative, but still breathing body). If we put in the effort to make a break in even the hardest ground, no matter how small it may be, new seeds can lodge there and new shoots sprout. Miniature fractures may be made by the businessperson who tries to do the right thing, despite pressure from peers and seniors to comply with unethical corporate agendas; by the scientist who disagrees with the scientific herd working unethically or making unscientific claims; or perhaps by you, adjusting your life style to break from the relentless drift of mass consumption and apathy. When you live as you believe – spending selectively, eating organically etc. – you are lifting your universe and, seeing you do it, others may help you with it and / or lift theirs, and so on, until we are all bearing our responsibilities to *the* universe.

If we do not, our failure to solve the environmental crisis will be catastrophic and irremediable from the perspectives of societies and communities. It will, of course, be the same from individuals' perspectives, but for individuals it may yet bring something spiritually positive to those who fought for the right cause. 'Character is that which can do without success' (Emerson). Character is formed by the choices and efforts made, and is stronger the greater the weight one attempts to carry. We considered above the greater grace and courage required to recover from failure and defeat and this is especially so where unsuccessful efforts have been for a common cause, but involved much personal self-sacrifice. Forever focussing on physical effects and visible 'success' we forget that failure often forges stronger characters than those fostered by some apparent 'success', which can often be contaminated by a consequent egotism. "The greatest test of courage on earth is to bear defeat without losing heart." (Robert G. Ingersoll). These views reinforce the importance of each of us doing what is right, regardless of what the rest of the world may be doing and regardless of physical results.

In the previous chapter we considered that Atlas' struggle was the same struggle for each of us. Atlas supporting a beach ball has no value and represents no achievement. He, and we, have to struggle, and struggle with the whole universe, not only because it represents the ultimate test but also because nothing less than the whole can live without the whole, the network of interconnections and interdependence which is Life. Our atlas will tell us where we are but our Atlas will tell us who we are. In this life we have no means other than physical effort by which to express what is in us, and hence what is in our universe (the reader will remember that we are all at the centres of our universe). Whilst physical effort is our only method of expression, its successful use is not necessarily accompanied by successful physical results. Nobody who makes the *right effort* and takes the *right action*, for the *right cause*, can ever be a 'loser' – whatever the physical results.

Saving the tiger (and all other species, including our own) from extinctions caused by human ignorance and arrogance, eliminating poverty and injustice generally, healing the world and our lives, is dependent on you, and me, and each of us. If we are banking ethically, eating organically, buying fair trade and environmentally-friendly products and services, meeting our responsibilities to other lives, then we are holding up our universe – regardless of whatever effects can be seen immediately or locally in the physical universe. We must make every effort to achieve this, whatever the rest of the world might be doing, and thereby realise our potential, our power.

Atlas reveals the awesome spiritual power we all possess, but which we so often neglect in favour of physical power, or its most common physical manifestation: money ('getting and spending, we lay waste our powers'). In chapter IV we contrasted spiritual power with physical power to interpret Jack London's suggested 'yardstick' of oneself with which one can measure the universe. The same relation is also in the reference above to his assessment of self control as 'gossamer wings' (since thought / choice / will cannot be measured physically) yet it has the steely strength to change the universe we measure. Now we can also see that the observation of Louise Hay in the previous chapter ('the power that created the universe beats in your heart') has a converse which is also true; since the power that beats in your heart creates the universe.

Atlas' brothers were Prometheus and Epimetheus. 'Prometheus' means forethought and 'Epimetheus' means after-thought or hindsight. The gods gave these two the task of allocating powers and abilities to the animals and man, newly created from earth and the sparks of heaven. It was agreed that Epimetheus would distribute the powers and abilities and Prometheus inspect the results. The various species are equipped with their powers such that some are strong but others swift, some small but able to fly or dwell underground, and so on and so forth, in order that no species will be destroyed. By the time Epimetheus comes to equip the last species, man, no powers remain to be distributed (having no forethought, he can only see his mistake in hindsight). To solve the problem Prometheus steals fire, and knowledge of its use, from the gods on our behalf. (This not only aids man's survival (eg. warmth, cooked food) but also allows an immense range of arts and skills to develop; from extracting and combining natural resources (including metals), chemistry in the laboratory and industry, energy of transport via steam, car and jet engines, to the generation of electricity via turbines). Prometheus also teaches man animal husbandry and knowledge necessary for civilisation (e.g. language, transport, astronomy). For stealing fire Prometheus was punished by Zeus; chained to Mount Caucasus, where an eagle consumed his liver. Overnight the liver would re-grow and the eagle return next day to consume it again. Eventually Heracles killed this eagle and rescued Prometheus, who was later reconciled with Zeus.

'Prometheus Bound' by Nicolas-Sébastien Adam (French, 1705–1778).
Printed by kind permission of the photographer Jastrow

Apparently liver does show some ability to regenerate itself and some scholars have suggested that this myth reveals that the ancient Greeks knew this. This author pretends no scholarly authority on physiology or mythology but themes in this book also fit within the framework of the myth…

Containing the sparks of heaven, and knowing the use of fire and free will, Man has to carry the burden of Atlas. Meeting or not meeting his responsibilities has repercussions for all, since it was Heracles who Atlas temporarily duped into holding the heavens on his shoulders. Had Heracles not managed to return Atlas' responsibilities to him, he would not have been free to rescue Prometheus, the benefactor of all mankind. The rescue of Prometheus is essential for us, as the gravity of our self-created environmental situation means forethought is desperately needed to rescue ourselves and civilisation.

Anticipating the consequences of our actions (if only immediately and locally) is the only way we can be responsible for our free will. If we really did not know what would or could result from our choices or actions, we would always be innocent. Epimetheus is often referred to in literature as rather stupid. However, this is due to his only being able to understand in retrospect, which makes him seem stupid – to those who have forethought. According to our principles, Prometheus might be thought equally stupid if he never learned from history (which sounds horribly familiar). The key and sole solution is to have *and use* both, which is why they are brothers (providing man's ability to see 'before and after' (Hamlet Act IV Sc. IV)) By using free will with fore and after thought, we may learn the lesson of the third brother, Atlas, to shoulder the responsibilities these attributes bring.

Man's physical helplessness reminds us of Thomson's lines in the first chapter referring to 'each bird, each insect flitting through the sky, (*being*) more sufficient for itself than thou!' and 'man, who madly deems himself the lord of all, is naught but weakness and dependence'; of Homer writing 'Of all that creep and breathe upon her, Earth breeds no feebler thing than man' and of the Biblical reference to foxes having holes and birds having nests but man having no where to lie down and rest. However, that physical helplessness points to another essential theme touched on in this book; it ensures we learn to co-operate, share, live with, care for, and eventually learn to love one another. Hence, helplessness is not so much a feature to be noted but a necessity for developing human relationships, and hence humans. This corresponds with the points made in the previous chapter about the need for developing collectively, if we would ensure and continue the ascent of man.

The above speculation also highlights the dangers of dismissing myth as falsehood. In the examples just given we can see the very quintessence of human life. They include developing our characters; facing our responsibilities, caring for and co-operating with other lives. Ironically, such myths are considered insubstantial fairy-tales – in societies almost totally characterised by image and falsehood.

Some of the multiple uses of the fire Prometheus brought us were mentioned above, and we are now in a position to draw together, from above and from previous chapters, ideas of fire and free will, to learn one of nature's most important lessons: By using practical abilities uniquely human, we can use fire to transform one thing into another and, moreover, do so according to our forethought and free will, by which we develop much of another uniquely human characteristic – our culture. Above we speculated briefly that these two unique abilities suggested some sort of correspondence between fire and free will. Now we can extend this correspondence since, as fire / free will transforms one thing into another in the physical world of earth, air and water, the spiritual fire of free will transforms us, our behaviour and character, in terms of our bodily earth, air and water, according to our flickering and changing choices.

Fire is latent within life (since life is essential for there to be fire – before photosynthetic organisms arose there was nothing to burn). Photosynthesis depends on light and, in the beginning, from both religious and scientific perspectives, light appears first. Light leads to life, and then to fire and free will. By free will, by fire, we may use our life to transform our earth, and thereby reach back into that most distant deep and sky of creation and bring to light the best of its many potentials.

We still use fire and free will to write our lives on Earth and in the heavens but by now our scribbles should not be causing stars to water heaven with their tears. It was Pythagoras who told us that the evening star is the same as (at a different time of year) the morning star, which is, strictly speaking, not a star but the planet Venus. Being the second planet from the sun and closer to Earth than the stars, it does not twinkle like a star but shines with a steady, undimmed white light, brighter than anything in the night sky except the moon, being brightest just after sunset or just before sunrise, which is why it became known as the evening or morning star. For millennia Venus has been an important aid to navigation. Perhaps she may also aid our inner navigation since Venus, as the Roman goddess of love, responds (as in the photograph below) most brightly to the moon's magic. While the light, like true love, is constantly bright, it is our challenge, and choice, to find the same constancy, by finding who we are and developing our character, and hence, having learned a little during the passage of the day, author for the evening something superior to the scribbles of our morning.

Writing on the earth and sky is easier the higher our vantage point. To author our best work, achieve the greatest development, we must climb to the highest peak of our soul's Himalayas, conquer the mountain of self and enjoy the best views. We must make every effort to reach the highest standards of morality and virtue by facing personal responsibilities to other lives. If not, we slide down the mountain of self to baseness and restricted views and live with those who have never attempted the climb, and others who have never even looked up. All lives compel some uphill paths, not to inflict pain but to reveal greater views. The choice whether to continue uphill or slide down the mountain of self is ours but, if we would fulfil our greatest potential, we must continue the climb, complete our life's pilgrimage. By following the reliable guides of nature, morality and virtue, we find our highest character and create some measure of certainty, since we are sure of our consistently healthy responses to life's uncertain, ever changing circumstances. In our usual back-to-front grasp of reality, we thought certainty was something independent of human choice, but now we can see that we can choose to establish something of it. We have within us what we seek. We may lose our name of Legion and settle for the simplicity and stability of a single character. The Upanishads refer to what is real as being that which remains constant amidst change, which is consistent with the general Hindu view of this ever-changing world as illusory (māyā). Eternal change around us can be met, if we choose, with our eternal constancy of character or, we might say, worldly illusions may be met with our own reality.

In James Hilton's novel 'Lost Horizon' the idyllic community of Shangri-La is hidden amongst the highest mountains. Our speculations would agree, but suggest that those mountains are not physical mountains, but the mountains of self, and that we approach Shangri-La by ascending spiritually. As we progress on our uphill journey, we get closer to Shangri-La because, as we climb upward, improving our character, we cannot help but improve our communities, and together we may create Shangri-La around us.

O that our souls could scale a height like this,
A mighty mountain swept o'er by the bleak
Keen winds of heaven; and, standing on that peak
Above the blinding clouds of prejudice,
Would we could see all truly as it is;
The calm eternal truth would keep us meek.

Robinson Jeffers (American poet 1887 – 1962)

(Excerpt from the poem 'A Hill-Top View' by Robinson Jeffers. The Aurora. Vol X. No. 5. February 1904. With thanks to Occidental College: Los Angeles, U.S.A., and Jeffers Literary Properties for kind permission to reprint this excerpt.)

Painting by Caspar David Friedrich (1774 - 1840)

Developing our character as highly as we can is best both for us and the community of which we form a part. However, shared objectives do not mean uniformity. Constancy of character need not equate to tedium. We may still retain our unique characteristics, our modes of expression, personal interpretations and senses of humour. We may still be creative and adventurous; exploring and seeking new experiences.

Whilst we do, we want to know that, whatever events occur, our family, friends and colleagues will not regularly be changing major features of their personality. To do so would render relationships untenable since we would, literally, not know who we are dealing with, and therefore whether they could be relied on, or even be dangerous etc. We need to know they will not wash their hands of situations when we need them to get their hands dirty. This reminds us of some observations on truth in the previous chapter and relates again to our themes of change and constancy, since truth is often considered to be constant and unchanging whereas we considered it to be growing and changing – because it involves us. *Truth grows and changes healthily* as a consequence of our *characters remaining constant* when they are crafted according to the guides of nature, morality and virtue.

We also like the security of loved ones loving us, and they do this because of who we are. If we change this too radically, we may be changing much else besides. Maintaining constancy of our own character also provides others with the security we want for ourselves. These reflections help us see something of the value of constancy, because love is dependent on 'who we are', and 'who we are' is dependent on our free will. Hence, our freely willed constancy of character helps us find love. Since our character choices are often dependent on our self control and since love is both the strongest and, at the same time, the most delicate of forces, perhaps we may say that love, like self control, is a poise of self that is as 'delicate as the fluttering of gossamer wings and at the same time as rigid as steel' (B47c) – the very quintessence of yin and yang combined harmoniously. From experience we know that the best blend and balance of yin and yang is achieved with, by and through love – remembering what was noted in the previous chapter that love is multi-faceted and more than the full-on fireworks of romantic passion, such that it includes compassion, care, kindness, concern, courtesy, sacrifice and suffering (sometimes voluntarily, sometimes not). With constancy of good character we establish wholesome, healthy, loving relationships and these is turn create wholesome, healthy societies. Sadly, so many modern societies are mostly loveless, as identified by Huxley in the previous chapter and like those referred to in Hosea 4: 1-3 as quoted in the Presentation to the Forest Guards above.

Following our guides of nature, morality and virtue to fully develop our characters brings a heavy load of considerations and responsibilities, under the weight of which we struggle. These guides do not make life easy, in fact on specific occasions and / or for short-term gain, it is often tempting to abandon them. Hence, far from being boring, maintaining the constancy of our character by self-control, is exacting and challenging.

We may monitor our progress by checking with nature's mirror, watching the reactions of the environment, animals and other people around us. The more intently we watch and listen, the more we may learn.

In accordance with some of the principles referred to in this book, it may be that I can only see, and have written of, my own partial, and possibly blurred and distorted, reflections. I am just a concerned individual trying to understand what I am seeing and hearing, and am most conscious of my ignorance, my fallibility and, as Jack London put it, my 'finity'. As pointed out in the Introduction, I am aware that experts on 'leaves and branches' may see much that is missing. However, what has been identified herein is so persistent in space and time, and identified by so many others, it surely cannot be entirely figments of my imagination. Even if my angle of view results in blurred and distorted appearances there is, even allowing for this, sufficient to testify to considerable substance in reality. This substance is so critical for all of us, we each need to check our views with others until a consensus is reached and then, if necessary, take appropriate action to preserve all that's made from 'green thoughts in green shades'.

The reader will know that I have made myself popular with governments, corporate giants, the media, some standard scientists, the scruffily dressed, the selfish and self-indulgent, those doing nothing about the environmental crisis and, no doubt, numerous others. Would I do this unless sincere? Remember Abe Lincoln (and for readers who might be unfamiliar with Western history, this American president was not usually regarded as the most handsome of men), who asked: 'If I were two-faced, would I be wearing this one?' What ulterior motives might I have? Even if some donations to LifeForce result from the book, they mean more unpaid work. More importantly, current circumstances make it likely that LifeForce will cease to exist in the not too distant future and this book is almost certainly the conclusion of this author's full-time efforts toward tiger conservation. So why write this, unless the case really is as ugly as presented and, at the same time, that which must be faced? If I am mistaken and, for example, the world is not controlled by the few and greedy, and this is not reflected in social, national, international and environmental crises; and tigers, wildlife and nature in general are thriving, and any reader can be bothered to correct me, please do so, that I may sleep more peacefully. However, if my reasoning is only partially correct and my impressions even half accurate, should readers not adopt the recommendations made herein and act accordingly? As mentioned, these recommendations only make the world a better place, so we may as well do them, whatever the state of the planet, or this author's imagination.

For whatever validity these perceptions might have, it is also true that fragments of philosophy have been offered without full or firm foundation, spirituality is considered only with regard to self development, the political, socio-economic and commercial suggestions are little more than ideas still to be developed and many may be considered naïve; even the environmental suggestions and conservation work are only briefly summarised.

For all that is absent from this book, what is left? What is left is at least some evidence of the immediate need for each and everyone to adjust (if necessary) their lifestyles, such that they 'husband and nurture' the natural environment – from which, in every sense, all else follows. Moreover, this evidence is based on a firm foundation, which you can stand on yourself – personal experience. You can check and supplement the evidence for yourself in your own investigations. You can explore the suggestions or viewpoints, spiritual or practical, and let nature and your experience of life guide those explorations. You can develop your rational and intuitive knowledge while exercising an interest in nature. Although personal experience can be deceived, it is also personal experience which eventually discovers the deception. Ultimately, life is lived, lessons learned, theories substantiated, science validated and art appreciated through personal experience. Nature is our reliable guide since 'nature never deceives us; it is always we who deceive ourselves.' (Rousseau) or 'We are betrayed by what is false within' (a line from Meredith's poem 'Love's Grave') or 'Not that which goes into the mouth defiles a man; but that which comes out of the mouth…' (Matthew 15:11)

If your explorations lead you to some of the viewpoints described above you will see that this book is more of a survival manual than any form of literature. While 'pass the tapes of your life-jacket around your back and tie them at the front' may be less than inspiring from a literary perspective, under some circumstances it may be the most valuable thing to read, in order that you can continue to enjoy life itself, including a more thorough exploration of all those topics to which full justice cannot be done in a survival manual. The problems are clearly defined. The tiger in particular, and the environment in general, can afford no further time before we adequately address them. For however few readers this book may reach, it is hoped that (if possible and / or practical) it might prompt them to adjust their life-styles such that their consumerism, and their earning and investment of money is as ethical and environmentally-friendly as possible, and (if they have not already) spread the word to their family and friends.

Plants and animals, without debating global warming, are rapidly moving north and south to reduce the effects of increasing temperatures. In this we see another example of allowing nature to be our guide and finding some independence from human opinions. As we are also totally dependent on our guide for all our essential needs, our most important consideration must surely be how we are treating our guide. It would seem a good idea to respect and care for it, since we will be lost without it and soon after that, without shelter, and then cold, thirsty and hungry. Yet, measured by all major socio-economic trends, we are currently despising, abusing and damaging our guide – while proclaiming our intelligence.

Perhaps you feel that you cannot totally rely on your own assessment of, for examples, the presence or absence of wildlife, pollution, the changing climate, the increasing severity of floods or the disappearance of tigers. If so, here is an alternative test; you might try asking people whether or not they care for and respect nature. If the majority response is blank ignorance or bland indifference; or the answer is 'no'; or even 'yes' but their life-styles do not match their affirmative answer, you can be sure we're in trouble. Or again, with regard to all the debate about human contributions to global warming, you could forget all the facts and figures and just consider whether or not the major motives behind our 'engineered' total dependence on fossil fuels by a few corporations are greed and power. The answer means that we can be sure we're in trouble. When profits take priority over people, society is poisoned, politically, educationally, commercially, socially and environmentally. Nature 'outside' will tell us what's 'inside' of us, and give us some time to change, before she changes things for us. Nature will teach us responsibility – individually and collectively, which is another reason why we can be sure environmental conditions are trying to tell us something.

Once we take action to protect and conserve nature, we leave the purity and relative simplicity of her laws and find ourselves in a jungle of entangled human views and opinions, incomplete data, heroes and villains, egos, ulterior motives, corruption, bias, the well-intentioned but ill-informed, the well-informed but ill-intentioned and the ill-informed and ill-intentioned. Yet nature still remains our guide and now, in addition to her constancy, we have the constancy of our character based on morality and virtue and, knowing who we are, we can decide on our actions and persist with them, even when the results seem physically ineffective and success nowhere to be found. Of course, it is not easy, we have to struggle and develop ourselves to carry the weight of responsibilities. Although we have found some certainty in nature and our characters, we also know that uncertainty and unanswered questions always remain, as does the necessity to press on in spite of them. Showing courage, persistence and a commitment to complete our tasks, play our roles, even when personal sacrifice is required of us. This is all part of the challenge and life's smelting process, part of the tiger's fire and the heat of the furnace, in which our potential for dignity and nobility, and our free-will decisions whether or not to exercise them, forge our chains, or set us free. We may choose bright orange or even pure white – or we may choose black, and the primeval darkness of Erebus, the product, according to Hesiod, of chaos and night.

If we look back on our journey together through the chapters laid out behind us we see that our day's march has taken us on the only narrow path that climbs to our current viewpoint: our first steps together took us through personal experience of nature to find two types of knowledge. We could have wandered from the path either side and spent a lifetime studying one or the other but, from our path, we can see the critical importance of balancing both rational and intuitive knowledge, and that nothing less than survival is dependent on *caring* (yin) for other lives in *practical* (yang) ways, the most important expression of which is, today, called conservation. By incorporating both aspects into our own lives we craft healthier, better balanced characters, and maybe, better karma. Again, we could have stepped off the path and spent a lifetime studying philosophy or religion – but find that lifetime curtailed, or very unhealthy, because we took no action according to our studies, since no philosophy, no art, no science and no religion is an end in itself. 'From beautiful moments engrossed in God, it is necessary to rush to the beggar, who calls for soup' (Master Eckhart. c. 1260 – 1328. German Christian Mystic). Whatever our occupation, we have to actively meet our personal responsibilities to others, which gives our life purpose and meaning. Carrying the weight of those responsibilities costs us some freedom and physical sacrifice, if not pain. Yet their weight develops our spiritual strength, which ultimately brings us health, wealth and freedom, in unity with and tolerance for other lives, human and non-human. As we look back, we find the path we have just reviewed is the middle path. It is narrow since it is the line of balance between opposing extremes either side which slope away and gradually steepen until they fall into a yawning abyss of excess each side, such as, for example, on one side, fabulous wealth wasted while, on the other, people and tigers die for want of pennies. As we approach the ideal balance, the path must of necessity be narrow, and our 'poise of self' must become ever more delicate – personally, socially, economically, environmentally '...for wide is the gate, and broad is the way, that leadeth to destruction...strait is the gate, and narrow is the way, which leadeth unto life, and few there be that find it.' (Matthew 7:13-14)

Narrow is the way to environmental health (and ever narrower are our chances of finding it, the longer we delay looking for it). However, we know, by any and every means available to us, it is the only path to life and health. We must exercise our powers urgently and decisively. We are still, but only just, living with tigers. We might not always be able to see them – but they are there. To save the physical tiger is to save important elements of ecosystems that affect global ecosystems, and therefore the quality of life, if not life itself. It is also to save your inner tiger, and qualities of life, to develop your own nobility and power; achieve balance and health; to find yourself and your freedom. Suicide or salvation depends on the choices and changes each of us make today. So seize your tiger's fire; smelt your moral mettle and, by the choices you make, the actions you take, dare frame *thy* fearful symmetries.

APPENDIX I

NOTES ON THE REACTIONS OF TIGERS TO THE SCENT OF CONSPECIFICS

Synopsis

Scent spraying occurs most frequently by all tigers on re-visiting areas for the first time each day. The only scent that elicited flehmen from the "owner" (of that scent), was the scent of the 'owner' in oestrus – and then not always. One female made a partial flehmen gesture on smelling her own 'normal' scent (that produced when not in oestrus) and one male sprayed on smelling his own scent. Other than these relatively few instances, in the vast majority of cases, no tiger showed any reaction to its own scent.

Four individuals (Trooper ♂, Kamal ♂, Topaz ♀, Jay ♀) sprayed much more frequently than the others, and of these, the two females sprayed most frequently of all. All four happen to be siblings, but this is not considered to be significant. What is considered to be significant is that these four are neither the most dominant, nor the most subordinate individuals i.e. they are the mid-range in the rank order, with so little between their status, individuals are regularly 'jostling' for new positions.

The only sprays not collected were those of the most dominant individual and the most subordinate individual i.e. the animals representing the extremes of the hierarchy. Both of these animals do spray (in the reserve etc.) but very infrequently. It seems significant that these two sprayed so rarely.

The most subordinate individual (a small female) and the most dominant individual (an average sized male) displayed no visible reaction to any scent presented to them, with only one exception on the part of the male (possibly linked with some interesting behaviour described in the main body of text).

Dominance can be indicated by the height at which a scent is located and, possibly, by the chemical composition of that scent. Flehmen appears to be concerned with assessment of female receptivity, probably in conjunction with Jacobson's organ. However, these results indicate that it also has other functions, unknown at present.

Introduction

Tigers in the wild and in captivity spray various objects in their environment with a mixture of urine and a 'marking fluid'. It can be seen as a "two-phase fluid, the whitish, oily or fatty marking fluid floating on the pale yellow urine" (Brahmachary and Dutta unpublished to date). It is thought that this not only serves for territory demarcation (Schaller 1967; McDougal 1977) but also, an indicator of the other tiger's identity, sex and, if female, her stage of oestrus (Schaller 1967, McDougal 1977, Brahmachary and Dutta). Scent spraying is not urination, it may be accompanied by it but remains a separate action. To spray, a tiger turns its hindquarters to point at an object and with rump slightly raised and tail held vertically, squirts the spray in anything from 1 – 6 bursts onto the object which is usually not more than 60cm away. To urinate, a tiger puts its hind feet slightly apart, lowers its hindquarters to squat and deposits the urine in a puddle on the ground (a tiger may occasionally spray in this position).

This paper attempts to expand the information available on tiger scent-marking behaviour by detailing reactions to scents and indicating possible functions of scent and the responses to it.

Description and daily routine

The tigers (a group of eight) were studied at Windsor Safari Park, Berkshire, England and represented two litters of four. One litter was born in late May 1977, and the other in early June 1977. Their heritage is unclear, but while one family appear to be specimens of the Indian sub-species the other family appear to be a cross-breed between the Indian (*Panthera tigris tigris*) and Siberian sub-species (*Panthera tigris altaica*).

	MALES	FEMALES
INDIAN RACE	Lancer	Sceptre
FAMILY	Rajah	Suli
INDIAN/SIBERIAN CROSS	Trooper	Topaz
FAMILY	Kamal	Jay

The tigers were released into a reserve at 10.00 a.m. each morning, where they remained until being caged overnight, when the Park was closed. The tiger night-quarters were an inter-connected block of nine usable cages each approximately 2.5m cubed, the upper half of the front wall being barred and open to the air. Each tiger had a cage to itself overnight which, amongst other reasons, allowed them to eat peacefully when fed each morning, excepting Tuesday and Friday which were 'starve days'.

For this reason, my experiments could only be conducted during the early morning on Tuesday and Friday. No work could be done after the cat reserves were closed, primarily because the tigers would not co-operate. After considerable preparation, the experiments began in January 1980 and finished in April 1980.

Methods

It will be useful to explain how the rank order amongst the tigers was assessed since this concept arises in the discussion of results.

Two types of event were observed where the tigers participating could be described as dominant or subordinate. The first was in a situation called a "pair confrontation" which involved one tiger (called the dominant) cowing the other in a ritualised manner by them exchanging blows and employing facial expressions termed by Leyhausen as 'aggressive threat' and 'defensive threat' (described more fully in Chapter II).

The second situation occurred at feeding time. In earlier days, as only four cages were available, it was necessary to feed the tigers as four pairs. It was therefore necessary over a period of time to experiment with different combinations of two individuals to achieve a peaceful feeding regime whereby each tiger received and ate its share e.g. If an animal termed a high dominant was put with a low subordinate, the dominant would take and eat both shares of meat, not allowing the other to feed. If two individuals of closer rank were put together the more dominant would take the first share of meat while the more subordinate would take the second and be able to eat it. Treating the second method of assessment as the more accurate index, it was possible to build up an idea of an individual's position in the rank order – if only the "absolute rank order" (Leyhausen 1965). Later, eight separate cages became available, allowing each tiger its own cage.

In order to obtain the uncontaminated scent of a tiger, the ninth cage, unused by any tiger overnight, was utilised. A tiger would be allowed to enter it alone and, hopefully within the time available, it would spray one of the three solid walls of the cage on which, at strategic positions, were stuck sheets of chemically inert paper. The paper used was 46 cm x 57 cm sheets of Whatman's Benchkote, which has an impermeable backing of polyethelene. It was originally positioned with the bottom edge of the paper at a height of approximately 1 m. above the cage floor. All three solid walls of the cage were covered with paper at this height. For reasons that will become clear later, it was also necessary to put paper above this i.e. so that the bottom edge of the upper paper was flush with the top edge of the lower paper. In this way the walls were covered from a height of 1m. to 1.92 m.

Although the tigers could see each other through the barred inter-connecting doors of the cages overnight, when these doors were opened in the morning and the tigers mixed with each other, scent spraying (and prusten) was noticeably very frequent by the majority of tigers. While the mixing was going on, an individual would be detoured into the ninth 'papered cage' and the 'impetus' of the social spraying seemed to induce him/her to spray the paper. Luckily, six tigers (three male, three female) did spray, and almost invariably in this situation.

It was also apparent that when the tigers entered the reserve for the first time each day, scent spraying was more frequent than at any other time throughout the day. So in two instances of re-visiting well known areas for the first time, scent spraying occurred more frequently than at any other time.

If a tiger, while exploring the cage, smelt a piece of paper and, in doing so, rubbed its muzzle on the paper, the paper was discarded and replaced, as it is assumed that the tiger, by virtue of it belonging to the Felidae, bears hypertrophied skin glands on the chin (Ewer 1973). Likewise the paper was discarded and replaced if the tiger happened to make a small exploratory lick. Paper was stored if, having been sprayed, it received no other mark or contamination whatsoever, excluding of course any fall-out from the air – which the scent is subject to under its functional conditions anyway. Impregnated paper was stored in airtight plastic containers under refrigeration.

Paper impregnated with an individual's scent was presented to all the tigers (including the "owner") one by one, by placing it against the bars of an empty cage midway along the block of nine. A tiger would be admitted to the cage and notes made from a distance, while the tiger explored the cage and smelt the paper. The tiger would then be moved on to the next cage and the next tiger moved into the 'presentation cage'. Of necessity (to prevent the tiger possibly ripping the paper down) the paper was placed on the outside of the bars. These bars were cleaned with 'Decon 90' (BDH), to ensure reactions were due only to the scented paper. The gaps in the bars allowed the rhinarium of the tiger to touch the paper but the bars prevented a tiger licking the paper, as it sometimes attempted to do. However attempted licking was classified as licking for the purposes of my notes.

Four responses of a tiger smelling a scent were listed:

1. Flehmen – full or partial
2. Licking
3   Spraying
4. No reaction

The first three may occur singly or in any combination. The last – 'No reaction' – means 'no visible and immediate reaction', whether or not the scent has any invisible and / or delayed effect was, of course, impossible to assess. 'Partial flehmen' is a lifting and curling of the lips and dropping of the lower jaw for brief periods (1-2 seconds). Full flehmen is the fully open mouth, wrinkled lips and tongue lolling out for long periods (up to 15 seconds), this sometimes occurred with visible salivation – sometimes dripping from the mouth.

Occasionally a tiger's lower jaw sagged open as it smelt the paper. Whether this aids the passage of aromatic molecules to the nasal apparatus and the vomeronasal organ by creating a 'through flow' situation, or whether this allowed aromatic molecules to enter the vomeronasal organ via its ducts, is not currently known. However, 'jaw sagging' was not listed as a separate response since it was impossible to know whether this was a reaction to the paper or a natural expression of life.

After smelling the paper some tigers sprayed the wall that was adjacent to the paper and at 90° to it (see diagram)

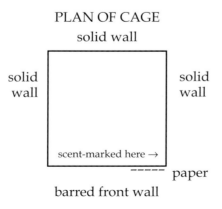

PLAN OF CAGE
solid wall

solid wall

solid wall

scent-marked here →

paper

barred front wall

This was recorded as "spraying" since this corner seemed to be interpreted as one place by the tigers. Identical observations were made by Van Den Brink (1977) concerning a couple of right-angled corners. He observed tigers smelling one side of the corner then turning at 90° and spraying the other side forming the right-angle. He comments "From the animal's behaviour, it became apparent that the places...were interpreted by the animals as one place". This would seem sensible in these experimental conditions as spraying would be inefficient against the barred wall, which was 90% air.

The scent of three individuals was presented to the tigers on the same day as collected – in two cases within the hour. However, I was unable to prevent delays between the collection and presentation of the other six sprays, which ranged from 7 to 21 days. This is unfortunate since it is assumed by many authors (Ewer 1973; McDougal 1977; Schaller 1967) that the age of a scent imparts some information and it may therefore have influenced the reaction of the tiger (refrigeration would make the scent seem fresher than it was but future tests would, ideally, dispense with any delays or utilise them systematically). Whatever the delay, a scent was presented to all the tigers one after the other, on the same day – the process usually lasting less than one hour.

Some tigers did not react to an impregnated paper that others did react to and this was considered to be a type of control experiment. However, in the little time that was left after the last experiment, some tigers were presented with a blank sheet of paper as a more rigorous control experiment. Although they sniffed it, no reaction was given by any (see results).

Most of the data from zoos indicate that tigresses have, on average, a 50 day oestrus cycle with, on average, a 7 day heat period (Schaller 1967). However, the ranges from which these averages are calculated are too wide to allow an accurate forecast of the heat-period for any individual tigress. Therefore, whether or not a tigress was on heat on any date that a scented paper was presented, was deduced from her behaviour and that of other tigers in response to her. Interestingly the two tigresses who had mated properly and frequently just prior to these experiments (during which time they sprayed some paper) both did so for exactly 7 days – the average period of receptivity.

Results and discussion

As the concept of a rank order is discussed below, here is a representation of that order. 'Closing brackets' indicate where the relative position of two animals is uncertain. Indeed these animals may be unsure themselves and offer each other mutual respect in accordance with Leyhausen's (1965) 'relative rank order' (as pointed out in the Synopsis, it is these individuals that spray most frequently). All females are subordinate to all males.

♂ ♂	Lancer	Most Dominant
	Rajah	
	Trooper)	
	Kamal)	↓
♀ ♀	Topaz)	
	Jay)	
	Sceptre	
	Suli	Most Subordinate

Below is a chart tabulating the results of the experiments. So if, for example, we want to know how Rajah reacted to the scent of Topaz 'on heat' we find Rajah at the top of a column and move down until we are on the row labelled Topaz 'on heat', to find that he smelled it for a prolonged time and then displayed full flehmen for 10 seconds.

RESPONSE OF

Lancer	Rajah	Trooper	Kamal	Topaz	Sceptre	Scep.OH	Jay	Suli	To scent of
NR	S	NR	P.F.	P.F.			NR	NR	Rajah 7D
NR	NR	NR	NR	P.S.		NR	S	NR	Trooper 17D
FF.5.L	NR	FF 3	NR	P.F.	NR		FF 4	NR	Kamal ND
NR	L FF 7	NR	NR	NR	NR		NR	NR	Topaz ND
NR	P.S. FF 10	P.F.	NR	P.S. FF 5+5+5	P.S. FF 10+5		P.S. FF 3	P.S.	Topaz 'on heat' 21D
NR	P.F.	FF 5+2 L	NR	P.F.	NR		P.F.	NR	Jay ND
PS	NR	NR	NR	P.S. S		NR	NR	P.S.	Jay 'on heat' 16D
NR	NR	NR	NR	P.F. S	NR		NR	NR	Sceptre 16D
NR	S	P.F.	NR	NR	NR		NR	NR	Male Cheetah 7D
	NR			NR	NR				Control

FF: Full Flehmen. Duration in seconds + duration in seconds of each subsequent gesture.

PF: Partial Flehmen

L: Licking. Although they can occasionally occur separately, licking and flehmen are probably linked actions, in that one accentuates the other.

S: Spraying

PS: Prolonged smelling (up to a minute)

NR: No reaction

7D: 7 Days delay between collection and presentation of scent.

ND: No Delay

Scep OH: Sceptre on heat. A blank square representing Sceptre's response to Rajah's scent was due to my being unable to induce her to smell the paper.

A short study of this table will yield most of the results listed in the Synopsis. Other results are discussed below with any relevant supplementary information.

The above table is not considered to be a standard manual of responses. Moreover, the responses would almost certainly change over time (i.e. if the same scents were presented repeatedly).

Particular locations were regularly used for scent marking. It would seem that the function of this is to ensure that other tigers, on recognising a location, can get a 'message' without having to hunt around and possibly miss it i.e. messages put on the 'notice board' are more likely to be read than those distributed at random around the environment.

All the tigers had been in the 'experimental' cage at least once (usually more times) before they sprayed it (and the attached paper) i.e. as the degree of exploratory behaviour diminished with each visit, the tendency to spray increased. Ewer (1973), talking of a pair of African civets (*Civettictis civetta*) comments "It seems that they must wait until some degree of familiarity has made the object less alarming before they are ready to mark it".

The exact function of flehmen is unclear although Ewer (1973) refers to the work of Knappe (1964) and Verbene (1970) who suggest that it seems to bring odours into contact with Jacobson's organ and observes that "flehmen is widespread possibly universal in the felids, which all possess a functional Jacobson's organ".

It seems safe to assume that flehmen serves to glean further information than is realised by sniffing alone. The fact that sniffing (sometimes prolonged) can take place without subsequently being followed by flehmen indicates that sniffing does serve an informative purpose in its own right. That this should sometimes be followed by flehmen, indicates that investigations have proceeded a stage further and that the molecules are being processed (probably by Jacobson's organ) for further information.

The scent of one female on heat (Topaz) elicited flehmen from two males. These two males (Rajah and Trooper) were the only two to have mated with her when she was on heat. The two males who showed no reaction to the female scents (produced when on heat or not) had not tried mating – possibly due to being sexually immature.

The scent of the other female (Jay) who had mated with one of the males (Rajah) but rebuffed attempts by the second (Trooper) to do so, elicited flehmen from them both but her 'on heat scent' did not. This is puzzling, especially as her 'on heat scent' was 16 days old as opposed to Topaz's 'on heat scent' that was 21 days old.

Jay repeatedly refused to let Trooper mate with her despite his numerous attempts, and allowed only Rajah to do so. As can be seen (see results chart) she did not respond to Rajah's scent but sprayed in response to Trooper's.

These two males responding with flehmen to the scents of these two females suggest that one function of flehmen may be to assess the receptivity of a female. "... it may be that Jacobson's organ has some special sensitivity to the odours emitted by the oestrus female" (Ewer 1973). Flehmen has long been suspected as a detector of female receptivity, at least with herbivores (Schaller 1967). However, it is evident (see results chart) that this cannot be the only function of flehmen – in tigers at least. The fact that both males and females can respond to male scents with flehmen shows that other information is being sought (some behaviour possibly relating to this is described below).

It might also be possible for females to assess whether a male is sexually mature by his scent. This would make sense since tigers maintain territories in the wild before they are sexually mature (McDougal 1977). Tigers certainly start to spray before they are sexually mature.

As these experiments were drawing to a close, I noticed that the relative height at which the tigers sprayed usually corresponded with their position in the rank order, the most dominant spraying highest and the subordinates lower according to their status. This is not a mechanical effect i.e. the bigger the tiger the higher the spray. Smaller, but dominant tigers sprayed higher than bigger but subordinate tigers.

Whilst this aspect was examined too late for complete records of accurate measurements to be made, it was possible to get a few measurements and a general idea of the relative heights. Where only one measurement is given this is the height of the approximate centre of the spray mark.

For example, Rajah made a very diffuse spray against a cage wall ranging from 1.63m at the top to 1.17m at the bottom, being 0.23m at its widest point. Usually, however, the lowest extension of his spray was much higher. When Rajah sprays high, some of the liquid is ejected at such a steep angle that some hits the underside of the up-raised tail. I have seen a tigress standing on her hind legs smelling the higher sprays.

Kamal also made an unusually diffuse spray ranging from 0.91m – 1.37m high, its width at the widest point being 0.17m. Lancer sprayed higher than Rajah did and Topaz sprayed slightly higher than the other females, although this could vary – she has sprayed as low as 0.71m and as high as 1.16m. Trooper has sprayed as high as 1.77m., but he is certainly not the most dominant nor does he always spray that high. Likewise, although not the most subordinate, Jay has sprayed as low as 0.73m (but this is unusual). Could the variable heights at which Topaz and Jay spray be linked with their inexact position in the rank order? Emphasising that much more work needs to be done are observations of two tigresses spraying tufts of grass on flat ground, which have subsequently been investigated by other tigers.

It is possible that not only the height can give information concerning status but also the chemical composition of the spray. With reference to the anal sac secretion of dogs Ewer (1973) suggests "... his status may be declared not only by his overt behaviour, but also by the olfactory characteristics of the secretion he emits".

There may be connection between this, the above paragraphs discussing flehmen, and the following speculation:

It can be seen from the results chart that Lancer (the most dominant individual) only responded to one scent – that of Kamal, a male – and he did so with full flehmen and licking. Kamal's scent was collected and presented to all tigers, including Lancer, on 4th February 1980. It is possible that this is linked with some very unusual behaviour I was fortunate enough to witness: At least four times within two days in February 1980, Lancer attacked and tried to kill Kamal. I have seen an endless number of fights, play and ritualised confrontations between tigers, but these incidents were like nothing I had seen before. Although captive tigers have no experience of killing, it has been known for captive tigers to be killed by captive-bred companions.

(It was noted in chapter II that Lancer intuitively knew where to bite the fake snake to 'kill' it. More evidence was provided by another incident when, due to a miscount, it was thought all tigers had been safely caged for the night. Lancer , however, was still in the Tiger Reserve, through which the neighbouring pride of lions had to pass to reach their night-cages. Two lionesses saw and attacked Lancer. He killed one lioness immediately and was in the process of killing the other when the incident was broken up by keepers in Land Rovers).

With regard to Lancer's attack on Kamal, he exerted tremendous energy and made every effort to get his teeth into Kamal's throat. Lancer's forequarters were laid across those of Kamal who was on his back (a submissive gesture usually respected by others). The struggling Kamal (a bigger tiger than Lancer) tried to push Lancer's head back with his paws and only just succeeded in keeping Lancer's teeth out of his throat. As Kamal managed to break free and make his way to another cage he was visibly shaken and constantly making prusten vocalisations (a gentle puffing of air through the almost closed mouth with vibrating upper lips, usually used in initial greetings signifying "no threat", which usually appeases aggressors). Lancer merely sat on his hind-quarters and looked at me through the bars. I was struck by the ruthlessness and violence of the attack.

Perhaps Kamal's scent contained some chemical 'message' which, after Lancer had investigated it by licking and flehmen, had contributed to Lancer's attack upon him. The 'message' may have been some semiochemical 'challenge' since Kamal had been contesting rank with his brother Trooper around this time and perhaps his 'semiochemical challenge' to Trooper was read by Lancer.

Factors possibly influencing responses to presented scents

1. If the height of the scent conveys any information, the presentation height (between 1 and 1.5m) may have affected that information.

2. The age of the tigers i.e. two males may have been sexually immature.

3. The tigers know each other very well.

4. Freshness may influence the information contained. For example, a one-hour old scent of a male cheetah was presented to Rajah. He smelt it for a prolonged time (1 min.) and displayed flehmen fully for 10 seconds. He smelt it again and again displayed flehmen fully for 5 seconds. He did this once more and then wandered off. When the same scent was presented to Rajah and the others (see results chart), 7 days later, he just sprayed after smelling it.

5. Due to the tigers being together for a large part of the day, they presumably have 'up-to-date information'. If I then presented them with a scent which 'contradicted' this information, they may have ignored it.

Thanks

I would like to thank Mr. A Thomas; Mr O. Bray; Mr F. Rendell; Miss S. Gardner; Miss A. Barten, and Mr A. Dearsley for their help in many varied ways during the course of this work.

References

1. Brahmachary, R.L and J. Dutta (unpublished to date) On the pheromones of a tigress.
2. Ewer, R.F. (1973) The Carnivores, London
3. Hashimoto, Y., Y. Eguchi and A. Arakawa, (1963) Histological observations on the anal sac and its glands of a tiger. *Jpn. J. Vet Sci*. 25: 29 – 32
4. Leyhausen, P. (1965) The communal organisation of solitary mammals *Symp. Zool. Soc. Lond*. 14: 249 – 263
5. McDougal C. (1977) The Face of the Tiger, London
6. Schaller G.B (1967) The Deer and the Tiger, Chicago.
7. Van den Brink, W.J. (1977) Urinespraying as scentmarking of Siberian tigers in Zurich Zoo. *Bijdr Dierkd* 47 (1) 145 – 148.

APPENDIX II

THE GOOD EARTH

A book entitled simply 'Biology' was written by an American lady, Helena Curtis, and published in 1968. It is exceptionally well-written and, despite being a text book, transmits an infectious enthusiasm for its subject. It has been recommended reading for undergraduates in universities. (In keeping with themes explored in previous chapters, Helena Curtis really does love the subject, and attributes her sustained enthusiasm to a total lack of scientific training! (pers. comm)). A brief quote is taken from a subsection on the soil 'In a natural ecosystem…organisms interact with one another and with their physical environment. As a result of these interactions, carbon, nitrogen, phosphates, and all other materials are cycled and recycled through the ecosystem. In terrestrial ecosystems, one of the most important elements in this recycling, and certainly the most complex, is the soil. Natural soils contain a variety of minerals, which are taken up by plant and animal bodies and then returned in discarded leaves and branches, animal excreta, and decomposing plant and animal bodies. In addition to these nonliving components, the soil contains a vast array of living creatures, a teeming underground world of animal life, of plant roots, of algae, fungi, bacteria, and protozoans. The insects, earthworms, and other invertebrates and the micro-organisms that live in the soil decompose the organic material, converting it to a form in which it can be used by plants and also, as a consequence, turning the soil and aerating it.

When the land is turned to agriculture, the subtle relationships of this soil world are destroyed. The minerals are removed from the land when the crop plants are harvested or consumed by cattle and other herbivores. Insecticides and fungicides and herbicides kill the micro-organisms of the soil…When the roots and other organic materials that bind the soil together are ripped up by the plough, the land becomes much more vulnerable to the effects of the weather. Wind and water erode the soil, and the topsoil, which contains the humus, is lost. Minerals are leached from the soil and washed away, eventually to the sea… How is it that our once sturdy little planet, on which life has persisted and even flourished for more than 3 billion years, has now become so fragile? The answer to this question can be found in a re-examination of the concept of mature and immature ecosystems. Any ecosystem under the "control" of man – and now man's influence is extending over the entire bio-sphere – is returned rapidly to an immature stage, a stage at which there are few species and therefore little complexity of interaction. A mature, complex ecosystem, with its complicated food webs, has many built-in checks and balances. Individual members of the plant and animal community may be sick or die, but the ecosystem itself is healthy and species tend to endure and in relatively stable numbers. Under agriculture, plants do not grow in complex communities, as they do in a forest, but in pure stands. A cornfield, for example, has little inherent stability. If not constantly guarded by man, it will be immediately overrun with insects and weeds. It is for this reason that insecticides and herbicides play such a large…role in our modern life. The susceptibility of modern crops to predators and parasites was tragically illustrated by the great potato famine of Ireland, which was caused by a fungus infection. The famine of 1845-1847 was responsible for more than 1 million deaths from starvation and initiated large-scale emigration from Ireland to the United States; within a decade, the population of Ireland dropped from 8 million to 4 million. Virtually the entire Irish potato crop was wiped out in a single week in the summer of 1846. As we noted previously, a number of plant geneticists are warning that the new strains of wheat and rice, which promise to contribute so importantly toward feeding the growing populations, will be particularly susceptible, because of their genetic uniformity and wide-spread distribution, to such disasters.' (B19)

'The National Academy of Sciences and the Royal Society, the leading scientific bodies of the US and Britain, said in their joint report of July 2000: "Modern agriculture is intrinsically destructive of the environment. It is particularly destructive of biological diversity. The widespread application of conventional agricultural technologies such as herbicides, pesticides, fertilizers and tillage has resulted in severe environmental damage in many parts of the world." At the beginning of the last century, most food was grown and distributed locally. At its end, just 20 multinational corporations dominated a food trade that had gone international. In spite of this, well over half the population in poor countries is still in farming families. So the most effective way to feed the majority of the world's poor is to ensure that small farmers have good access to thriving local markets, that they are not forced off the land, do not have to buy seed, are helped with appropriate research and technology and have control over water in their locality. The price they get for their produce must not be undercut by subsidised imports.

Two-fifths of the world population is malnourished. Half of these are hungry. The other half eats too much unhealthy junk food. This is hardly surprising because most nutrition research is now funded by and for industrial agribusiness. It is in their interest to develop and advertise food that will appeal to the rich not the poor, to encourage growing for export rather than to meet local needs, to make farmers dependent on purchased seed, chemicals, and machinery. It is not in their interests to make farmers self-sufficient. There is no world shortage of food. The US has huge surpluses. India exports grain and meat to wealthy countries and even considers dumping excess grain at sea. Poverty, not lack of food, in an increasingly wealthy and unequal world, condemns a billion people to live daily with the horror that they and their families may not have enough, or anything, to eat.

Aid from the rich to the poor is inadequate. Whereas Denmark donates over 1% of its GDP in aid the US gives only 0.1%. But aid is also an admission of failure; it would not be necessary, other than for disaster-relief, if the world had a fair economic system.

The twenty companies that dominate the food trade would like us to believe that increasingly specialized crops, genetic engineering and new chemicals are required to feed the world.

Arable land is constantly being lost because chemicals destroy the quality of soil. Dependence on chemicals puts poor farmers in debt and drives them from the land. Nitrates seep into ground and poison drinking water. Persistent synthetic chemicals (EDC's (Endocrine Disrupting Chemicals) and POPs (Persistent Organic Pollutants)) endanger human and animal health and reproduction. The short-term advantage of herbicides and pesticides soon turns into a long-term hazard as resistance develops and the balance of predators is upset.

Diversity is fundamental to all life. The current use of only high-yield and GM crops is a tendency towards monoculture, so is contrary to sound science. During the 20th century three-quarters of the genetic diversity of agricultural crops was lost, 100,000 varieties of rice have been reduced to a few dozen and three-quarters of the world's rice now descends from a single plant… The Irish experience with potatoes was just one warning that monoculture is the herald of starvation…In 1896 Professor Shaler of Harvard University said: "If mankind can't devise and enforce ways of dealing with the earth which will preserve the source of life, we must look forward to a time when our kind, having wasted its inheritance, will fade from the earth." Since then America has lost half its topsoil. It can take at least 500 years to develop an inch of topsoil, so the damage is immense…With intensified use of pesticides in the US the proportion of crops lost to pests has increased from 32% to 37%. Many pests are now resistant to pesticides…'

(B10 reprinted by kind permission of Alastair Sawday Publishing Co.)

Before chemical farming, innumerable birds would follow the plough to eat from the rich, living soil that had been exposed. No birds follow modern ploughs. (There is good evidence to show that ploughs damage the soil and some farms act as practical demonstrations that cultivation can be conducted without them). Modern agricultural techniques have killed the soil, which can no longer grow crops without being drenched in chemicals. Vast areas of single species crops have so far, luckily, been free of a pathogen that would devastate them. Is relying on luck the best and safest future we can secure for agriculture, and our children? The following quotes were included in issue No. 4 of LifeForce Charitable Trust's newsletter 'LifeLines':

'One of the principal justifications for the Green Revolution has been the argument that the new agricultural technology is needed to feed the world's hungry. In an age of scarcity, so the argument goes, only increased production will solve the problem of hunger, and only large-scale agribusiness is able to produce more food. This argument is still used, long after detailed research has made it quite clear that the problem of world hunger is not at all a technical problem; it is social and political. One of the most lucid discussions of the relation between agribusiness and world hunger can be found in the work of Frances Moore Lappe and Joseph Collins, founders of the Institute for Food and Development Policy in San Francisco. Extensive research has led these authors to conclude that scarcity of food is a myth and that agribusiness does not solve the problem of hunger but, on the contrary, perpetuates and even aggravates it. They point out that the central question is not how production can be increased, but rather what is grown and who eats it, and that the answers are determined by those who control the food-producing resources. Merely to introduce new technologies into a system marred by social inequalities will never solve the hunger problem; on the contrary, it will make it worse. Indeed, studies of the impact of the Green Revolution on hunger in the Third World have confirmed the same paradoxical and tragic result again and again. More food is being produced, yet more people are hungry. As Moore Lappe and Collins write, "In the Third World, on the whole there is more food and less to eat."

Research co-directed by Moore Lappé and Collins has shown that "there is no country in the world in which people could not feed themselves from their own resources and that the amount of food produced in the world at present (*first published 1986 – author*) is sufficient to provide about eight billion people – more than…the world's population – with an adequate diet. Nor can scarcity of agricultural land be considered a cause of hunger. For example, China has twice as many people per cultivated acre as India, yet in China there is no large-scale hunger. Inequality is the main stumbling block in all current attempts to fight world hunger.

Agricultural 'modernization' – mechanized large-scale farming – is highly profitable for a small elite, the new corporate 'farmers' and drives millions of people off the land. Thus fewer people are gaining control over more and more land, and once these large landholders are established they no longer grow food according to local needs but switch to more profitable crops for export, while the local population starves. Examples of this vicious practice abound in all countries of the Third World. In Central America at least half of the agricultural land – and precisely the most fertile land – is used to grow cash crops for export while up to 70 percent of the children are undernourished. In Senegal vegetables for export to Europe are grown on choice land while the country's rural majority goes hungry. Rich, fertile land in Mexico that previously produced a dozen local foods is now used to grow asparagus for European gourmets. Other landowners in Mexico are switching to grapes for brandy, while entrepreneurs in Colombia are changing from growing wheat to growing carnations for export to the United States.

World hunger can be overcome only by transforming social relations in such a way that inequality is reduced at every level. The primary problem is not the redistribution of food but the redistribution of control over agricultural resources. Only when this control is democratized will the hungry be able to eat what is produced. Many countries have proved that social changes of this kind can be successful. In fact, 40 percent of the Third World population now lives in countries where hunger has been eliminated through common struggle. These countries do not use agriculture as the means to export income but rather use it to produce food first for themselves. Such a 'food first' policy requires, as Moore Lappé and Collins have emphasized, that industrial crops should be planted only after people have met their basic needs, and that trade should be seen as an extension of domestic need rather than being determined strictly by foreign demand.

At the same time, we who live in industrialized countries will have to realize that our own food security is not being threatened by the hungry masses in the Third World, but by the food and agricultural corporations that perpetuate this massive starvation. Multinational agribusiness corporations are now in the process of creating a single world agricultural system in which they will be able to control all stages of food production and to manipulate both food supply and prices through well-established monopoly practices. This process is now well under way. In the United States almost 90 percent of the vegetable production is controlled by major processing corporations, and many farmers have no choice but to sign up with them or go out of business.

World-wide corporate control of food production would make it impossible ever to eliminate hunger. It would, in effect, establish a Global Supermarket in which the world's poor would be in direct competition with the affluent and thus would never be able to feed themselves. This effect can already be observed in many Third World countries, where people go hungry although food is grown in abundance right where they live. Their own government may subsidize its production and they themselves may even grow and harvest it. Yet they will never eat any because they are unable to pay the prices resulting from international competition.

In its continual efforts to expand and increase its profits, agribusiness not only perpetuates world hunger but is extremely careless in the way it treats the natural environment, to the extent of creating serious threats to the global ecosystem. For example, giant multinational companies such as Goodyear, Volkswagen, and Nestle are now bulldozing hundreds of millions of acres in the Amazon River basin in Brazil to raise cattle for export. The environmental consequences of clearing such vast areas of tropical forest are likely to be disastrous. Ecologists warn that the actions of the torrential tropical rains and the equatorial sun may set off chain reactions that could significantly alter the climate throughout the world.

Agribusiness, then, ruins the soil on which our very existence depends, perpetuates social injustice and world hunger, and seriously threatens global ecological balance. An enterprise that was originally nourishing and life-sustaining has become a major hazard to individual, social, and ecological health."' (B51 reprinted by kind permission of Institute for Food and Development Policy, 398 60th Oakland, CA 94618 USA)

Hence, we can see that, during the latter half of the 20th century, much malnutrition and starvation has been the result of people being unable to purchase food locally, due to socio-economic systems prevailing globally, and not due to natural environmental conditions. However, continued abuse of nature by those same socio-economic systems will increasingly make the environment a factor in food shortages (e.g. rising sea levels (i.e. salt water) will render low lying arable land barren) and must ultimately make it the major factor – which will force us to readjust our socio-economic systems. When we do, the environment will eventually restore the bounty we previously misused and abused, in another of nature's cycles – although this cycle is more easily described than experienced.

'The influence of the pharmaceutical industry on the practice of medicine has an interesting parallel in the influence of the petrochemical industry (chemicals isolated or derived from petroleum) on agriculture and farming. Farmers, like doctors, deal with living organisms that are severely affected by the mechanistic and reductionist approach of our science and technology. Like the human organism, the soil is a living system that has to remain in a state of dynamic balance to be healthy. When the balance is disturbed...disease will occur, and eventually the whole organism may die and turn into inorganic matter. These effects have become major problems in modern agriculture because of the farming methods promoted by the petrochemical companies. As the pharmaceutical industry has conditioned doctors and patients to believe that the human body needs continual medical supervision and drug treatment to stay healthy, so the petrochemical industry has made farmers believe that soil needs massive infusions of chemicals, supervised by agricultural scientists and technicians, to remain productive. In both cases these practices have seriously disrupted the natural balance of the living system and thus generated numerous diseases. Moreover, the two systems are directly connected, since any imbalance in the soil will affect the food that grows in it and thus the health of the people who eat that food.

...Solar energy is the natural fuel that drives the soil cycles, and living organisms of all sizes are necessary to sustain the whole system and keep it in balance. Thus bacteria carry out various chemical transformations, such as the process of nitrogen fixation, which make nutrients accessible to plants; deep-rooted weeds bring trace minerals to the soil surface where crops can make use of them; earthworms break up the soil and loosen its texture; and all these activities are interdependent and combine harmoniously to provide the nourishment that sustains all life on earth.

The basic nature of living soil requires agriculture, first and foremost, to preserve the integrity of the great ecological cycles. This principle was embodied in traditional farming methods, which were based on a profound respect for life. Farmers used to plant different crops every year, rotating them so that the balance in the soil was preserved. No pesticides were needed, since insects attracted to one crop would disappear with the next. Instead of using chemical fertilizers, farmers would enrich their fields with manure, thus returning organic matter to the soil to re-enter the biological cycle.

This age-old practice of ecological farming changed drastically about three decades ago (*pub. 1982 – author*), when farmers switched from organic to synthetic products, which opened up vast markets for the oil companies. While the drug companies manipulated doctors to prescribe ever more drugs, the oil companies manipulated farmers to use ever more chemicals. Both the pharmaceutical industry and the petrochemical industry became multi-billion-dollar businesses. For the farmers the immediate effect of the new farming methods was a spectacular improvement in agricultural production, and the new era of chemical farming was hailed as the "Green Revolution". Soon, however, the dark side of the new technology became apparent, and today it is evident that the Green Revolution has helped neither the farmers nor the land nor the starving millions. The only ones to gain from it were the petrochemical corporations.

The massive use of chemical fertilizers and pesticides changed the whole fabric of agriculture and farming. The industry persuaded farmers that they could make money by planting large fields with a single highly profitable crop and controlling weeds and pests with chemicals. The results of this practice of single-crop monocultures were great losses of genetic variety in the fields and, consequently, high risks of large acreages being destroyed by a single pest. Monocultures also affected the health of the people living in the farming areas, who were no longer able to obtain a balanced diet from locally grown foods and thus became more disease-prone.

With the new chemicals, farming became mechanized and energy-intensive, with automated harvesters, feeders, waterers, and many other labour-saving machines performing the work that had previously been done by millions of people. Narrow notions of efficiency helped to conceal the drawbacks of these capital-intensive farming methods, as farmers were seduced by the wonders of modern technology.

The reality, of course, was far less encouraging. While American farmers were able to triple their corn yields per acre and, at the same time, cut their labor by two-thirds, the amount of energy used to produce one acre of corn increased fourfold. The new style of farming favoured large corporate farmers with big capital and forced most of the traditional single-family farmers, who could not afford to mechanize, to leave their land. Three million American farms have been eliminated in this way since 1945, with large numbers of people forced to leave the rural areas and join the masses of the urban unemployed as victims of the Green Revolution.

...In this industrialized system, which treats living matter like dead substances and uses animals like machines, penned in feedlots and cages, the process of farming is almost totally controlled by the petrochemical industry. Farmers get virtually all their information about farming techniques from the industry's sales force, just as most doctors get their information about drug therapy from the drug industry's "detail men." The information about chemical farming is almost totally unrelated to the real needs of the land. As Barry Commoner (*an active environmentalist and author*) has noted, "One can almost admire the enterprise and clever salesmanship of the petrochemical industry. Somehow it has managed to convince the farmer that he should give up the free solar energy that drives the natural cycles and, instead, buy the needed energy – in the form of fertilizer and fuel – from the petrochemical industry."

In spite of this massive indoctrination by the energy corporations, many farmers have preserved their ecological intuition, passed down from generation to generation. These men and women know that the chemical way of farming is harmful to the land, but they are often forced to adopt it because the whole economy of farming – tax structure, credit system, real estate system, and so on – has been set up in a way that gives them no choice. To quote Commoner again, "The giant corporations have made a colony of rural America."

Nevertheless, a growing number of farmers have become aware of the hazards of chemical farming and are turning back to organic, ecological methods. Just as there is a grass-roots movement in the health field, there is a grass-roots movement in farming. The new organic farmers grow their crops without synthetic fertilizers, rotating them carefully and controlling pests with new ecological methods. Their results have been most impressive. Their food is healthier and tastes better, and their operations have also been shown to be more productive than those of conventional farms. The new organic farming has recently sparked serious interest in the United States and in many European countries. The long-term effects of excessive 'chemotherapy' in agriculture have proven disastrous for the health of the soil and the people, for our social relations, and for the entire ecosystem of the planet. As the same crops are planted and fertilized synthetically year after year, the balance in the soil is disrupted. The amount of organic matter diminishes, and with it the soil's ability to retain moisture. The humus content is depleted and the soil's porosity reduced. These changes in soil texture entail a multitude of interrelated consequences. The depletion of organic matter makes the soil dead and dry; water runs through it but does not wet it. The ground becomes hard-packed, which forces farmers to use more powerful machines. On the other hand, dead soil is more susceptible to wind and water erosion, which are taking an increasing toll. For example, half of the topsoil in Iowa has been washed away in the last twenty-five years, and in 1976 two-thirds of America's agricultural counties were designated drought disaster areas. What is often called 'drought,' 'wind breaking down the land,' or 'winter-kill,' are all consequences of sterile soil.

The massive use of chemical fertilizers has seriously affected the natural process of nitrogen fixation by damaging soil bacteria involved in this process. As a consequence crops are losing their ability to take up nutrients from the soil and becoming more and more addicted to synthetic chemicals. Because their efficiency in absorbing nutrients this way is much lower, not all the chemicals are taken up by the crop but leach into the ground water or drain from the fields into rivers and lakes.

The ecological imbalance caused by monocropping and by excessive use of chemical fertilizers inevitably results in enormous increases in pests and crop diseases, which farmers counteract by spraying ever larger doses of pesticides, thus fighting the effects of their overuse of chemicals by using even more. However; pesticides often can no longer destroy the pests because they tend to become immune to the chemicals. Since World War II, when massive use of pesticides began, crop losses due to insects have not decreased; on the contrary, they have almost doubled. Moreover, many crops are now attacked by new insects that were never known as pests before, and these new pests are becoming increasingly resistant to all insecticides. Since 1945 there has been a sixfold increase in the use of chemical fertilizers and a twelvefold increase in the use of pesticides on American farms. At the same time increased mechanization and longer transport routes have contributed further to the energy dependence of modern agriculture. As a result, 60 percent of the costs of food are now costs of petroleum. As the farmer Wes Jackson puts it succinctly: "We have literally moved our agricultural base from soil to oil." When energy was cheap, it was easy for the petrochemical industry to persuade farmers to change from organic to chemical farming, but since the costs of petroleum began their steady climb, many farmers have realized that they can no longer afford the chemicals they now depend upon. With every enlargement of farming technology the indebtedness of farmers increases as well. Even in the 1970's an Iowa banker remarked quite frankly, "I occasionally wonder whether the average farmer will ever get out of debt." If the Green Revolution has had disastrous consequences for the well-being of farmers and the health of the soil, the hazards for human health have been no less severe. Excessive use of fertilizers and pesticides has sent great quantities of toxic chemicals seeping through the soil, contaminating the water table and showing up in food. Perhaps half the pesticides on the market are mixed with petroleum distillates that may destroy the body's natural immune system. Others contain substances which are related specifically to cancer. Yet these alarming results have barely affected the sale and use of fertilizers and pesticides. Some of the more dangerous chemicals have been outlawed in the United States, but the oil companies continue to sell them in the Third World, where legislation is less strict, as the drug companies sell dangerous prescription drugs. In the case of pesticides all populations are directly affected by this unethical practice because the toxic chemicals come back on fruits and vegetables imported from Third World countries.' (B13 © 1982 Fritjof Capra reprinted by kind permission of HarperCollins Publishers Ltd.)

The most nutritious food is fresh and locally grown (because it contains the elements and compounds that make up other parts of that locality – such as our bodies). Local farms and small-holdings not only feed local people but also work against vast profits and power being channelled into a few people's pockets. If we continue along the agribusiness path, the problems grow ever deeper roots – insect resistance to chemicals, poisoning of the soil, potentially catastrophic dangers to major food supplies and the natural ecology, and the manipulation of macro-economics by a few individuals. All that agribusiness ultimately grows is greed. Physical results reflect the values and priorities of the people who profit from and promote agribusiness; for example, pesticides and greed are 'equivalent' in the sense that the former are the physically poisonous manifestations of the latter 'character poison'. They are reflections of each other through a 'mirror-line' between spiritual and physical realms. Together they reinforce each other and greed spreads further afield. Since greed is poisonous and all things are connected, it ultimately poisons the greedy who value short-term profit more than long-term health and life (which is real wealth, as Ruskin said "there is no wealth but life"). The problem is not complex but simple: Whether in agriculture or other arenas, the pursuit of greed, power and maximum profit for a few will ultimately mean poverty for all.

Where still possible, we can choose to buy food from smaller, localised, organic farms. LifeLines 4 quotes farmer Michael Ableman visiting organic farms 'Puzzled when workers passed me carrying buckets of beautiful vegetables, I got down on my knees and parted the weeds. There before me were healthy rows of red and yellow peppers, squash and tender lettuces. (*The farmer*) knows that weeds protect and nourish the soil and that he can grow a crop for nature together with one for humanity. My friend Steve Beck...shows me his orchard...filled with healthy, producing apple trees that have never been pruned...No one would think these farmers would get away with such unorthodox practices but…they've learned exactly how much of a helping hand to lend to nature and when to leave well enough alone. Like many of my friends in farming I've experimented with numerous techniques. Some failed but many succeeded and now there are places on my farm where I can thrust my arm into the soil up to my elbow and come up with dark, rich earth that is so alive that you can see it move. This is the true measure of my success. It has taken time – nature's process is slow, deeply rooted, and with every cycle of the seasons the land grows a little fuller and stronger, and I grow a little wiser.' (B1)

'Why is organic produce more expensive? Because the market is distorted. Market fundamentalism does not apply when agribusiness can influence federal bodies. Society, not the farmers, carries the costs of pesticide contamination, polluted water and other health, chemical-management and environmental impacts associated with industrial farming – not to mention the $20 billion annual subsidies of the 2002 Farm Security Act. Organic food shows what the true cost of food would be in an undistorted economy…' (B10 reprinted by kind permission of Alastair Sawday Publishing Co.)

'Every time you spend money, you're casting a vote for the kind of world you want.' (Anna Lappé (daughter of Frances Moore Lappé, quoted above) author and co-founder, with her mother of The Small Planet Institute)

Ableman: 'Although good production is a key to financial viability, success must be measured in other terms as well. I see it in the children who have never been on a farm before as they leave after a tour with carrots or strawberries in their hands and memories of goats and geese. I like knowing that even here, surrounded by roads and suburban development, a family of red-tailed hawks lives in our orchard and that our neighbours stroll through the farm, reconnecting with a distant part of themselves. As our soil grows rich and strong, it's good to know there's no debt to the bank for fertilizers and pesticides and that our land improves every year. This is our investment and a savings we know we can depend on.

"Very few farmers farm from the heart" (*farmer*) Harter says, "they farm from the pocket book. These things that they do, all the inputs they think that it takes – chemicals, machines – it's a trap. There's nothing in technological systems that can perpetuate itself the way life can – to recycle, purify, heal. Nature's got everything it needs to produce food." But what is the true cost of food? Is the bill being paid well beyond the checkout counter? Who pays for the subsidies farmers receive to produce this food? And what is the cost to our health as soils become exhausted and depleted food and poisons find their way to our kitchen tables and into our bodies? How about the farm workers whose hands do the hoeing and harvesting – what toxic materials are they exposed to? Perhaps the greatest debt in this spiralling bill is being paid by the earth. It is being eroded, compacted and polluted. We are part of this process, and we can be part of the solution – each time we make a purchase we contribute to a whole chain of food consequences extending from the intimate to the global environments. Active participation in that food process challenges us to see beyond the cold, neat rows of the supermarket, where digital displays, studio lighting and triple layer, four colour packaging create the illusion of bounty, security and unlimited choice.

I think of the markets in Peru or in Africa, where abundant colours flood together in living, moving masses of humanity and goods – where the foods are alive and culturally connected to each pueblo or tribe that produced them, where markets are as much gathering places for social exchange as they are for food. One old woman in Burundi told me she had come some thirty kilometres to the market not to shop but to see her friends…

My sense of responsibility as a farmer has heightened since seeing the faces of those who will eat my food – no intermediary, no package to hide behind, no truck to load for distant ports. In this relationship nurturing replaces factory production. Knowing and seeing those I am feeding humanizes the process, returning life to the fields and real care to every step. I can tell the person who is buying my corn that we just picked it hours before, that this year melons or tomatoes will be late due to the cool temperatures, that all our food is grown with compost and free of chemicals.

Little questions – "Where was this grown?" "When was it picked?", "What materials were used on it?", "How is the land where it grew being cared for?" – can start a profound change within ourselves and within a system that removes everything that is real and basic from our lives. Small steps like putting in a garden can change a neighbourhood, and then a whole town. When everyone starts asking and taking responsibility, then greater changes begin to happen. The problems of our farmland and production of our food no longer belong to the two percent of the population we call farmers. When we rejoin the food process we begin to see ourselves as farmers, and the whole planet as our farm to be nurtured and cared for.

And when we rejoin the food process we rejoin the environmental process as well: we begin to understand more precisely what part of our planet belongs to us for food, for fibre and for fuel – and what part must be left sacred to nature. We must bring the interconnections among our food, our health, our communities and our environment for the worst of reasons – that we may not survive if we do not – and for the best of reasons – that we might embark on the wonderful adventure of creating a society in which the beauty of our food is felt in every aspect of our lives. By the simple act of reconnecting with our food, we will nourish and revitalize ourselves and our earth. The act of eating then becomes an act of caring – for our bodies and those of our families, and for the body of the earth of which we partake.' (B1)

'And when a horse stops work and goes into the barn there is a life and a vitality left, there is a breathing and a warmth, and the feet shift on the straw, and the jaws champ on the hay, and the ears and the eyes are alive. There is a warmth of life in the barn, and the heat and smell of life. But when the motor of a tractor stops, it is as dead as the ore it came from. The beat goes out of it like the living heat that leaves a corpse. Then the corrugated iron doors are closed and the tractor man drives home to town, perhaps twenty miles away, and he need not come back for weeks or months, for the tractor is dead. And this is easy and efficient. So easy that the wonder goes out of work, so efficient that the wonder goes out of land and the working of it, and with the wonder the deep understanding and the relation. And in the tractor man there grows the contempt that comes only to a stranger who has little understanding and no relation. For nitrates are not the land, nor phosphates; and the length of fiber in the cotton is not the land. Carbon is not a man, nor salt nor water nor calcium. He is all of these, but he is much more, much more; and the land is so much more than its analysis. The man who is more than his chemistry, walking on the earth, turning his plow point for a stone, dropping his handles to slide over an outcropping, kneeling in the earth to eat his lunch; that man who is more than his elements knows the land that is more than its analysis. But the machine man, driving a dead tractor on land he does not know and love, understands only chemistry; and he is contemptuous of the land and of himself.' (B66 reprinted by kind permission of the Penguin Group)

502

APPENDIX III

EXCERPT FROM
'THE LITTLE EARTH BOOK'
by James Bruges
International 'Agreements' directly or indirectly affecting tigers via their economic repercussions

WTO

'The WTO grew out of the GATT but things have gone disastrously wrong. After 55 years half the world's population lives on less than $2 a day and half those on less than $1. Around the world poor farmers are committing suicide because trade rules are destroying their livelihood. The WTO has been hijacked by corporate interests and its purpose is now to promote trade: Full stop. There is no higher authority, and corporate free trade, "market fundamentalism" has become the governing principle of the world.

The WTO – deliberately – now ensures that the weak cannot protect themselves against the strong. The WTO aims to weaken national government. A strong government in a poor country might discourage the export of raw commodities so that value can be added to them within its own borders. It might also exclude imports that have been cheapened unfairly by subsidies in rich countries. These are ways in which the poor can climb out of poverty. But they are forbidden.

Under WTO rules governments are not allowed to favour local firms, prevent foreigners having a controlling interest in local companies, favour trade partners or subsidise domestic industry (though it has not prevented massive US an EU subsidies to their farmers and exporters). Governments are not allowed to interfere in markets to pursue social objectives such as racial, ethnic or gender equality, nor to favour friendly countries that might have special needs. The rules work to the advantage of corporations which benefit from economies of scale, which can undercut to capture a market, which are immune to local consumer feedback and which can shift their production at short notice to countries with lower wages and fewer environmental or labour regulations. In all these fields manufacturers, suppliers, retailers and farmers in poor countries are at a disadvantage. It is hardly believable but the WTO sets maximum, not minimum, standards of environmental protection.

Trade spreads films, music, language, business methods and attitudes. The WTO is therefore establishing a single culture, globally. But modern communications make everyone aware of stark and growing inequality disintegrating societies, collapsed economies, violent reaction from disaffected groups and environmental crises.

The WTO claims to arrive at decisions by consensus. The Quad (Canada, EU, Japan and the US) sets the agenda and detailed wording of its decisions are hammered out in Green Room meetings to which awkward delegates are excluded or forcibly ejected. Green Room decisions are then presented as "consensus" and binding on all. Objectors are often neutralized by phone calls from heads of state to the delegate's government (George Bush made fifteen such calls during the Cancun meeting). So, formal disputes have largely been limited to differences among the rich.

For the notorious WTO meeting in Seattle in 1999 the chair was the head of the US delegation and delegates from poor countries were sidelined and ignored both in preparations and during the conference. At the following Doha meeting, Europe and the US undertook to reduce subsidies and both reneged on their promises. Subsequent meetings were held in remote locations behind police barriers, vividly demonstrating that the WTO had lost legitimacy...The EU was responsible for the collapse of the Cancun talks by refusing to withdraw new issues. The US had anyway decided to deal unilaterally – "WTO or no WTO we plan to do just what suits us" said one US ambassador...The primary objective of a world trade organization should be to encourage and enable the poor to add value to their commodities and crops within their own communities and boundaries. Countries with poor communities must be encouraged to use appropriate subsidies, tariffs and import quotas, but for these restrictive measures to be reduced on a sliding scale as their economies strengthen. Rich countries should remove all fiscal measures that promote exports or benefit established companies, but not those measures that help small businesses to serve a local market. This policy was pioneered by the American Founders in their struggle against the tyranny of British companies and led to Alexander Hamilton's "infant industry protection" policy that regulated US trade from 1789.

TRIPs (Trade Related Intellectual Property Rights)

The TRIPs agreement protects patent rights – almost all of which belong to western companies – and countries are no longer allowed to make patent regulations to suit domestic conditions. The TRIPs agreement is a restriction on trade in favour of corporations, a blatant infringement of the WTO's own free trade agenda. It limits the use and development of knowledge, paralyses scientific research, benefits only the rich, prevents technology-transfer to the poor, denies affordable access to life-saving medicines, limits farmers' use of traditional knowledge, reduces bio-diversity and even allows nature's life forms to become private property.

GATS (General Agreement on Trade Services)

Came into being in 1995 following pressure from multinational corporations (MNCs), but details are still being worked out. The European Commission admits: "the GATS is first and foremost an instrument for the benefit of business." There has been widespread protest in poor countries as they see their services taken over by foreign companies but, after nine years, the WTO has carried out no independent research into its effects.

The rich say that many poor countries have not been able to afford adequate investment in their service sectors so multinational corporations will help them with both capital and expertise – the rose-tinted view of privatisation.

Under the GATS, national governments must submit to certain rules when handing over services for privatization. Countries are free to decide which sectors they will subject to GATS rules though the aim is for all to be privatised in the end. The GATS enables corporations to invest, acquire land and take over essential services in any country that signs up. Health, education, electricity, water, sanitation, post, telecommunications, transport, banks, investment, insurance, radio, television, film, garbage collection, setting up of retail stores, construction, tourism, land – they all fall within the orbit of the GATS. The preamble to the GATS has many statements to reassure its critics. But the preamble is not legally binding. The rest of the document is legally binding and it specifies that governments must not regulate in any ways that are a hindrance to trade. Even a government's right to hold back essential services is being eroded in current discussions. Article Vl.4, the "Necessity Test," makes the GATS Dispute Panel arbiter with veto powers over whether a government's regulations conflict with free trade imperatives. Bureaucrats that meet in secret determine what a government can or can't do. National parliaments are thus demoted to mere advisory bodies within their own countries.

Many consider the GATS to be the most evil and dangerous of all interventions by the WTO in the affairs of poor countries…

Trick 1

The process is irreversible. If a government or a dictator has privatised a service and listed it to the GATS, such as railways, health or water, a subsequent democratically elected government cannot take it out.

Trick 2

The regulation of trade is enforced by sanctions. Sanctions by poor nations are a scarcely noticed pinprick for the rich. Sanctions and withdrawal of assistance by rich nations can destroy the poor.

Trick 3

Only rich-nation businesses benefit. One cannot conceive of companies from poor countries bidding for health, education or water services in the US or France or the UK.

Trick 4

A country is not free to encourage its own expertise and indigenous culture by, for example, limiting the number of foreign citizens working as architects.

Trick 5

Awkward negotiators from poor countries are withdrawn following a phone call to their governments from a powerful country.

Trick 6

A poor country may be persuaded to bargain away a particular service because it is desperate to retain, say, favourable tariffs on textiles.

Trick 7

It is virtually impossible for indigenous companies to compete with MNCs – either to get started or to survive.

Trick 8

A country may not realize what it is letting itself in for. Having listed tourism, for example, it may not be able to limit the number of hotels provided by foreign companies at an historic site.

Trick 9

Negotiators from poor countries are frequently excluded from critical meetings.

Trick 10

Countries cannot insist on foreign firms working jointly with domestic firms, or that a proportion of shareholders be domestic, or that some assets be held within the country to cover liability for damages.'

(Reprinted by kind permission of Alastair Sawday Publishing Co. www.sawdays.co.uk or www.fragile-earth.com)

APPENDIX IV

TIGER ECONOMIES, TIGERS AND ECONOMIES

Western media often refer to capitalism and capitalists as the 'creators of jobs' or 'creators of wealth'. This seems to make sense since employment is mostly available, in industrialised societies, at companies and other businesses, the majority of which are capitalist enterprises. Yet the Einstein quote in chapter IV referred to capitalism ensuring 'an army of unemployed'. How can both claims be true?

One reason has become so common as to now be accepted as a necessity by almost all concerned: A company makes millions of pounds profit but a few million less than in previous years. The workforce must be cut to reduce costs as part of remedial measures to regain previous levels of profit. For example, it was reported in late 2008 that the telecoms company BT would cut 10,000 jobs before the end of the financial year, despite pre-tax profits for the second quarter of that year (the latest figures then available) being £590,000,000. This type of event happens so often that even those who will be made redundant accept their loss of livelihood as due to what seems to be some law of physics. Let us pause for a moment – profits were still in the order of many millions of pounds. Even if they had been reduced to hundreds, it's still a profit i.e. that which remains after all costs and expenses have been accounted for, including salaries.

So, from one perspective, there is no need to cut the labour force and put families into dire financial straits regardless of their skills, loyalty and reliability. If the company made a loss this might be more understandable but it would still be a decision for the company owners, who might be influenced by social relationships with and loyalty to, their staff and a collective willingness to suffer leaner times together ('leaner' than £590,000,000 profit).

However, a characteristic feature of modern capitalism is that privately owned companies have long since become a tiny minority. Big companies with the largest workforces are mainly joint-stock companies – owned by shareholders. There are, of course, advantages to joint-stock companies; for example, large scale enterprises, that would be financially impossible for most private companies, become possible, whilst limiting the risk of loss for each participant to the shares they can afford to buy (even this safeguard has now been eroded. Just prior to the current financial crash, the purchase of shares could be made on 'margin' i.e. purchasing with a very small down payment and taking a loan to pay the balance). However, along with the benefits of joint-stock companies comes a separation between the owners, workers and products. It is suggested that this separation is a critical and negative factor (as it is in the previous examples of agriculture, medicine and government). In terms of joint-stock companies, separation means that shareholders may have never seen the product, the people who make it or ever lived in the locality, or even the country, where the company is located; and so are far distant, and in more than one sense. Moreover, what were once predominantly joint owners (who may have had some interest in the company they co-owned) are now mainly traders in shares – their sole purpose is to make profit by selling the shares. If, as in our example, reduced profits result in reduced value of their shares or reduced dividends, shareholders look to transfer their investment to companies offering bigger dividends or better value (higher priced) shares. So, in order to retain shareholders and the viability of the company on the stock market, a company with reduced profits cuts costs by a number of measures, including making workers redundant. This is all common practice and if we buy and sell shares according to the sole criterion of maximising our profits, we are part of this system.

Shareholders' appreciation of, or pride in the people and / or the product were concepts made redundant long before the first workers, as was a willingness to occasionally take lean when there's no fat. The current system must always produce fat, and lots of it, so that wallets can also become fat, and their owners obese (in more than one sense), while others become lean. This is a major reason why hard working, decent people are deprived of their livelihoods and join the 'army of unemployed'. Those who retain their positions are humble and grateful to be 'lucky enough' to have work and less likely to make demands on their employers lest they be replaced with those from the 'army' outside. Profit for the few takes priority over the majority's livelihoods.

Unemployment is also due to smaller businesses collapsing in recessions and depressions. 'Recessions' and 'depressions' lend an academic air to economic disasters, allowing them to be talked about as if they are expressions of natural laws, over which we have no control. In reality, they are the products of mismanagement and nearly always driven by commercial greed and stupidity. Unemployment is also caused by extensive cuts in public spending, made by governments to help the national economy survive those recessions and depressions – as in the U.K. in 2010 where drastic cuts were being made at the same time as the banks, which caused the recession, were counting their returning profits and calculating their bonuses.

Now we can resolve the apparent conflict between Einstein (and many other observers) saying capitalism creates an army of unemployed, while modern media refer to capitalism as a creator of jobs. Capitalism, due to its priorities of mass production and maximum profit for a few, creates some employment, but much more unemployment (could it be instructive that the media only refer to the first category?)

Unemployment, recessions and depressions have, of course, consequent and harmful effects, creating socio-economic, and then environmental, imbalances. For example, in the context of tiger conservation, the unemployed are often forced to utilise any remaining natural resources, including tiger habitats, for their own survival. Particular circumstances may lead to petty crimes, such as taking wood from the forest, which can escalate into serious offences when, for example, they are challenged by Forest Guards. This author has knowledge of whole villages congregating and threatening to burn down the Forest Department compound holding the confiscated wood. All manner of problems and violence are created in the forests, while a few count their profits in cities or countries many miles away.

The subtleties and complexities of stock markets may make them appear as highly sophisticated, sharp-witted business to the naïve or ill-informed and it is true that stock markets do involve abstruse and complicated features, especially since stock markets have persuaded the brightest graduates (especially mathematicians) to work for them. However, much of the complexity and sophistication arises from trying to make something from nothing, to become rich by doing nothing. Hence, from a spiritual perspective, laziness is added to greed as another symptom of spiritual illness. In the context of previous chapters, such people are trading their tigers for herd like animals or even parasites and insects – both metaphorically and literally (since insects can multiply as consequences of ecological imbalances such as extinctions of larger species).

'Herd behaviour' is also more than metaphor because it literally describes the trends behind many stock markets' peaks and troughs, despite technical explanations or pretentious labels. A 'bull' market is aptly named since it is the bovine acquiescence of many buyers clamouring to buy rising shares. This increases their price still further which, in turn, attracts more buyers. Similarly, when the herd turns the other way (a 'bear' market) the prices of particular shares tumble in self-perpetuating free-fall. These fluctuations can happen completely independently of what is happening in the real world. They are rooted in human psychology and provide another example of our theme of unhealthy extremes, since the boom is generated by the rush to attain maximum (greed) and the bust is generated by fear; the rush to shed what can only provide minimum i.e. when greed is greater than fear there is a bull market but when fear is greater than greed there is a bear market. Can a community, now a global one, ever be healthy when its economic foundations are built on greed and fear?

Boom and bust can also, of course, be triggered by real events but, again, these are not some mysterious, unidentifiable causes but often the results of stupid and / or immoral behaviour such as; selling bad debts disguised as investments, hiding debt from the balance sheets, loaning more than the total value of securities held, loaning more than the value of what is purchased by the loan, and loaning to known defaulters. The highly paid and high-powered executives who have to be, we are told, paid fantastic salary packages to secure their expertise, have presided over such practices. Consider what your decision would have been with regard to loaning thousands of dollars to somebody with neither a job nor any other form of income, no assets, poor credit history and knowing the value of the loan would be greater than the value of the asset on which it would be secured (most usually in recent years, a house). If your 'business nose' is twitching with the scent of a sure-fire deal, and your decision would be to say 'yes' to the loan, then you should surely be fired! However, those highly paid 'executives' who approved such loans for years stayed in their senior positions – contributing significantly to the financial crisis (for everybody but themselves). When such executives sold, as a 'package', these very high risk mortgages mixed with a few low risk mortgages (don't be duped by labels for these packages such as 'Structured Investment Vehicles' or 'Collateralised Debt Obligations'), they are no different to a market trader hiding mouldy turnips or rotten apples under a few good ones, selling them and rapidly moving on. At time of writing, the financial crisis has proved the financial pundits right: we really do have to pay dearly for having people of this calibre running our financial institutions.

The reader may think all such insanity is now over and lessons have been learned. However, the same practice of 're-packaging' high risk debts with mortgages and selling them on is now being repeated (The Week 19/09/09). 'Securitisation', if strictly controlled, can be a valid means by which aggregates of debt can be traded amongst banks, but strict control is precisely what is lacking, both before the crash and, incredibly, after it.

Moreover, banking practices themselves become ever further removed from the real world. For example, the value of derivatives can appear as current credit – before the future on which they are speculating, has come to pass. Prices can also fluctuate independently of real values and hence distribution of wealth within society is forever fluctuating independently of real value i.e. the energy (in terms of matter or labour) the stock represents.

Since scientists have been increasingly recruited into stock markets, they have designed computer programmes to detect tiny changes in share value, which then prompt buying or selling just ahead of the majority (HFT – High Frequency Trading or simply high-speed trading. Details from The Week 18/09/10). Two-tenths of a second is sufficient to give an advantage, which may only translate into pennies gained but, over many millions of transactions, pennies accumulate into millions of pounds. Of course, all the largest companies now use these computer programmes, leaving average and private investors with distinct disadvantages, while increasing the pace of the whole mad race trying to gain something for nothing. Ultimately all is at the expense of the environment...and then life on earth, including investment firms and shareholders.

Since shareholders are not computers it might be thought that they could collaborate to reverse the trends they have established; they could *choose* to be satisfied with less than maximum, *choose* to tolerate lean times with the workers, *choose* not to follow the herd etc. However, such developments only offer slim hopes of having any significant effect as share ownership has become divided between a minority of shareholders with massive shareholdings (e.g. pension companies) and a majority of shareholders with relatively few shares each (moreover, most shareholders, traditionally, were individuals who bought with their own money, now companies buy shares using other people's money. The same pattern prevails in banking insofar as traditional merchant banks used, and risked, their own money on their investments. Since the recent mingling of retail and merchant banking, other people's money is gambled). So, even when the *majority of shareholders* vote for a particular action, *majority shareholdings* determine the result. Those with majority shareholdings may even be sitting on the boards of other businesses, whose major shareholders are the directors of the former company, so sub-groups appear which make decisions to favour themselves, regardless of other shareholders, staff, customers, citizens, governments – or tiger habitat. These are just a few of the ways in which capitalism compromises environmental and social security.

At risk of being repetitive, the only influence left to us is to choose which products we purchase from which company. We began by looking at falling profits provoking redundancies. Obviously, reducing profits by withholding our custom must result in redundancies, so how will this help? It can help since our selective custom will be making other companies expand and seek more labour. These companies will be respecting the environment and observing ethical conduct. We may even prompt the revival of people buying shares in companies that make or do something they are interested in or passionate about, and they would find more than monetary rewards in the product or service (partly because, following nature and morality, their product or service is good for all) or, perhaps, in the skill, sheer hard work of the employees, pride in good workmanship, high standards and customer satisfaction. Weathering storms together can weld more than metal in such factories. With this sort of ownership, a company will usually become successful in the long-term (and make money!)

In the meantime the global system of capitalism, dominated by stock markets, the WTO, IMF and World Bank, has impoverished a significant proportion of the world's population. This (in Asia) is threatening the tiger's continued existence, since those threats are produced by the socio-economic conditions of people living in or near tiger habitat.

For decades Western corporations have taken advantage of the relatively cheap labour in developing countries, rather than employ their own citizens, who need higher wages. This factor has combined with other aspects of deregulation and globalisation to allow these nations and their businesses to become significant and powerful global economies, some in Asia having been called 'tiger economies'. Sadly, these businesses are following exactly the same pattern as Western capitalism, with the same old, injurious emphasis on maximum profit for a few in minimum time. H.G. Wells referred to the possibilities of 'economic life without the wasting disease of profiteering' but virtually all capitalist economies now have this wasting disease. What have been called 'tiger economies' will soon be minus the tiger, and soon after that, minus the economies, since the source of all wealth is the natural environment, which is being seriously damaged as a consequence of improperly regulated capitalism. While the distribution of wealth via man-made systems is imbalanced, nature's systems will restore balance by bringing about their collapse.

Stock markets now represent a major index of economic health for many communities. A rapid fall in share prices (much of which, as we saw above, is man-made and born of greed, fear, laziness and stupidity) is dramatically intoned in news reports, and that day labelled as 'black' for the history books. If, collectively, we had any sense, 'black' days should be identified as those on which another forest falls, more topsoil disappears, species are declared extinct etc. – and for many reasons but, in this context, if only because stock markets are based on the environment.

Media and some apologists for people on extremely large 'salary packages' also attach the 'creators of wealth' label to individuals, trying to cover greed's ugly nakedness with implications of rare abilities from which we all benefit. Firstly, we know that all wealth is created by nature. Human enterprise can harvest it, transform it, and distribute it, but humans can never create it. Secondly, some of the largest salary packages are those of senior personnel in banks, financial houses and investment brokers, such as those 'creators of wealth' we have just considered 'selling rotten apples' and crashing economies. Thirdly, much investment is not only unethical but also causes serious damage to natural ecosystems – the source of all wealth as just identified in the first point. So, in reality, the vast majority of wealth created by the current system is short-term, for a few people, and is preparing poverty for all in the long-term. Other wealth can be generated by technology but again this is for the few who own it. They use it to access or generate vast markets and thereby acquire monopolies, forcing consumers to comply with their prices, product or service range. In addition, technology replaces human workers and thereby increases unemployment.

An exclusive focus on money, as opposed to the work which earns it, can gradually change what we mean by 'earn'. We all know, physically, mentally and spiritually when we have earned our due. Hence we know it is often ridiculous to refer to the lucrative salary and bonus packages of senior corporate personnel as having been 'earned'. They are merely 'received'. Some may counter that, for example, wealthy financiers work hard; put in long hours at an office and tolerate associated stress and responsibility. This may be so, just as it is for millions of others. However, lucrative salary and bonus packages can represent, from global perspectives, one million times (or more!) what is earned by low paid workers, yet it is impossible for any one human being to work one million times harder than another (or be one million times more intelligent, or responsible, or skilled, or whatever…) Differentials are fine and can be justified on the basis of incentives and / or genuine disparities in ability and / or effort but they need to be kept within margins as revealed to us by nature, common sense, compassion and care for each other and our communities. Those on lucrative salary and bonus packages are actually *receiving* rewards *earned* by other people and / or due to monopolising a resource 'owned' by all. Receiving more than is earned leads to obesity (not necessarily, or only, physically) and, as an old saying has it, if one receives something for nothing, somebody else might suffer. Billions – not pounds; people – suffer daily. A primary focus on people, with a secondary focus on money, brings health and life. A primary focus on money brings disease, damage and deaths.

Capitalism can create wealth for a community if governments enforce fair taxation, distribution of profits and legal constraints (most importantly; environmental protection). So capitalism's ability to 'create wealth' holds some truth but, when controlled by the few and greedy, governments are manipulated, tax evaded, legislation changed or avoided, profits hoarded, and the environment abused. As power and influence grow, competition can be bought out or eliminated. These factors imbalance the scales still further and widen the financial gap between ever-fewer, ever-richer rich people and ever-more numerous, poorer poor people. The widening gap between the rich and obese and the skeletal poor provides the most graphic example of imbalance in the global community. As levels of inequality increase, so does social unrest and society becomes increasingly dysfunctional. Ultimately the system as a whole starts to break down either economically (financial depressions or severe recessions), socially (general strikes; social welfare cannot cope with the needy; judicial system cannot cope with increasing law-breakers; street riots) and / or environmentally (abuse of life-support systems leads to breakdowns of those systems). Unless controlled by strict and enforced legislation, capitalism will create poverty for all.

APPENDIX V

THE MAXIMA AND MINIMA OF SCIENCE AND THE CALCULUS OF COMPASSION

As mentioned in Chapter II, science can be a fascinating and, when used properly, useful human discipline. However, it is increasingly represented, particularly by the media, as the only source of truth, encouraging a sense of dependence upon it, if not intimidation by it. There's nothing wrong with science in and of itself, but we currently use it in an imbalanced way and have allowed it to become a dominant force within society. Once again, agriculture offers a good example: corporate interests used scientific development and endorsement of pesticides, fungicides and herbicides to convince farmers to use them and governments to subsidise them. Within the constraints of the research and its applications, the chemicals produced the required results: abundant and massive crops - before the farmers' eyes. Few, if any, businessmen or scientists investigated or were even interested in the long-term effects on the soil, micro-organisms, plants, animals, the wider environment and man. Science did its job within the limits set for it by vested interests but might well have warned of dangerous ramifications and repercussions, had it not been confined to particular agendas. In the context of 'purpose' we see the critical importance of human values, since the purpose for which science is used will determine what it finds. If science does represent a pure and independent method of investigation in a philosophical sense, it is forever constrained by the limitations and / or the agendas of the humans who fund and practise it. Rather than learn the lesson, science (in the context of our example) now seeks cures for diseases caused by chemical poisons, instead of helping us find our way back to naturally healthy arrangements.

Science and technology give rise to material benefits and power. Inevitably therefore military, commercial and political interests largely dominate its development. This results in scientific research being restricted almost exclusively to the material world - the only concern of military, commercial and political agendas, usually concerned only with the exploitation of nature. Science, as currently practised, is also freed, by agreement, from ethical considerations, while providing an increasing power and control to its practitioners and sponsors.

This trend developed most rapidly during and after the Enlightenment (referred to briefly below) but it reminds us of Koestler referring to the invention of the telescope (just pre-dating the

Enlightenment of the 17-18th centuries): 'It was indeed a new departure. The range and power of the main sense organ of *homo sapiens* had suddenly started to grow in leaps to thirty times, a hundred times, a thousand times its natural capacity. Parallel leaps and bounds in the range of other organs were soon to transform the species into a race of giants in power - without enlarging his moral stature by an inch. It was a monstrously one-sided mutation – as if moles were growing to the size of whales, but retaining the instincts of moles…the intellectual giants of the scientific revolution were moral dwarfs. They were, of course, neither better nor worse than the average of their contemporaries. They were moral dwarfs only in proportion to their intellectual greatness. It may be thought unfair to judge a man's character by the standard of his intellectual achievements, but the great civilizations of the past did precisely this; the divorce of moral from intellectual values is itself a characteristic development of the last few centuries. It is fore-shadowed in the philosophy of Galileo, and became fully explicit in the ethical neutrality of modern determinism. The indulgence with which historians of science treat the Founding Fathers is based on precisely that tradition which the Fathers introduced – the tradition of keeping intellect and character as strictly apart as Galileo taught us to separate the "primary" and "secondary" qualities of objects. Thus moral assessments are thought to be essential in the case of Cromwell or Danton, but irrelevant in the case of Galileo, Descartes or Newton. However, the scientific revolution produced not only discoveries, but a new attitude to life, a change in the philosophical climate. And on that new climate, the personalities and beliefs of those who initiated it had a lasting influence. The most pronounced of these influences, in their different fields, were Galileo's and Descartes'' (B43 Excerpt from The Sleepwalkers (© 1959 The Estate of Arthur Koestler) is reproduced by permission of PFD (www.pfd.co.uk) on behalf of The Estate of Arthur Koestler.)

Now a new climate is (literally!) being produced by the products and processes of industrialised multinationals. The combination of capitalism, science and technology has greatly magnified power in the hands of a few senior executives whose moral stature has not increased proportionately to that power. Since the sorts of people seeking these positions are not usually paragons of virtue, the disproportion between vastly increased power and moral stature makes an even more exaggerated contrast than would be the case for their average contemporary. Today the power acquired is such that the decisions of a few individuals have effects on global scales of magnitude - but they are most often prompted by the smallest and meanest of personal motives. Despite this, morality may have remained alive and well had religious morals remained a foundation on which people built their lives. However, '…The mechanical universe could accommodate no transcendental factor. Theology and physics parted ways not in anger, but in sorrow…because they became bored with and had nothing more to say to each other…To…science, the parting of the ways seemed at the beginning to be an unmitigated boon. Freed from mystical ballast, science could sail ahead at breathtaking speed to its conquest of new lands beyond every dream. Within two centuries it transformed the mental outlook of *homo sapiens* and transformed the face of his planet. But the price paid was proportionate: it carried the species to the brink of physical self-destruction, and into an equally unprecedented spiritual impasse. Sailing without ballast, reality gradually dissolved between the physicist's hands; matter itself evaporated from the materialist's universe…in the two centuries that followed, the vanishing act continued. Each of the "ultimate" and "irreducible" primary qualities of the world of physics proved in its turn to be an illusion. The hard atoms of matter went up in fireworks; the concepts of substance, force, of effects determined by causes, and ultimately the very framework of space and time turned out to be as illusory as the "tastes, odours and colours" which Galileo had treated so contemptuously. Each advance in physical theory, with its rich technological harvest, was bought by a loss in intelligibility. These losses on the intellectual balance sheet, however, were much less in evidence than the spectacular gains; they were light-heartedly accepted as passing clouds which the next advance would dissolve.' (B43 Excerpt from *The Sleepwalkers* (© 1959 The Estate of Arthur Koestler) is reproduced by permission of PFD (www.pfd.co.uk) on behalf of The Estate of Arthur Koestler.)

Well, even if science is practised without morality, surely we can rely on commerce and / or the State to oversee developments to ensure its moral and virtuous use? Unfortunately, we cannot. Even prior to the divorce of science from morality, an increasingly wealthy Commerce parted company with morality as part of the enormous social changes wrought by the Reformation (16th century). Despite the efforts of, for examples, Luther and Calvin, this period saw commercialism triumph over traditional Christian values while greater and greater fortunes accumulated into fewer and fewer hands. For example; the charging of interest on money became legal and widespread. Previously it had been forbidden by the social ethics of Christianity and, for example, in Florence, Italy, the financial capital of mediaeval Europe, bankers were fined for charging interest, while in Coventry, England, it was on a par with adultery and fornication. Economic and commercial conduct formed an important part of maintaining traditional standards of personal morality (B68). Today in England, Italy and most of the Western world, charging interest, adultery and fornication are all practised as a normal part of life and no connections are noted, or even noticed, between their consequences and nature's environmental mirror. With regard to charging interest, an overwhelming majority of modern societies have forgotten there is a choice, but there are a few 'alternative' banks which do not charge or pay interest – the JAK bank in Sweden for example. It began in Denmark but these banks are strongly opposed by the other banks since, whilst interest-free banking has economic benefits for the society in which they occur, interest-charging banks would lose out financially (B10 by kind permission of Alastair Sawday Publishing Co.). We have already considered in chapter V some of the dangers of compound interest accruing indefinitely.

An increasing separation between the State and religious morals followed the Renaissance (15th and 16th centuries), Reformation and Enlightenment and has, in the majority of nations, been growing wider right up to the present day. However, the State has not adopted any independent form of philosophical alternative as a basis for its operations but has increasingly come under the influence of commerce, which has been eager to maintain any split between State and Church. Since all nations on Earth now practice some form of capitalism, the power of commerce is dominant, yet few call for a separation between State and Commerce.

When material is the overwhelmingly dominant factor, be it in the State, science, commerce or life in general, it represents 'the pendulum' at one end of its swing. The restricted view from this position means that more traditional views of life can no longer be seen. However, adopting this position, and divorcing commerce and science from morality (as has the West in particular) was, and still is, a choice. Nothing has been revealed in Scripture or discovered by science that indicates they must be separated.

Nor is there any necessity for science to be divorced from religion. In fact, closer examination reveals they are not in conflict. The supposed points of difference, compared to the complementary corpus each represents for the other, are minor and cannot bear the weight given them by those who gain materially or personally by promoting the artificial schism. The supposed points of difference have been magnified disproportionately.

As religion and morality continued to separate from trading and banking, workers were being replaced by the new technology of the industrial revolution, while profits and power concentrated in the pockets and hands of a few businessmen. The vast majority of people lost their skills and the security of their medieval social structures. Many were dispossessed of the land on which their lives had been self-sufficient, and where their domestic animals had been treated with care and respect. (Within a couple of centuries, animal husbandry had become battery hens and closely confined cattle, pigs and sheep, mechanised milking, artificial insemination, and injections of drugs and hormones. The industrialisation of farming and our food is the industrialisation of life – little wonder that we have become near identical numbered products in the society it produces.) Mass unformity and mass unemployment followed, and the jobless and homeles migrated to cities and towns in hope of finding work, more often than not as general labourers (a process currently being repeated in various 'developing' countries).

The Reformation, the Enlightenment and the Industrial Revolution did not, of course, happen overnight. These mass movements were preceded by the Renaissance, which is usually seen only as a marvellous revival of classical art, literature and learning. However, it too contained some unhealthy seeds which would sprout during the Reformation e.g. individual artists and artisans began to be replaced by general labourers (building, say, a repeating pattern of arches and pillars along a façade) and elements (identified by Ruskin) of conformity and uniformity began to prevail in art and life. (In the preceding Gothic style of mediaeval times, architecture and construction, for examples, had studied the human relationship with nature. Gothic architecture reflected human unity and integration with nature, views shared by both rulers and ruled.) The Renaissance saw growing divisions between rich patrons and poor labourers and the distancing of all people from nature.

The Renaissance (15th - 16th centuries) and the Reformation (16th century) preceded the Enlightenment (17-18th centuries), which saw vigorous developments in the pursuit and practice of reason and the scientific method. In 'Civilisation' Clark comments that the Enlightenment's emphasis on reason and empiricism produced great achievements yet, with the exception of Carlyle and Ruskin, no writers apparently noticed it had also produced the demise of crafts and skills, the darkest sides of industrial society and economics that ensured the rich became richer.

We live within strict constraints of time and energy so whenever yang is over-emphasised, yin must be under-emphasised. If the pendulum is disturbed it can only move in one direction.

The enormous social changes of the Renaissance, Reformation and Enlightenment moved the pendulum toward technology and an exclusive rationalisation of our experiences and our interpretation of nature in general. The pendulum moved so rapidly it travelled past the ideal balance point and, up to and including modern society, Intellect (used in the sense of pure reason) gained such favour as to occasionally, if not regularly, let go of its brother's hand altogether (referring to the Oscar Wilde quote in chapter IV). In the modern world, Intellect might even sneer at its brother dismissively (in the context of yin and yang, we should say 'sister'). Not only is this improper in itself but, like all arrogance, it forgets that it is inseparably connected with everything else, that it too needs, as part of the whole, what it sneers at. The whole is only healthy when the constituent elements are in a balanced relationship. Leaving its sibling meant that Intellect left all but reason and '…after throwing off the shackles of canon and dogma, (*Intellect found*) fresh slavery for itself in scientific formalism.' (B65) We now worship Science and are confined by our devotion to its dogma. Despite the efforts of the Romantics, the Enlightenment reduced all of our varied experience to reason alone and so, in some significant ways, led us into a new dark age. '…it is strange that the very first recorded system of philosophy in the world, the very first attempt to solve the Great Question by the light of reason alone, should differ scarcely at all from the last. The human brain fails now, as it failed then.' (B65) From our explorations, we can now see that it is not so strange, since reason working alone will always fail us - because we neither work, nor live, by reason alone. Similarly to the suggestion in chapter IV of a 'Capcomm party' in politics, maybe we need a new discipline of 'Sci-relig' (to replace the current sacrilege?!)

This extremely brief historical tour is to emphasise that the current 'conventional wisdoms' and dominance of science and technology, seemingly so solid and immovable, are relatively recent developments, merely a few centuries old, and represent the view from one end of the pendulum's swing. We still have a choice to re-balance the pendulum. It is not intended here to denigrate the Enlightenment's achievements or the powers of reason. The only intention is to bring balance by paying equal regard to intuition, emotion, religion, yin; to encourage religion and rationalism, to join hands once more for the health of both; for Earth; for life.

The pendulum has swung between heart and head, religion and science (when the latter is portrayed as atheistic), social responsibility and personal greed, before now. Why should our present position, at the end of the last major swing, be worth any special attention? Why not wait for the next swing? The important difference is that now the scale of our influence is global and there may not be another swing – well, not in any way that we want to imagine. The analogy of the pendulum also incorporates the idea of ticking off, the counting down, of nature's patience.

In the television series 'Civilisation' Sir Kenneth Clark examined examples of the first complex, man-made scientific instruments made during the Enlightenment, and considered that answers to enquiries as to whether something will work or pay are different to answers to enquiries as to whether or not it is God's will. He says that only in recent decades are we beginning to sense that these various beautiful instruments and their offspring will bring about our downfall. Tennyson told of his surprise at a Brahmin destroying a microscope because it revealed secrets man should not be privy to (Tennyson, H. *Alfred Lord Tennyson: A Memoir*. Macmillan. London 1898). Perhaps Tennyson (1809 – 1892) thought we had outgrown the view still prevalent in Chaucer's time (1342 – 1400), referred to in the Canterbury Tales, advising us that 'One shouldn't be too inquisitive in life, Either about God's secrets or one's wife. You'll find God's plenty all you could desire; Of the remainder better not enquire' and 'God has some secrets that we shouldn't know. How blessed are the simple, aye, indeed, That only know enough to say their creed!' Even Einstein commented: "It is strange that science, which in the old days seemed harmless, should have evolved into a nightmare that causes everyone to tremble."

Science and modern technology have provided the means for virtually instant total destruction with nuclear forces. They have also allowed us to damage and degrade the environment globally whilst seducing us into thinking that we are clever and in control. At the same time, science can encourage us to believe that adherence to common and / or religious codes of morality is a consequence of primitive superstitions and that we can rely on our own judgements, including personal 'value judgements' (which supposedly include morals and virtues).

In contrast, one universal impression, agreed by anyone who studies nature (including some scientists), whether for minutes or decades, is that of our overwhelming ignorance, and that we had best adapt ourselves to nature as our guide (as plainly perceptible to our unaided senses by attentive proximity to nature) along with morality and virtue – which are neither primitive, nor subject to individuals' opinions or values.

Since human history began, history has been teaching us that we are, in the main, the authors of our lives. Maybe many civilisations have preceded our currently known history of civilisation beginning approximately 7000–10,000 years ago. From what we know of civilisations within this time period, we find that they deteriorated due to internal imbalances. However, the fall of previous civilisations were geographically confined. The one we are orchestrating now is global and, as the very institutions developed to protect us are the elements most seriously imbalanced, civilisation now depends on each and everyone making their choices and taking action, however relatively small that action may be, to promote the well-being of society. Whether we are selling turnips to each other, or technology to nation states, conducting ourselves without regard for morality, will ensure our activities are ultimately harmful to the buyers…and, since all things are connected…the sellers, the turnips, the technology…tigers…and everything else on the planet – 'What goes around comes around'. The divorce of morality from our conduct in science, business, commerce or any other activity is the most dangerous detour from the path of prosperity for individuals, society and the environment. Following the guides as mentioned, takes the focus of attention away from self; develops character and mutually supportive characters; while knitting the community into a healthy, wholesome unit.

Books on the Enlightenment, concerned only with the development of reason tend, for obvious reasons, to describe it as a dawning light leading us out from primitive and purblind ignorance. Technically and practically this view can be justified, but other essential elements of life were lost in darkness. Without the ballast of these other elements, reason operating alone will imbalance the whole, until it reaches an extreme position and triggers a backlash - and all imbalances must be temporary because they make the pendulum move.

By caring for other people and life forms, facing our personal and moral responsibilities, balancing reason with intuition, we eliminate extremes, the maxima and minima, and as a result, well-proportioned characters grow exponentially – the calculus of compassion.

Although (at the same time as Leibniz) Newton discovered the calculus, perhaps the calculus of compassion is at least part of, by his own account, that 'ocean of truth which lay all undiscovered' before him. In the face of nature, practically and spiritually speaking, we are as small children. Paddling at the edge of that ocean of truth, we may compare our views more healthily and usefully, and with mutual co-operation, by keeping yin and yang in harmony, and making sure Intellect does not let go of his sister's hand.

Detail from the painting '94 Degrees in the Shade' by Sir Lawrence Alma-Tadema, OM, RA (1836–1912)
(With thanks to Bridgeman Art Library)

BIBLIOGRAPHY

Books (when quoted in the main text are identified by a 'B' followed by a number, corresponding to their listing below)

1) Ableman, M.   From the Good Earth.
   Thames and Hudson. London 1993

2) Alexander, R. McNeill   Animal Mechanics.
   Sidgwick and Jackson. London 1968

3) Allen, Hugh   The Lonely Tiger.
   Faber & Faber. London. 1960

4) Bazé, William   Tiger! Tiger!
   Elek Books.London 1957

5) Best, J.W.   Tiger Days.
   John Murray. London 1931

6) Beston, Henry.   The Outermost House.
   Selwyn & Blunt. London. 1928

7) Blixen, Karen   Out of Africa.
   Putnam & Co. Ltd. London. 1937

8) Brander, A.A. Dunbar   Wild Animals in Central India.
   Edward Arnold. London 1923

9) Briggs, J.C.   Francis Bacon and the Rhetoric of Nature.
   Harvard University Press 1989

10) Bruges, James.   The Little Earth Book.
   Sawday Publishing Co. Ltd. Bristol. 2005

11) Buch, M.N.   The Forests of Madhya Pradesh.
   Madhya Pradesh Madhyam, Bhopal, India. 1991

12) Burton, R.G.   The Book of the Tiger.
   Hutchinson & Co. London 1933

13) Capra, F. The Turning Point.
  Simon & Schuster. New York 1982

14) Carson, R. Silent Spring.
  Houghton Mifflin Co. U.S.A. 1962

15) Christie, John. Morning Drum.
  BACSA 1983

16) Clark, K. Civilisation.
  BBC and John Murray. London 1969
  Animals and Men.
  Morrow & Co.inc. New York 1977

17) Cooper, James Fennimore The Last of the Mohicans.
  Carey & Lea U.S.A. 1826

18) Corbett, Jim. Man-Eaters of Kumaon. O.U.P. 1946
  Man-Eating Leopard of Rudrayprayag. O.U.P. 1948
  My India. O.U.P. 1952
  Jungle Lore. O.U.P. 1953
  The Temple Tiger. O.U.P. 1954

19) Curtis, Helena Biology.
  Worth Publishers Inc.NewYork 1968

20) Dale, T. and Carter, V.G. Topsoil and Civilization.
  University of Oklahoma Press. 1955

21) Denis, A. Cats of the World.
  Constable. London. 1964

22) Doyle, C.W. Dr. The Taming of the Jungle
  Archibald Constable. London 1899

23) Durant, W. The Story of Philosophy.
  Simon and Schuster. New York 1926

24) Eddington, Sir A. Space, Time and Gravitation.
  C.U.P. 1920

25) Einstein, A. Out of my Later Years.
  Philosophical Library. N. York 1950

26) Ewer, R.F. The Carnivores.
  Weidenfeld & Nicolson.London1973

27) Fölsing, Albrecht

Albert Einstein.
Viking 1997

28) Föllmi, Olivier

India.
Harry N. Abrams. New York 2005
Excerpt from the Introduction by Radhika Jha

29) Gelbspan, Ross

Boiling Point: How Politicians, Big Oil and Coal, Journalists and Activists Are Fueling the Climate Crisis – And What We Can Do to Avert Disaster.
Basic Books (2004)
The Heat Is On: The Climate Crisis, the Cover-Up, the Prescription.
Perseus Books Group; Updated 1998

30) Gordon-Cumming, R.G.

Wild Men and Wild Beasts.
Edmonston & Douglas. Edinburgh 1871

31) Haining, P.

The Spitfire Log.
Souvenir Press. London 1985

32) Hamilton, E. and Cairns, Huntingdon. (Eds.)

Plato: The Collected Dialogues.
Princeton University Press 1961

33) Hanley, P.

Tiger Trails in Assam.
Robert Hale & Co. London, 1961

34) Huxley, Aldous.

The Perennial Philosophy.
Chatto & Windus, London 1946

35) Jepson, Stanley (ed.)

Big Game Encounters.
H.F.&G. Witherby Ltd.London 1936

36) Jones, Henry.

Browning as a Philosophical and Religious Teacher.
Thomas Nelson and Sons. c. 1891

40) Jung, C.G.

Memories, Dreams, Reflections.
Collins and Routledge & Kegan Paul. London 1963

41) Kala, D.C.

Jim Corbett of Kumaon. Ankur Publishing House, New Delhi 1979

42) Kipling, Rudyard.

(a) The Jungle Book. Macmillan & Co.1895
(b) Captains Courageous. Macmillan & Co.1897
(c) Kim. Macmillan & Co.1901

43) Koestler, Arthur

The Sleepwalkers.
Hutchinson. London 1959

44) Leyhausen, Paul   Cat Behaviour.
Garland Press. New York 1979

45) Levinson, Charles   Vodka Cola.
Gordon & Cremonesi London. 1979

46) Linzey, Andrew and   Animals on the Agenda.
    Dorothy Yamamoto (eds.)   University of Illinois Press 1998

47) London, Jack   (a) The Call of the Wild. Macmillan 1903
(b) The Sea Wolf. Macmillan 1904
(c) White Fang. Macmillan 1906

48) Lorenz, K. and   Motivation of Human and Animal Behaviour.
    Leyhausen, P.   Van Nostrand Reinhold. 1973

49) Marshall, Edison   Shikar and Safari.
Museum Press. London. 1950

50) McDougal, Charles   The Face of the Tiger.
Rivington Deutsch. 1977

51) Moore Lappé and Collins   World Hunger: Twelve Myths.
Grove Press. New York 1986

52) Moray, N.   Attention: Selective Processes in Vision and Hearing.
Hutchinson Educational.London 1969

53) Perry, Richard   World of the Tiger.
Cassell. London 1964

54) Quennell, Marjorie   Everyday Things in Archaic Greece
    and C.H.B.   B.T. Batsford Ltd. 1931

55) Ross, Nancy Wilson.   Three Ways of Asian Wisdom.
Simon & Schuster. 1966

56) Russell, Bertrand   Portraits from Memory.
Allen & Unwin Ltd. 1956

57) Shaffer, P.   Equus.
André Deutsch. London 1973

58) Schaller, George B.   (a) The Deer and the Tiger. University of Chicago Press. 1967
(b) The Serengeti Lion. University of Chicago Press. 1972
(c) Serengeti: A Kingdom of Predators. Collins. London 1973.

59) Schumacher, E.F.   Small is Beautiful.
            Blond & Briggs Ltd. London 1973

60) Seymour, John.   Getting it Together.
            Michael Joseph 1980

61) Singer, June.   Blake, Jung and the Collective Unconscious.
            Nicolas-Hays inc.Maine U.S.A. 2000

62) Smith, Anthony   The Body.
            Viking 1986

63) Smythies, E.A.   Big Game Shooting in Nepal.
            Thacker & Co, Calcutta. 1942

64) Standing Bear, Luther Land of the Spotted Eagle.
            Houghton Mifflin. U.S.A. 1933

65) Steel, Flora. A.   India through the Ages.
            Routledge & Sons. London 1908

66) Steinbeck, J.   The Grapes of Wrath.
            Viking Penguin U.S.A. 1939

67) Szamosi, G.   The Twin Dimensions.
            McGraw-Hill 1986

68) Tawney, R.L.   Religion and the Rise of Capitalism.
            John Murray. London 1926

69) Vessantara   Tales of Freedom.
            Windhorse Publications 2000

70) Walker, D.   Harry Black.
            Collins. London 1956

71) Wardrop, A.E.   Days and Nights with Indian Big Game.
            Macmillan and Co., Limited 1923

72) Watts, P.M.   Nicolaus Cusa: A Fifteenth Century Vision of Man.
            E.J. Brill. Leiden 1982

73) Whitrow, G.J.   Einstein: The Man and his Achievement.
            Dover Publication, Inc. New York 1973

74) Wheen, F.   How Mumbo Jumbo Conquered the World.
            Fourth Estate. London. 2004

Articles and Papers from Journals (when quoted in the main text are identified by a 'J' followed by a number, corresponding to their listing below)

1) Abbot, D.H., Baines, D.A., Faulkes, C.G. Jennens, D.C., Ning, P.C.Y.K. and Tomlinson, A.J. 'A Natural Deer Repellent: Chemistry and Behaviour' *'Chemical Signals in Vertebrates'*. Kluwer academic / Plenum Publishers New York

2) Asa, Cheryl. S. (1993) Relative Contributions of Urine and Anal-Sac Secretions in Scent Marks of Large Felids. *Amer. Zool.*, 33:167-172

3) Beauchamp, G.K., Yamazaki, K. and Boyse, (1985). The chemosensory recognition of genetic individuality. *Sci. Amer.*, July, 66-72.

4) Bertram, B.C.R. (1975) Social factors influencing reproduction in wild lions. *J. Zool., Lond.* 177, 463 – 482

5) Bradshaw C. J.A., Warkentin I. G., Sodhi N. S. (2009) Urgent preservation of boreal carbon stocks and biodiversity. *Trends in Ecology & Evolution*, Vol. 24, Issue 10: 541-548

6) Didier, R (1950) Etude systématique de l'os pénien des mammifères: Famille des Félidés. *Mammalia* 14, 78-94

7) Eaton, R.L.
   - (1970) Hunting behaviour of the cheetah. *J. Wildl. Mgmt.* 34, 56 – 57
   - (1970) The predatory sequence, with emphasis on killing behaviour and its ontogeny, in the cheetah (Acinonyx jubatus Schreber). *Ibid.* 27, 492 – 504

8) Eccles, R. (1982) Autonomic innervation of the vomeronasal organ of the cat. *Physiol Behav* 28: 1011 – 1015

9) Eccles, R.M., Phillips, C.G., & Wu, C.P. (1968) Motor innervation, motor unit organisation and afferent innervation of M. extensor digitorum communis of the baboon's forearm. *J. Physiol.* 198, 179 – 92

10) Fitch W.T. and Reby, D. (2001) Laryngeal descent in deer. *Proc. R. Soc. Lond. B* pp.1669 – 1675

11) Hepper, P.G. (1987). The discrimination of different degrees of relatedness in the rat: evidence for a genetic identifier. *Anim. Behav.*, 35, 549-54.

12) Hernandez-Péon, R., Scherrer, R. H. & Jouvet, M. (1956) Modification of electrical activity in the cochlear nucleus during "attention" in unanesthetized cats. *Science*, 123: 331–32.

13) Holecamp, K.E., and L. Smale. (1995) Rapid change in offspring sex ratios after clan fission in the Spotted Hyena. *The American Naturalist* 145, no.2: 261-262

14) Jerge, C.R. (1963) Organisation and function of the trigeminal mesencephalic nucleus. *J. Neurophysiol.* 26, 379 – 92

15) Kruuk, W. & Turner, M. (1967) Comparative notes on predation by lion, leopard, cheetah and wild dog in the Serengeti area, East Africa. *Mammalia* 31, 1 – 27

16) Lepri, J.J., Wysocki, C.J., Gerber, K. and Lisk, R.D. 'The Vomeronasal Organ of the Prairie Vole: Role in Chemosignal Activation of Female Reproduction and Observations of Fine Structure' *'Chemical Signals in Vertebrates'*. Kluwer academic / Plenum Publishers New York

17) Leyhausen, Paul.
    a) (1965) The Communal Organisation of Solitary Mammals. *Symp. Zool. Soc* 14, 249-262
    b) (1965) Uber die Funktion der relativen Stimmungshierarchie (dargestellt am Beispiel der phylogenetischen und ontogenetischen Entwicklung des Beute-fangs von Raubtieren). *Z. Tierpsychol.* 22, 412-94

18) Lopez, Barry. The Language of Animals. *Wild Earth* Vol. 8 No.2 (POB 455, Richmond, Vt 05477, U.S.A.)

19) Melese-d'Hospital, P.Y. and Hart, B. (1985) Vomeronasal Organ Canulation in Male Goats: Evidence for Transport of Fluid from Oral Cavity to Vomeronasal Organ During Flehmen. *Physiology & Behavior* Vol. 35, pp. 941-944.

20) Müller-Schwarze, D. 'Leading them by Their Noses: Animal and Plant Odours for Managing Vertebrates' *'Chemical Signals in Vertebrates'*. Kluwer academic / Plenum Publishers New York

21) Packer, C. et al. (2005) Ecological Change, Group Territoriality and Population Dynamics in Serengeti Lions. *Science* Vol. 307 pp. 390-393

22) Perry, Ted. (1971/2) Modified and embellished version of Chief Seattle's 1854 Treaty Oration. Please also see reference to Smith, Dr. Henry A.

23) Rasmussen, L.E.L. and Hultgren, B. 'Gross and Microscopic Anatomy of the Vomeronasal Organ in the Asian Elephant (Elephus maximus)' *'Chemical Signals in Vertebrates'*. Kluwer academic / Plenum Publishers New York

24) Ren, L. Miller, C. Lair, R. Hutchinson, J.R. (2010) Integration of biomechanical compliance, leverage and power in elephant limbs. *Proceedings of the National Academy of Sciences,* U.S.A..

25) Rogers, Peter. Facing the Freshwater Crisis. *Scientific American.* August 2008 pp. 28-35

26) Smith, Dr. Henry A. (1854) Chief Seattle's Treaty Oration Ver.1 Column in *Seattle Sunday Star* October 29th 1887.

27) Stoddart, M. (1980) Vertebrate Olfaction. *Endeavour, New Series* Volume 5 No.1 Pergamon Press.

28) Taylor, A. & Davey, M.R. (1968) Behaviour of jaw muscle stretch receptors during active and passive movements in the cat. *Nature Lond.* 220, 301 – 2

29) Ward, A.E. (Dec. 1951) A Cushion for a Tiger. *The Lantern* (staff magazine of Oxford University Press) vol. XVIII no. 3 pp. 66-9

30) Weisbrot, M. (2002) The Mirage of Progress. *The American Prospect* Vol. 13 No.1.

31) Weissengruber, G.E., Forstenpointner, G., Peters, G., Kübber-Heiss, A., Fitch, W.T. (2002) Hyoid apparatus and pharynx in the lion (Panthera leo), jaguar (Panthera onca), tiger (Panthera tigris), cheetah (Acinonyx jubatus) and domestic cat (Felis silvestris f. catus). *Journal of Anatomy* 201 (3) , 195–209.

Acknowledgements

With thanks to Jonathan Gordon and Lesley Williams for much appreciated accommodation in England while a significant proportion of this book was written.

Thanks also to Andrew Thompson for reading an early manuscript of this book, and to Michael Martin for proof reading a later and full manuscript.

For help with editing some images, thanks go to Jason Powell and Stuart Bebb (www.stuartbebb.com).

Photo Credits

pp. 302, 304, 306, 362 Giles Clark

p. 120 Albert Einstein and related rights ™/© of HUJ. Represented exclusively by GreenLight, LLC

pp. viii, 8 (tree against moon), 14, 35, 130, 135-6 (without starburst and amber colour), 207, 233, 244, 263, 292, 339, 346, 351, 407, 421, 424, 465, 519 and cover image www.istockphoto.com

pp. 26, 198, 231, 250 Adrian Macer (www.mdhphotos.com)

pp. 89, 97, 104, 120 Oxford University Press

p. 331 Satpuda Foundation (www.satpuda.org)

pp. 60, 103, 105, 114, 121-6, 156. 160-1, 168, 191-2, 197, 240-1, 288, 336, 354, 396, 456-7 Andrew Thompson

pp. 5, 17, 18, 29 (L.R.), 53, 78-9, 115, 146-7, 177, 185, 186-7, 210, 216-7, 221, 237, 243, 266, 268-9, 275, 281, 294-5, 299, 300, 310, 322, 325, 327-8, 332, 344, 347, 349, 358-9, 364, 367, 370-1, 381, 388, 390, 397, 412-3, 430, 444, 477, 481-2 Geoff Whittle (www.thetotalimagegroup.co.uk)